Statistical Mechanics for Thermophysical Property Calculations

Statistical Mechanics for Thermophysical Property Calculations

Richard L. Rowley

Professor of Chemical Engineering
Brigham Young University
Provo, Utah

PTR Prentice Hall, Englewood Cliffs, New Jersey 07632

Library of Congress Cataloging-in-Publication Data

Rowley, Richard L.
    Statistical mechanics for thermophysical property calculations/
by Richard L. Rowley.
        p. cm.
    Includes bibliographical references and index.
    ISBN 0-13-030818-8
        1. Materials—Thermomechanical properties.   2. Statistical
mechanics.   3. Statistical thermodynamics.   4. Statistical physics.
    I. Title.
    TA418.24.R69   1994
    620.1'121—dc20   93-45530
                                                                      CIP

Acquisitions editor: *Betty Sun*
Cover design: *Design Solutions*
Cover design director: *Eloise Starkweather-Muller*
Copyeditor: *Betsy Winship*
Art production manager: *Gail Cocker-Bogusz*
Production coordinator (Buyer): *Alexis R. Heydt*

© 1994 by PTR Prentice Hall
Prentice-Hall, Inc.
A Paramount Communications Company
Englewood Cliffs, New Jersey 07632

The publisher offers discounts on this book when ordered in bulk quantities.
For more information, contact Corporate Sales Department, PTR Prentice
Hall, 113 Sylvan Avenue, Englewood Cliffs, NJ 07632.
Phone: 201-592-2863; FAX: 201-592-2249.

Printed in the United States of America

10 9 8 7 6 5 4 3 2 1

ISBN 0-13-030818-8

Prentice-Hall International (UK) Limited, *London*
Prentice-Hall of Australia Pty. Limited, *Sydney*
Prentice-Hall Canada Inc., *Toronto*
Prentice-Hall Hispanoamericana, S.A., *Mexico*
Prentice-Hall of India Private Limited, *New Delhi*
Prentice-Hall of Japan, Inc., *Tokyo*
Simon & Schuster Asia Pte. Ltd., *Singapore*
Editora Prentice-Hall do Brasil, Ltda., *Rio de Janeiro*

to Vickie

CONTENTS

APPENDICES
(All Appendices are correlated to chapter numbers)

PREFACE

There are many excellent textbooks on statistical mechanics, written at a variety of levels and from a variety of perspectives. Chemists, physicists, and a few engineers have written texts focusing on material particularly applicable to their disciplines. Such books have ranged in level from introductory texts, suitable for upper division undergraduates, to quite advanced monographs, primarily suited for use by specialists and researchers. It has been my experience that most introductory texts are quite fundamental in scope, mainly intended to assist in developing in-depth understanding of statistical mechanical theory. Applications of the principles are often only made to very idealized systems. The opposite holds true for the monographs. They are often applications oriented, but directed to a very narrow audience of specialists. The fundamentals are not handled very well for the nonspecialist who needs to understand the limitations and strengths of the applications. This book arose out of a desire to teach chemical engineering students the use of statistical mechanics to estimate and calculate thermophysical properties with a text written for the student; a book that includes important fundamentals without ponderous proofs and abstract concepts that are still developing.

One often hears the witticism that with many sciences you can calculate almost anything, but only approximately; with statistical mechanics you can calculate almost nothing, but nearly exactly. While there is still some truth to the witticism, recent advances in applied statistical mechanics have made it a powerful tool for chemical engineers, mechanical engineers, chemists, and physicists interested in property estimation and prediction of "real" fluids and solids. The objective of this book is to provide an abbreviated introduction to the fundamentals, with more focus on the application of those principles to calculating properties of materials. The book was written for the chemical engineer, mechanical engineer, or chemist who requires a moderate understanding of theory and fundamentals of statistical mechanics, but who is particularly interested in calculating property values based on fundamentals at a molecular level.

The pedagogy used is consistent with these objectives. Theory is kept brief and to the point, using examples to illustrate concepts. Proofs are omitted when they provide little additional information to the student about applications of principles. Problems at the end of each chapter are grouped according to the subtopics in the chapter so that the student can become more aware of the relationship of applications to particular principles. Use of these presentation styles is intended to make the book a teaching text rather than an encyclopedic reference of statistical mechanical techniques. The latter purpose is also very important, but other texts already available fill that need excellently. As a teaching text, simple examples, simulations, and models are used to provide the reader with a concrete feel for how statistical mechanics can be used to obtain thermophysical properties.

An additional objective of this text is to make available to students some of the major advances that have occurred in statistical mechanical methods for thermophysical property calculation over the past decade. Some of the recent advances are due to carefully constructed assumptions associated with analytical solutions, some are due to new mathematical techniques, and some are due to the combination of simple models with fundamental theory. Computer simulation of properties has become a very important technique for thermophysical property estimation. The widespread accessibility of high-performance computers has opened to students and professionals alike the capability of using Monte Carlo and molecular dynamics simulations to obtain thermophysical properties and to model thermophysical phenomena. Two of the largest chapters in this book deal with these numerical simulation techniques and their application to property prediction. Again the emphasis is on teaching applications, and so computer source code is used to guide the discussion of the methodology.

Exploration of the relationship between dependent and independent variables is an important learning mode for the student of thermophysical properties. Typical example problems in a textbook have not lent themselves very well to active study by the student. The ready accessibility of computers to today's students makes it possible to provide students with *dynamic* examples, examples that allow students to interactively change independent variables and observe resultant effects. Computer visualization of the concepts and applications can assist students in gaining a more concrete feel for what can otherwise be abstract and difficult to grasp. Included in this text and keyed to the examples are dynamic computer examples that allow the students to explore properties, principles, and phenomena far beyond the examples reproduced in the text. It is not uncommon for books to include companion diskettes. Generally, however, the diskette provides data or specific computational algorithms. I view the purpose of the diskette enclosed in this book very differently. It is designed to be an integral part of the course, particularly the teaching/learning process that comes by use of examples. The diskette provides opportunity for students to examine the examples in the book dynamically and interactively, change conditions, extend the illustration to more complex situations, visualize more fully the concept, and make property computations more conveniently. The programs can be used as class demonstrations, but they are particularly effective when students "play" with them on their own, "seeing what happens when ... ." This kind of use can be further promoted by assigning problems that are to be done with the diskette simulations and examples.

The book is intended to be a one-semester course at the first-year graduate level, although properly prepared seniors might also be included. The first part of the book contains the basic principles of statistical mechanics. The second part of the book makes application to simple models and ideal systems. This includes ideal gases and solids. The third and largest section presents methodologies for calculation of thermophysical properties of real fluids and solids. Also contained in this section are the computer simulation methods.

I hope that this applications-oriented approach to teaching about thermophysical properties and their calculation from first principles will be of benefit to others. It matches my style of learning and that of many of my students. I should also mention that because the intent was to teach through specific applied examples, I have omitted from the book many other topics that have a great deal of promise for future thermophysical property calculations. I have rather chosen to focus on methods that can be used right now to calculate thermophysical properties. There is rapid progress being made in this area and my hope is that the methods discussed in the book will become quickly outdated as new, more powerful techniques are developed.

INSTRUCTIONS FOR EXAMPLES DISKETTE

PURPOSE OF DISKETTE

The enclosed diskette contains 33 dynamic examples keyed to the examples in the text with the diskette icon ▓▓ . Also contained on the diskette are useful data and source codes keyed to the Appendices. The dynamic examples fall into two major categories: (1) interactive opportunities to change variables and parameters in order to observe thermophysical property response to the change, and (2) thermophysical property computation programs for the more complex methods. For both classes of examples, the purpose of the dynamic examples is to enhance the student's understanding of often difficult concepts and the interrelationship of thermophysical properties and independent variables over and above what can be done by static examples on the printed page. This is accomplished through graphics visualization and interactive adjustability of conditions.

HARDWARE REQUIREMENTS

Adequate computer hardware is at least a 386-level DOS machine with a hard drive and at least an EGA-graphics monitor and adapter card. **The examples can not be run from the enclosed floppy diskette, but must first be installed on the hard drive.** This requires 2.3 Mb of hard disk space. Additionally, the examples all use conventional memory and some may require up to 580K of conventional RAM. Thus, the machine should have 640K of conventional memory. DOS 5.0 or higher is required and additional RAM memory is beneficial especially if a DOS or WINDOWS memory manager is employed to load much of the operating system into high memory. To free up as much conventional memory as possible, I advise unloading TSR (terminate-and-stay-resident) programs that may not only occupy valuable memory but occasionally interfere with the examples. A mouse is strongly encouraged for user interaction, although the programs are fully functional with keyboard control.

INSTALLATION

To use the dynamic examples, the software must first be installed onto a hard drive. To do this use one of the two options below:

Option 1: Using the Installation program

1. Place the provided diskette in drive A: (or B:) and make that the default drive by typing A: (or B:).
2. Type INSTALL. The program will load a graphical installation screen. The window in the lower left of the screen is an interactive area to customize the installation. It allows you to change the drive that your source diskette is in and the default directory (normally C:/statmech) that you want to create. Accept the defaults or change them and then click on "OK."
3. The appropriate files are then automatically copied to the new subdirectory on your hard disk. It may take a few minutes to copy "EXAMPLES.EXE" so be patient. When the graphical screen is replaced by a message box, the copying step is complete. Select "OK" in the message box or press the space bar.
4. The installation program then de-compresses (or inflates) each of the example programs into your subdirectory. Finally a graphical interface returns indicating successful installation. Click on "OK" or press the space bar.

Option 2. Using DOS Commands

1. Create a subdirectory on your hard drive using the MKDIR DOS command.
2. Copy EXAMPLES.EXE from the floppy to the new subdirectory on the hard drive.
3. Change to the new subdirectory on your hard drive and type EXAMPLES. This will begin the inflation process for the examples and will complete the installation.

LIST OF EXAMPLES ON DISKETTE

RUNNING THE EXAMPLES

Once loaded onto the hard disk, the examples can be accessed by setting their subdirectory as the default and typing "BOOKMENU." When the installation program is run, the new subdirectory automatically is set as the default directory. Later you will either have to specifically change to the directory, for example:

C:> CD /statmech,

or set up the same information as a WINDOWS application before running the program. At the prompt C:/statmech/, typing "BOOKMENU" will bring up the menu interface which allows the user to select from any of the 33 examples.

USER INTERFACE

A consistent user interface is maintained throughout the examples. The interface is essentialy that which has been accepted as the MICROSOFT© standard. Menu bars, list boxes, selections, and so forth may all be accessed with either the mouse or the keyboard, although it is often easier with the mouse. Brief instructions on the various interface devices are given below for both keyboard and mouse use.

Menu Items

The red bar at the top of the screen contains various pull-down menus and options. For most examples these include the main menu categories of "File," "Modify," "Simulate," "About," and "Help." Access to the options available in these menus is available in three ways:

1. *Mouse*—With the mouse, click on the menu item on the bar to drop down the options available; then click on the desired submenu.
2. *Keyboard*—When the [ALT] key is pressed, a letter in the menu is high-lighted. Pressing the key for that letter then opens the menu making the options available. Thus, [ALT + F] opens the "File" menu. The selection is then made by using the cursor control keys to highlight the choice and then pressing [RETURN].
3. *Hot Keys*—Many submenu items have been set up to function with hot keys. These are shown to the right of the submenu item. For example, to the right of "Exit" in the "File" menu is the parenthetical key "(^X)." This indicates that pressing [CTRL + X] from the keyboard immediately executes the option "Exit" without ever opening the menu. Other hot keys are associated with the most common menu choices.

As mentioned, most examples include the menu items "File," "Modify," "Simulate," the example name (which is an "About" menu), and "Help." The "File" menu allows the user to either "Escape" [ESC] back to the original default values for the simulation or "Exit" the example. The "Modify" menu allows users to change variables and system parameters. The "Simulate" menu is used to initiate the action once the options are set. [CTRL] + R], for Run, is the usual hot-key method for beginning the calculation or simulation. By clicking on the example's title in the middle of the menu bar, a window is displayed that describes the program. A brief help menu that explains the functions of each of the menu and submenu items is available by pressing F1, [ALT + H] or clicking on "Help."

Other Interface Units

The examples also have other types of input features that can be accessed from the keyboard or mouse. These are briefly described below:

1. *List Boxes*—List boxes display a list of preselected options from which a single selection can be made. With the mouse, one can use the slide bar at the right to view all the options and to make a selection. The selection is made by clicking on the appropriate choice. Selections are made from the keyboard by using the cursor keys as well as [PgUp] and [PgDn] keys to highlight the desired choice; and then pressing [RETURN].

2. *Variable Boxes*—Often variables are modified in a variable box containing a rangebar. With the mouse, set the variable by dragging the slide bar to the appropriate place or clicking on the arrows at the end of the bar until the position marker is adjusted appropriately; then click on the "OK" button. To use the keyboard, position the slide marker with the horizontal cursor control keys. The [TAB] key is then used to switch from one input field to the next. Use the [TAB] key to set action to the "OK" button (as determined by the change of color from low to high intensity), then select "OK" by pressing the [SPACEBAR].

3. *Option Boxes*—Often you may choose one option from two or three choices, such as which starting condition, initial configuration, or units are to be used. This is conveniently done with an option box consisting of a group of options and the command button, usually marked "OK." With the mouse, simply click on the open circle preceding your choice. Your selection is marked by the change from an open to a solid circle while all nonselected choices retain an open circle in front of them. When satisfied with the selection, click the "OK" command button. With the keyboard, the option selection is made by using the [TAB] key to move between selections—note that the selection option changes to upper case

when it has received the focus—and then pressing [SPACEBAR] to select the choice.

4. *Text Input*—Text input is typed in from the keyboard after first selecting the desired input line. Selection is made by clicking with the mouse or using the [TAB] keyboard method of stepping through the available selection choices. Normal editing keys such as delete, back-delete, home, end and so on are available for textual input in these fields. In fields where default text is provided, pressing [RETURN] retains the default value, typing any character erases the default value and begins inserting what you type, and using the right arrow key moves the cursor to the right for editing of the default text.

EXITING THE PROGRAM

Exiting any example always returns the user to the BOOKMENU screen ready for another Example selection. Exit from the program itself must be from BOOKMENU by choosing the "Exit" option of the "File" menu.

ADDITIONAL APPENDIX MATERIAL

When the installation of the software is complete, several appendix files will have been transferred also to the same subdirectory as the examples. You may access these files with any ASCII editor. They contain useful data too voluminous to include in the Appendix and computer source codes.

DISCLAIMER

The examples on the enclosed diskette are for instructional and educational purposes only. They are "as-is" software with no guarantee of accuracy or machine compatibility. The owner is free to make personal copies of the software and to use results of the programs for educational purposes. Use of any results from the programs for design purposes or publications is discouraged and may only be done at the user's own risk. Neither the author nor the publisher will bear any responsibility for the accuracy or use of thermophysical properties obtained from the enclosed codes. Presently there is no availability of the programs for the McIntosh.

1

THE FOUNDATION TOOLS

1.1 THE EMERGENCE OF STATISTICAL PHYSICS

The foundation of statistical mechanics was laid early in the nineteenth century with the development of classical thermodynamics. Upon that solid foundation has been built a science that links macroscopic observations to the microscopic world of molecules. Interestingly, classical thermodynamics makes no assumption about the constituent nature of matter. Yet, when combined with the fields of mechanics, quantum mechanics, and statistics, thermodynamics provides powerful insight into the link between molecular phenomena and macroscopic thermophysical properties.

In the late 1800s, men of particular vision promoted an atomistic view of matter and realized that macroscopic properties of matter must be a result of the multitude of interactions in the material. Science during that period held firmly to determinism, believing that an understanding of the motion of each particle would enable one to predict all future states of the system and the resultant thermodynamic or macroscopic properties. In trying to understand why liquids formed, J.D. van der Waals used the concept of interacting particles to show how a single equation of state could predict the continuity of liquid and gas states. In his Ph.D. thesis van der Waals wrote[1]:

> We have therefore to explain why it is that particles attracting one another and only separated by empty space do not fall together: and to do this we must look around for other causes. These we find in the motion of the molecules

themselves, which must be of such a nature that it opposes a diminution of volume and causes the gas to act as if there were repulsive forces between its particles.

In this single paragraph, van der Waals identifies two concepts that still form the basis of current fluid theories: (1) matter is composed of molecules that must be in continuous motion, and (2) the interplay between interparticle attractions, repulsions, and the motion of the particles gives rise to the properties of the fluid.

Attributing liquid behavior to the interactions and movement of the molecules was not a popular belief at the time. A hostile attitude toward atomism permeated physics at the turn of the century. Atomism's foes included several celebrated scientists, and bitter polemics between atomists and nonatomists were common. During this time, the cause of atomism was championed by Ludwig Boltzmann, who passionately insisted on the reality of atoms. In a defiant statement concluding one of his papers, Boltzmann exclaims,[2] "I think I can still safely say of molecules: nevertheless they do move!"

Boltzmann intensely sought the molecular origins of the laws of thermodynamics, recognizing in the second law a key to understanding that link. He forged that link by re-interpreting Clausius's statement of the second law (that heat cannot be converted altogether into mechanical work) in terms of molecular probability, the natural propensity of a large collection of particles toward molecular disorder. Boltzmann became the father of a new science, statistical mechanics. Others would follow and further establish the validity and procedures of the method. For example, early in the twentieth century, both Einstein and Gibbs independently worked out a mathematical procedure that allowed them to relate the thermodynamic state of the system to the statistics of the molecular states.

Still, calculation of thermophysical properties based on statistical probabilities represented a bold new way of thinking, a paradigm shift aided by apparent discrepancies unresolvable from the deterministic view. Experiments designed to reveal the nature of light and electrons both yielded the same deterministic paradox. While the wave nature of light had been well established through such phenomena as interference patterns, the photoelectric effect could only be understood by assuming a constituency of small particles or photons.

The paradox on the nature of light deepened when the now famous two-slit experiment was performed with an electron beam. Electrons fired at a phosphorescent screen produced tiny flashes of light where the electron struck the screen. When the experiment was carried out with two slits, an interference pattern resulted just as it did when light was used in the experiment. When the experiment was repeated with first one slit covered and then the other, no combination of the two experiments could explain the two-slit interference pattern. Even when the intensity was lowered so that only one electron was present in the apparatus at a time, the interference pattern persisted! How could such results possibly be explained? Furthermore, scientists found that shooting electrons through a single hole produced inexplicable results. As the size of the hole was reduced, the impact position of the electron on the screen became less, rather than better, defined. What we now understand is that the smaller the hole, the more accurately we know the location of the particle at a particular time, but the less we know about its velocity and subsequent impact position. By focusing on a position experiment, velocity information is lost. Similarly, focus on a particle experiment causes a lose of detectability of the wavelike character of light. The particle or wave nature of the subatomic realm manifests itself according to the kind of measurement performed. These troubling paradoxes forced physicists to relinquish complete determinism of subatomic particles. A new mechanics formulation was called for.

The new quantum mechanics formulations (several different but equivalent methods were independently developed at the same time) by Heisenberg and Schrödinger in the 1920s were attempts to explain the matter-wave paradox. Somewhat surprising was the realization that the new way of thinking could only be viewed as statistical rather than deterministic. One has no way to know the electron's history, because position and velocity cannot be simultaneously determined. One can only talk about the probability of finding *an* electron (not *one particular* electron) in a certain location. Just as an actuary may calculate the probability of death as a function of age and obtain quite accurate insurance tables for prediction of death rates in large populations without knowing which individuals will die at particular ages, so also physicists accepted the view that there is no connection between a given electron's present and future positions, only that there is a certain probability of finding an electron at each region in space.

The paradigm shift, the new physics,[3,4] made acceptance of statistical mechanics relatively easy. It has now become a powerful method for calculating thermophysical macroscopic properties from statistical analysis of the microstates of the constituent molecules, fulfilling a dream of the early atomists of the late nineteenth century. As we shall see, the use of statistical mechanics does not preclude deterministic ideas. Molecules are much larger and more massive than electrons, and one can still predict macroscopic properties from computer simulation of the classical motion of the particles. Even so, the computation of macroscopic properties from a necessarily small representation must rely on statistics.

1.2 WHAT IS STATISTICAL MECHANICS?

Unlike thermodynamics, the science of statistical mechanics is based on the molecular concept of matter. It contains the link between the microscopic states of matter and the observed macroscopic properties sought by the atomists of the late nineteenth century. If indeed the observed properties of matter are entirely determined by microscopic forces and interactions, then the properties themselves should also be directly calculable from those microscopic interactions, provided one is clever enough. Although this is a large caveat, statistical mechanics has become a powerful tool for prediction of thermophysical properties.

Calculation of macroscopic properties from all molecular interactions is an impossible task. The use of statistics empowers the application of mechanics to so many particles (10^{22} for a small macroscopic system), and the task becomes merely difficult instead of impossible. Just as a small sample from a large population allows statisticians to calculate expected properties of the overall population, so also statistics may be used to compute properties of macroscopic systems from the probabilities of inherent molecular states. Ironically, it is the very enormity of particle numbers in a macroscopic system that makes the statistical treatment viable. Statistical distributions become very narrow about the mean as the population within the distribution increases, and the entire distribution may be replaced by the most probable value in the limit of very large populations. Together, thermodynamics and statistics serve as tools to bridge the gap between the sciences that deal with molecular properties and the desired macroscopic properties as shown in Figure 1.1.

In actuality, the methods employed in bridging microscopic motion and macroscopic properties are often, of necessity, complex. These computational difficulties have unfortunately limited engineering applications of statistical mechanics. For many years the methods were applicable only to idealized systems of little interest to chemical engineers. Considerable progress is now being made, however, in the application of statistical mechanics to real fluids, nonideal mixtures, complex polymers, and even large biological molecules. Important and accurate computations of macroscopic properties from intermolecular forces are now being made by chemical engineers. This book is intended to be pragmatic and is written for the chemical engineer who desires an introduction to the field. It focuses as much as possible on applications rather than rigorous derivations of the underlying theories of statistical mechanics. Readers wishing to obtain experience in the latter areas should consult any of a number of excellent texts including McQuarrie,[5] Reed and Gubbins,[6] Tolman,[7] and Hill.[8]

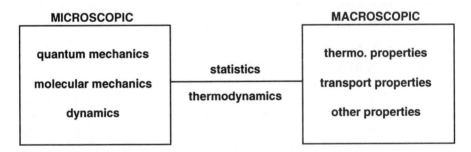

Figure 1.1 The relationship of microscopic sciences to macroscopic properties in statistical mechanics.

To emphasize further the concepts of problem solving and the application of statistical mechanics, this book is also problem oriented.

Another area of rapid progress related to statistical mechanics is that of molecular simulation, either by molecular dynamics (MD) or Monte Carlo (MC) methods. Rather than bridging the gap between microscopic and macroscopic phenomena entirely with statistics, simulations use a relatively small collection of particles to represent the macroscopic system, employing computational tricks such as periodic boundary conditions to make the representation efficacious. Statistical methods are then used to obtain macroscopic properties from averages of the mechanical variables. In MD calculations, the classical equations of motion are solved for all particles in the representative sample, and properties are computed from time averages of the molecular mechanical properties. In MC techniques, large numbers of possible system configurations are generated and properties are computed from averages of these configurations weighted in proportion to their probability. Traditionally, computer simulations have been instrumental in testing the assumptions of various statistical mechanical theories. Comparison of theory to simulation rather than experiment permits separation of assumptions about intermolecular forces from the underlying assumptions of the theory because both theory and simulation can use the same intermolecular force model. More and more often, however, MD and MC simulations are now being used to calculate the properties of real fluids. Simulation is rapidly becoming a viable method of property prediction and estimation.

In the remaining sections of this chapter, a brief introduction and review of the basic tools needed in statistical mechanical calculations are presented. Chemical engineers generally have a good background in thermodynamics and so that foundation science is not reviewed here. The topics of mechanics, quantum mechanics, and statistics may be less familiar or less honed by the chemical engineer and so are briefly discussed. The coverage of these topics is intended only to provide rudimentary capabilities sufficient for use in subsequent chapters.

1.3 CLASSICAL MECHANICS

1.3.1 Newtonian Mechanics

Let us start with a simple representation of a system of particles and later add the complexities that may be required to model real fluids. Consider a system composed of particles whose motion is governed by classical mechanics. Newton's second law,

$$F = ma = m\ddot{r}, \tag{1.1}$$

constitutes an equation of motion for a particle because its solution, subject to initial conditions on the position and velocity, yields information about subsequent particle positions and velocities as shown in Example 1.1.

The dynamics of many interacting molecules are of course much more complex, but the principle is the same. Given an initial set of positions and velocities for all of the particles, Newton's equations of motion could theoreti-

---

Example 1.1   Determine the trajectory of a 1.0-kg ball thrown from a height of 100 m into the air at an initial velocity of 50 m/s and an angle of 45° with respect to the ground.

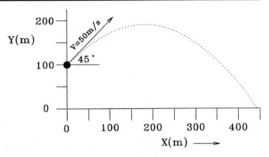

To determine the position and velocity of the ball at any later time, Newton's equation of motion can be integrated. First the equation is separated into x and y components:

$$F_x = m\ddot{x} \quad F_y = m\ddot{y} \ .$$

If the y direction is taken as vertical, there is no component of force in the x direction and the force in the y direction is that due to gravity, or

$$F_x = 0 \quad F_y = mg\cdot\cos\phi = -mg \ ,$$

where the negative sign results from the fact that ϕ, the angle the gravitational force makes with the positive y axis is 180°. Combination of the above equations and integration with respect to time yields the following differential and algebraic equations:

$$\ddot{x} = 0 \quad \dot{x} = c_1 \qquad x = c_1 t + c_2$$
$$\ddot{y} = -g \quad \dot{y} = -gt + c_3 \qquad y = -\frac{1}{2} gt^2 + c_3 t + c_4 \ ,$$

where c_i are integration constants to be obtained from initial conditions on position and velocity. The initial conditions described in the problem can be written mathematically as

$$x|_{t=0} = 0 \qquad \dot{x}|_{t=0} = v\cdot\cos\theta = (50 \text{ m/s}) \ [\cos(45°)] = 35.4 \text{ m/s}$$
$$y|_{t=0} = 100 \text{ m} \qquad \dot{y}|_{t=0} = v\cdot\sin\theta = (50 \text{ m/s}) \ [\sin(45°)] = 35.4 \text{ m/s} \ ,$$

and these equations can be used to determine the integration constants. Elimination of the c_i yields,

$$x = 35.4t \text{ m} \qquad \dot{x} = 35.4 \text{ m/s}$$
$$y = (100 + 35.4t - 4.9t^2) \text{ m} \qquad \dot{y} = (35.4 - 9.8t) \text{ m/s} \ .$$

From these equations, the position and velocity of the ball can be calculated at any subsequent time, and the entire trajectory can be mapped out as shown by the dashed line in the figure.

cally be solved to obtain positions and velocities of the particles at some later time, provided an accurate expression for the forces between the molecules is available. The results of such calculations also depend on the degree to which the particles behave classically rather than quantum mechanically. In Newton's formulation of the equations of motion, the total energy of a many particle system must be found from the positions and velocities of the particles as the sum of the kinetic and potential energies. For a conservative system, the kinetic energy depends only on particle velocities, while the potential energy depends only on their positions. Thus,

$$E(r,v) = \sum_i \frac{m_i v_i^2}{2} + U(r) . \tag{1.2}$$

The force between pairs of particles is related to the potential energy of the pair by

$$F = -\nabla U \qquad \text{(for conservative systems)}. \tag{1.3}$$

1.3.2 Lagrangian Mechanics

While Newton's law is convenient for calculating velocities and positions in Cartesian coordinates, the form of the equation may be different in other coordinate systems. As can be seen in Example 1.2, Newton's equation of motion is not invariant under transformation from one coordinate system to another. In the example, the r component of the equation of motion in polar coordinates,

$$m\ddot{r} = F_r + mr\dot{\theta}^2 , \tag{1.4}$$

is seen to contain an additional term, the centrifugal force, introduced by the coordinate transformation. To use Newton's equation in different coordinate systems, one must either go through the coordinate transformation procedure or be prepared to add to Equation (1.1) any additional forces that apply to the new coordinate system. Neither procedure is ideal and so other formulations of the basic laws of mechanics have been formulated which eliminate this difficulty.

Lagrange's equations of motion are independent of the coordinate system. The equations can be obtained by differentiation of the Lagrangian, L, defined as the difference between the kinetic and potential energies,

$$L = K - U . \tag{1.5}$$

In terms of general coordinates, q_k, the kinetic energy, K, can be written as a function of the generalized velocity, $\dot{q}$, as

$$K = \frac{m\dot{q}^2}{2}.$$ (1.6)

For the conservative systems (those for which the force can be obtained from

---

Example 1.2 A problem related to the orbit of planets about the sun is the Kepler problem. Consider an object of mass m moving about a fixed central object of mass M. Determine the equation of motion in polar coordinates.

The force and potential between the two objects are given by Newton's gravitational law,

$$\mathbf{F} = -\frac{MmG\mathbf{r}}{r^3} \qquad U = -\frac{MmG}{r},$$

where the vector $\mathbf{r}$ is directed from M to m. The equation of motion becomes

$$m\ddot{\mathbf{r}} + \frac{MmG\mathbf{r}}{r^3} = 0.$$

In Cartesian coordinates the equations for the x and y components of the position vector then become

$$\ddot{x} + \frac{GMx}{r^3} = 0 \qquad \ddot{y} + \frac{GMy}{r^3} = 0,$$

where $r^2 = x^2 + y^2$. Polar coordinates are quite natural for this problem and transformation is achieved with the identities

$$x = r\cos\theta \qquad y = r\sin\theta.$$

The transformation yields

$$m\left(\ddot{r} - \dot{\theta}^2 r + \frac{GM}{r^2}\right)\cos\theta - m(2\dot{\theta}\dot{r} + r\ddot{\theta})\sin\theta = 0$$

$$m\left(\ddot{r} - \dot{\theta}^2 r + \frac{GM}{r^2}\right)\sin\theta + m(2\dot{\theta}\dot{r} + r\ddot{\theta})\cos\theta = 0.$$

The easiest simplification procedure is to multiply the top equation by $\cos\theta$, multiply the bottom equation by $\sin\theta$, and add the two resultant equations together. This gives the final form of the equation of motion in polar coordinates,

$$m\ddot{r} = m\dot{\theta}^2 r - \frac{GmM}{r^2}.$$

As can be seen, an additional term arises when r and θ are used as the independent coordinates. Physically, this term represents the centrifugal force.

---

the gradient of the potential) dealt with in this book, the Lagrangian equation of motion is

$$\frac{\mathrm{d}}{\mathrm{d}t}\left(\frac{\partial L}{\partial \dot{q}_j}\right) - \frac{\partial L}{\partial q_j} = 0 \, . \tag{1.7}$$

The important feature of Equation (1.7) is that one obtains the final differential equations from it by differentiating with respect to q_j and $\dot{q}_j$ whether the coordinates are in terms of (x, y, z), (r, θ, ϕ), or any other set of coordinates. An example of this is given in Example 1.3.

Many interesting systems have constraints on their motion. The normal equations of motion must be restricted by an additional relationship in order to describe the actual motion that occurs. For example, the bead in Example 1.3 is constrained to slide on the wire. Similarly, you might envision obtaining the motion of a diatomic molecule by solving the equations of motion for each of the two atoms subject to a constraint of fixed distance (bond length) between them. This kind of constraint is called *holonomic* because it can be written in the form $g(\boldsymbol{r}, t) = 0$, independent of the velocities. Or, you might envision solving the equations of motion for a many-particle system subject to the constraint that the temperature of the system (i.e., the kinetic energy) is fixed. This would impose a *nonholonomic* constraint, one which depends on the velocities of the particles, i.e., $g(\boldsymbol{r}, \dot{\boldsymbol{r}}, t) = 0$. There are many other examples of constraints, both holonomic and nonholonomic, that are of interest. While Lagrange's equation can be readily solved subject to holonomic constraints, nonholonomic constraints are more difficult to handle.

Lagrange's method of undetermined multipliers can be used as a general procedure to solve differential equations subject to constraints. Before applying the method to the equations of motion, consider a related problem. Suppose we wish to find the extremum of a function $f(x_1, x_2, \ldots, x_n)$, where the x_i are independent variables. The extremum is found by setting the total differential to zero,

$$\mathrm{d}f = \sum_{i=1}^{n} \left(\frac{\partial f}{\partial x_i}\right)_{x_{j \neq i}} \mathrm{d}x_i = 0 \, . \tag{1.8}$$

Because each x_i is independent, the corresponding coefficient for $\mathrm{d}x_i$ must independently vanish, yielding n simultaneous independent equations,

$$\left(\frac{\partial f}{\partial x_i}\right)_{x_{j \neq i}} = 0 \qquad (i = 1, 2, \ldots n) \, . \tag{1.9}$$

These n equations can, at least in principle, be solved for all x_i values at the extremum condition.

Example 1.3   Use Lagrange's equation
to obtain the equation of motion for a
bead which can slide on a rotating wire
in force-free space.

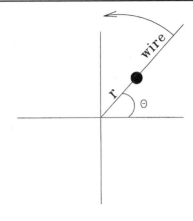

For a single particle in two dimensions, the potential energy is zero, and
therefore the Langrangian is just equal to
the kinetic energy,

$$L = K = \frac{1}{2}m(\dot{x}^2 + \dot{y}^2).$$

This equation can be transformed to polar
coordinates in a manner analogous to that
of Example 1.2 to obtain

$$L = \frac{1}{2}m\dot{r}^2 + \frac{1}{2}mr^2\dot{\theta}^2.$$

The new coordinates are r and θ with corresponding velocities $\dot{r}$ and $\dot{\theta}$. Langrange's
equations of motion are given by Equation (1.7) regardless of the coordinate system, so

$$\frac{d}{dt}\left(\frac{\partial L}{\partial \dot{r}}\right) - \frac{\partial L}{\partial r} = 0 \qquad \frac{d}{dt}\left(\frac{\partial L}{\partial \dot{\theta}}\right) - \frac{\partial L}{\partial \theta} = 0.$$

Thus,

$$\frac{d}{dt}m\dot{r} - mr\dot{\theta}^2 = 0 \Rightarrow \ddot{r} = r\dot{\theta}^2$$

$$\frac{d}{dt}(mr^2\dot{\theta}) = 0 \Rightarrow r\ddot{\theta} = -2\dot{r}\dot{\theta}.$$

The second equation is not needed for this problem. If the wire is rotating at an angular
velocity, ω, then the angular velocity of the bead is also constrained to the same value
or $\dot{\theta} = \omega$. The equation of motion for the bead is, therefore,

$$\ddot{r} = r\,\omega^2,$$

which describes the well-known result that the bead moves outward because of centripe-
tal acceleration.

If all of the x_i are not independent (i.e., if there is a constraint on the
system which relates two or more of the variables), Equation (1.8) can still be
satisfied because groups of terms may still cancel. For m constraint equations
represented by

$$g_k(x_1, x_2, ..., x_n) = 0 \qquad (k = 1, 2, ..., m) \,, \tag{1.10}$$

an auxiliary function, F, can be defined which involves m undetermined constant multipliers, λ_k,

$$F = f - \sum_{k=1}^{m} \lambda_k g_k \,. \tag{1.11}$$

The extremum condition applied to our new auxiliary function requires that

$$\left(\frac{\partial F}{\partial x_i} \right)_{x_{j \neq i}} = 0 \,. \tag{1.12}$$

To the original n unknown variables, we have added m additional unknowns (λ_k). This doesn't seem much like progress! But, we have also increased the number of equations to $m + n$. The n derivative equations (1.12) and m constraint equations (1.10) constitute a solvable set of simultaneous equations. Example 1.4 illustrates a simple application of the method.

The method of undetermined multipliers is also the most common method of solving the Lagrangian equation subject to holonomic constraints. Generally the pth constraint equation can be written in the form

$$\sum_k a_{pk} dq_k = 0 \,, \tag{1.13}$$

or when differentiated with respect to time, as

$$\sum_k a_{pk} \dot{q}_k = 0 \,. \tag{1.14}$$

The equations of motion subject to the imposed constraints are then obtained from the modified Lagrange equation,

$$\frac{d}{dt}\left(\frac{\partial L}{\partial \dot{q}_k} \right) - \frac{\partial L}{\partial q_k} = \sum_p \lambda_p a_{pk} \,. \tag{1.15}$$

The additional term in Equation (1.15) is the constraint force. In fact, Equation (1.15) can be generalized to[9]

$$\boxed{\frac{d}{dt}\left(\frac{\partial L}{\partial \dot{q}_k} \right) - \frac{\partial L}{\partial q_k} = S \tag{1.16}}$$

where S represents all nonconservative forces. That is, any force not obtainable from the potential, such as friction, appears in S. An added advantage of this method is that the constraint force is simultaneously determined from the solution

Example 1.4   What is the volume of the largest rectangular box that can be placed inside the ellipsoid

$$\frac{x^2}{a^2} + \frac{y^2}{b^2} + \frac{z^2}{c^2} = 1$$

so that its edges will be parallel to the coordinate axes?

We wish to maximize V, the volume of the box, subject to the constraint that the corners also satisfy the above equation. With the box centered at zero (so that the origin is coincident with that of the ellipsoid), the volume of the box is given by $V = (2x)(2y)(2z) = 8xyz$. We can find the values of x, y, and z that maximize V by forming the auxiliary function

$$F = 8xyz - \lambda \left(\frac{x^2}{a^2} + \frac{y^2}{b^2} + \frac{z^2}{c^2} - 1 \right).$$

There are now four unknowns (x, y, z, λ) which can be found at the extremum from the ellipsoid equation and the three derivative equations:

$$\left(\frac{\partial F}{\partial x} \right)_{y,z} = 8yz - \frac{2x\lambda}{a^2} \quad \left(\frac{\partial F}{\partial y} \right)_{x,z} = 8xz - \frac{2y\lambda}{b^2} \quad \left(\frac{\partial F}{\partial z} \right)_{x,y} = 8xy - \frac{2z\lambda}{c^2}.$$

Solution of these equations is most easily done by multiplying the above three equations by x, y, and z, respectively, to obtain

$$x^2 = V_{max}\frac{a^2}{2\lambda} \quad y^2 = V_{max}\frac{b^2}{2\lambda} \quad z^2 = V_{max}\frac{c^2}{2\lambda}.$$

These equations can then be substituted into the constraint (ellipsoid) equation to obtain $V_{max} = 2\lambda/3$. Thus,

$$x_{max} = \frac{a}{\sqrt{3}} \quad y_{max} = \frac{b}{\sqrt{3}} \quad z_{max} = \frac{c}{\sqrt{3}},$$

and the maximum volume is given by $V_{max} = 8x_{max}\, y_{max}\, z_{max} = 1.54abc$.

Although not needed, the undetermined multiplier, λ, may also be determined from the above equations. It is $3V_{max}/2$ or $2.309abc$.

of the undetermined multipliers. An example will best serve to illustrate how to solve constrained equations of motion using the undetermined multiplier method. Example 1.5 illustrates the method for a hoop rolling down an inclined plane.

Example 1.5   Find the equation of motion for a hoop of mass M and radius R that rolls down an inclined plane.[9]

The hoop is constrained to roll down the plane, i.e., the displacement down the plane must equal the length of hoop that has been in contact with the surface. Using the coordinate system shown in the figure, one can state this constraint mathematically as,

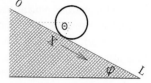

$$R d\theta - dx = 0 \quad \text{(rolling constraint)}.$$

The kinetic energy, analogous to Example 1.3, is the sum of the displacement and rotational kinetic energies,

$$K = \frac{1}{2}M\dot{x}^2 + \frac{1}{2}MR^2\dot{\theta}^2 .$$

The potential energy is due to the gravitational field and can be expressed as,

$$U = Mg(L - x)\sin\phi .$$

Finally, the Lagrangian is the difference between the kinetic and potential energy,

$$L = \frac{1}{2}M\dot{x}^2 + \frac{1}{2}MR^2\dot{\theta}^2 - Mg(L - x)\sin\phi .$$

To solve the problem, we first find the appropriate partial derivatives with respect to the generalized coordinates:

$$\left(\frac{\partial L}{\partial \dot{x}}\right) = M\dot{x} \quad \left(\frac{\partial L}{\partial x}\right) = Mg\sin\phi \quad \left(\frac{\partial L}{\partial \dot{\theta}}\right) = MR^2\dot{\theta} \quad \left(\frac{\partial L}{\partial \theta}\right) = 0 .$$

A direct comparison of the constraint equation to Equation (1.13) allows us to identify $a_x = -1$ and $a_\theta = R$. These coefficients of λ, together with the above derivatives, can be substituted into the generalized Lagrangian, Equation (1.15), to obtain,

$$M\ddot{x} - Mg\sin\phi + \lambda = 0 \quad MR^2\ddot{\theta} - \lambda R = 0 .$$

These two equations plus the constraint equation can now be solved for the three unknowns, λ, $\ddot{x}$, and $\ddot{\theta}$. This is most easily done by differentiating the constraint equation with respect to time and using the result to eliminate $\ddot{\theta}$ from the x and θ equations. Finally,

$$\lambda = \frac{1}{2}Mg\sin\phi \quad \ddot{x} = \frac{\lambda}{M} = \frac{1}{2}g\sin\phi \quad \ddot{\theta} = \frac{\ddot{x}}{R} = \frac{1}{2}\frac{g\sin\phi}{R} .$$

These equations govern the motion of the hoop down the inclined plane. From the final equation, it can be observed that the hoop rolls down the plane with only half the acceleration with which it would slip down the plane. Note also that in solving the problem in this manner, we have also obtained the constraint or friction force directly,

$$F_c = a_x\lambda = -\frac{1}{2}Mg\sin\phi .$$

1.3.3 Hamiltonian Mechanics

The natural variables of Lagrange's equation are position and velocity. Actually, a more convenient formulation for the equations of motion is Hamilton's which uses position and momentum as the natural variables. Like Lagrange's equation, Hamilton's formulation retains the convenient property of form-invariance with respect to the coordinate system. The Hamiltonian, H, is the total energy of the system, the sum of the kinetic and potential energies. For a single particle in a conservative system, H can be written in terms of the momentum and position as

$$H(p,q) = K(p) + U(q) = \frac{p^2}{2m} + U(q) . \tag{1.17}$$

Hamilton's equations of motion are quickly derived from Equation (1.17) by partial differentiation to obtain

$$\left(\frac{\partial H}{\partial p_j}\right)_{P_{k \neq j}, q_k} = \dot{q}_j \tag{1.18}$$

$$\left(\frac{\partial H}{\partial q_j}\right)_{q_{k \neq j}, P_k} = -\dot{p}_j \tag{1.19}$$

where use has been made of Equation (1.3) in the form

$$\left(\frac{\partial U}{\partial q_j}\right)_{q_{k \neq j}, P_k} = -F_j .$$

Thus, given initial states for each particle's momentum and position and a form for the intermolecular potential as a function of position, all future states of the system can be determined as illustrated in Example 1.6. There is, of course, a limit to the accuracy of this kind of calculation. The minimum uncertainty in calculated momenta and positions, Δp and Δq, is governed by the Heisenberg Uncertainty Principle:

$$\Delta q \Delta p \geq h . \tag{1.20}$$

As was illustrated by the two-slit experiment discussed in Section 1.1, the more accurately experiments attempt to define exact particle positions, the less accurately velocities, hence subsequent particle positions, can be determined.

Example 1.6   As shown below, a particle is attached to a wall with a spring which has a force constant f. Determine the equation of motion for this one-dimensional harmonic oscillator relative to an equilibrium position at $x = 0$.

The potential energy of this system is given by $U = \frac{1}{2}fx^2$. We use Hamilton's equation of motion to obtain,

frictionless surface

$$\left(\frac{\partial H}{\partial x}\right)_{p_x} = \left(\frac{\partial U}{\partial x}\right)_{p_x} = fx = -\dot{p}_x = -m\ddot{x} \, ,$$

or $m\ddot{x} + fx = 0$. The solution of this equation is

$$x = \alpha \sin \sqrt{f/m}\, t + \beta \cos\sqrt{f/m}\, t \, .$$

Suppose initially the ball is at the equilibrium position ($x = 0$ at $t = 0$) and is given an initial velocity of v_0. These initial conditions on position and velocity can then be used to determine α and β. Application of the initial condition on position requires that $\beta = 0$; application of the initial condition on velocity requires $\alpha = (m/f)^{1/2}v_0$. Thus, the final solution is

$$x = v_0\sqrt{m/f} \sin(\sqrt{f/m}\, t)$$

which describes a periodic oscillatory motion about the equilibrium distance from the wall.

The frequency of the oscillations can be found by dividing $\sqrt{f/m}$ by 2π. In terms of the frequency, the solution is therefore

$$x = 2\pi\nu v_0 \sin(2\pi\nu t) \, ,$$

where

$$\nu \equiv \frac{1}{2\pi} \sqrt{\frac{f}{m}} \, .$$

1.4 QUANTUM MECHANICS

On a macroscopic level, energies appear to be continuous. Any value of energy appears to be available to the system with appropriately small changes in conditions. For example, it appears that the temperature difference between two systems might be made infinitely small if we had a perfect method with unlimited accuracy to control and measure temperature. Physicists before about 1920 also believed the analogy to apply for atomic energy levels. Study of atomic spectra and other experimental work, however, could not be reconciled with classical mechanics. The new mechanics developed in the 1920s gave excellent predictions of observed spectra and resolution to the previous paradoxes. The price paid for this new capability was acceptance of the fact that energy is indeed quantized at the microscopic level. Just as ordinary wave behavior is restricted to certain integral numbers of nodes, so also microscopic energy levels are discrete rather than continuous. The energy of most macroscopic systems still appears continuous because the finite energy levels of so many microscopic particles can combine to yield virtually any value of energy within the precision of our best instruments. Even on a molecular scale, the energy of the system may be treated as a continuum if the temperature is sufficiently high relative to the separation between energy levels to populate a wide range of states. We will find that generally translational motion of particles can be treated classically because of the close spacing between translational energy levels, while electronic and vibrational motion usually must be treated quantum mechanically. Rotational degrees of freedom may sometimes be treated classically if temperatures are adequately high.

Quantum mechanics is based on the dual nature of matter. Particles of small mass can be treated using wave mechanics rather than particulate mechanics. This is done in terms of the wave function, Ψ, which represents the displacement of a wave as it fluctuates with time and position, $\Psi = \Psi(q,t)$. The spatial and temporal dependence of Ψ is most conveniently expressed with complex variables as

$$\Psi = A \exp\left[2\pi\, i\left(\frac{q}{\lambda} - \nu t\right)\right],\qquad(1.21)$$

where A is the amplitude of the wave, λ is the wavelength, and ν is the frequency. Ultimately we wish to replace the wave variables ν and λ with the particle variables of mass and velocity. It was difficult for physicists of the early 1900s to accept the link between wave and particle variables, but the work of Einstein, Bohr, and others ultimately yielded what have now become standard relations,

$$E = h\nu = mC^2 = \frac{p^2}{m} \qquad (h = 6.624 \times 10^{-27}\text{erg}\cdot\text{s}) \qquad(1.22)$$

$$\lambda = \frac{C}{\nu} = \frac{p}{m\nu} = \frac{h}{p},$$

where h is Planck's constant, C is the velocity of light, and E is the particle or wave energy. The above identities can be used to express the wave equation as,

$$\Psi = A \exp\left[2\pi i\,\frac{(pq - Et)}{h}\right] = A\pi\psi,\qquad(1.23)$$

where the separated[*] temporal and spatial parts are defined, respectively, as

$$\tau = \exp\left(- \frac{2\pi iEt}{h} \right) \tag{1.24}$$

and

$$\psi = \exp\left(\frac{2\pi ipq}{h} \right). \tag{1.25}$$

We are only interested in the wave function as a means of calculating system mechanical properties such as p and E. These are readily obtained from differential operations on Ψ. For example,

$$\left(\frac{\partial \Psi}{\partial q} \right)_t = A\tau \left(\frac{\partial \psi}{\partial q} \right)_t = \Psi \left(\frac{\partial \ln\psi}{\partial q} \right)_t = \frac{2\pi ip\Psi}{h} \tag{1.26}$$

or

$$p\Psi = \frac{h}{2\pi i} \left(\frac{\partial \Psi}{\partial q} \right)_t. \tag{1.27}$$

Similarly,

$$\left(\frac{\partial \Psi}{\partial t} \right)_q = A\psi \left(\frac{\partial \tau}{\partial t} \right)_q = \Psi \left(\frac{\partial \ln\tau}{\partial t} \right)_q = - \frac{2\pi iE\Psi}{h} \tag{1.28}$$

or

$$E\Psi = - \frac{h}{2\pi i} \left(\frac{\partial \Psi}{\partial t} \right)_q. \tag{1.29}$$

As can be seen, operation on the wave function yields the product of the mechanical variable and the wave function, that is, the mechanical variable is an eigenvalue. Thus, in quantum mechanical calculations of mechanical properties (energy, coordinates, momenta, etc.), wave function operators replace the variables. Equations (1.27) and (1.29) serve to define the operators corresponding to p and E, i.e.,

---

[*]While it is true that p implicitly depends on t and that E implicitly depends on p, only two variables are independent. Once the state of the system is fixed by the specification of two independent variables, the remaining dependent variables are also fixed. Selection of q and t as the independent variables is convenient because of our intuitive feel for spatial and temporal coordinates.

$$p \Leftrightarrow \hat{p} = \frac{h}{2\pi i}\nabla \tag{1.30}$$

$$E \Leftrightarrow \hat{E} = -\frac{h}{2\pi i}\frac{\partial}{\partial t}. \tag{1.31}$$

We can also formulate the Hamiltonian operator by replacing momentum in Equation (1.17) with the momentum operator. Thus,

$$H = \sum_i \frac{p_i^2}{2m_i} + U \Leftrightarrow \hat{H} = -\sum_i \frac{h^2}{8\pi^2 m_i}\nabla_i^2 + U. \tag{1.32}$$

For a conservative system $H = E$, and Equations (1.29) and (1.32) can be combined to yield the Schrödinger equation,

$$\hat{H}\Psi = -\sum_i \frac{h^2}{8\pi^2 m_i}\nabla_i^2\Psi + U\Psi = E\Psi = -\frac{h}{2\pi i}\frac{\partial \Psi}{\partial t}. \tag{1.33}$$

Originally, the Schrödinger equation was thought to be a direct replacement for the classical equations of motion but with the added capability of predicting the quantized behavior observed in atoms. While the equation is the quantum mechanical equivalent of the equations of motion in classical mechanics, Ψ was found not to reflect an actual mechanical location of a selected electron, rather only the spatial probability of finding any electron. Solution of the Schrödinger equation subject to appropriate boundary conditions permits calculation of the wave function as illustrated in Example 1.7.

As we shall see in the next section, Ψ is essentially a probability distribution function and can be used to find expected or average values of mechanical properties. In general the expectation value of a property J, represented by $<J>$, is calculated from

$$<J> = \frac{\int \Psi^* \hat{J} \Psi \, dq}{\int \Psi^* \Psi \, dq}, \tag{1.34}$$

where * indicates the complex conjugate of the function. The denominator of Equation (1.34) represents the probability of finding the particle somewhere in the space over which the integral is performed. It is really just the expectation value of 1, meaning that the particle must be found somewhere, and is therefore a normalizing factor for the probability.

To calculate quantum mechanical properties, one solves the Schrödinger equation for Ψ and uses it in Equation (1.34) to find expectation values of properties. This procedure is illustrated in Example 1.8.

Generally, for a given set of boundary conditions, many solutions will satisfy the Schrödinger equation. The most general solution is obtained using

Example 1.7   Calculate the energy levels available to a single particle confined to a one-dimensional region of length L by infinite potentials at either end. This is the classical "particle-in-a-box" problem.

Schrödinger's equation can be written as,

$$-\frac{h^2}{8\pi^2 m}\frac{d^2\psi}{dx^2} + U_0\psi = E\psi ,$$

where the amplitude and temporal part of Ψ have been divided out. This equation can be rearranged to yield,

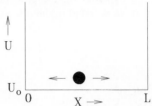

$$\frac{d^2\psi}{dx^2} + \frac{8\pi^2 m}{h^2}(E - U_0)\psi = 0 .$$

The equation is now in a form for which we readily recognize the general solution:

$$\psi = \alpha\sin\gamma x + \beta\cos\gamma x$$

with

$$\gamma = \sqrt{8\pi^2 m(E - U_0)/h^2} .$$

Because the potential at either end of the "box" is infinite, the probability distribution must vanish at the boundaries, i.e., the boundary conditions are

BC 1: $\psi = 0$ at $x = 0$ BC 2: $\psi = 0$ at $x = L$.

Application of BC 1 requires $\beta = 0$, and subsequent application of BC 2 requires that $\gamma = n\pi/L$, where n is an integer. Thus, the nth particular solution is

$$\psi_n = \alpha_n\sin\left(\frac{n\pi x}{L}\right)$$

and the available energy levels are discrete, characterized by the quantum number n:

$$E_n = U_0 + \frac{n^2 h^2}{8mL^2} .$$

the superposition principle. If Ψ_n is the nth solution, the general solution is given by

$$\Psi = \sum_n C_n \Psi_n = \sum_n c_n\psi_n\tau_n , \qquad (1.35)$$

where both the amplitude A_n and C_n have been absorbed into the new normalization constant c_n. Then, for example, the kinetic energy of a particle in either of the two lowest energy states could be found as in Example 1.8, but Ψ would be given by

Example 1.8   Find the average kinetic energy for the particle in the box, shown in Example 1.7, if it is constrained to a single energy level.

To find E_n, the probably $\wp_n$ must first be normalized to 1 to ensure that the particle is found in the nth energy level. Thus,

$$\int_0^L \Psi_n^* \Psi_n \, dx = 1 = c_n^2 \tau_n^* \tau_n \int_0^L \sin^2 \left(\frac{n\pi x}{L} \right) dx .$$

But,

$$\tau^* \tau = \exp \left[\frac{2\pi i E t - 2\pi i E t}{h} \right] = 1 .$$

The above integral is easily found to be $L/2$, and so the normalization constant is given by $c_n = (2/L)^{1/2}$. The complete normalized wave function for the nth quantum state is therefore:

$$\Psi_n = \sqrt{\frac{2}{L}} \exp \left(-\frac{2\pi i E_n t}{h} \right) \sin \left(\frac{n\pi x}{L} \right) .$$

The average or expectation value of the kinetic energy can be found from the wave function in accordance with Equation (1.34), i.e.,

$$\langle K \rangle = \int_0^L \Psi_n^* \left(-\frac{h^2}{8\pi^2 m} \right) \frac{d^2 \Psi_n}{dx^2} dx = -\frac{h^2}{8\pi^2 m} c_n^2 \tau^* \tau \int_0^L \psi_n^* \frac{d^2 \psi_n}{dx^2} \, dx$$

$$= \frac{c_n^2 h^2 n^2}{8mL^2} \int_0^L \sin^2 \left(\frac{n\pi x}{L} \right) dx$$

or

$$\langle K \rangle = \frac{n^2 h^2}{8mL^2} .$$

$$\Psi = c_1 \tau_1 \psi_1 + c_2 \tau_2 \psi_2 .$$

1.5 STATISTICS

Application of either classical or quantum mechanics to macroscopic systems containing on the order of 10^{23} molecules is obviously impractical, probably impossible. Instead, we use statistical techniques to obtain expectation or average values of variables. Rather than count specific particles, we use probability distributions to represent the system. The expectation value of a function is then found by statistically averaging the function using the probability distribution. We consider both discrete and continuous distributions because quantum mechanics requires the former and classical mechanics requires the latter.

1.5.1 Discrete Distributions

When computing properties with statistics, we must realize that the result of any one event is not determined. We may predict an expected outcome based on many events, not the outcome of any single event. For example, we don't know when we flip a coin whether the result will be heads or tails, but we do expect to see approximately 50,000 heads in 100,000 coin tosses because the probability of heads is $1/2$ for each toss. We desire then to be able to determine the average or expected value (called the expectation) for a large number of events.

Suppose we have three discrete, independent variables x_1, x_2, and x_3. If the probability of occurrence for each of these three variables is identical, then obviously the average value is found from

$$<x> = \frac{x_1 + x_2 + x_3}{3} \, .$$

The average is found in this manner because all three events are equally probable. What we are actually doing is multiplying the occurrence by its probability,

$$<x> = \frac{1}{3}x_1 + \frac{1}{3}x_2 + \frac{1}{3}x_3 \, .$$

In general, the probability of an event can be found by dividing the number of successful occurrences by the total number of tries. For example, normally one would expect a six to be turned up one out of six times a die is thrown. The desired event is one out of six equally possible outcomes, and so the probability is 1/6. If a "loaded" die is thrown 600 times and six is obtained 200 times, then the probability of obtaining a six is 1/3, rather than 1/6, for the loaded die.

One uses such probabilities to find the expectation or mean value of a discrete function by taking the product of the function and its probability. If $F(x)$ is the value of a discrete function at x and $\wp(x)$ is the probability of x, then

$$<F> = \sum \wp(x)F(x) \, . \tag{1.36}$$

This is illustrated in Example 1.9.

Only simple algebra is required to prove three quite useful theorems about expectation values. The relationships shown in Table 1.1 can be viewed as convenient ways to calculate expectation values. For example, one can find the expectation value of the sum of two variables simply by adding the individual expectation values of the two variables. These three theorems can, of course, be generalized to more variables.

TABLE 1.1   Theorems on Expectation Values

Relation	Condition of Validity
$<cx> = c<x>$	c is a constant
$<x + y> = <x> + <y>$	
$<xy> = <x><y>$	for independent x and y

A function may also be multivariate. In this case, we may be interested in the joint probability, or the probability that x and y are simultaneously satisfied as in Example 1.9. The expectation value for multivariate distributions is a simple extension of Equation (1.36),

$$<F> = \sum_x \sum_y ...F(x,y,...)\, \wp(x,y,...)\,, \tag{1.37}$$

where $\wp(x, y, ...)$ is the joint probability of x, y, ... simultaneously occurring. The joint probability can be found from the conditional probability, $\wp_{x|y}$, which is the probability that x occurs given that y does. In evaluating $\wp(x, y)$ from $\wp_{x|y}$, it is important to remember that probabilities of sequential events multiply. Thus the probability that y occurs multiplied by the probability that x occurs given that y already has, yields the joint probability,

$$\wp(x,y) = \wp_{x|y} \cdot \wp_y\,. \tag{1.38}$$

If the probabilities are independent (if the probability that x occurs does not depend on the occurrence of y), then the conditional probability $\wp_{x|y}$ is simply $\wp_x$ and

$$\wp(x,y) = \wp_x \cdot \wp_y \qquad \text{(for independent probabilities)}\,. \tag{1.39}$$

As in the univariant case, multivariant probabilities are always normalized to unity.

1.5.2 Continuous Distributions

Let f represent a continuous distribution of events as a function of b, for example, that shown in Figure 1.2. The probability of events occurring in the infinitesimal range $b + db$ is denoted $\wp db$. It is simply the fraction of total events associated with that range, i.e.,

$$\wp\, db = \frac{f\, db}{\displaystyle\int_{-\infty}^{\infty} f\, db}\,. \tag{1.40}$$

$\wp$ is called the probability density function because it represents a fractional

Example 1.9   Suppose a poll of 30 married couples is taken and can be considered representative of the population of a city as a whole. In the poll, couples are asked how many children and how many dogs they have. The following results were obtained, where *n(x)* represents the number of couples having *x* children and *n(y)* represents the number of couples with *y* dogs:

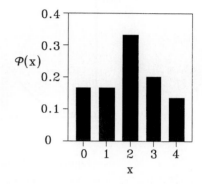

$\mathcal{P}(x)$

x or *y*	0	1	2	3	4	total
n(x)	5	5	10	6	4	30
n(y)	15	10	5	0	0	30

The probability of a married couple having *x* children is found by dividing *n(x)* by the total, $\Sigma n(x)$. The probability distribution is discrete since only integer numbers of children and dogs are viable. The resultant discrete probability distribution is shown at the right. Note that the distribution is normalized so that $\Sigma \mathcal{P}(x) = 1$. Once the probability distribution is known, expectation values may be found from Equation (1.36).

(a) What is the average number of children per married couple in this city?

$$\langle x \rangle = 1 \times \frac{1}{6} + 2 \times \frac{1}{3} + 3 \times \frac{1}{5} + 4 \times \frac{2}{15} = 2$$

(b) If all homes contain one master bedroom plus one additional bedroom for every two children, what is the average number of bedrooms in the homes of the married couples in this city? The number of bedrooms can be written down as a function of the number of children as $r(x) = 1 + \text{INT}[(x + 1)/2]$. The average number of bedrooms is then given by

$$\langle r \rangle = \Sigma \, r(x) \mathcal{P}(x) = 1 \times \frac{1}{6} + 2 \times \frac{1}{6} + 2 \times \frac{1}{3} + 3 \times \frac{1}{5} + 3 \times \frac{2}{15} = 2.2$$

(c) If the number of dogs owned by a married couple is independent of the number of children that they have (it almost certainly is not), then what is the probability that a married couple in this city has both two children and no dogs? Because dog ownership and the number of children are to be considered independent, the joint probability is just the product of the two independent probabilities and

$$\mathcal{P}_{(x = 2, \, y = 0)} = \mathcal{P}_{(x = 2)} \, \mathcal{P}_{(y = 0)} = \frac{1}{3} \times \frac{1}{2} = 0.167$$

(d) What is the average number of dogs among people with at least one child?

$$\langle y \rangle = 1 \times \frac{10}{30} + 2 \times \frac{5}{30} = \frac{2}{3} \text{ (if dogs and children are independent)}$$

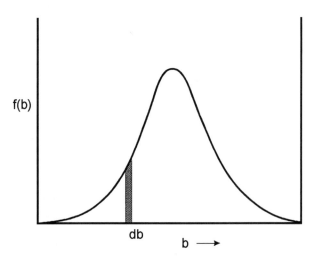

Figure 1.2   Continuous distribution function.

probability associated with each value of the independent variable. $\wp$ is simply the normalized form of the density distribution function f. As in the discrete case, the probability density is normalized. Obviously from Equation (1.40),

$$\int_{-\infty}^{\infty} \wp \, db = 1 \, . \tag{1.41}$$

Relations analogous to Equations (1.37)–(1.39) also apply for continuous distributions:

$$<F> = \frac{\displaystyle\int_{b}\int_{c} ... \, Ff(b,c, ...) \, db \, dc \, ...}{\displaystyle\int_{b}\int_{c} ... \, f(b,c, ...) \, db \, dc \, ...} = \int_{b}\int_{c} ... \, F \, \wp(b,c, ...) \, db \, dc \, ... \, , \tag{1.42}$$

$$\wp(b) = \int_{c} ... \, \wp(b,c, ...) \, dc \, ... \, , \tag{1.43}$$

and

$$\wp(b,c) = \wp(b) \, \wp(c) \quad \text{(for independent probability densities).} \tag{1.44}$$

Notice from Equation (1.43) that if we want $\wp$ as a function of only a particular subset of variables, independent of the values of the remaining variables, we simply integrate the multivariate distribution function with respect to each of the nonselected variables over their whole domain.

The *variance* of a random variable is another important quantity in statistics, because it describes the dispersion or scatter of the values of the random variable about the mean. The variance is defined by

$$V(x) = \langle (x - \langle x \rangle)^2 \rangle . \tag{1.45}$$

The *standard deviation*, σ, is also commonly used. It is defined as the positive square root of the variance.

The variance is actually only one of many *moments* which can be used to describe a distribution function and its shape. The rth moment of a random variable x about the mean, also called the rth central moment, is defined by

$$\mu_r = \langle (x - \langle x \rangle)^r \rangle . \tag{1.46}$$

It follows that $\mu_0 = 1$, $\mu_1 = 0$, and $\mu_2 = V(x)$. Thus the second moment is the variance about the mean.

The third and fourth moments are generally normalized with respect to the standard deviation. They provide information about the shape of the distribution. The coefficient of *skewness*, $\alpha_3 = \mu_3/\sigma^3$, indicates the asymmetry of the distribution about the mean. A positive value of α_3 means that the distribution is skewed to the right, and a negative value implies that there is more area to the left of the mean. The coefficient of *kurtosis*, $\alpha_4 = \mu_4/\sigma^4$, indicates the "peakedness" of the distribution. A narrow, high peak corresponds to a large kurtosis; a low, broad peak is described with a small value of α_4. The Gaussian or *normal* distribution with which you are undoubtedly familiar is symmetric about the mean ($\mu_3 = 0$) and has a kurtosis of 3.

Together, the mean, variance, and higher order moments can be used to describe the distribution. This is particularly useful in systems for which the functionality of the distribution is not known. For example, we will apply this concept later by representing the unknown polar interactions between molecules with a multipole expansion in terms of various charge separation moments.

1.5.3 Counting

Statistics also helps in counting degeneracies or different arrangements of equally probable distributions. For example, let Q represent the set of letters {A,B,C,D,E}. We might ask, "In how many different orders can these five letters be arranged without using the same letter twice?" We may select any of the five letters for the first position. For each choice of the first letter, there are four remaining letters from which to select the second letter, and so on. This procedural logic reveals that the total number of unique arrangements is $5 \cdot 4 \cdot 3 \cdot 2 \cdot 1 = 5!$ (five factorial). A short-hand notation is

$$_N P_N = N! \, , \tag{1.47}$$

read as *permutations* of N things taken N at a time.

We might also be interested in permutations of a subset of Q. For example, how many unique two-letter arrangements can be made from the five letters comprising Q? Obviously, we again may choose any of the five letters for the first position and any of the remaining four for the second, or 20 different permutations. This kind of counting is readily done using permutations of N things taken X at a time, or

$$_N P_X = \frac{N!}{(N-X)!} \, . \tag{1.48}$$

Counting arrangements using permutations assumes that all of the elements of the set are unique. Often order within the arrangement is not important. For example, if we choose two letters from Q and the selection order is not important, then the combinations {AE} and {EA} are not unique and we must divide out from the permutations the possible internal ways of arranging the letters. If ordering is of no consequence in determining unique arrangements, then one should calculate *combinations* of N things taken X at a time rather than permutations:

$$_N C_X = \frac{N!}{X! \, (N-X)!} \, . \tag{1.49}$$

Molecules of the same kind are indistinguishable and so we will use combinations to count the number of unique distinguishable arrangements. Example 1.10 illustrates the use of combinations in counting only distinguishable states. Notice that in this example there are six distinguishable states. If permutations $_4 P_4$ had been used to count the states, we would have arrived at 24 unique states. The extra factor of four accounts for the indistinguishable arrangements obtained by switching the order of the identical X's and O's in the six arrangements shown.

Equation (1.49) can be used in combinatorial analysis to determine the probability of particular events occurring, remembering that the probability is

---

Example 1.10   How many unique orderings of four molecules are possible if each is composed of two identical molecules of type O and two of type X?

There are six possible unique orderings since

$$_4 C_2 = 4!/(2! \cdot 2!) = 4 \cdot 3/2 = 6.$$

The six cases can be represented diagrammatically as:

1) *XXOO*   2) *XOXO*   3) *XOOX*
4) *OOXX*   5) *OXOX*   6) *OXXO*

---

given as the number of occurrences of the desired event divided by the total number of events. Example 1.11 (from ref.10) illustrates this kind of analysis.

Equation (1.49) is also the equation for the coefficients of a binomial distribution. Similarly, the number of orderings for groupings of more than two particles are the coefficients of a multinomial distribution. Generalizing, we may write the distribution density of N things taken N_1, N_2, ... at a time as

---

Example 1.11   A box contains eight red, three white, and nine blue balls. If three balls are drawn at random, determine the probability that (a) all three are red, (b) two are red and one is white, (c) at least one is white, (d) one of each color is drawn, and (e) the three balls are drawn in the order red, white, blue.[10]

(a) Combinations can be used to count the number of successful events since the order in which the balls are drawn is not important. Then,

$$\wp(3r) = \frac{_8C_3}{_{20}C_3} = \frac{14}{285}.$$

Note that another way to approach the problem is to use joint probabilities. Let r_i represent a red ball drawn on the ith draw. Then the probability of drawing three red balls is given by,

$$\wp_{(3r)} = \wp_{(r_1)} \; \wp_{(r_2|r_1)} \; \wp_{[r_3|(r_2,\, r_1)]} = \frac{8}{20} \times \frac{7}{19} \times \frac{6}{18} = \frac{14}{285}.$$

(b)

$$\wp_{(2r,\, 1w)} = \frac{(_8C_2)(_3C_1)}{_{20}C_3} = \frac{7}{95}$$

(c)

$$\wp_{(\geq 1w)} = 1 - \wp_{(0w)} = 1 - \frac{_{17}C_3}{_{20}C_3} = 1 - \frac{34}{57} = \frac{23}{57}$$

Note: This could also be calculated as $\wp_{(1w)} + \wp_{(2w)} + \wp_{(3w)} = [(_3C_1)(_{17}C_2) + (_3C_2)(_{17}C_1) + (_3C_3)]/_{20}C_3$.

(d)

$$\wp_{(1r,\, 1w,\, 1b)} = \frac{(_8C_1)(_3C_1)(_9C_1)}{_{20}C_3} = \frac{18}{95}$$

(e)

$$\wp_{(r_1,\, w_2,\, b_3)} = \frac{1}{3!} \; \wp_{(1r,\, 1w,\, 1b)} = \frac{1}{6} \times \frac{18}{95} = \frac{3}{95}$$

or alternatively,

$$\wp_{(r_1,\, w_2,\, b_3)} = \wp_{(r_1)} \; \wp_{(w_2|r_1)} \; \wp_{(b_3|w_2,\, r_1)} = \frac{8}{20} \times \frac{3}{19} \times \frac{9}{18} = \frac{3}{95}$$

$$f(N_1, N_2, \ldots) = \frac{N!}{\Pi_j N_j!} \quad (N = \sum_j N_j) . \qquad (1.50)$$

An important feature of multinomial distributions is that $\sigma \to 0$ as N becomes large. The variance of the distribution decreases so rapidly that the peak narrows to a single value. In the limit of infinite N, the distribution completely collapses to a single spike. In this limit, the entire distribution can then be replaced by the maximum term.

To appreciate this more fully, let us examine the location of the maximum in a distribution. For large N, discrete distributions become continuous, so we consider only the continuous case. The maximum in the distribution, which represents the most probable state, can be found by differentiating the distribution (or more conveniently, $\ln f$) with respect to N_1 and setting the derivative to zero. Thus, from Equation (1.50), written for the binomial case,

$$\left[\frac{d \ln f(N_1)}{dN_1} \right]_{max} = \left\{ \frac{d}{dN_1} [\ln N! - \ln N_1! - \ln(N-N_1)!] \right\}_{max} = 0 . \qquad (1.51)$$

The $\ln N!$ term is common in statistics and can be replaced by a convenient and accurate approximation that becomes exact for the large number of particles dealt with in statistical mechanics. The simplification is made by writing $\ln N!$ as the sum of logarithms. This sum can be replaced by an integral for large values of N. Thus,

$$\ln N! = \sum_{x=1}^{N} \ln x \simeq \int_1^N \ln x \, dx = (x \ln x - x) \Big|_1^N = N \ln N - N .$$

The final relation

$$\ln N! \simeq N \ln N - N \qquad (1.52)$$

is called Stirling's approximation. Although it is shown in Equation (1.52) as an approximation, it is exact in the limit $N \to \infty$. Equation (1.51) can be solved for the value of N_1 at which the maximum in $f(N_1)$ occurs. After some algebra, one finds that $N_1^* = N/2$.

If one expands $\ln f(N_1)$ in a Taylor's series expansion about the maximum and truncates the resultant expression after the second-order term (the first-order term is obviously zero since the first derivative vanishes at the maximum), one can show that the binomial distribution becomes Gaussian for large N, i.e.,

$$f(N_1) = f(N_1^*) \exp \left[- \frac{2(N_1 - N_1^*)^2}{N} \right] . \qquad (1.53)$$

The usual form for a Gaussian or normal distribution is commonly written in terms of the standard deviation σ,

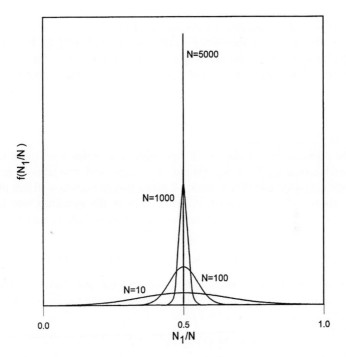

Figure 1.3   Normalized binomial distribution as a function of N.

$$f(x) = \frac{1}{\sqrt{2\pi}\,\sigma} \exp\left[-\frac{1}{2}\left(\frac{x-<x>}{\sigma}\right)^2\right]. \tag{1.54}$$

A comparison of Equations (1.53) and (1.54) reveals that σ is on the order of $N^{1/2}$ for the bivariate system considered here. This provides us with the relation sought between the width of the curve and N. For example, approximately 99.9% of the area under a normal distribution is contained within an area of 3σ on either side of the maximum. Even for 10^{20} particles, a distance of 3σ is only 3×10^{10}, an extremely small number compared to the possible range of the distribution 10^{20}! Figure 1.3 illustrates how rapidly the variance of a normalized Gaussian distribution decreases with increasing N. On this scale, the distribution becomes a spike centered at the maximum distribution for values of N as low as 5,000.

The reason for this relative decrease in the variance with increasing N is the very large number of possible ways of generating the maximum distribution relative to the number of ways of producing values at the ends of the distribution. With this many particles there are so many more possible combinations when $N_1 = N_1^*$ than at any other value, that the maximum term simply overwhelms the number of other possible combinations at other N_1 values. This point can be further examined by the simple experiment illustrated in Example 1.12. Certainly, for values of N approaching that required for thermodynamic systems, the distribution of states can be replaced with its maximum value without loss of accuracy or generality. Thus,

$$f(N_1) = f(N_1^*) \, \delta_{N,N/2} = f^*, \qquad (1.55)$$

where δ is the Kronecker delta.

The replacement of the entire distribution with the maximum term is a key simplification in the development of a statistical mechanical method of computation. It simplifies the statistics without loss of accuracy so that properties can be formulated from the most probable state of the system. Consider a sum of M positive quantities, T_i. Let S be the sum of these values, and let T_i^* be the largest of the T_i's. Since the T_i's are all positive,

$$T_i^* \leq S \leq MT_i^* \text{ or } \ln T_i^* \leq \ln S \leq (\ln M + \ln T_i^*) \, . \qquad (1.56)$$

If, as in the distributions discussed above and the molecular systems to be discussed in this book, T_i^* varies with M as $\exp(M)$, then $\ln M \ll \ln T_i^*$ for large M. Therefore,

$$\ln T_i^* \leq \ln S \leq \ln T_i^* \text{ or } S = T_i^* \, . \qquad (1.57)$$

As before, we see that the sum can be replaced by the most probable term. Ironically, the extremely large, incomprehensible number of particles that precluded the application of deterministic mechanics to the whole system actually provides the simplification that allows a statistical method to be applied to the mechanics.

Example 1.12   Perform a simple experiment with coins to see how the breadth of a distribution becomes small relative to the domain of possible outcomes as N increases. In this case, N will be the number of coins in a group that are tossed and N_1 represents the number of heads. Flip four coins as a group and count the number of heads. Repeat this process for 10 trials and then plot the number of occurrences of zero, one, two, three, and four heads in the 10 trials. Repeat this procedure using a group of 10 coins, then once again for a group of 20 coins. Notice that as N is increased, the probability of getting all tails or all heads greatly diminishes and the distribution moves away from the ends of the domain. Also, the number of ways in which approximately 50% heads can occur rapidly increases and begins to dominate the distribution.

REFERENCES

1. van der Waals, J.D. *On the Continuity of the Gaseous and Liquid States* (1873), as cited in Rowlinson, J.S. ed., *J.D. van der Waals: Continuity of Gaseous and Liquid States,* Studies in Statistical Mechanics, Vol. 14, Elsevier, Amsterdam, 1988.

2. Boltzmann L. *The Development of the Methods of Theoretical Physics* (1899), as cited in E. Broda, *Ludwig Boltzmann,* Ox Bow Press, Woodbridge, CT, 1983, p. 43.

3. Cline B.L. *Men Who Made a New Physics,* University of Chicago Press, Chicago, 1987.

4. Gregory, B. *Inventing Reality: Physics as a Language,* John Wiley, New York, 1990.

5. McQuarrie, D.A. *Statistical Mechanics,* Harper & Row, New York, 1976.

6. Reed, T.M., and Gubbins, K.E. *Applied Statistical Mechanics,* McGraw-Hill, New York, 1973.

7. Tolman, R.C. *The Principles of Statistical Mechanics,* Oxford University Press, London, 1967.

8. Hill, T.L. *An Introduction to Statistical Thermodynamics,* Addison-Wesley, Reading MA, 1960.

9. Goldstein, H. *Classical Mechanics,* 2nd ed., Addison-Wesley, Reading, MA, 1980, p. 48.

10. Spiegel, M.R. *Probability and Statistics, Schaum's Outline Series,* McGraw-Hill, New York, 1975.

PROBLEMS

MECHANICS

1. The mechanics of objects launched from Earth and from orbiting objects, such as the Space Shuttle, require information about the size and mass of the Earth. For the problems posed here, assume that the radius of the Earth is 6.37×10^3 km and that its mass is 5.97×10^{24} kg.

(a) The minimum energy required to move an object from the surface of the Earth to an infinite distance beyond the pull of Earth's gravitational field is the escape energy. The upward velocity of the object at the Earth's surface required to provide this amount of energy is the escape velocity. Calculate the Earth's escape velocity in km/s assuming negligible air resistance (the system is therefore conservative) and no effects due to the presence of the moon and other celestial bodies.

(b) If a satellite is launched from the Space Shuttle at an altitude of 150 km above the surface of the Earth, at what horizontal speed, relative to the Earth not the Shuttle, must the satellite have if it is to have a circular orbit?

(c) The moon's orbit is nearly circular with a period of 27.32 days. Calculate the center to center distance from the Earth to the moon.

2. Suppose two point molecules of relative masses $m_2 = 1$ and $m_2 = 2$ are constrained to motion in one dimension. Further suppose that they have zero velocity relative to each other at a point where they are separated from each other by a dimensionless distance of $x = 2.5$, and that the potential between the molecules is given by

$$U = 4 \left(x^{-12} - x^{-6} \right).$$

   (a) Plot on the same graph the potential energy U and the intermolecular force up to a distance of $x = 3$.
   (b) Write down the differential equation and appropriate initial conditions which could be numerically solved to obtain $x = x(t)$. Do not attempt to solve the problem, but sketch on a t vs. x plot the general behavior that you would expect to see if you did solve the problem.

3. The motion of a two-particle system can be conveniently split into the motion of the center of mass and the relative motion of the two particles.[5] Consider two particles of mass m_1 and m_2 moving in one dimension. The potential energy depends only on the distance between the two particles, $U = U(x_{12})$, where $x_{12} = x_1 - x_2$, and the total energy of the system is given by

$$E = \frac{1}{2}m_1\dot{x}_1^2 + \frac{1}{2}m_2\dot{x}_2^2 + U(x_{12})$$

and the center of mass coordinate is defined by

$$X = \frac{(m_1 x_1 + m_2 x_2)}{(m_1 + m_2)}.$$

Derive an expression for the total energy in terms of the center of mass, X, and the relative coordinate, x_{12}. Your answer should be in terms of the total mass, $M = m_1 + m_2$, and the reduced mass, $\mu = m_1 m_2/M$.

4. Transform the Cartesian-coordinate expression for L given in Example 1.3 to the polar coordinate version.

5. A rope of length L is draped over a frictionless, massless pulley.[9] A weight of M_1 is attached to one end of the rope and a weight of M_2 is attached to the other end. Determine the equation of motion for this system using Lagrange's method. *Hint*: Let x be the distance from one weight to the top of the pulley, then the distance from the top of the pulley to the other weight is $L - x$.

6. Derive Lagrange's equations of motion for a particle of mass m moving in two dimensions while being attracted coulombically $[(U(r) = -C/r]$ to a fixed center.[9] Here C is a constant of charge. The angular momentum, l, of the particle is given by

$$l = mr^2\dot{\theta}.$$

Show that the angular motion is conserved, i.e., $dl/dt = 0$.

7. A silo is to be built as a right circular cylinder with a hemispherical roof. The silo is to have a specified volume V, but the surface area (including the floor) is to be minimized to decrease the heat transfer. What dimensions should the silo have?

8. Use the Lagrangian in polar coordinates and the method of constraints to determine the equation of motion for a bob of mass M at the end of a frictionless pendulum

of length D. Also determine the constraint force felt by the pendulum rod as a function of angle. (Note that this problem can be solved more simply by formulating the Lagrangian to already include the constraint, but the constraint force is not immediately apparent from this latter approach).

QUANTUM MECHANICS

9. (a) Calculate the expectation value of the kinetic energy for a particle "in a box" if it can occupy the two lowest states. That is, assume the wave function to be given by

$$\Psi = C_1 \tau_1 \psi_1 + C_2 \tau_2 \psi_2 \quad \text{with } C_1 = C_2 .$$

(b) Suppose that instead of $C_1 = C_2$ as in part (a), it is observed that the value of the kinetic energy of the particle is twice that of the lowest stationary state. What values of C_1 and C_2 would satisfy this observation?

10. What is the expectation value for the linear momentum p_x of a particle in a one-dimensional box? What is the expectation of p_x^2? Explain the difference in your results.

STATISTICS

11. (a) The Gaussian distribution may be written as[6]

$$p(x) = A \exp \left[- \frac{(x - <x>)^2}{2\sigma^2} \right] .$$

Calculate the normalization constant A.

(b) For a gas at equilibrium at temperature T, the fraction of molecules having an x component of velocity in the range v_x to $v_x + dv_x$ was shown by Maxwell to be

$$f(v_x)dv_x = \sqrt{\frac{m}{2\pi kT}} \exp \left(- \frac{mv_x^2}{2kT} \right) dv_x .$$

Similar expressions hold for the v_y and v_z velocity components. This is a Gaussian centered at $v_x = 0$ with $\sigma = (kT/m)^{1/2}$. Show that $f(v_x)$ is normalized.

(c) Find $<v_x>$ and $<v_x^2>$.

(d) Find the mean deviation and the mean-square deviation of v_x.

(e) Show that $<1/2mv_x^2> = 1/2kT$ and that $<1/2mv^2> = 3kT/2$.

12. Show that $<(x - <x>)^2> = <x^2> - <x>^2$.

13. Consider the sum

$$\sum_{N=0}^{M} \frac{M!\, x^N}{N!(M-N)}.$$

where x is of the order of 1 while M and N are both of the order 10^{20}. First show that the logarithm of the sum is exactly $M \ln(1+x)$, and then calculate the logarithm of the maximum term. *Hint*: Recall the binomial expansion.

14. Show from Equation (1.51) that the maximum in a binomial distribution occurs when $N_1 = 1/2N$.

15. Five journals and four textbooks are randomly placed on a shelf.[10] Determine the probability that three specific textbooks will be found together on the shelf.

16. A ball is drawn at random from a box containing six red balls, four white balls and five blue balls.[10] Determine the probability that the ball drawn is (a) red, (b) white, (c) blue, (d) not red, and (e) either red or white.

17. Three balls are drawn successively from the box of problem 6.[10] Find the probability that they are drawn in the order red, white, and blue if each ball is (a) replaced and (b) not replaced.

18. Four red balls, three white balls, and five blue balls are arranged in a row.[10] If all the balls of the same color are indistinguishable, how many different arrangements are possible?

19. A circular arrangement of lights contains seven sockets. Given seven different colored bulbs, how many different color arrangements can be made (a) with no restrictions on color combinations, and (b) if two particular colors may not be adjacent?

20. In how many ways can a committee of three be chosen from 10 people?

21. If you are dealt a poker hand from a normal, shuffled 52-card deck, what is the probability of obtaining (a) four aces, (b) a full house, and (c) two pair.

22. Evaluate 1000!.

23. The joint probability density function of two variables x and y is given by

$$\wp(x,y) = \begin{bmatrix} cxy & 0\le x\le 4; & 1\le y\le 5 \\ 0 & & \text{otherwise} \end{bmatrix}$$

(a) Determine c, the normalization constant.
(b) Determine $\wp(x)$, the probability distribution of x, independent of the y value.
(c) Are the probabilities $\wp(x)$ and $\wp(y)$ independent?
(d) Compute $<x + y>$.
(e) What is the conditional probability $\wp(x|y = 3)$?

2

THE PARTITION FUNCTION

The objective of this chapter is development of a relationship between observed thermodynamic properties and the immense number of molecular states and interactions inherent in the macroscopic manifestation of those properties. The relationship involves the partition function, obtained using the statistics of large numbers applied to the molecular states. Exact equations are then derived between the partition function and thermodynamic properties. While this relationship draws us closer to an ultimate capability of calculating macroscopic properties from molecular motion and interactions, it must be viewed as only a step toward the solution of the problem rather than the solution itself. In actuality, the difficulties of the many-body problem are still present, just concealed within the partition function. The partition function can be calculated rather easily for the noninteracting systems, as is shown in Chapters 3 and 4, but the complexity of molecular interactions makes its evaluation quite difficult for the nonideal, real fluids for which thermophysical properties are needed in actual processes. Methods for dealing with these difficulties inherent in the interacting many-body problem in fact constitutes the subject matter of the remainder of the book subsequent to Chapter 4.

2.1 TIME AND ENSEMBLE AVERAGES

Measured quantities (e.g., pressure, temperature, and density) arise from molecular motion, the mechanics of the constituent molecules as they interact and "collide" while in constant thermal motion. Unfortunately, we have no sensor that can detect the relationship between molecular motion and macroscopic properties. Indeed the heart of the Heisenberg uncertainty principle is that no such device can be made. The smaller the sensor, the more attuned it is to the position of the molecules, but the more the sensor is affected by the momenta of the particles themselves. The small mass of a very tiny sensor is affected by the very molecular momenta it tries to measure. The best that we can even hope for is a probe that measures a spatial average of molecular states at an instant in time, or a temporal average of molecular states at a particular position. Virtually all real sensors, of course, do neither. Because of their size and response time, they really only view an average over both time and space of what is happening on a molecular level. Thus we do not see the mercury level in a thermometer wildly fluctuating due to molecular collisions; the large number of molecules contacting it and the rapidity with which the collisions occur preclude this. The same is true of most, but not all, probes with which we measure the properties of the fluid. Einstein actually helped prove atomism by calculating the size of a probe that could be used to see fluctuations—something about the size of a dust or pollen particle. Such an experiment had already been carried out, unbeknownst to Einstein. The rapidly fluctuating, seemingly random motion of smoke and pollen particles observed by Robert Brown, later called Brownian motion, was nicely explained by Einstein's calculations.

Thus experimental measurements of macroscopic properties are really averages of molecular properties with respect to time or position, almost always both. To obtain useful thermophysical property calculations from molecular states, we must use statistical averaging techniques that are realistic and consistent with experiment. Imagine a hypothetical probe small enough that very localized measurements could be made. If the response time of the probe were incredibly fast, we could see molecular scale fluctuations as shown in Figure 2.1. The local instantaneous value of a molecular property J would fluctuate about some mean value $<J>$. The value of J measured by the instrument would be simply the time average of J found from

$$<J> = \lim_{t \to \infty} \frac{1}{t} \int_0^t J \, dt' \qquad (2.1)$$

for continuous systems, or from

$$<J> = \lim_{t \to \infty} \frac{1}{t} \sum_i J_i \Delta t_i \qquad (2.2)$$

for discrete systems.

Another way to look at time averages is in terms of the evolution of the momentum and position coordinates of the particles that comprise the system. Consider a single spherical particle. Three coordinates ($x, y,$ and z in a Cartesian

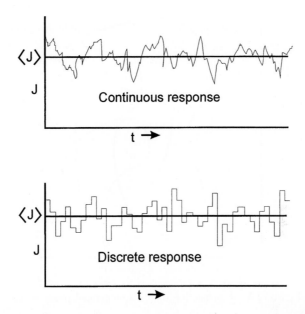

Figure 2.1   Time averages from continuous and discrete response functions.

coordinate system) are required to specify the position of the particle and three are required to specify its momentum. A single point on a six-dimensional plot would then completely represent the state of the particle, its position, and momentum. Now extend this concept to a system containing N spherical particles. The complete state of the system (and theoretically therefore all instantaneous properties) is identified if $3N$ momenta and $3N$ positions are specified. One could therefore imagine a point, plotted in $6N$-hyperspace, representing a unique state of the system with specific values for the momentum and position of each particle. As molecules move and interact, their positions and momenta continuously change, so the point representing the instantaneous state of the system in this $6N$-dimensional hyperspace, called *phase space,* evolves. The progression of the system can be viewed as a trajectory in $6N$ phase space. Phase space is difficult to portray graphically on two-dimensional paper, but a representation of the projection of a phase-space trajectory into two dimensions can be obtained by collapsing all momentum axes into one momentum axis and all position axes into a single position axis, as shown in Figure 2.2. Example 2.1 is a simple two-dimensional illustration of the concept of a trajectory in phase space.

While each point in phase space represents a unique state of the molecular system, there is enormous redundancy of such microscopic states that collectively produce the same macroscopic value of the property J. For example, the same

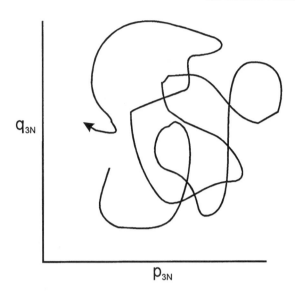

q_{3N}

p_{3N}

Figure 2.2   A projection of 6N dimensional phase space.

value of J is obtained from two microstates of a pure fluid which differ only by the interchange of positions or momenta of two identical particles; that is, the property is independent of molecular identity. The trajectory of the system through phase space therefore generates time-dependent fluctuating values of the macroscopic properties analogous to that depicted in Figure 2.1. The time average of the property is weighted by how much time the system spends in macroscopically degenerate loci of phase space.

Viewed in this way, one might imagine yet another way to find an average macroscopic property from the trajectory in phase space. We could disregard the chronological order of the phase-space points through which the system passes, and simply weight the average by the macroscopic degeneracy of the phase-space points through which the system travels, regardless of when the system passes through them. In this case, the average is found from the probability of observing the system in particular states from an instantaneous representation of the phase-space states available to the system. Figure 2.3 illustrates a cloud of phase points, the density of which represents the probability of the system being found in that particular region of phase space. A static collection of representative phase points through which the system would pass in time is called an ensemble, and the expectation value of J found statistically from this instantaneous representation is called the ensemble average:

$$<J> = \sum_i \wp_i J_i . \tag{2.3}$$

An ensemble is therefore a mental collection of a very large number of

Example 2.1   The concept of phase space is more easily understood through a graphical example of a familiar object. Here we examine the trajectory through phase space of the one-dimensional harmonic oscillator illustrated in Example 1.6. The program on disk illustrates the phase-space trajectory of the motion illustrated in Example 1.2.

Because only one momentum and one position coordinate are required to fix a single, one-dimensional oscillator in phase space, the plot is two-dimensional. To make it general, we use dimensionless coordinates. From Example 1.6, the dimensionless position can be written as

$$x^+ = \frac{x}{v_0\sqrt{m/f}} = \sin\sqrt{f/m}\ t\ .$$

The dimensionless momentum is found by differentiating the position equation. Thus,

$$p_x^+ = p_x/p_0 = \cos\sqrt{f/m}\ t\ .$$

In order to plot in phase space, momentum must be expressed as a function of position. This is done by solving for t from the position equation and substituting into the momentum equation to obtain

$$p^+ = \cos\left[\pm|\sin^{-1}(x^+)|\right]\ .$$

This is represented in phase space by the circular trajectory shown to the right.

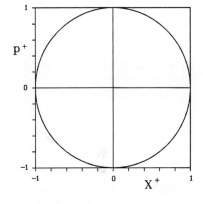

Note that $\sin^{-1}(x^+)$ is multivalued, but calculators generally return only the principal value for the inverse trigonometric functions. Because the domain of the argument of the sin function in the x^+ equation is from 0 to 2π, we must be sure to include the appropriate sign with the principle angle in the above equation to cover the appropriate domain.

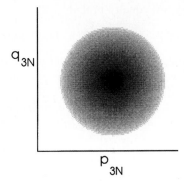

Figure 2.3 Representation of the density of states in phase space.

macroscopic replicas of the actual system, replicas with identical macroscopic properties, but which may vary in molecular phase-space coordinates. An instantaneous average based on these replicas should be identical to a time average if the same regions of phase space have been sampled. This is a statement of the Ergodic hypothesis, presented here without proof.

Postulate I (Ergodic Hypothesis).   Time averages are equivalent to ensemble averages.

$$<J> = \sum_i J_i \wp_i = \lim_{t \to \infty} \sum_i J_i \Delta t_i \tag{2.4}$$

The Ergodic hypothesis is the foundation upon which the methods of statistical mechanics rest, asserting that statistical averages are identical to the time-averaged properties obtained from laboratory sensors.

Ensemble averages are commonly used to calculate thermodynamic properties from statistical mechanics. Both ensemble and time averages are important in computing thermodynamic properties from molecular computer simulations. Molecular dynamics simulations solve the equations of motion and calculate particle trajectories in time; time averages are then used to obtain thermodynamic properties. On the other hand, Monte Carlo simulations deal specifically with the probability of generating ensembles, and use ensemble averages to obtain macroscopic properties.

A second postulate upon which we base development of the statistical mechanical method asserts that all states of the same energy level are equally probable. For a closed system of fixed V, quantum state i depends only upon the energy of that state, E_i. The principle of equal a priori probabilities assumes that nothing but the level of energy affects the relative probability of states. Without further information there is no reason to believe that any states of a particular energy level are more probable than others. We assume that they are fully degenerate.

Postulate II (Equal a Priori Probabilities).   All quantum states of the same energy are equally probable.

$$\wp_i = \wp_i(E_i) \tag{2.5}$$

Postulate II is of fundamental importance in linking microscopic states to expectation values. It permits development of a distribution function dependent solely upon the energy quantum state.

Ensembles are convenient representations of the statistical distribution of system states constrained to particular conditions. Depending upon the system constraints, one of several different ensembles may lend itself more directly to the types of properties to be calculated. Of course all ensemble representations provide the same results, but different ensembles are convenient for specific properties and conditions. Some of the more widely used ensembles are discussed in the following section.

2.2 ENSEMBLES

2.2.1 Microcanonical Ensemble

For isolated systems, the number of molecules, the volume, and the total energy of the system are constrained to be constant. Therefore, the most convenient ensemble for isolated systems is the microcanonical or NVE (since N, V, and E are fixed) ensemble. This is depicted in Figure 2.4 where each block represents an ensemble member having macroscopic properties N, V, and E identical to every other ensemble member. Each member represents a point in phase space for the complete system, and the phase-space domain is restricted to those points which produce the same values of N, V, and E.

We can mentally construct the ensemble of Figure 2.4 by putting together a large number of replicates of the system all having the same number of molecules and the same volume. The walls around the ensemble are adiabatic, rigid, and impermeable. Initially, the walls between the ensemble members are rigid, diathermal, and impermeable. Once the energy in each ensemble member has equilibrated to the mean value for the ensemble, the walls surrounding that member are instantaneously changed to adiabatic walls, making it an isolated

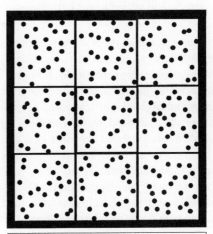

All boxes have the same volume, contain the same number of particles, and have the same energy; but the microstates are different.
Microcanonical = N, V, E constant

Figure 2.4 Depiction of microcanonical or NVE ensemble.

system. The temperature, pressure, and other properties of each ensemble member will naturally fluctuate about some mean value as in Figure 2.1, but the energy, volume, and number of particles will remain fixed. We seldom measure properties in the laboratory under these conditions, and so the microcanonical ensemble is not used extensively in statistical mechanical calculations. It is, however, the most naturally suited ensemble for molecular dynamics simulations in which conservative equations of motion are used. In such simulations, Newton's equations of motion are generally used to generate the phase-space trajectory of the system in a box of constant N and V. Because energy is a constant of the motion, all points generated are members of a microcanonical ensemble.

Because of the importance of the canonical ensemble in thermophysical property calculations, we will use it to develop the link between thermophysical properties and the ensemble partition function. We will then summarize relationships between the various ensembles and thermophysical properties in tables. Before moving on to the canonical ensemble, however, we should point out that the microcanonical partition function $\Omega(E)$ represents the total number of states of energy E available to the system. The ratio of the number of ensemble members in a particular state divided by $\Omega(E)$ is a probability of that state occurring. Postulate II tells us that because all states in the microcanonical ensemble have the same energy, each is equally probable. Example 2.2 illustrates that $\Omega(E)$ can be thought of as a volume of a thin shell in phase space. This volume is then readily calculated from geometric mensuration formulas for such simple cases as the one illustrated in the example.

2.2.2 Canonical Ensemble

The canonical or NVT ensemble is particularly useful for calculating thermodynamic properties because ensemble members are at constant temperature rather than energy as shown in Figure 2.5. One can mentally construct such an ensemble by juxtaposing replicas of the system in the sense that each contains the same number of particles and occupies the same volume. The ensemble members are enclosed by diathermal, rigid, impermeable walls. The whole ensemble is placed in a very large heat reservoir maintained at T. After thermal equilibration of all ensemble members, the wall around the entire ensemble is instantly made adiabatic to isolate now the ensemble from the heat bath and fix the total energy of the ensemble at E. The rigid, impermeable walls guarantee the same N and V for each ensemble member, and because each member can exchange heat with the other ensemble members, T is also constant and uniform throughout the ensemble. In essence, the other ensemble members serve as a heat reservoir for each member to maintain a constant T. Although T is constant and identical for each replicate system, the energy does fluctuate. This construct is strictly figurative, a visualization aid toward understanding the meaning of an NVT ensemble.

Example 2.2 Consider the harmonic oscillator of Example 1.6. (a) Determine the volume of phase space occupied by an oscillator whose energy is less than or equal to E, i.e., $\Omega(\leq E)$. (b) Determine the microcanonical partition function $\Omega(E)$ for the oscillator in terms of Δ, the allowed variation in the fixed value of E.

The Hamiltonian for the one-dimensional oscillator is

$$H(p,q) = \frac{p^2}{2m} + \frac{fq^2}{2}.$$

The surface of constant energy, E, is given by $H(p,q) = E$. Thus,

$$\frac{p^2}{2mE} + \frac{fq^2}{2E} = 1.$$

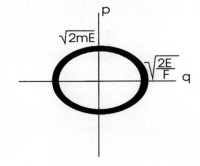

(a) Note that this is the equation of an ellipse in two-dimensional p-q phase space with intercepts $(2mE)^{0.5}$ and $(2E/f)^{0.5}$, respectively, as shown in the figure at the right. The area enclosed by the ellipse includes all states with $H \leq E$, and from geometry this is simply

$$\Omega(\leq E) = \pi\sqrt{2mE}\ \sqrt{\frac{2E}{f}} = 2\pi E\ \sqrt{\frac{m}{f}}.$$

(b) The area enclosed by the thin shell of width Δ illustrated in the figure represents the microcanonical partition function $\Omega(E)$. The area of the shell is

$$\Omega(E) = \pi\sqrt{2m(E + \Delta)}\ \sqrt{\frac{2(E + \Delta)}{f}} - 2\pi E\ \sqrt{\frac{m}{f}}$$

$$= 2\pi\sqrt{\frac{m}{f}}\,(E + \Delta - E).$$

Finally, the microcanonical partition function is obtained as

$$\Omega(E) = 2\pi\Delta\sqrt{\frac{m}{f}}.$$

The canonical ensemble is the workhorse of statistical mechanical computations. There are several other useful ensembles, but the NVT ensemble is the most common and will be the main focus throughout this text. Once an ensemble is chosen, our task is to determine the probability distribution of members in an ensemble. From these probabilities, the partition function can be obtained and related to thermodynamic properties.

Suppose that there are N members of a canonical ensemble. Remember, each ensemble member represents the whole macroscopic system of N molecules in a particular microscopic state. Let N_i represent the number of ensemble members in state i having energy E_i, then simple counting requires

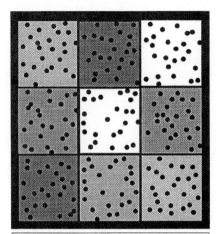

All boxes have the same volume, contain the same number of particles, and are at the same temperature; but the microstates and energies (shading) are different. Canonical = N, V, T constant

Figure 2.5 Representation of the canonical or NVT ensemble.

$$N = \sum_i N_i \tag{2.6}$$

$$E = \sum_i N_i E_i . \tag{2.7}$$

Our task is to find a way to calculate the relative number of systems (ensemble members) in each of the possible quantum states. There are in fact many ways to distribute N systems among the various microscopic, or quantum, states. We know that for *any one of these distributions,* the probability of finding N_j ensemble members in the jth state is

$$\wp_j = \frac{N_j}{N} . \tag{2.8}$$

But, this is just one of the many possible distributions. We really need to replace N_j in Equation (2.8) with the expectation value $<N_j>$ calculated from all the possible distributions of N ensemble members among the various accessible quantum states. Because the ensemble itself is isolated, the second postulate applies, and we may obtain the distribution function by statistically computing the total number of ways to distribute N things, N_j at a time. This is simply the multinomial distribution function [Eq. (1.50)] obtained from combinatorial counting

$$f = \frac{N!}{\Pi_i N_i!},$$ (2.9)

based on equal probabilities for these energetically degenerate states. This distribution function can then be used to find the expectation value of N_j and finally the probability of N_j systems in quantum state j. However, the degeneracy of microscopic states leading to the same thermodynamic properties is enormous and, as we saw in Chapter 1, the distribution f can be replaced with its maximum term, f^*, without loss of accuracy. These steps in finding the probability of having N_j systems in state j can be summarized mathematically by

$$\wp_j = \frac{<N_j>}{N} = \frac{1}{N} \frac{\sum\limits_N N_j f}{\sum\limits_N f} = \frac{1}{N} \frac{N_j^* f^*}{f^*} = \frac{N_j^*}{N}.$$ (2.10)

As an aid to understanding the steps taken for the general, abstract case, consider a simple, concrete example presented by Hill[1] and illustrated in Example 2.3.

According to Equation (2.10), the problem of calculating the probability of state j has been simplified to one of finding the maximum of the distribution, f^*. Lagrange's method of undetermined multipliers is particularly suited to this task because the maximum must be found subject to the constraints posed in Equations (2.6) and (2.7). It is equivalent, but much simpler to maximize $\ln f$ than f, and so we write the auxiliary function to be maximized subject to constraints as

$$F = \ln f + \alpha\left(N - \sum_i N_i\right) + \beta\left(E - \sum_i N_i E_i\right)$$

$$= \ln N! - \sum_i \ln N_i! + \alpha\left(N - \sum_i N_i\right) + \beta\left(E - \sum_i N_i E_i\right),$$ (2.11)

where α and β are the two undetermined multipliers for the constraint equations. By utilizing Stirling's approximation [Eq. (1.52)] and differentiating with respect to N_j, one obtains

$$\left(\frac{\partial F}{\partial N_j}\right)_{N_{k \neq j}} = -\ln N_j^* - \alpha - \beta E_j = 0,$$ (2.12)

or

Example 2.3 Suppose there are only four members of the ensemble; i.e., $N = 4$. Further suppose that there are only three possible energy states E_1, E_2 and E_3 which these four systems may occupy. What is the probability of observing quantum state 1?

Let N_i represent the number of systems (out of the four possible) which are in energy state E_i. One particular distribution might be D1 = $\{N_1 = 1, N_2 = 2, N_3 = 1\}$; another might be D2 = $\{N_1 = 2, N_2 = 0, N_3 = 2\}$. The probability of quantum state 1 in D1 is $\wp_1 = 1/4$; in D2 it is 2/4 or 1/2. This is summarized in the table. However, there are many ways to obtain sets D1 and D2 from 4 particles, and Postulate II indicates that each of them is equally probable because they would all have equivalent energies. The degeneracies of these two distributions are therefore

	E_1	E_2	E_3
D$_1$	1	2	1
D$_2$	2	0	2
$\wp_{Ei}(D_1)$	1/4	1/2	1/4
$\wp_{Ei}(D_2)$	1/2	0	1/2

$$f(D1) = \frac{4!}{1!\ 2!\ 1!} = 12 \quad f(D2) = \frac{4!}{2!\ 0!\ 2!} = 6 \ .$$

The overall probability of observing quantum state 1 is therefore

$$\wp_1 = \frac{1}{N} <N_1> = \frac{1}{4}\left(\frac{1 \times 12 + 2 \times 6)}{12 + 6}\right) = \frac{1}{3} \ .$$

The final simplification shown in Equation (2.10) cannot be illustrated in this example because of the small numbers chosen. Nevertheless, it is not difficult to imagine that if there is an overwhelmingly large number of ways in which to achieve one particular distribution, then the most probable distribution will predominate and the average N_j will approach N_j^*.

$$N_j^* = e^{-\alpha}e^{-\beta E_j}. \tag{2.13}$$

The first undetermined multiplier, α, can be obtained from Equation (2.6). If $N = \Sigma N_j$ is true for *all* possible distributions, it is certainly true for the most probable, that is,

$$N = \sum_j N_j^* = \sum_j e^{-\alpha}e^{-\beta E_j}. \tag{2.14}$$

Thus,

$$e^{-\alpha} = \frac{N}{\displaystyle\sum_j e^{-\beta E_j}} \ . \tag{2.15}$$

We have nearly achieved the objective of finding the probability distribution of states in the canonical ensemble. When Equations (2.13) and (2.15) are substituted into Equation (2.10), we obtain

$$\wp_k = \frac{e^{-\beta E_k}}{\sum\limits_{j} e^{-\beta E_j}} . \tag{2.16}$$

This probability distribution can then be used to find expectation values of any mechanical property, J, which depends upon the microscopic states of the system. Because the denominator of $\wp_k$ is a normalization term for the distribution of all possible states, it is a recurring group which appears in all canonical ensemble averages. For convenience, it is therefore given a specific symbol, Q:

$$Q(N,V,\beta) = \sum\limits_{k} e^{-\beta E_k}. \tag{2.17}$$

Q is the canonical ensemble partition function, so called because it is a sum over all the states partitioned by their energy level. The ensemble averages are now formed as before,

$$<J> = \sum\limits_{k} \wp_k J_k = \sum\limits_{k} \frac{J_k e^{-\beta E_k}}{Q} . \tag{2.18}$$

For example, the thermodynamic internal energy, U, and pressure, P, are found from the expectation values for the energy and pressure

$$U = <E> = \sum\limits_{j} E_j \wp_j = \sum\limits_{j} \frac{E_j e^{-\beta E_j}}{Q} \quad \text{and} \tag{2.19}$$

$$P = <P> = \sum\limits_{j} P_j \wp_j = \sum\limits_{j} \frac{P_j e^{-\beta E_j}}{Q} , \tag{2.20}$$

respectively.

In order to complete the description of ensemble averages, β must yet be identified. This can be done by relating the expectation values for pressure and energy, based on the canonical ensemble, to their thermodynamic equivalents. Recall from thermodynamics that

$$\left(\frac{\partial U}{\partial V}\right)_{T,N} = T\left(\frac{\partial P}{\partial T}\right)_{V,N} - P . \tag{2.21}$$

If we can replace the partial derivatives in the above equation with known expressions, a solvable relationship for β will be obtained. The procedure is straightforward, though algebraically tedious. We form the expectation values for E and P and then differentiate these in accordance with Equation (2.21). Two important facts are essential to keep in mind when computing the derivatives. First, quantum states are not a function of temperature. Recall from the particle-in-the-box example of Chapter 1 that $E_j = E_j(N,V)$; or conversely, $E_j \neq E_j(T)$. The relative *populations* of energy levels are a function of temperature—higher energy levels will be populated only at higher temperatures—but the quantum states or levels are themselves independent of temperature (see Example 2.4). Therefore, the work required to effect a change in volume with fixed N is given by $dE_j = -P_j dV$ where P_j is the pressure of quantum state j. Thus,

$$P_j = -\left(\frac{\partial E_j}{\partial V}\right)_N. \tag{2.22}$$

Second, β is the undetermined multiplier for the constraint on energy and is therefore a constant with respect to the independent variables of the quantum energy levels; that is, $\beta \neq \beta(N,V)$.

To find $(\partial U/\partial V)_{T,N}$, Equation (2.19) is differentiated with respect to V to obtain

$$\left(\frac{\partial U}{\partial V}\right)_{T,N} = \sum_j \frac{\left(\frac{\partial E_j}{\partial V}\right)_{T,N} e^{-\beta E_j}}{Q} - \beta \sum_j \frac{E_j \left(\frac{\partial E_j}{\partial V}\right)_{T,N} e^{-\beta E_j}}{Q} + \beta \sum_j \sum_k \frac{E_j e^{-\beta E_j} \left(\frac{\partial E_k}{\partial V}\right)_{T,N} e^{-\beta E_k}}{Q^2},$$

which simplifies to

$$\left(\frac{\partial U}{\partial V}\right)_{T,N} = -<P> + \beta<E \cdot P> - \beta<E> <P>, \tag{2.23}$$

in view of Equations (2.19) and (2.20).

Similarly, to find $(\partial P/\partial T)_{V,N}$, Equation (2.20) can be differentiated to obtain

$$\left(\frac{\partial <P>}{\partial T}\right)_{V,N} = \left[\sum_j \left(\frac{\partial E_j}{\partial V}\right)_N \frac{E_j e^{-\beta E_j}}{Q} - \sum_j \sum_k \left(\frac{\partial E_j}{\partial V}\right)_N \frac{E_k e^{-\beta E_k} e^{-\beta E_j}}{Q^2}\right] \cdot \left(\frac{\partial \beta}{\partial T}\right)_V,$$

or, more simply,

$$\left(\frac{\partial P}{\partial T}\right)_{V,N} = \left(\frac{\partial \beta}{\partial T}\right)_V (-<P \cdot E> + <P><E>). \tag{2.24}$$

Substitution of Equations (2.23) and (2.24) for the partial derivatives in Equation (2.21) yields

$$\beta(<P \cdot E> - <E> <P>) = -T\left(\frac{\partial \beta}{\partial T}\right)_{V,N} (<P \cdot E> - <E><P>),$$

which can be solved to obtain

$$\beta = \frac{1}{kT}. \tag{2.25}$$

The constant k results from the integration. Equation (2.25) was obtained in general for any system, so we can apply it to any particular system to obtain the value of k. This is conveniently done for an ideal gas (in Chapter 3), and k, Boltzmann's constant, is found to have the value: $k = 1.3806 \times 10^{-16}$ ergs/(mol·K).

The relationship between the canonical ensemble of microscopic states and the thermodynamic energy and pressure is now complete. Our experience in differentiating Q in the above derivation can be used to write the relationships expressed in Equations (2.19) and (2.20) in a more compact form:

$$U = -\left(\frac{\partial \ln Q}{\partial \beta}\right)_{V,N} = kT^2\left(\frac{\partial \ln Q}{\partial T}\right)_{V,N} \quad \text{and} \tag{2.26}$$

$$P = kT\left(\frac{\partial \ln Q}{\partial V}\right)_{N,V}. \tag{2.27}$$

One task yet remains before we can calculate all of the thermodynamic properties from the canonical ensemble: an expression for the entropy, S, must be obtained.

For a fixed number of particles, S is related to U and PV through the thermodynamic identity

$$dS = \frac{(dU + PdV)}{T}. \tag{2.28}$$

U may also be written in terms of the probability distribution $\wp_i$ as $U = \sum_i \wp_i E_i$, whereupon dU can be expanded to

$$dU = \sum_i [\wp_i dE_i + E_i d\wp_i]$$

$$= \sum_i \left[\wp_i\left(\frac{\partial E_i}{\partial V}\right)_N dV + E_i d\wp_i\right] \tag{2.29}$$

$$= -PdV + \sum_i E_i d\wp_i.$$

A combination of Equations (2.28) and (2.29) results in

$$dS = \frac{\sum_i E_i d\wp_i}{T}. \tag{2.30}$$

Interestingly, this expression leads to an equation for S entirely in terms of the probability distribution when Equation (2.16) is solved for E_k in terms of $\wp_k$ and used to replace E_i. This converts Equation (2.30) to

$$dS = -\frac{\sum_i [\ln \wp_i d\wp_i + \ln Q d\wp_i]}{\beta T}. \tag{2.31}$$

However, the second term is zero because $\Sigma(d\wp_i) = d(\Sigma \wp_i) = 0$ (since $\Sigma \wp_i = 1$). We therefore obtain the important relationship between the thermodynamic entropy and the microscopic probability density function

$$dS = -k \sum_i \ln \wp_i d\wp_i. \tag{2.32}$$

Equation (2.32) can be integrated to obtain absolute entropy. In actuality, we still only obtain relative values of the entropy, but the integration constant is commonly set to zero to maintain compatibility with the third law entropies defined in thermodynamics. This fixes the reference entropy at zero for any perfectly ordered substance at 0 K. The nonzero entropy of an incompletely ordered crystalline material at 0 K is due to the different ways in which the molecules fit into the lattice, and it can be computed from these equations, as illustrated in Example 2.4 for a very simple case. From the equations derived above, several equivalent forms of the relationship between absolute entropies, Q, and $\wp_i$ can be obtained:

$$S = \frac{U}{T} + k\ln Q$$

$$S = -k \sum_i \wp_i \ln \wp_i \tag{2.33}$$

$$S = -k\langle \ln \wp \rangle$$

The derivation of these equations is left as an exercise at the end of the chapter. The last of Equations (2.33) is well known. The form of it used in Example

Example 2.4   Calculate the third law entropy of a crystal of CO at 0 K assuming that the relatively similar sizes of C and O atoms permit the molecules to align as CO or OC equally well in the lattice.

At 0 K, all ensemble members would be in the ground energy state E_0, which is by convention taken to be 0. Thus, from Equation (2.33) we obtain

$$S_0 = -k\wp_0\ln\wp_0 .$$

If there were no degeneracy in the ground state, that is, if CO could only fit into the lattice in one orientation, then S would be 0, since $\wp_0 = 1$. For convenience, let W represent the degeneracy or number of ways in which each molecule can fit into the lattice (assume equal probabilities for this). Then for one molecule

$$S_0 = -k\sum_{i=1}^{W} \frac{1}{W}\ln\frac{1}{W} = k\ln W .$$

This latter equation is the actual inscription on Boltzmann's memorial.[2] This equation is identical to the expression obtained for S from the microcanonical ensemble (cf. Table 2.2) because the energy is also constant.

For the N molecules of CO, each molecule can be oriented equally likely in one of two ways so $W = 2^N$. Thus,

$$S_0 = Nk\ln 2 .$$

One mole of a substance contains Avagadro's number of molecules, and $Nk = R$ (the ideal gas constant). The molar entropy is therefore 1.38 cal/mol·K. The value reported in the literature is 1.0 cal/mol·K, slightly lower than the calculated value. This is to be expected since the C and O atoms are not exactly the same size and both orientations are therefore not equally likely.

2.4 is carved in Boltzmann's grave marker[2] as a memorial to him and the development of statistical mechanics that arose from his studies of the relationship between entropy, the probability of microscopic states, and the direction of spontaneous processes.

Because thermodynamic properties can all be obtained by appropriate partial differentiation of the Helmholtz free energy, A, it is most common to formulate the link between the canonical ensemble and macroscopic properties in terms of A. From the equations developed in this section and the identity $A = U - TS$, one can easily show that

$$A = -kT\ln Q . \qquad (2.34)$$

The other thermodynamic properties can be readily derived from this equation using standard thermodynamic identities. For convenience, Table 2.1 summarizes these relations.

Calculation of thermodynamic properties from microscopic states is thus a problem of computing the partition function Q. It is important to understand just what states we must sum over in Equation (2.17) to compute Q. The formal summation can actually be handled in two different ways. The development used in this text has focused on all separate states, regardless of degeneracy within an energy level. That is, we sum over all quantum states available to the ensemble members. On the other hand, we might also choose to sum over all unique quantum states. In this case we must multiply each term in the sum by its appropriate degeneracy, $W(E_j)$. The two methods are obviously equivalent and can be written as

$$Q(N,V,T) = \sum_j e^{-\beta E_j} = \sum_{E_j} W(E_j) e^{-\beta E_j}. \tag{2.35}$$

Explicitly expressing the two methods for summing states will help avoid confusion later on.

The canonical partition function plays a central role in thermophysical property calculations. Once Q is obtained, it can be used in conjunction with the relationships in Table 2.1 to obtain desired thermodynamic properties. We also see from Equation (2.16) that the probability of various states can be directly ascertained from the canonical partition function. The probability function can then be used in the normal way to obtain expectation values of various quantities.

TABLE 2.1   Thermodynamic Properties from the Canonical Partition Function

$Q = \sum_i \exp\left(-\dfrac{E_i}{kT}\right)$	$G = -kT\ln Q + kTV\left(\dfrac{\partial \ln Q}{\partial V}\right)_{N,T}$
$A = -kT\ln Q$	$H = U + PV$
$U = kT^2\left(\dfrac{\partial \ln Q}{\partial T}\right)_{N,V}$	$C_V = \left(\dfrac{\partial U}{\partial T}\right)_{N,V}$
$P = kT\left(\dfrac{\partial \ln Q}{\partial V}\right)_{N,T}$	$C_P = \left(\dfrac{\partial H}{\partial T}\right)_{N,P}$
$S = k\ln Q + \dfrac{U}{T}$	$\mu_i = -kT\left(\dfrac{\partial \ln Q}{\partial N_i}\right)_{T,V,N_{j\neq i}}$

Example 2.5 illustrates the use of Q in finding state probabilities and expectation values for a particle in a one-dimensional box.

2.2.3 Grand Canonical Ensemble

Several other useful ensembles can also be defined. One that is often useful for systems in which phase equilibrium is involved is the grand canonical ensemble. This ensemble fixes the chemical potential of each component, but permits the number of particles within individual ensemble members to fluctuate. When applied to phase equilibrium problems, the equilibrium conditions are naturally satisfied by fixing the chemical potential of each component to the same value in both phases, allowing the number of molecules in each phase to adjust appropriately.

To form figuratively the grand canonical ensemble, we might imagine enclosing each member within a diathermal, permeable wall. The collection of such members could then be placed in a large heat and particle reservoir until the temperature and number of particles in each ensemble member reaches equilibrium. After equilibration, the entire system is isolated from the surroundings so that the total energy and number of molecules of the ensemble are fixed. Of course the energy and number of molecules in each ensemble member may still fluctuate. In this mental construct, the immense number of neighboring ensemble members serves as a virtually infinite source of heat and molecules. Flow of heat and movement of molecules between ensemble members occur in response to driving forces of inequalities in temperature and chemical potential to ensure that the temperature and number of molecules in each ensemble member remain fixed. The grand canonical ensemble is therefore one of constant V, T, and μ as depicted in Figure 2.6.

Derivation of the partition function for the grand canonical ensemble is analogous to that for the canonical ensemble. The maximum distribution, found subject to the particular constraints of the ensemble, is used to obtain the probability distribution function. In this case, the three constraint equations

$$N = \sum_N \sum_j N_{Nj} \tag{2.36}$$

$$E = \sum_N \sum_j N_{Nj} E_{Nj} \tag{2.37}$$

$$\eta = \sum_N \sum_j N N_{Nj} \tag{2.38}$$

are used to fix the total number of ensemble members, the total energy, and the total number of particles. In the above equations, N_{Nj} represents the number of

Example 2.5   Consider a system of 20 independent particles in a one-dimensional box of length L. Determine the probability of finding a particle in each of the lowest five energy states (i.e., $0 \leq n \leq 4$) at a dimensionless temperatures of $T^+ = 1$ and $T^+ = 4$. Here, T^+ is defined by $T^+ = T \cdot (8mL^2k/h^2)$. Then determine the expectation value for the energy of the system.

The energy level for a noninteracting particle in a box is given by

$$E_n = \frac{n^2h^2}{8mL^2} \qquad (n = 0, 1, 2 \ldots),$$

and therefore a dimensionless energy can be defined as

$$E^+ \equiv \beta E_n = \frac{n^2}{T^+}.$$

We can then write out the canonical partition function

$$Q = \sum_j e^{-\beta E_j} = 1 + e^{-4/T^+} + e^{-9/T^+} + e^{-16/T^+} + \ldots$$

and sum this rapidly converging series at each temperature to yield $Q(T^+ = 1) = 1.386$ and $Q(T^+ = 4) = 2.272$. The probability of finding a particle in a particular state is found from the partition function using Equation (2.16),

$$\wp_n(T^+) = \frac{e^{-n^2/T^+}}{Q}.$$

At the desired temperatures, the probabilities obtained in this manner are:

T^+	$\wp_0$	$\wp_1$	$\wp_2$	$\wp_3$	$\wp_4$
1	0.721	0.263	0.013	8.9×10^{-5}	8.1×10^{-8}
4	0.440	0.343	0.162	0.046	0.008

Notice how temperature changes the occupation probability, not the energy levels themselves. For the specified system of 20 independent particles, the probability of finding one particle in any state is 20 times its probability listed in the table.

Expectation values are found from probability distribution functions in the usual manner. In terms of the dimensionless energy,

$$<E^+> = \sum_{n=0}^{\infty} \frac{n^2}{T^+} \wp_n.$$

From the values above, we obtain $<E^+> = 0.319$ at $T^+ = 1$ and 0.390 at $T^+ = 4$.

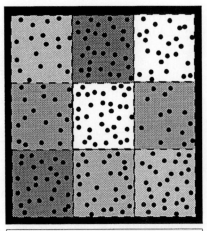

All boxes have the same volume, the same chemical potential, and are at the same temperature; but the microstates, energy, and number of particles vary.
Grand Canonical = μ, V, T constant

Figure 2.6 Depiction of grand canonical or μVT ensemble.

ensemble members that have both N particles and are in state j (quantum energy level E_j). The distribution of ensemble members is, as before, a multinomial distribution,

$$f = \frac{N!}{\prod_N \prod_j N_{Nj}!}. \tag{2.39}$$

The joint probability distribution of finding N molecules in state j is

$$\wp_{Nj} = \frac{\langle N_{Nj} \rangle}{N} = \frac{N_{Nj}^*}{N}, \tag{2.40}$$

analogous to Equation (2.10).

The maximum in the distribution is again found using the method of undetermined multipliers, maximizing $\ln(f)$ subject to the constraints of Equations (2.36) to (2.38). When the auxiliary expression is differentiated and set equal to zero at the maximum, one obtains

$$N_{Nj}^* = e^{-\alpha}e^{-\beta E_{Nj}}e^{-\gamma N}, \tag{2.41}$$

for the most probable number of ensemble members which have both N molecules and are in energy state E_j. The three undetermined multipliers α, β, and γ must yet be determined.

We can eliminate α entirely by substituting Equations (2.36) and (2.41) into Equation (2.40), whereupon the joint probability distribution can be written as

$$\wp_{Nj} = \frac{e^{-\beta E_{Nj}} e^{-\gamma N}}{\Xi},$$ (2.42)

with the grand canonical partition function Ξ defined by

$$\Xi = \sum_N \sum_j e^{-\beta E_{Nj}} e^{-\gamma N}.$$ (2.43)

As with the canonical partition function, the undetermined multipliers are found by requiring expectation values of mechanical variables to correspond to their thermodynamic counterparts. This also provides the connection between thermodynamic properties and Ξ. Because the steps used to obtain the connections are analogous to those shown in the derivation of the equations for the canonical ensemble, we shall omit many of the mathematical details in outlining this process.

Expectation values for the energy, pressure, and number of particles can be found in the usual way [cf. Equation (2.18)] from the probability function. Thus,

$$U = <E> = \frac{\sum_N \sum_j E_{Nj} e^{-\beta E_{Nj}} e^{-\gamma N}}{\Xi} = -\left(\frac{\partial \ln\Xi}{\partial\beta}\right)_{V,\gamma}$$ (2.44)

$$P = <P> = -\frac{\sum_N \sum_j \left(\frac{\partial E_{Nj}}{\partial V}\right)_{\beta,\gamma} e^{-\beta E_{Nj}} e^{-\gamma N}}{\Xi} = \frac{1}{\beta}\left(\frac{\partial \ln\Xi}{\partial V}\right)_{\beta,\gamma}$$ (2.45)

$$N = <N> = \frac{\sum_N \sum_j N e^{-\beta E_{Nj}} e^{-\gamma N}}{\Xi} = -\left(\frac{\partial \ln\Xi}{\partial\gamma}\right)_{V,\beta}.$$ (2.46)

Strictly for ease of notation, let $g = \ln\Xi$. Because $g = g(\beta,\gamma,V)$, the total differential of g is

$$dg = \left(\frac{\partial g}{\partial\beta}\right)_{\gamma,V} d\beta + \left(\frac{\partial g}{\partial\gamma}\right)_{\beta,V} d\gamma + \left(\frac{\partial g}{\partial V}\right)_{\beta,\gamma} dV$$

$$= -<E>d\beta - <N>d\gamma + \beta<P>dV.$$ (2.47)

To recast Equation (2.47) into a form identifiable with a thermodynamic relation, we add $d(\beta<E> + \gamma<N>)$ to both sides to obtain

$$d(g + \beta<E> + \gamma<N>) = \beta dU + \gamma dN + \beta P dV . \tag{2.48}$$

The multiplier β can be shown to still be $1/(kT)$. Actually, this is obvious if we simply view the canonical ensemble as a subset of the grand canonical ensemble; one for which all the particle numbers are fixed at N. From thermodynamics,

$$dS = k\beta(dU - \mu dN + P dV) . \tag{2.49}$$

Because Equations (2.48) and (2.49) are written in terms of identical, independent differentials dU, dN, and dV, the coefficients multiplying these terms must be the same in the two equations. Thus, $\gamma = -\beta\mu$, and

$$dS = k d(\ln\Xi + \beta U - \beta\mu N) . \tag{2.50}$$

As was done with the canonical ensemble, the differential entropy may be integrated; compatibility with third law entropies is maintained by setting the integration constant to zero. Thus,

$$S = k\ln\Xi + \frac{U}{T} - \frac{\mu N}{T} . \tag{2.51}$$

Now that the γ undetermined multiplier has been identified, the grand canonical partition function can be more compactly written as

$$\Xi = \sum_N \sum_j e^{-\beta E_{Nj}} e^{\beta\mu N} = \sum_N Q(N,V,T) e^{\beta\mu N}, \tag{2.52}$$

from which a complete prescription for calculation of thermodynamic properties can again be developed. Equations (2.44), (2.45), (2.46), (2.51), and (2.52) can be used to obtain the relationships compiled in Table 2.2 between thermodynamic properties and the grand canonical ensemble.

For reference purposes, we summarize in Table 2.3 the main connection formulas between several commonly used ensembles and thermodynamic properties.

2.3 CLASSICAL STATISTICAL MECHANICS

As we saw in the particle-in-the-box example, energy levels are a function of volume, not temperature. The temperature does, however, determine the population of the energy levels. If the temperature is high enough that kT is large relative to the spacing of the energy levels, then a large number of quantum states can be populated. For a large number of particles, the many possible ways in which the quantum states can be populated leads to a large number of

TABLE 2.2   Thermodynamic Properties and the Grand
Canonical Partition Function

$$\Xi = \sum \cdots \sum \exp\!\left(\frac{N_\alpha\mu_\alpha + \cdots N_\zeta\mu_\zeta - E_i}{kT}\right) \qquad N_\alpha = kT\!\left(\frac{\partial\ln\Xi}{\partial\mu_\alpha}\right)_{T,V,\mu_{\beta\neq\alpha}}$$

$$P = kT\!\left(\frac{\partial\ln\Xi}{\partial V}\right)_{T,\mu_\alpha} = \frac{kT}{V}\ln\Xi \qquad U = kT^2\!\left(\frac{\partial\ln\Xi}{\partial T}\right)_{V,\mu_\alpha} + \sum_\alpha \mu_\alpha N_\alpha$$

$$H = U + PV$$

$$S = k\ln\Xi + \frac{U}{T} - \sum_\alpha \frac{\mu_\alpha N_\alpha}{T}$$

$$G = \sum_\alpha N_\alpha\mu_\alpha \qquad A = \sum_\alpha N_\alpha\mu_\alpha - kT\ln\Xi$$

$$C_V = \left(\frac{\partial U}{\partial T}\right)_{V,N_\alpha} \qquad C_P = \left(\frac{\partial H}{\partial T}\right)_{P,N_\alpha}$$

total energy quantum states, giving the appearance of a continuum of energy possibilities. In such cases, classical rather than quantum statistical mechanics may be used. This criterion of kT greater than the energy level spacing is generally true for translational degrees of freedom, except at very low temperatures. Other degrees of freedom are generally treated quantum mechanically as we shall see in the next chapter.

The position and momentum of monatomic particles (i.e., the system's position in phase space) are fixed with the specification of $6N$ coordinates. If the molecules are not monatomic, additional coordinates are required to specify the system's location in phase space. The center of mass of each particle is still established with three momentum and three position coordinates, but, additionally, atoms within the molecule must be located relative to the center of mass. Rotation and vibration within the molecule are internal degrees of freedom which change the positions and orientations of the atoms relative to a coordinate system fixed at the molecular center of mass. Suppose each molecule possesses F degrees of freedom (independently variable directions of motion of parts of the molecule). Then NF momenta and NF positions are required to identify the location of the system in phase space. Note that this is consistent with our previous description for systems with purely translational degrees of freedom for which $F = 3$ and $6N$ phase space coordinates are required. In general, the number of degrees of freedom for a molecule containing M atoms is $3M$.

TABLE 2.3   Formulas Linking Thermodynamic Properties to
Common Ensembles

A. Microcanonical Ensemble: $\Omega(N,V,E)$

$$S = k\ln\Omega$$

$$\frac{P}{kT} = \left(\frac{\partial\ln\Omega}{\partial V}\right)_{N,E}$$

$$\beta = \left(\frac{\partial\ln\Omega}{\partial E}\right)_{N,V}$$

$$\frac{\mu}{kT} = -\left(\frac{\partial\ln\Omega}{\partial N}\right)_{V,E}$$

B. Canonical Ensemble: $Q(N,V,T)$

$$A = -kT\ln Q$$

$$P = kT\left(\frac{\partial\ln Q}{\partial V}\right)_{N,T}$$

$$S = k\ln Q + kT\left(\frac{\partial\ln Q}{\partial T}\right)_{N,V}$$

$$\mu = -kT\left(\frac{\partial\ln Q}{\partial N}\right)_{V,T}$$

C. Grand Canonical Ensemble: $\Xi(\mu,V,T)$

$$P = \frac{kT}{V}\ln\Xi = kT\left(\frac{\partial\ln\Xi}{\partial V}\right)_{\mu,T}$$

$$N = kT\left(\frac{\partial\ln\Xi}{\partial\mu}\right)_{V,T}$$

$$S = k\ln\Xi + kT\left(\frac{\partial\ln\Xi}{\partial T}\right)_{V,\mu}$$

D. Isothermal-Isobaric Ensemble: $\Delta(N,T,P)$

$$G = -kT\ln\Delta$$

$$V = -kT\left(\frac{\partial\ln\Delta}{\partial P}\right)_{N,T}$$

$$S = k\ln\Delta + kT\left(\frac{\partial\ln\Delta}{\partial T}\right)_{N,P}$$

$$\mu = -kT\left(\frac{\partial\ln\Delta}{\partial N}\right)_{T,P}$$

As illustrated in Example 2.6, specification of NF momenta and NF positions is required to locate the system in phase space at any instant in time. It is convenient to represent this instantaneous position in phase space as Γ, a shorthand notation for specification of NF q and p values. The chronological sequence of these phase-space points generates a trajectory through phase space. One can then find time-averaged values, instead of ensemble averages, of

Example 2.6   How many coordinates must be specified to locate NO_2 in phase space?
NO_2 has 3 atoms so the maximum number required would be 18; i.e., $F = 9$ so
there are 9 momenta and 9 positions required. The modes are identified below:

3 translational modes for the center of mass (x, y, z)

3 vibrational modes

3 rotational modes

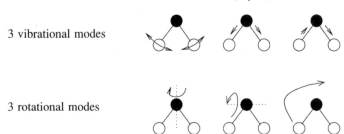

mechanical variables over the region of phase space available to the system.
For example, the energy of the system can be calculated from the time average
of the energy of the instantaneous phase-space points by

$$<E> = \lim_{t \to \infty} \left[\frac{1}{t} \int_0^t E(\Gamma)dt \right] . \tag{2.53}$$

We will not make a notational distinction between expectation values computed
via ensemble and time-averaging methods. Indeed, the Ergodic hypothesis asserts
that they are equivalent. Thus the expectation value of the energy could be
formulated equally well as

$$<E> = \lim_{N \to \infty} \left[\int_\Gamma \wp_N(\Gamma)E(\Gamma)d\Gamma \right] , \tag{2.54}$$

where $\wp_N(\Gamma)$ is the probability density distribution of system points in phase
space, and the integral is performed over the entire region of phase space
accessible to the system. Thus,

$$d\Gamma = dp_1 dp_2 ... dp_{NF} dq_1 dq_2 ... dq_{NF} . \tag{2.55}$$

In Equation (2.54), $\wp \, d\Gamma$ represents the normalized probability that an ensemble
member is located in phase space between Γ and $\Gamma + d\Gamma$. We were able to
easily determine a similar probability distribution function in the form of Equation (2.16) for the discrete case in the canonical ensemble; can we now transform
it to the more specific case of a continuous distribution function? This transformation is performed by recognizing that as the number of discrete, populated
levels becomes large, summations may be replaced by integrals, and closely

spaced energy levels may be replaced by the classical Hamiltonian. Both of these replacements are possible due to closeness of the energy level spacings relative to the energy of the system. With these replacements, the classical expression for $\wp_N$ is

$$\wp_N(\Gamma) = \frac{e^{-\beta H}}{\int e^{-\beta H} d\Gamma}. \tag{2.56}$$

The analogy between Equations (2.16) and (2.56) is in fact so close that it is tempting to identify the denominator as Q. But, we must be careful not to alter the definition of Q from Equation (2.17); that is, Q has been defined once and we must make certain that we don't unknowingly redefine it. We must make sure that in the limit of large numbers of states, the classical and quantum mechanical descriptions agree. Due to counting differences, the classical canonical partition function is actually,

$$Q_{cl} = \frac{1}{N! h^{NF}} \int_\Gamma e^{-\beta H} d\Gamma. \tag{2.57}$$

The factor $N!$ results from overcounting indistinguishable particles. In the quantum mechanical definition of Q, the sum is over experimentally distinguishable quantum states. In the classical expression, the integral is over all momentum and position coordinates regardless of whether the particles are distinguishable or not. Because N indistinguishable particles can be ordered in $_NP_N$ ways, a factor of $N!$ must be divided out. The h^{NF} factor results from the finite size of $d\Gamma$. Points in classical phase space are not "points" in the mathematical sense; each occupies a finite volume because the Heisenberg uncertainty principle precludes exact simultaneous knowledge of both p and q. The uncertainty in each phase space coordinate produces a volume of phase space occupied by each point; $\Delta p \Delta q = h$. The extra volume of phase space included in the integral of Equation (2.57) is therefore h^{NF}. This volume must be divided out to maintain consistency with the definition of Q. Example 2.7 illustrates this with a concrete example. We first calculate the total number of states for a particle in a three-dimensional box and compare this with the direct calculation of the occupied volume of classical phase space.

The classical partition function for mixtures is analogous to Equation (2.57). It can be written down by inspection from this equation as long as one is careful to divide by the proper statistical factors. Thus,

$$Q_{cl} = \frac{1}{(N_a! \, N_b! \, \ldots)(h^{NF_a + NF_b + \cdots})} \int \ldots \int e^{-\beta H} d\Gamma_{N_a} d\Gamma_{N_b} \ldots. \tag{2.58}$$

As we have seen, the partition function is the key to obtaining thermodynamic properties. We developed the classical form of the partition function

Example 2.7   Let us determine the number of quantum states of energy E or less for a particle contained in a cubic box of edge length L and compare this to the volume of classical phase space occupied by the system.[3]

For a particle in a three dimensional box, solution of the Schrödinger equation yields

$$E_{n_x,n_y,n_z} = \frac{h^2}{8mL^2}(n_x^2 + n_y^2 + n_z^2) \qquad (n_i = 0, 1, 2, \ldots)$$

with the corresponding wave function

$$\psi_{n_x,n_y,n_z}(x,y,z) = A \sin\left(\frac{n_x \pi x}{L}\right) \sin\left(\frac{n_y \pi y}{L}\right) \sin\left(\frac{n_z \pi z}{L}\right).$$

We now constrain the system to have an energy of E or less; i.e.,

$$(n_x^2 + n_y^2 + n_z^2) \leq \frac{8mL^2E}{h^2}.$$

Note the form of this equation. It represents the number of lattice points (the n values) within a sphere of radius and volume,

$$r = \sqrt{\frac{8mL^2E}{h^2}} \qquad \text{and} \qquad V = \frac{4\pi}{3}\left(\frac{8mL^2E}{h^2}\right)^{3/2},$$

respectively. Now, n are *positive* integers, but the volume of the sphere would include points from $-n$ to n for each of the three coordinates. Therefore, the actual number of energy states is only the first octant of the sphere defined above. The total number of states is therefore 1/8 of the volume of the sphere, or

$$\Omega(\leq E) = \frac{4\pi}{3}\left(\frac{2mL^2E}{h^2}\right)^{3/2} = \frac{4\pi}{3}\frac{V(2mE)^{3/2}}{h^3}.$$

To find the corresponding volume occupied by the system in classical phase space, we simply integrate $\int dx\,dy\,dz\,dp_x\,dp_y\,dp_z$ over the domain of system phase space to obtain

$$\Gamma(\leq E) = \int_0^V d\boldsymbol{q} \cdot \int_{p^2 \leq 2mE} d\boldsymbol{p} = V \cdot \frac{4\pi}{3}(2mE)^{3/2}.$$

As expected, the two quantities are related by the relationship

$$\Omega(\leq E) = \frac{\Gamma(\leq E)}{h^3}.$$

because it is quite easily evaluated for the translational motion of noninteracting molecules. The simplest example of such a system is a monatomic ideal gas, and Example 2.8 illustrates the methods used to evaluate the classical partition function for this case. The final result for the monatomic, ideal gas can be written as

---

Example 2.8   Calculate the classical partition function for an ideal gas of N monatomic identical molecules.

By ideal gas, we mean one in which the molecules do not interact. Therefore, the potential energy is zero and the Hamiltonian becomes

$$H = \sum_{i=1}^{3N} \frac{p_i^2}{2m}$$

since $F = 3$ (translational degrees of freedom only). The classical partition function is therefore

$$Q = \left[\frac{\int \ldots \int dq_1 dq_2 \ldots dq_{3N}}{N! \, h^{3N}} \right] \left[\int \ldots \int \exp\left(\frac{\Sigma p_i^2}{2mkT} \right) dp^{3N} \right]$$

The $3N$ integrals in the leftmost bracket are taken over the volume of the system, and may be separated out from the momentum integrals because there is no potential energy term. The integral with respect to the coordinates can be immediately performed to obtain V^N, a factor of V for each particle's coordinate triplet. Because each particle is identical, the argument of the sum of squared momenta may be expanded and written as a product of the exponentials. Thus,

$$Q = \frac{V^N}{N! \, h^{3N}} \left[\int_{-\infty}^{\infty} \exp\left(-\frac{p^2}{2mkT} \right) dp \right]^{3N}$$

The momentum integral is now in a form available in integral tables (see Appendix 2). With $x = p^2$ and $n = \beta/2m$, it can be written as

$$\int_{-\infty}^{\infty} \frac{e^{-nx}}{2\sqrt{x}} \, dx = \sqrt{\frac{\pi}{n}},$$

or

$$Q_{cl}^{id} = \frac{V^N}{N!} \left(\frac{2\pi mkT}{h^2} \right)^{\frac{3N}{2}}.$$

$$Q_{cl}^{id} = \frac{V^N}{N! \, \Lambda^{3N}},\tag{2.59}$$

where Λ is the de Broglie wave length given by

$$\Lambda = \sqrt{\frac{h^2}{2\pi mkT}}.\tag{2.60}$$

The technique used in Example 2.8 is common in evaluation of the partition function and is worth detailing here. The momentum integrals involve exponentials whose arguments are a sum of terms. But, the exponential of a sum can be simplified by writing it as a product of the exponentials themselves. Because the particles are indistinguishable, this product of N terms can be replaced by a single integral term raised to the Nth power.

This same simplification can also be exploited in the quantum mechanical determination of noninteracting particles ($U = 0$). In this case, the quantum state of the system, E_i, can be written as a sum of individual molecular quantum states ϵ_j for the N monatomic, noninteracting molecules:

$$E_i = \sum_{k=1}^{N} \sum_{j} \epsilon_{kj},\tag{2.61}$$

where the first index refers to molecule number and the second indicates the quantum state for that molecule. Thus the total partition function factors into a product of molecular partition functions,

$$Q = \sum_{i} e^{-\beta E_i} = \left(\sum_{j} e^{-\beta \epsilon_{1j}} \right) \left(\sum_{j} e^{-\beta \epsilon_{2j}} \right) \cdots \tag{2.62}$$

$$= \left(\sum_{j} e^{-\beta \epsilon_j} \right)^N = q^N.$$

We will find it much more convenient to calculate molecular partition functions, q, than the system or total partition function, Q. For the case of distinguishable particles

$$Q = q^N,\tag{2.63}$$

as shown in Equation (2.62). For indistinguishable particles, we must again divide out the over-counting factor to obtain

$$Q = \frac{1}{N!} q^N.$$ (2.64)

As we have seen, the $N!$ and h^{3N} terms in Equation (2.57) are necessary to maintain numerical equivalency between the classical and quantum mechanical definitions of Q. No rigorous proof was made for the inclusion of these terms, but we did see in Example 2.7 how the h^{3N} term appears naturally from the calculation of a volume in phase space. As further evidence of the necessity of including these terms, we may examine the high-temperature limit of a quantum mechanical solution where the results should be equivalent to those obtained from a classical solution. This is illustrated in Example 2.9 for a particle in a three-dimensional box, and we find equivalent results for both treatments, quantum mechanical and classical, in the limit of high temperatures.

The student may at this point wonder about the ubiquity of the particle-in-a-box example used so far in this book. It is not solely its simplicity which recommends it for illustration of procedures and concepts, but also its direct application to thermophysical properties. Particles confined in a volume V which do not interact with each other constitute an ideal gas. The energy levels calculated from solution of the Schrödinger equation correspond to the translational levels for monatomic gas molecules. The partition function obtained in Example 2.9 therefore represents the starting point in Chapter 3 for determination of ideal gas properties. The equivalency of the quantum mechanical and classical descriptions at temperatures high relative to the energy-level spacings permits us to use more convenient classical mechanics on that portion of the problem for which the energy levels are quite close together. The resultant Q is called the semiclassical partition function. This simplified form of the partition function will be the starting point for our thermophysical property calculations throughout the remainder of the text.

2.4 SEMICLASSICAL PARTITION FUNCTION

Translational modes are conveniently treated classically while internal degrees of freedom usually must be treated with quantum statistical mechanics. It is therefore common to divide the canonical partition function into translational and internal parts. This is done by assuming the Hamiltonian may be split into a term describing the kinetic energy of the center of mass (cm) and one that involves the intermolecular (int) degrees of freedom, including vibration, rotation, and electronic transitions:

$$H = H_{cm} + H_{int}.$$ (2.65)

Such a separation is rigorous only when the motion of the center of mass is independent of the internal modes. This is certainly not true in general for polyatomic molecules which interact through nonspherical potentials. For exam-

Example 2.9 Calculate the quantum mechanical partition function for a single particle in a three-dimensional box of volume V at high temperatures.

The one-dimensional particle-in-a-box energy levels were found in Example 1.7 to be

$$\epsilon_i = n^2 h^2 / (8mL^2) \ .$$

The three-dimensional solution is similarly

$$\epsilon_i = h^2(n_x^2 + n_y^2 + n_z^2)/(8mV^{2/3})$$

where n_j is the quantum number for translational motion in the j direction.

The quantum mechanical partition function is

$$Q = \frac{1}{N!} \left\{ \sum_{n_x} \sum_{n_y} \sum_{n_z} \exp\left[-\frac{h^2(n_x^2 + n_y^2 + n_z^2)}{8mV^{2/3}kT} \right] \right\}^N$$

which can be written for a cubic box as

$$Q = \frac{1}{N!} \left[\sum_n \exp\left(-\frac{h^2 n^2}{8mV^{2/3}kT} \right) \right]^{3N} .$$

At high temperatures, virtually all of the quantum states are populated, and the possible system states become nearly continuous. Therefore, the sum can be replaced by an integral,

$$Q = \frac{1}{N!} \left[\int_0^\infty \exp\left(-\frac{h^2 n^2}{8mV^{2/3}kT} \right) dn \right]^{3N} ,$$

which can be integrated to yield

$$Q = \frac{V^N}{N!} \left(\frac{2\pi mkT}{h^2} \right)^{\frac{3N}{2}} .$$

This is exactly the same result obtained from the classical partition function for an ideal gas.

---

ple, one can imagine a head-on collision between the two molecules shown in Figure 2.7a inducing compression–expansion vibrational motion along the bonds. Likewise, coupling between translational and rotational motion is expected in Figure 2.7b as the two extended atoms collide, producing oppositely directed torques in the two molecules. In spite of these easily imagined counter examples, Equation (2.65) serves as a good first approximation for many systems. Problems involving coupled motion are quite complex, and the simplicity

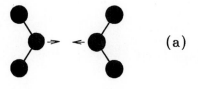

(a)

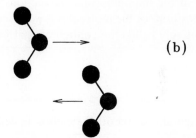

(b)

Figure 2.7 Molecular translational "collisions" expected to induce (a) vibrational motion and (b) rotational motion.

obtained by the separation is often worth the loss of generality. Equation (2.65) therefore serves as a useful approximation for many real systems. Nevertheless, one should be aware of the degradation of this assumption for polyatomic molecules at relatively high densities.

Linear separation of the Hamiltonian in Equation (2.65) factors the partition function. We take advantage of the convenient property of exponentials, $e^{x+y} = e^x e^y$, to write

$$Q = Q_{cm}(N,V,T) \cdot Q_{int}(N,T) . \tag{2.66}$$

Note that the internal partition function does not depend upon volume. Under the assumption of independence between the translational and internal Hamiltonians, the energy levels for the internal degrees of freedom depend only on the intramolecular structure of the molecule.

Factoring the partition function in this manner permits us to treat Q_{cm} classically and Q_{int} quantum mechanically. The advantage of so doing is the simplicity with which the center-of-mass Hamiltonian can be evaluated, as in Example 2.8. Translational states are relatively close together, and the classical treatment is generally valid for temperatures above about 50 K. Because H_{cm} is

$$H_{cm} = \sum_{i=1}^{N} \frac{p_i^2}{2m} + U(q) , \tag{2.67}$$

the classical partition function may be written as

$$Q_{cm} = \frac{1}{N!h^{3N}} \int \ldots \int e^{-U/kT}\, dq^{3N} \int \ldots \int \exp\left[-\frac{\sum\limits_{i}(p_{ix}^2 + p_{iy}^2 + p_{iz}^2)}{2mkT} \right] dp^{3N}. \qquad (2.68)$$

The $3N$ momentum integrals are independent of position and may therefore be evaluated as in Example 2.8. The $3N$ integrals over coordinates depend upon the form of the intermolecular interactions which in turn is a function of the relative positions of the molecules (system configuration). These latter integrals are collectively called the configurational partition function, Z. Thus,

$$Q = \frac{ZQ_{int}}{\Lambda^{3N}N!}. \qquad (2.69)$$

The configurational partition function is defined as

$$Z = \int \ldots \int e^{-U/kT}\, dq^{3N}. \qquad (2.70)$$

Under the two assumptions made in this section, the canonical partition function can be divided into the product of the translational and internal partition functions. The former can be further separated into the configurational partition function and a readily integrable portion due solely to the kinetic energy of the molecules. The assumptions involved, while not exact for real systems, are thought to be quite accurate. They reduce the complexity of calculating thermophysical properties immensely because the very difficult problem of coupling between the center-of-mass and internal modes is avoided. Equations (2.69) and (2.70) will be the starting point for most of the calculations discussed in later chapters. By these procedures, the problem of thermodynamic property computation has been reduced to the separate calculation of the internal and configurational partition functions.

2.5 FLUCTUATIONS

The development of partition functions from various ensembles relies on the assumption that the distribution of states can be replaced by the maximum in the distribution. We have argued the case for this assumption in terms of the large number of ensemble members involved which causes the maximum in the distribution to completely outweigh the remainder of the distribution. In view of the discussion in Chapter 1 concerning the moments of a distribution and their ability to describe completely the distribution function, we may justifiably wonder what the variance or standard deviation of the distribution function is in these ensembles. Obviously the real system still contains fluctuations in properties about the mean value as depicted in Figure 2.1, but how large are these fluctuations?

The variance of the distribution depends upon the ensemble chosen. This is contrary to the thermodynamic properties which are independent of the ensemble used in their evaluation. That the variance, V, does indeed depend on the chosen ensemble is readily established by considering $V(E)$ for the microcanonical and canonical ensembles. By definition $V(E) = 0$ for the microcanonical ensemble because all members must have the same energy. On the other hand, T rather than E is fixed in the canonical ensemble and $V(E) \neq 0$.

To find $V(E)$ in the canonical ensemble, we write

$$V(E) = \langle (E - \langle E \rangle)^2 \rangle = \langle E^2 - 2E\langle E \rangle + \langle E \rangle^2 \rangle = \langle E^2 \rangle - \langle E \rangle^2. \tag{2.71}$$

The first term of Equation (2.71) can be conveniently rewritten as

$$\langle E^2 \rangle = \frac{1}{Q} \sum_j E_j^2 e^{-\beta E_j} = -\frac{1}{Q} \left[\frac{\partial (\langle E \rangle Q)}{\partial \beta} \right]_V$$

$$= -\left(\frac{\partial \langle E \rangle}{\partial \beta} \right)_V - \langle E \rangle \left(\frac{\partial \ln Q}{\partial \beta} \right)_V$$

$$= kT^2 \left(\frac{\partial \langle E \rangle}{\partial T} \right)_V + \langle E \rangle^2 = kT^2 C_V + \langle E \rangle^2 .$$

The $\langle E \rangle^2$ terms cancel when the above equation is substituted into Equation (2.71), leaving

$$V(E) = kT^2 C_V . \tag{2.72}$$

The *relative* magnitude of the standard deviation is $\sigma/\langle E \rangle$. As an approximation of the breadth of the distribution about $\langle E \rangle$, we may use ideal gas values. In the next chapter we shall see that $\langle E \rangle$ is on the order of NkT and C_V is on the order of Nk. This provides an order of magnitude estimate for $\sigma/\langle E \rangle$ of $N^{-1/2}$— indeed a very small quantity for macroscopic systems (i.e., at the most about 10^{-10}). Incidently, Equation (2.72) is of interest for more than just computing the size of the fluctuations. If one looks at the equation from the opposite perspective, the relation implies that heat capacities can be determined from fluctuations. This is particularly useful in simulations, and Equation (2.72) provides a direct calculational route for heat capacities from fluctuations observed in the simulation. This concept is further illustrated in Example 2.10.

The computation of $V(N)$ in a grand ensemble is analogous to that for $V(E)$ in the canonical ensemble. We therefore leave out the mathematical details (and pose it as an exercise for the student at the end of the chapter). The result

Example 2.10   Use the results of Example 2.5 and the fluctuation formula, Equation (2.72), to calculate dimensionless heat capacity C_V^+ for the particle in the box at $T^+ = 1$ and 4.

The dimensionless heat capacity is $C_V^+ = C_V/k$, so the fluctuation formula may be written as

$$C_V = \frac{<E^2> - <E>^2}{kT^2},$$

or

$$C_V^+ = \frac{<E^2> - <E>^2}{k^2T^2} = <E^{+2}> - <E^+>^2.$$

Substitution of the energy as a function of n into the first term yields

$$<C_V^+> = \sum_n \left(\frac{n^2}{T^+}\right)^2 \wp_n - <E^+>^2.$$

The argument in the summation is again a converging sequence (though not as rapidly as before) and we tabulate and sum these values to obtain

T^+	$1^4\wp_n/T^{+2}$	$2^4\wp_n/T^{+2}$	$3^4\wp_n/T^{+2}$	$3^4\wp_n/T^{+2}$	$3^4\wp_n/T^{+2}$	$4^4\wp_n/T^{+2}$
1	0.263	0.208	0.007	2×10^{-5}	6×10^{-9}	2×10^{-13}
4	0.021	0.162	0.235	0.129	0.033	0.004

with

$$\sum_n \left(\frac{n^2}{T^+}\right)^2 \wp_n = \begin{cases} 0.484 & \text{at } T^+ = 1 \\ 0.585 & \text{at } T^+ = 4 \end{cases}.$$

Finally, we obtain for the heat capacity $<C_V^+> = 0.382$ at $T^+ = 1$ and 0.433 at $T^+ = 4$.

$$V(N) = kT\left(\frac{\partial <N>}{\partial \mu}\right)_{V,T} \tag{2.73}$$

is obtained by this procedure. This can be put in a more common form by using the thermodynamic identity

$$Nd\mu = Vdp \text{ (constant } T) \tag{2.74}$$

to obtain

$$\left(\frac{\sigma}{<N>}\right)^2 = \frac{kT\kappa}{V}, \tag{2.75}$$

where κ is the isothermal compressibility defined by

$$\kappa = -\frac{1}{V}\left(\frac{\partial V}{\partial P}\right)_T. \tag{2.76}$$

For an ideal gas, $\kappa = 1/P$ and, therefore, $kT\kappa/V = 1/N$. Again, one obtains an expression for the relative fluctuations that is extremely small for macroscopic systems. In fact, relative σ values are the same order of magnitude for both fluctuations of energy in the canonical ensemble and number fluctuations in the grand canonical ensemble.

Having completed this excursus on fluctuations, we return in the next chapter to our main theme of calculating the partition function for various systems. We start with the simplest case, that of an ideal gas.

REFERENCES

1. Hill, T.L., *An Introduction to Statistical Thermodynamics,* Addison-Wesley, Reading, MA, 1960.
2. Broda, E., *Ludwig Boltzmann,* Ox Bow Press, Woodbridge, CT, 1983.
3. Kubo, R., *Statistical Mechanics,* North-Holland, Amsterdam, 1965.
4. Reed, T.M., and Gubbins, K.E., *Applied Statistical Mechanics,* McGraw-Hill, New York, 1973.
5. McQuarrie, D.A., *Statistical Mechanics,* Harper & Row, New York, 1976.

PROBLEMS

PHASE SPACE

1. Use the results of Example 1.1 to determine:
  (a) the dimensionality of phase space for this system,
  (b) how many possible two-dimensional projections of the system's trajectory in phase space there are if switching the ordinate and abscissa are counted as unique projections, and
  (c) how many possible two-dimensional projections of the system's trajectory in phase space there are if switching the ordinate and abscissa are not considered unique.
  (d) Finally, plot any four of the two-dimensional projections determined in part c.

2. Consider the motion of a particle (of unit mass) attached at right angles to walls by springs which impart simple harmonic motion to the particle in two directions. The frequency and amplitude of the vibrations in the two directions are identical, but the phase constants are different. In analogy with Example 1.6, the equations of motion can be solved to obtain positions normalized with respect to the amplitude of the harmonic motion

$$x = \cos(\omega t + \delta)$$

$$y = \cos(\omega t + \alpha)$$

where δ and α are the two different phase constants. Plot the $x - y$, $p_x - x$ and $p_x - p_y$ projections of the phase space trajectories for motion of the mass if (a) $\delta = \alpha$, (b) $\delta = \alpha + \pi/2$, and (c) $\delta = \alpha - \pi/4$.

3. Two free, noninteracting particles are confined to one dimension between 0 and L.

   (a) If the energy is constrained to be between E and $E+\Delta$, compute the microcanonical ensemble partition function $\Omega(E)$.

   (b) Compute the volume of phase space occupied by the system if the total system energy is constrained to be less than E.

4. A mass moves in the x direction with momentum p_x, is elastically reflected by the wall at $x = L$, moves in the $-x$ direction with momentum p_y, and is elastically reflected by the wall at $x = 0$.[3]

   (a) Sketch the trajectory in phase space.

   (b) Find the volume of phase space $\Omega(\leq E)$.

   (c) Find the number of quantum states with energy below E and compare the result with $\Omega(\leq E)$ for large E.

5. Find the volume of phase space occupied by an ideal gas of N molecules[3] contained in a box of volume V. You should do this problem using the classical definition and the fact that a unit sphere in n-dimensional space is equal to $\pi^{n/2}/\Gamma(n/2 + 1)$ where Γ is the gamma function.

PARTITION FUNCTIONS

6. A new energy scale is defined by writing $E'_i = E_i - E_0$, where E_0 is the energy of the ground (lowest) energy level.[4] For this new energy scale there are corresponding values of U', Q', and S' given by

$$U' = \sum_i \wp_i(E'_i)E'_i \qquad Q' = \sum_i e^{-\beta E'_i} \qquad S' = k\ln Q' + \frac{U'}{T}.$$

Relate U' and Q' to U and Q and show that S' is the same entropy as that defined for the canonical partition function.

7. Show that for a two-component system

$$\Xi(\mu_1,\mu_2,T,V) = \sum_{N_1} \sum_{N_2} Q(N_1,N_2,V,T)\lambda_1^{N_1}\lambda_2^{N_2}$$

where $\lambda_i = e^{\beta\mu_i}$. Derive from this expression the corresponding thermodynamic connection formula.

8. Using a method similar to that used in the derivation of the canonical and grand canonical ensembles, show that the partition function appropriate to an isothermal-isobaric ensemble is

$$\Delta(N,P,T) = \sum_V Qe^{-PV/kT},$$

and derive the principal thermodynamic connection formula for this ensemble.

9. Starting with the primary connection formula for the canonical ensemble, Equation (2.34), derive the thermodynamic equations shown in Table 2.1.

10. A rigid diatomic molecule rotates freely in three dimensions in a zero potential-energy field.[4] The Hamiltonian may be expressed in terms of the moment of inertia as

$$H = \frac{1}{2I}\left(p_\theta^2 + \frac{p_\phi^2}{\sin^2\theta}\right),$$

where $0 \le \theta \le \pi$ and $0 \le \phi \le 2\pi$ and

$$p_\theta = I\dot{\theta} \quad \text{and} \quad p_\phi = I\dot{\phi}\sin^2\theta.$$

Evaluate the classical molecular partition function, Q_{cl}, (excluding the $N!$ term). Note that there are only two applicable coordinates, θ and ϕ, because the distance between the atoms is fixed and translational motion is not considered.

11. The partition function of an ideal gas of diatomic molecules in an external electric field $\mathscr{E}$ is[5]

$$Q(N,V,T,\mathscr{E}) = \frac{[q(V,T,\mathscr{E})]^N}{N!},$$

where

$$q(V,T,\mathscr{E}) = V\Lambda^3 \cdot q_r \cdot q_v \cdot \left(\frac{kT}{\mu\mathscr{E}}\right)\sinh\left(\frac{\mu\mathscr{E}}{kT}\right),$$

$$q_r = \frac{8\pi^2 IkT}{h^2}, \qquad q_v = \frac{\exp(-h\nu/2kT)}{1 - \exp(-h\nu/kT)},$$

I is the moment of inertia of the molecule, ν is the molecule's fundamental vibrational frequency, and μ is the molecule's permanent dipole moment. Using this partition function and the thermodynamic relation

$$dA = -SdT - PdV - N<\mu>d\mathscr{E},$$

show that

$$<\mu> = \mu\left[\coth(\beta\mu\mathscr{E}) - \frac{1}{\beta\mu\mathscr{E}}\right],$$

where $<\mu>$ is the average dipole moment of a molecule in the direction of the external field. Then sketch the functionality of the dimensionless dipole moment ($\mu^+ = <\mu>/\mu$) result versus the dimensionless field $\mathscr{E}^+$ ($\mathscr{E}^+ = \beta\mu\mathscr{E}$) from $\mathscr{E}^+ = 0$ to $\mathscr{E}^+ = \infty$ and interpret what you see.

12. Derive Equations (2.33) starting from Equation (2.32).

13. Derive the *classical* canonical partition function for an ideal monatomic gas contained within a cubic box of length L on a side if the particles experience a gravitational field in the z direction; that is, the potential energy of each particle is given by $U(z) = mgz$.

14. A catalyst surface has M sites each of which can adsorb one gas molecule.[3] Suppose that the catalyst is in contact with an ideal gas of chemical potential μ. Also assume that an adsorbed molecule has energy $-\epsilon$ compared to molecules in the free state. Let N represent the number of molecules adsorbed on the surface of the catalyst.

   (a) Show that the canonical partition function for N particles adsorbed is

$$Q(N,\mu,T) = Ae^{N\beta\epsilon},$$

   where A is related to the number of possible arrangements of the N particles. You should show what A is in your answer.

   (b) Show that the grand canonical partition function can be written as

$$\Xi = [1 + e^{\beta(\epsilon + \mu)}]^M.$$

   Hint: Remember the multinomial expansion for $(1 + x)^M$.

   (c) From the formula for Ξ obtained in part b, find $<N>$ and the fractional coverage of the catalytic sites ($\theta = <N>/M$). This is the so-called Langmuir isotherm.

15. For a system of N independent, indistinguishable, one-dimensional, simple harmonic oscillators of force constant f, evaluate the classical partition function in terms of N, T, and ν where

$$\nu = \frac{1}{2\pi}\sqrt{\frac{f}{m}}.$$

In so doing, you should realize that the potential energy term of an harmonic oscillator is given by $U(x) = 1/2fx^2$. Does your result agree with the quantum mechanical expression in the appropriate limit? Prove that it does or does not. *Hint:* A useful integral is

$$\int_{-\infty}^{\infty} e^{-ax^2} \, dx = \sqrt{\frac{\pi}{a}} \, .$$

FLUCTUATIONS

16. Derive Equation (2.75).

17. Show that the fluctuation in energy in a grand canonical ensemble is

$$\sigma_E^2 = kT^2 C_V + \left(\frac{\partial <E>}{\partial <N>}\right)_{T,V} \mu \sigma_N^2 \, .$$

18. Derive an expression for pressure fluctuations in the canonical ensemble.

19. Show that in a two-component, open, isothermal ensemble that

$$<N_1 N_2> - <N_1><N_2> = kT\left(\frac{\partial <N_1>}{\partial \mu_2}\right)_{V,T,\mu_1} = kT\left(\frac{\partial <N_2>}{\partial \mu_1}\right)_{V,T,\mu_2} \, .$$

20. Rederive the expression for the heat capacity for a particle in a box

$$<C_V^+> = \sum_n \left(\frac{n^2}{T^+}\right)^2 \wp_n - <E^+>^2$$

using the result from Example 2.5 and the identity

$$C_V = \left(\frac{\partial E}{\partial T}\right)_V$$

directly, rather than the fluctuation formula derived in the text.

21. Consider N gas noninteracting gas molecules[3] contained in volume V. Let n be the number of molecules in a part of the vessel of volume v. Because the particles are noninteracting, the probability of finding a certain molecule in v is equal to v/V. Find the probability distribution $f(n)$. Then determine $<n>$ and $V(n)$.

3

THERMOPHYSICAL PROPERTIES OF IDEAL GASES

3.1 METHODOLOGY

The starting point for calculation of thermodynamic properties of ideal gases is the canonical, semiclassical partition function of Equation (2.69),

$$Q = \frac{ZQ_{\text{int}}}{\Lambda^{3N}N!} . \tag{3.1}$$

By definition there are no intermolecular interactions between ideal gas molecules. This simplifies considerably the configurational partition function Z defined in Equation (2.70). Because U is zero for an ideal gas, each set of triple integrals over the three coordinates yields a factor of V,

$$Z = \int \cdots \int e^{-\beta U} dq^{3N} = V^N . \tag{3.2}$$

Thus,

$$Q = \frac{V^N}{\Lambda^{3N}N!} Q_{\text{int}} , \tag{3.3}$$

and the problem of obtaining thermophysical properties for the ideal gas reduces to one of evaluating the partition function for the internal degrees of freedom.

We must now decide how to treat the internal degrees of freedom. As we have seen, the spacings between energy levels relative to the thermal energy of the molecules determine whether classical or quantum mechanics are appropriate. When the thermal energy is high relative to the spacing, many energy levels are populated and the various possible linear combinations of particle energies yield nearly continuous values for the total system energy. Within molecules, energy level spacings are in the order $\epsilon_n > \epsilon_e > \epsilon_v > \epsilon_r > \epsilon_t$, where the subscripts have the following meanings:

n = nuclear-spin states
e = electronic states
v = vibrational states
r = rotational states
t = translational motion

Above about 50 K, the thermal energy, kT, is considerably greater than the translational energy level spacing, and translational motion can be treated classically. Except for a few diatomic molecules, rotational modes can also be treated classically at normal temperatures. Vibrational, electronic, and nuclear-spin energy levels are generally sufficiently energetically separated that a quantum mechanical description is required even at very high temperatures.

A complete and rigorous calculation of Q_{int} would be very difficult due to coupling between different internal modes. However, the calculations can be greatly simplified with reasonable approximations of independence between various modes. For example, the Born-Oppenheimer approximation assumes that electron movement is rapid relative to the movement of the much more massive nuclei. Electrons therefore "see" virtually fixed nuclear positions during transitions between states, and so we make the assumption that the electronic partition function is independent of other internal modes. Similar time-scale considerations suggest that the other internal modes may also be approximated as independent motions, though the degree of validity for these assumptions varies from mode to mode. Probably the least amenable to this assumption of independence is the coupling between rotational and vibrational modes. One can easily visualize rotation affecting vibration and vice versa. Nevertheless, the rigid rotator model assumes rotational and vibrational independence and appears to be a reasonably good approximation in many cases, as evidenced by favorable comparisons of experimental and calculated values. For the rather simple molecules treated in this book, the assumption of independence does not lead to significant errors in thermophysical properties. While we will not treat rotational–vibrational coupling in this book, more specialized monographs[1] should be consulted if there is reason to believe that the actual potential is more complicated.

Under the approximation of independence, the molecular energy level for the internal modes can be represented as a simple sum of terms,

$$\epsilon_{int} = \epsilon_r + \epsilon_v + \epsilon_e + \epsilon_n . \qquad (3.4)$$

Expansion of the exponential term in the partition function factors the molecular partition function into individual modes,

$$q_{int} = q_r \cdot q_v \cdot q_e \cdot q_n . \tag{3.5}$$

Because the $N!$ term required for indistinguishable molecules was included with the translational portion of the partition function in Equation (3.1), the total internal-mode partition function Q_{int} is related to the corresponding molecular partition functions by

$$Q_{int} = q_{int}^N . \tag{3.6}$$

The total partition function is then written as

$$Q = \frac{V^N}{\Lambda^{3N} N!} (q_r \cdot q_v \cdot q_e \cdot q_n)^N . \tag{3.7}$$

A particularly nice feature of this factorization becomes evident when thermodynamic properties are calculated. Because Q is a product of terms, $\ln Q$ (upon which the thermodynamic properties depend as shown in Table 2.1) separates the various modes into a sum of terms,

$$\ln Q = N\ln V - 3N\ln\Lambda - \ln N! + N \sum_L^{\text{modes}} \ln q_L . \tag{3.8}$$

Additionally, the operators that relate thermodynamic properties to $\ln Q$ are linear. This means that the formulas in Table 2.1 produce a term-by-term contribution to the overall property; that is, a property J can be computed by applying the formulas of Table 2.1 to each mode and summing the results:

$$J = J_{\text{trans}} + \sum_L^{\text{int modes}} J_L . \tag{3.9}$$

No new or additional formulas are necessary to evaluate the J_L; we simply replace Q in the equations of Table 2.1 with q_L. In applying this procedure to pure components, the $N!$ term for indistinguishable particles and the configurational integral, V^N, though not strictly part of the translational partition function, are often grouped together (for the ideal gas case) into J_{trans}. For convenience, these formulas are repeated in Table 3.1 where the division between the translational (t) and internal (i) partition functions are separately shown.

We now specifically show how to calculate the contribution to the thermo-dynamic properties of ideal gases for each mode. The information used to calculate the internal degrees of freedom is obtained from spectroscopic data. The student is encouraged to review appropriate sources on quantum chemistry and spectroscopy of molecules. The discussion here is on the use of spectroscopic data for calculation of properties without intent to explain the molecular source of the equations and nomenclature used by the spectroscopist.

TABLE 3.1 Thermodynamic Properties
of Ideal Gases

Translational	Internal
$U_t = NkT^2 \left(\dfrac{\partial \ln q_t}{\partial T} \right)_V$	$U_i = NkT^2 \left(\dfrac{\partial \ln q_i}{\partial T} \right)_V$
$P_t = NkT \left(\dfrac{\partial \ln q_t}{\partial V} \right)_T$	$P_i = 0$
$H_t = U_t + NkT$	$H_i = U_i$
$C_{V_t} = \left(\dfrac{\partial U_t}{\partial T} \right)_V$	$C_{V_i} = \left(\dfrac{\partial U_i}{\partial T} \right)_V$
$C_{P_t} = C_{V_t} + Nk$	$C_{P_i} = C_{V_i}$
$S_t = Nk\ln\dfrac{q_t}{N} + \dfrac{U_t}{T} + Nk$	$S_i = Nk\ln q_i + \dfrac{U_i}{T}$
$A_t = -NkT\ln\dfrac{q_t}{N} - NkT$	$A_i = -NkT\ln q_i$
$G_t = -NkT\ln\dfrac{q_t}{N}$	$G_i = A_i$
$\mu_t = -kT\ln\dfrac{q_t}{N}$	$\mu_i = -kT\ln q_i$

3.2 TRANSLATIONAL PROPERTIES

It is convenient to group the configurational partition function with the translational for ideal gases because the configurational partition function is easily and explicitly evaluated as V^N. We will not do so for nonideal fluids. Actually, the calculation of Z is the prime difficulty for nonideal systems and will occupy the bulk of this text. Another reason for grouping Q_{trans} and Z together into J_{trans} for ideal gases is that both of these partition functions depend upon the volume, while none of the internal modes do. This means that the pressure is independent of the internal modes, as shown in Table 3.1, and the equation of state is calculated entirely from the translational–configurational partition function using

$$P = kT\left(\frac{\partial \ln Q}{\partial V}\right)_{T,N}.$$

From Equation (3.8), we find that

$$\left(\frac{\partial \ln Q}{\partial V}\right)_{T,N} = \frac{N}{V},$$

and we immediately retrieve the ideal-gas equation of state,

$$PV = NkT. \tag{3.10}$$

The translational contribution to the internal energy is given by

$$U_t = kT^2\left(\frac{\partial \ln Q_t}{\partial T}\right)_{V,N}. \tag{3.11}$$

Because Λ is the only temperature-dependent part of $\ln Q$ [see Equation (3.8)], the derivative in Equation (3.11) reduces to

$$\left(\frac{\partial \ln Q_t}{\partial T}\right)_{V,N} = -3N\left(\frac{\partial \ln \Lambda}{\partial T}\right)_{V,N} = -3N\left(\frac{\partial(-\frac{1}{2}\ln T)}{\partial T}\right)_{V,N} = \frac{3N}{2T}. \tag{3.12}$$

Thus,

$$U_t = \frac{3}{2}NkT. \tag{3.13}$$

Other translational properties are similarly derived from the formulas given in Table 3.1.

3.3 NUCLEAR-SPIN PROPERTIES

Separation between nuclear energy levels is extremely large (on the order of 10^{-6} ergs). This means that virtually all molecules are in the ground nuclear state except when $T > 10^8$ K. We will thus simplify q_n to just the ground-state degeneracy W_0; that is,

$$q_n = \sum_{\epsilon_j} W(\epsilon_j)e^{-\beta\epsilon_j} = W(\epsilon_0)e^0 = W(\epsilon_0) \, .$$

Because q_n is a constant below about 10^8 K, the nuclear-spin contribution to thermodynamic properties except entropy is zero . This is because of the derivative relationship between $\ln q$ and the thermodynamic properties except entropy as shown in Table 3.1. The contribution to entropy is itself a constant; which we also set to zero to again maintain compatibility with third law entropies. In general then, there is no nuclear-spin contribution to any thermodynamic properties for temperatures below about 10^8 K; that is,

$$\left[\begin{matrix} \ln q_n &= 0 \\ q_n &= 1 \end{matrix}\right] \quad (T < 10^8 \text{ K}) \, . \tag{3.14}$$

3.4 ELECTRONIC AND VIBRATIONAL PROPERTIES

The electronic molecular partition function relative to the ground state of $\epsilon_0 = 0$, in terms of energy levels, is given by

$$q_e = \sum_{\epsilon} W(\epsilon)e^{-\beta\epsilon} = W(\epsilon_0) + W(\epsilon_1)e^{-\beta\epsilon_1} + \dots , \tag{3.15}$$

or, in terms of frequencies, as

$$q_e = W(\epsilon_0) + W(\epsilon_1)e^{-\beta h\nu_1} + \dots . \tag{3.16}$$

Often electronic energy levels are so far apart that all molecules are in the ground electronic state. At temperatures where only the ground state is populated, $\ln q_e$ is a constant and does not contribute to thermodynamic properties, analogous to the situation for $\ln q_n$. Unlike the case for nuclear spin, however, a few simple, common molecules do have populated excited electronic states even near room temperature, and for these molecules, we must use Equation (3.16) to obtain the electronic contribution to the thermodynamic properties.

It is convenient to take the separated, unexcited atoms as a reference energy for molecules. This permits different compounds of the same elements to be referenced to the same energy ground state so that changes in thermodynamic properties can be determined for reactions. Figure 3.1 depicts the ground and first excited electronic states of a diatomic molecule separated by ϵ_1. In this figure, D_e is the depth of the electronic potential well. Because we take the unexcited, separated atoms as the reference state, the zero of energy is represented by the top of the energy well at large values of r, the internuclear separation distance. Relative to this reference, the energy at the bottom of the potential

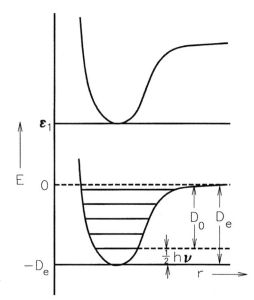

Figure 3.1 Schematic of the electronic and vibrational levels of a diatomic molecule.

well is $-D_e$. We can therefore shift the reference energy of Equation (3.16) to the separated atoms reference by subtracting D_e from each energy term to obtain,

$$q_e = W_0 e^{\beta D_e} + W_1 e^{-\Theta_{e1}/T} + \dots . \qquad (3.17)$$

Values of the electronic energy levels are now referenced to the separated atoms as shown in Figure 3.1. Here Θ_e is a characteristic electronic excitation temperature given by $\Theta_e = (\epsilon - D_e)/k$.

As mentioned in Chapter 2, there are generally $3m$ degrees of freedom in a polyatomic molecule of m atoms. In addition to the three translational modes, there are three molecular rotational modes for nonlinear molecules, one around each principal axis drawn through the molecular center of mass, or two rotational modes for linear molecules. Rotation about the bond axis of a linear molecule does not yield a degree of freedom because no distinguishable orientations are produced. The remaining degrees of freedom are vibrational modes. There are therefore

$$F_v = 3(m - 1) - F_r \qquad (3.18)$$

vibrational degrees of freedom, where F_r is 2 for linear and 3 for nonlinear molecules. Examples of vibrational modes for NO_2 are depicted in Example 2.6.

Consider for a moment a diatomic molecule. According to Equation (3.18), $m = 2$, $F_r = 2$, and $F_v = 1$. This single vibrational degree of freedom is the stretching mode of a harmonic oscillator; that is, the distance between atomic centers oscillates as the bond stretches and contracts. The potential energy versus internuclear separation for this vibrational mode is that depicted in Figure 3.1. The quantum mechanical solution of the harmonic oscillator problem yields quantized energy levels located at

$$\epsilon_{nv} = \left(n + \frac{1}{2}\right)h\nu \qquad n = 0, 1, 2, \dots \qquad (3.19)$$

relative to the bottom of the potential well. These quantized, stretching frequencies, depicted as horizontal lines in Figure 3.1, increase in energy from the vibrational ground-state energy, which is $\frac{1}{2}h\nu$ above the bottom of the potential well, to the dissociation energy of the molecule. If this stretching mode is energized to a quantum state n, where n is sufficiently high that $\epsilon_n > D_e$, then the diatomic molecule has sufficient energy to dissociate into separate atoms. The vibrational partition function for the jth mode of the F_v vibrational modes is

$$q_{vj} = \sum_n e^{-\beta\epsilon_{nj}}, \qquad (3.20)$$

which becomes, upon substitution of Equation (3.19),

$$q_{vj} = e^{-\beta h\nu_j/2} \sum_{n=0}^{\infty} e^{-nh\beta\nu_j}. \qquad (3.21)$$

The infinite summation in Equation (3.21) is coincidently of a convenient form that can be replaced by a closed algebraic form. The sum is an infinite geometric series of the form

$$\sum_{n=0}^{\infty} e^{-nx} = (1 - e^{-x})^{-1}. \qquad (3.22)$$

Equation (3.22) permits the vibrational molecular partition function to be written as

$$q_{vj} = \frac{e^{-\frac{1}{2}\beta h\nu_j}}{1 - e^{-\beta h\nu_j}}. \qquad (3.23)$$

For polyatomic molecules with F_v vibrational modes, a similar equation may be written for each mode. Because the total vibrational energy is the sum of the energies of the individual, independent modes, the vibrational partition function factors into the product of partition functions for the various vibrational modes by the usual expansion of the exponential of a sum. The molecular vibrational partition function can then be written as

$$q_v = \prod_{j=1}^{F_v} \frac{e^{-\frac{1}{2}\beta h v_j}}{1 - e^{-\beta h v_j}} . \tag{3.24}$$

It is generally convenient to combine the electronic and vibrational partition functions because a cancellation of terms occurs. In the diatomic molecule depicted in Figure 3.1, the ground-state vibrational level of the electronic ground state is at an energy of $\frac{1}{2}hv - D_e$ relative to the separated atoms. For simplicity we define D_0 as

$$D_0 = D_e - \sum_{j=1}^{F_v} \frac{1}{2}hv_j . \tag{3.25}$$

D_0 values are commonly tabulated as dissociation energies, and a few values are provided in Tables 3.2, 3.3, and 3.4. Also given in these tables are values of the vibrational frequencies for a few molecules given in units of characteristic vibration temperatures. These latter quantities are related to the vibrational frequencies by

$$\Theta_v = \frac{hv}{k} . \tag{3.26}$$

In terms of D_0 and Θ_v, the electronic and vibrational partition functions may be written as

$$q_e = W_0 e^{\beta D_0} \prod_j e^{\Theta_{vj}/2T} + W_1 e^{-\Theta_{e1}/T} + \dots \tag{3.27}$$

and

$$q_v = \prod_j \frac{e^{-\Theta_{vj}/2T}}{1 - e^{-\Theta_{vj}/T}} , \tag{3.28}$$

respectively. When only the ground electronic state is populated, the cancellation of the ground-state vibrational frequency that occurs by writing the electronic and vibrational partition functions together makes a combined vibrational–electronic partition function convenient. In this case,

$$q_{ve} = W_0 e^{\beta D_0} \prod_j \frac{1}{1 - e^{-\Theta_{vj}/T}} \quad \text{(no excited electronic states)} . \tag{3.29}$$

TABLE 3.2   Electronic Energy Levels for Atoms[2]

Atom	State	W	$\Theta_e(10^3 \text{ K})$
H	0	2	0.0
	1	2	118.4
He	0	1	0.0
	1	3	230.0
Li	0	2	0.0
	1	2	214.7
O	0	5	0.0
	1	3	0.232
	2	1	0.348
	3	5	22.86
	4	1	48.6
F	0	4	0.0
	1	2	0.580
	2	6	147.4

TABLE 3.3   Molecular Constants for Diatomic Molecules[2]

Molecule	W_e	D_0 (kcal/mol)	Θ_v (K)	Θ_r (K)
H_2	1	103.2	6215	85.3
D_2	1	104.6	4394	42.7
Cl_2	1	57.1	808	0.351
Br_2	1	45.4	463	0.116
I_2	1	35.6	308	0.0537
O_2	3	118.0	2256	2.07
N_2	1	225.1	3374	2.88
CO	1	255.8	3103	2.77
NO	2	150.0	2719	2.45
HF	1		5960	30.2
HCl	1	102.2	4227	15.02
HBr	1	92.4	3787	12.02
HI	1	70.5	3266	9.06

If excited electronic states are involved, then Equations (3.27) and (3.28) should be used instead of Equation (3.29).

It is important to realize that the product in Equation (3.29) is over all vibrational modes. While there is often a degeneracy in vibrational modes, such

TABLE 3.4 Molecular Constants for Polyatomic Molecules[2]

Molecule	D_0 (kcal/mol)	Rotational (K)			Vibrational (K) Θ_V		
		Θ_A	Θ_B	Θ_C			
CO_2	381.5	0.561			(2)954	1890	3360
H_2O	219.3	40.1	20.9	13.4	2290	5160	5360
NH_3	276.8	13.6	13.6	8.92	1360	4800	(2)4880
					(2)2330		
ClO_2	90.4	2.50	0.478	0.400	640	1360	1600
SO_2	254.0	2.92	0.495	0.422	750	1660	1960
N_2O	263.8	0.603			(2)850	1840	3200
NO_2	221.8	11.5	0.624	0.590	1900	1980	2330
CH_4	392.1	7.54	7.54	7.54	(3)1870	(2)2180	4170
					(3)4320		
CH_3Cl	370.7	7.32	0.637	0.637	1050	(2)1460	1950
					(2)2140	4270	(2)4380
CCl_4	308.8	0.082	0.082	0.082	(2)310	(3)450	660
					(3)1120		

as two scissor modes possessing the same vibrational frequency, each frequency, degenerate or not, must be included in Equation (3.29) as separate Θ_V values. An alternative, but equivalent method, is to compute a single q_v for each unique vibrational energy level. The total molecular vibrational partition function is then the product of the q_v for each energy level raised to the power of the degeneracy for that level. As a third alternative, one could calculate the vibrational thermodynamic property for each unique frequency and multiply the property itself by the degeneracy when summing to obtain the total q_v. We can represent these three methods mathematically. Let $\mathscr{R}$ be the operator on q that yields property R. Then we may obtain R by (1) operating on the product of all q for individual frequencies, (2) operating on the product of all *unique* frequencies raised to the appropriate power for the degeneracy of each, or (3) operating on each *unique* frequency and summing the frequency contributions to the thermodynamic property times the appropriate degeneracy; that is,

$$R = \mathscr{R}\left(\prod_{\text{modes}} q_{ve}\right) = \mathscr{R}\left(\prod_{\text{energies}} q_{ve}^{W_\Theta}\right) = \sum_{\text{energies}} W_\Theta \mathscr{R}(q_{ve}) . \qquad (3.30)$$

Table 3.4 lists the degeneracies of characteristic vibrational temperatures in parentheses preceding the corresponding value for Θ_V. In both the third and second methods illustrated above, we calculate the vibrational–electronic partition function using Equation (3.29). This partition function is then used in conjunction with the equations given in Table 3.1 to obtain the vibrational–

electronic contribution to the desired thermodynamic property. In the first method given above, we instead calculate the total molecular partition function and then apply the operator to obtain the total thermodynamic property.

3.5 ROTATIONAL PROPERTIES

The rotation of a rigid object about its center of mass can be defined in terms of three principal moments of inertia I_A, I_B, and I_C. A coordinate system can always be oriented in a rigid body such that all products of inertia vanish leaving only these three principal moments of inertia. The moments of inertia, as implied by the name, tell us about the second moment of the mass distribution within the molecule. The principal moments of inertia can be found from exact structural information on the molecule. For example, I_A, the principal moment of inertia in the x direction (in a coordinate system chosen with the origin at the center of mass and oriented such that the *products* of inertia vanish) can be found by summing over the point masses within the molecule times the squared distances from the center of mass in the y and z direction:

$$I_A = \sum_j m_j[(y_j - y_{cm})^2 + (z_j - z_{cm})^2] \, .$$

Consider the simple example sketched in Figure 3.2, that of a diatomic, homonuclear molecule such as O_2. We can find the principal moment I_A by summing the squared y distances from the center of mass of the two atoms multiplied by the atomic masses. This is readily seen to be a second moment and an inertial resistance to rotation about the x axis.

For nonlinear molecules, we could analogously obtain all three principal moments of inertia, I_A, I_B, and I_C, given the positions of the atoms within the molecule. Ordinarily, however, we would proceed from the opposite direction

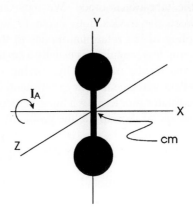

Figure 3.2 Principal moment of inertia I_A for a diatomic molecule.

and obtain information about the molecular structure from spectroscopic data. Values for the moments of inertia are generally calculated from characteristic rotational temperatures, Θ_r, observed spectroscopically. The relationship between the principal moments and Θ_r is

$$\Theta_\alpha = \frac{h^2}{8\pi^2 k I_\alpha}. \tag{3.31}$$

The symmetry of atoms within a molecule of course has considerable influence on the distribution of mass within the molecule and, correspondingly, with the relative magnitudes of the three principal moments of inertia. Molecules in which all three principal moments are equal are called "spherical tops," those with two equal are "symmetric tops," and those with three different moments are "asymmetric tops." The quantum mechanical problem of the rotation of a molecule can be solved in closed form for all three types of molecules, but the problem for asymmetric tops is much more difficult than that for either the spherical or symmetric top. Unfortunately, most molecules are asymmetric tops. Linear molecules are particularly simple to deal with, and so we will start with them. We will then proceed to polyatomic molecules, generalizing the results for the different symmetries that may be found in real molecules.

3.5.1 Linear Molecules

Linear molecules have two rotational modes characterized by equivalent moments of inertia. For example, the diatomic molecule shown in Figure 3.2 is oriented with its bond along the y axis. In this case, the x and z moments of inertia are equal, and the y moment vanishes because there is no mass distribution about the center of mass in the x and z directions. Linear molecules will therefore have only one characteristic rotational temperature as can be seen in Tables 3.3 and 3.4.

The simplest rotational model for molecules is that of a rigid rotator. In this model, bond lengths are fixed; that is, the rotational mode is independent of the vibrational mode. We have already discussed the fact that coupling between the modes does occur to some extent. Anharmonic motion due to coupling of the rotational modes to the vibrational modes is known to occur. Nevertheless, coupling is usually a small perturbation to the decoupled solutions, and the results obtained by solving the decoupled problem are generally in excellent agreement with experiment. The quantum-mechanical solution of the rigid-rotator problem for a linear molecule is straightforward (this is the obvious advantage of decoupling the problem), and it yields energy levels quantized as,

$$\epsilon_r = J(J+1)\frac{h^2}{8\pi^2 I} \quad J = 0, 1, \ldots, \tag{3.32}$$

where J is the rotational quantum number. The degeneracy of the Jth rotational energy state is

$$W(J) = 2J + 1 . \tag{3.33}$$

Before substituting the energy levels and degeneracy into the rotational partition function, we must take care not to overcount the number of states for molecules which possess some symmetry. If the molecules possess rotational symmetry, then we must divide out the so-called *symmetry number*, σ. This number corresponds to the number of distinct rotations that produce indistinguishable configurations.

Determining σ is not always easy. One must carefully examine the symmetry within the molecule. Consider, for example, the homonuclear and heteronuclear diatomic molecules depicted in Figure 3.3. In the heteronuclear case, the linear molecule is unsymmetrical, and a rotation of 180° about either the x or the z axis produces a distinct new configuration. While the total partition function for the heteronuclear molecule would involve no overcounting since each rotation state is unique, the partition function must be divided by two to eliminate the duplicate states counted in the rotation of this symmetric molecule. After a 180° rotation, all of the states generated in the next 180° of rotation produce equivalent states or indistinguishable configurations which have already been counted. Thus $\sigma = 1$ for the heteronuclear diatomic molecule, while $\sigma = 2$ for the homonuclear. We will explicitly divide the partition function by σ, recognizing that σ will be unity for molecules with no symmetry. Thus, we write for the rotational molecular partition function of a linear molecule

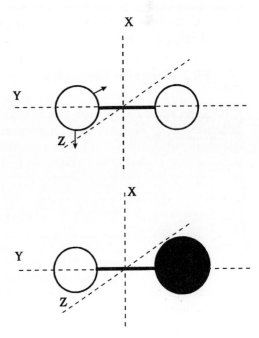

Figure 3.3 Rotational degrees of freedom in homonuclear and heteronuclear linear molecules.

$$q_r = \frac{1}{\sigma}\sum_{J=0}^{\infty}(2J + 1)e^{-J(J+1)\Theta_r/T}. \tag{3.34}$$

At sufficiently high temperatures, we should be able to use classical mechanics rather than quantum mechanics, and Equation (3.34) should approach that obtained from classical mechanics. In the classical limit, the summation in the partition function can be replaced by an integral which can be analytically integrated. Thus,

$$q_r = \frac{1}{\sigma}\int_0^{\infty}(2J + 1)e^{-J(J+1)\Theta_r/T}dJ = \frac{1}{\sigma}\int_0^{\infty}e^{-x\Theta_r/T}\,dx = \frac{T}{\sigma\Theta_r}, \tag{3.35}$$

where we have used the transformation of variables $x = J(J + 1)$ to make the solution more easily recognized. The classical limit is applicable for T/Θ_r larger than about five. Such is often, but not always, the condition of interest for calculations involving diatomic molecules. If the classical limit is appropriate, then the analytical solution

$$q_r = \frac{T}{\sigma\Theta_r} \quad \left(\text{for } \frac{T}{\Theta_r} > 5\right) \tag{3.36}$$

is more convenient to use than Equation (3.34). One should keep in mind, however, that Equation (3.34) is the more general case and the one that should be used when $T < 5\Theta_r$.

3.5.2 Nonlinear Molecules

As previously mentioned, the classical limit is adequate for q_r of nonlinear molecules at all but very low temperatures. The most general case of the rotational partition function for an asymmetric top is tedious to solve, but the classical limit is analogous to Equation (3.36):

$$q_r = \frac{\sqrt{\pi}}{\sigma}\left(\frac{T^3}{\Theta_A\Theta_B\Theta_C}\right)^{1/2}. \tag{3.37}$$

Rather than view Equation (3.34) separately from Equation (3.37), we can view Equation (3.37) as the general equation for the classical limit of all nonlinear molecules. To do so, we view each moment of inertia as contributing $(T/\Theta)^{1/2}$ to the partition function. Using this viewpoint, Equation (3.37) is seen to readily simplify to

$$q_r = \frac{\sqrt{\pi}}{\sigma}\left(\frac{T}{\Theta_r}\right)^{3/2} \qquad (3.38)$$

for a spherical-top molecule because all three moments of inertia are equal. Likewise, it becomes

$$q_r = \frac{\sqrt{\pi}}{\sigma}\left(\frac{T^3}{\Theta_A^2\Theta_B}\right)^{1/2} \qquad (3.39)$$

for a symmetric-top molecule because two of the principal moments are equal.

It is sometimes difficult to arrive at the correct value of the symmetry number for polyatomic molecules. If the molecule is asymmetric, then $\sigma = 1$. If the molecule is linear and symmetric about the center of mass, then $\sigma = 2$ because a 180° rotation about either axis perpendicular to the bond produces an equivalent configuration. If some symmetry exists in a polyatomic molecule then we must carefully count the degeneracy about the axes of rotation as illustrated in Example 3.1.

Example 3.1 Determine the rotational symmetry numbers for ammonia and methane.

The ammonia molecule is geometrically oriented as a triangular pyramid. Rotation about the axis drawn through the upper point of the pyramid and perpendicular to the base repeats the same configuration every 120° since all of the hydrogen atoms are indistinguishable. The other two axes do not yield any additional symmetry since rotation about these axes always generates unique configurations. Thus, $\sigma = 3$.

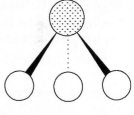

Methane is a tetrahedral molecule. There are obviously three equivalent rotations about the axis in the figure as is the case with ammonia. However, there are four different hydrogens that could be put at the top position, generating 3×4, or 12, equivalent configurations. Thus, $\sigma = 12$.

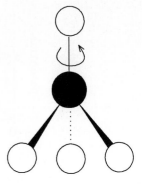

3.5.3 Internal Rotations

Molecules such as ethane possess yet another degree of freedom, internal rotations around the carbon–carbon bond. In Figure 3.4, we look end to end down the carbon–carbon bond in an ethane molecule. Rotation around this bond will swing the hydrogens on either carbon into different positions relative to each other. As shown in this figure, steric interactions between hydrogen atoms on opposite carbon atoms are best avoided when they are in a staggered configuration relative to each other. This is represented by the minimum in the intermolecular potential energy function. We will take the angle between two reference hydrogens, one on either carbon, to represent the degree of rotation about the carbon–carbon bond, beginning with the staggered conformation arbitrarily taken as $0°$ as in Figure 3.4. As rotation about the bond occurs, the potential energy increases due to the steric hindrance of the hydrogens and they pass by each other. The maximum in the potential, V_0, occurs when the hydrogen atoms are fully eclipsed. Continued rotation would produce additional staggered conformations at $120°$ intervals.

The torsional motion of intramolecular rotation about a central bond is not active in either Raman or infrared spectroscopy. Direct information about intramolecular rotational frequencies is therefore not readily available. Comparison of experimental thermodynamic properties to values obtained using statistical mechanics offers a way of obtaining information about the value of the internal energy barrier V_0. However, exact inclusion of internal rotation is difficult. Sometimes it can be included by treating the rotation as either a free rotation or as harmonic oscillation using the formulas already derived. For example, if

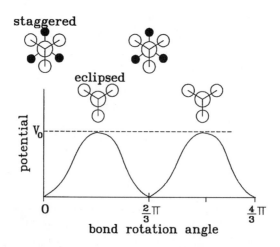

Figure 3.4 Potential as a function of the angle of rotation about the carbon–carbon bond in ethane.

$kT >> V_0$, then the internal rotation is virtually uninhibited. Free rotations can be treated with the same methods used in the previous section for the rigid rotor model. On the other hand, if $kT << V_0$ then the configuration is essentially trapped in the staggered conformation. The torsional motion will be oscillatory in this case, and the harmonic oscillator model used to evaluate vibrational modes becomes appropriate for evaluating the motion. Unfortunately, the energy barrier to internal rotation relative to kT is often in an intermediate range so that configurational transitions cannot be treated accurately with either limiting case. In this circumstance, one must deal explicitly with hindered or restricted rotational motion. Schröedinger's equation is difficult to solve analytically for this case, but some researchers have used numerical solutions to obtain eigenvalues for the energy and the corresponding contributions to thermodynamic properties as a function of V_0. Alternatively, the value of V_0 can be accurately obtained by molecular mechanics simulations of the variation of the potential with spatial movement of pieces of the molecule. Once a model for the potential as a function of rotation angle has been determined by such techniques, the contribution of conformational transitions and internal rotation to the thermodynamic properties can be included quite nicely with molecular dynamics simulations performed using site–site potential models.[3,4] We will not deal further with analytical computations of intramolecular rotational degrees of freedom in this chapter, as the effects on the properties of ideal gases are generally quite small. Conformational effects and hindered intramolecular rotations really only play a role in the thermodynamic properties at much higher densities, generally only for liquids.

Table 3.5 summarizes the contributions to the molecular partition function that we have discussed in this section. Contributions of each mode to a specific thermodynamic property can be computed separately using the formulas of Table 3.1. The sum of these contributions then yields a value for the total thermodynamic property. We now have all of the fundamentals in place for looking in more detail at the calculation of total thermodynamic properties of ideal gases. This is best done by example. The final section of this chapter therefore consists mainly of different applications of the above formulas so that the student can get a better feel for performing the calculations.

3.6 THERMODYNAMIC PROPERTIES OF IDEAL GASES

Individual contributions to the thermodynamic properties of an ideal gas from the various intramolecular modes of a molecule can be calculated as we have described in the previous sections. In accordance with Equation (3.9), we then sum all of the contributions to obtain a value for the total property. For convenience, a summary of some of the thermodynamic properties is made in Tables 3.6

and 3.7 for linear and nonlinear molecules, respectively. Use of these equations is illustrated in Examples 3.2 through 3.5.

In Tables 3.5 to 3.7, we have used $q_t = V/\Lambda^3$ as the molecular partition function for translational motion. As mentioned previously, we generally think of the $N!$ term that appears in Equations (3.1) and (3.3) as belonging to the translational partition function. The $N!$ term has not yet been explicitly included in the molecular partition functions shown in these tables. The total partition function is therefore obtained from

---

TABLE 3.5   Summary of Molecular Partition Functions

A. Nuclear Spin

$q_n = 1$ $(T < 10^8 \text{ K})$

B. Electronic and Vibrational

$$q_e = W_0 e^{\beta D_0} \prod_j e^{\Theta_{vj}/2T} + W_1 e^{-\Theta_{el}/T} + \dots$$

$$q_v = \prod_j \frac{e^{-\Theta_{vj}/2T}}{1 - e^{-\Theta_{vj}/T}}$$

$$q_{ve} = W_0 e^{\beta D_0} \prod_j (1 - e^{-\Theta_{vj}/T})^{-1} \qquad \text{(only ground electronic state populated)}$$

C. Rotational

Linear Molecules:

$$q_r = \frac{1}{\sigma} \sum_{J=0}^{\infty} (2J + 1)e^{-J(J+1)\Theta_r/T} \qquad \text{(general quantum expression)}$$

$$q_r = \frac{T}{\sigma\Theta_r} \qquad \text{(classical limit: } T/\theta_r > 5)$$

Nonlinear:

$$q_r = \frac{\sqrt{\pi}}{\sigma}\left(\frac{T^3}{\Theta_A\Theta_B\Theta_C}\right)^{1/2} \qquad \text{(classical limit)}$$

D. Translational

$$q_t = \frac{V}{\Lambda^3}$$

$$Q = \frac{q_t^N}{N!} \prod_{i=\text{int}} q_i^N , \tag{3.40}$$

from which the total thermodynamic properties shown in the tables have been formulated. As usual, properties are related to the logarithm of Q and Stirling's approximation is used to evaluate the $\ln N!$ term. Notice the appearance of an additional N in the translational part of A and S in Tables 3.6 and 3.7 resulting from the $N!$ term.

For mixtures of ideal gases, the partition function can again be factored into molecular partition functions, but the counting of indistinguishable molecules must be done as in Equation (2.58). Thus the total partition function is

$$Q = \frac{q_a^{N_a} \cdot q_b^{N_b} \cdot \cdots}{N_a! N_b! \cdots} = \prod_i \frac{q_i^{N_i}}{N_i!} , \tag{3.41}$$

where all of the previous equations for the molecular partition functions again apply to the mixture. The separate $N!$ for each component in the denominator of Equation (3.41) arises from the distinguishability of a and b molecules. These

TABLE 3.6 Thermodynamic Properties of Ideal Gases
Containing *Linear* Molecules

$$q = \left(\frac{2\pi mkT}{h^2} \right)^{3/2} V \cdot \frac{T}{\sigma \Theta_r} \cdot \left[\prod_{j=1}^{3m-5} (1 - e^{-\Theta_{vj}/T})^{-1} \right] \cdot W_0 e^{D_0/kT}$$

$$-\frac{A}{NkT} = \ln \left[\left(\frac{2\pi mkT}{h^2} \right)^{3/2} \frac{Ve}{N} \right] + \ln \left(\frac{T}{\sigma \Theta_r} \right) - \sum_{j=1}^{3m-5} \left[\ln(1 - e^{-\Theta_{vj}/T}) \right] + \frac{D_0}{kT} + \ln W_0$$

$$\frac{U}{NkT} = \frac{3}{2} + 1 + \sum_{j=1}^{3m-5} \left(\frac{\Theta_{vj}/T}{e^{\Theta_{vj}/T} - 1} \right) - \frac{D_0}{kT}$$

$$\frac{C_V}{Nk} = \frac{3}{2} + 1 + \sum_{j=1}^{3m-5} \left(\frac{\Theta_{vj}}{T} \right)^2 \left[\frac{e^{\Theta_{vj}/T}}{(e^{\Theta_{vj}/T} - 1)^2} \right]$$

$$\frac{S}{Nk} = \ln \left[\left(\frac{2\pi mkT}{h^2} \right)^{3/2} \frac{Ve^{5/2}}{N} \right] + \ln \left(\frac{Te}{\sigma \Theta_r} \right) + \sum_{j=1}^{3m-5} \left[\frac{\Theta_{vj}/T}{e^{\Theta_{vj}/T} - 1} - \ln(1 - e^{-\Theta_{vj}/T}) \right]$$
$$+ \ln W_0$$

$$PV = NkT$$

TABLE 3.7   Thermodynamic Properties of Ideal Gases Containing *Nonlinear* Molecules

$$q = \left(\frac{2\pi mkT}{h^2}\right)^{3/2} V \cdot \frac{1}{\sigma}\left(\frac{\pi T^3}{\Theta_A\Theta_B\Theta_C}\right)^{1/2} \cdot \left[\prod_{j=1}^{3m-6}(1 - e^{-\Theta_{vj}/T})^{-1}\right] \cdot W_0 e^{D_0/kT}$$

$$-\frac{A}{NkT} = \ln\left[\left(\frac{2\pi mkT}{h^2}\right)^{3/2}\frac{Ve}{N}\right] + \ln\left[\frac{1}{\sigma}\left(\frac{\pi T^3}{\Theta_A\Theta_B\Theta_C}\right)^{1/2}\right] - \sum_{j=1}^{3m-6}[\ln(1 - e^{-\Theta_{vj}/T})] + \frac{D_0}{kT}$$
$$+ \ln W_0$$

$$\frac{U}{NkT} = \frac{3}{2} + \frac{3}{2} + \sum_{j=1}^{3m-6}\left(\frac{\Theta_{vj}/T}{e^{\Theta_{vj}/T} - 1}\right) - \frac{D_0}{kT}$$

$$\frac{C_V}{Nk} = \frac{3}{2} + \frac{3}{2} + \sum_{j=1}^{3m-6}\left(\frac{\Theta_{vj}}{T}\right)^2\left[\frac{e^{\Theta_{vj}/T}}{(e^{\Theta_{vj}/T} - 1)^2}\right]$$

$$\frac{S}{Nk} = \ln\left[\left(\frac{2\pi mkT}{h^2}\right)^{3/2}\frac{Ve^{5/2}}{N}\right] + \ln\left[\frac{1}{\sigma}\left(\frac{\pi T^3 e^3}{\Theta_A\Theta_B\Theta_C}\right)^{1/2}\right]$$
$$+ \sum_{j=1}^{3m-6}\left[\frac{\Theta_{vj}/T}{e^{\Theta_{vj}/T} - 1} - \ln(1 - e^{-\Theta_{vj}/T})\right] + \ln W_0$$

$$PV = NkT$$

terms in turn give rise to the ideal mixing free energy and entropy that occurs just due to interspersing one kind of molecule in another even without any interactions. As the reader should show in Problem 12 at the end of the chapter, when the logarithm of Equation (3.41) is taken, the individual $\ln(N!)$ terms yield the ideal mixing contribution to entropy-related properties. Of course, nonideal mixtures cannot be factored into individual component contributions as in Equation (3.41), but we will wait to later chapters to handle that situation.

     Examples 3.2 to 3.5 illustrate the calculation of thermodynamic properties for ideal gases. The student should study these examples and try others. The program on diskette for Example 3.3 can be used to provide answers for other problems that the student may wish to examine. In doing these calculations by hand, one should be careful to ensure that the units are consistent throughout. Another common problem is to find an overflow error when trying to compute q. This usually occurs when one attempts to take products or quotients of the

Example 3.2   Compute the molar internal energy of CCl_4 at 500 K.

From Table 3.6, $(U/NkT)_t = 3/2$ and $(U/NkT)_r = 3/2$. Strictly for notational convenience, define

$$L_j = \frac{\Theta_{vj}/T}{e^{\Theta_{vj}/T} - 1},$$

so that the vibrational/electronic contribution is given by

$$\left(\frac{U}{NkT}\right)_{Ve} = \sum_j L_j.$$

The values of Θ_{vj} and their degeneracy are obtained from Table 3.4 and are shown below with the corresponding values of L_j:

j	0	1	2	3
Θ_v	660	310	1120	450
L_j	0.4812	0.7218	0.2669	0.6166
W	1	2	3	3

We must remember to sum over all vibrational states or, equivalently, multiply each L_j for unique energy levels by the corresponding degeneracy. Thus,

$$(U/NkT)_{ve} = 0.4812 + (2)(0.7218) + (3)(0.2669) + (3)(0.6166)$$
$$-[(308{,}800 \text{ cal/mol})/(500 \text{ K})(1.987 \text{ cal/mol·K})] = -306.25,$$

where the value of D_0 for CCl_4, 308.8 kcal/mol, was also obtained from Table 3.4.

Finally, the total dimensionless internal energy is given by the sum of the contributions:

$$(U/NkT) = 3/2 + 3/2 - 306.25 = -303.25,$$

and the molar internal energy is found by setting N to Avagadro's number to obtain $U = -304.3$ kcal/mol. This value is relative to the dissociated atoms; the dissociation energy is obviously the primary contribution. Since no reactions are involved, it is more convenient to choose as a reference the molecule in its ground state, in which case the molar internal energy is given by

$$U = -304 \text{ kcal/mol} + D_0 = 4.5 \text{ kcal/mol}.$$

very large or very small numbers inherent to molecular-based calculations. This problem can be avoided by carefully taking products and quotients in an appropriate order to minimize the potential problem and by calculating $\ln Q$ rather than Q values. It is, after all, $\ln Q$ that one is after to obtain thermophysical property values.

Example 3.3 Calculate the enthalpy of reaction at 1000 K for the ideal gas-phase reaction $N_2 + O_2 = 2\, NO$.

All of the molecules involved in this reaction are linear and at the requested temperature, $T/\Theta_r \gg 5$ permitting the use of the formulas in Table 3.6. The heat of reaction can be written as

$$\Delta H_{rxn} = 2H_{NO} - H_{O_2} - H_{N_2}.$$

Enthalpy is related to internal energy by $H = U + PV$ as shown in Table 3.1. We can thus write

$$\Delta H_{rxn} = 2U_{NO} - U_{O_2} - U_{N_2} + PV(2 - 1 - 1) = 2U_{NO} - U_{O_2} - U_{N_2}.$$

Because the number of molecules is conserved during reaction, the enthalpy and internal energy change are seen to be equivalent. We can therefore simply use the equation for U in Table 3.6,

$$\frac{U}{NkT} = \frac{3}{2} + 1 + \frac{\Theta_v/T}{e^{\Theta_v/T} - 1} - \frac{D_0}{kT}$$

to determine ΔH_{rxn}. Thus,

NO:

$$\frac{U}{NkT} = 2.5 + \frac{2.719}{e^{2.719} - 1} - \frac{150{,}000}{(1.987)(1000)} = -72.799$$

O_2:

$$\frac{U}{NkT} = 2.5 + \frac{2.256}{e^{2.256} - 1} - \frac{118{,}000}{(1.987)(1000)} = -56.622$$

N_2:

$$\frac{U}{NkT} = 2.5 + \frac{3.374}{e^{3.374} - 1} - \frac{225{,}100}{(1.987)(1000)} = -110.667$$

Combining the above results, we obtain

$$\Delta H_{rxn} = NkT[(2)(-72.799) + 56.622 + 110.667] = 180.3 \text{ kJ/mol}$$

The next chapter considers properties of crystalline solids. It is interesting to note that the random nature of gases and the ordered structure of solids make them both much easier to treat with statistical mechanics than liquids. The structural middle ground of liquids, not entirely ordered nor entirely random, makes calculation of the configurational partition function difficult. The solids dealt with in Chapter 4 will be treated much like we have treated ideal gases. Though the molecules do interact, their restriction to lattice sites within the crystal permit us to treat the molecules as though they are independent.

Example 3.4   Compute the equilibrium constant for the gas-phase dissociation of Cl_2 at 1000 K.

The dissociation reaction is

$$Cl_2 \rightleftarrows 2Cl,$$

for which the equilibrium constant is given by

$$K(T) = \exp(-\Delta G^0/RT).$$

Here ΔG^0 is the standard state Gibbs free energy, usually at 1 atm. The pressure will only affect the translational mode since the internal degrees of freedom are independent of volume. Let v_i represent the stoichiometric coefficient of the ith component (including appropriate sign). Thus, $v_{Cl} = 2$, $v_{Cl_2} = -1$, and $\Delta G^0 = \sum_i v_i G^0_i$.

The free energies are obtained from the formula given in Table 3.1,

$$G^0_L = -N_0 kT \ln(q^0_L/N_0),$$

where N_0 is Avagadro's number and the subscript L represents each mode (translational, rotational, etc.). We will consistently use the index L for different modes and i for different components in this example. Thus,

$$K(T) = \prod_L \prod_i (q_{Li}^0/N_0)^{v_i} = \prod_L K_L(T).$$

This equation expresses the equilibrium constant as a product of the individual internal mode equilibrium constants. Alternatively, K can be calculated as

$$K(T) = \prod_i [(q^0/N)_t \cdot q_{ev} \cdot q_r]^{v_i}.$$

We choose this latter method in what follows. Note that the standard state indication only needs to be made on the translational portion of the partition function.

Cl atoms:

Since monatomic, there are no rotational or vibrational modes for Cl atoms. The translational partition function is simply

$$q^0_t/N = V^0/(N\Lambda^3) = kT/[(1 \text{ atm})(\Lambda)] = 1.712 \times 10^8,$$

where we have substituted the equation of state $PV = NkT$ to obtain V^0 from the known value of P. We have also evaluated Λ at 1000 K from Equation (2.60).

The electronic partition function is found from the ground and first excited states of Cl atoms. Cl happens to be a case where the first excited state is low enough to make a contribution to the partition function. For the ground level $\epsilon_0 = 0$ with a degeneracy of 4, and for the first excited state $\epsilon_1 = 1.765 \times 10^{-13}$ ergs with a degeneracy of 2.

Thus, the electronic partition function is given by

$$q^0_e = 4 + 2 \cdot \exp\{-1.765 \times 10^{-13} \text{ ergs}/[(1.386 \times 10^{-16} \text{ ergs/K})(1000 \text{ K})]\}$$
$$= 4.557.$$

The total partition function for Cl atoms is the product of the translational and electronic partition functions, or $q^0_{Cl}/N = (1.712 \times 10^8)(4.557) = 7.80 \times 10^8$.

Example 3.4   Continued

Cl$_2$ Molecules:

For molecular Cl$_2$ the partition function is found from

$$q^0(Cl_2)/N = (q^0/N)_t \cdot q_r \cdot q_{ve} \, .$$

The translational and rotational partition functions are, respectively,

$$(q^0/N)_t = kT/(P^0 \cdot \Lambda^3) = 4.74 \times 10^8 \text{ and } q_r = T/(\sigma\Theta_r) \, .$$

Note that the classical limit is acceptable for q_r since at this temperature T/Θ_r is 2849, much greater than 5. From Table 3.3, $\Theta_r = 0.351$ K. Because the molecule is homonuclear and linear, $\sigma = 2$, and $q_r = 2849/2 = 1424.5$.

The vibrational/electronic partition function is given by

$$q_{Ve} = \frac{W_0 e^{D_0/kT}}{1 - e^{-\Theta_{vj}/T}} = 5.452 \times 10^{12} \, ,$$

where $W_0 = 1$, $\Theta_v = 808$ K and $D_0 = 57.1$ kcal/mol, as obtained from Table 3.3. The total molecular partition function for Cl$_2$ is therefore given by the product of the values for the various modes, or

$$(q^0/N)_{Cl_2} = (4.74 \times 10^8)(1424.5)(5.45 \times 10^{12}) = 3.681 \times 10^{24} \, .$$

Finally, for the dissociation of Cl$_2$ to Cl, the equilibrium constant is given by

$$K(1000 \text{ K}) = \frac{(q^0/N)^2_{Cl}}{(q^0/N)_{Cl}} = \frac{(7.80 \times 10^8)^2}{3.681 \times 10^{24}} = 1.65 \times 10^{-7} \, .$$

REFERENCES

1. Gray, C.G., and Gubbins, K.E. *Theory of Molecular Fluids. Vol. 1: Fundamentals*, Clarendon Press, Oxford, 1984.

2. McQuarrie, D.A. *Statistical Mechanics*, Harper & Row, New York, 1976.

3. Rowley, R.L., and Ely, J.F. "Non-equilibrium molecular dynamics simulations of structured molecules. Part I. Isomeric effects on the viscosity of butanes," *Mol. Phys.* **1991**, *72*, 831.

4. Rowley, R.L., and Ely, J.F. "Non-equilibrium molecular dynamics simulations of structured molecules. Part II. Isomeric effects on the viscosity of models for *n*-hexane, cyclohexane and benzene," *Mol. Phys.* **1991**, *72*, 831.

5. Reed, T.M., and Gubbins, K.E. *Applied Statistical Mechanics*, McGraw-Hill, New York, 1973.

Example 3.5 Compute the chemical potential of CO_2 at 400 K and 1 atm.
The chemical potential is related to Q by

$$\mu = \left(\frac{\partial A}{\partial N}\right)_{T,V} = -kT\left(\frac{\partial \ln Q}{\partial N}\right)_{T,V} = -\left[\frac{\partial}{\partial N}\ln\left(\frac{V^N \Pi_i q_i^N}{\Lambda^{3N}N!}\right)\right]_{T,V}.$$

We then perform the differentiation:

$$\frac{\mu}{kT} = -\left(\frac{\partial N\ln V}{\partial N}\right)_{T,V} - \sum_i \left(\frac{\partial N\ln q_i}{\partial N}\right)_{T,V} + 3\left(\frac{\partial N\ln \Lambda}{\partial N}\right)_{T,V} + \left(\frac{\partial (N\ln N - N)}{\partial N}\right)_{T,V}$$

$$= -\ln V - \sum_i \ln q_i + 3\ln\Lambda + \ln N$$

$$= -\ln\frac{kT}{P} - \ln W_0 - \frac{D_0}{kT} + \sum_v \ln(1 - e^{-\Theta_v/T}) - \ln\left(\frac{T}{\sigma\Theta_r}\right) + \frac{3}{2}\ln\left(\frac{h^2}{2\pi mkT}\right).$$

The values for the constants contained in this equation are obtained from Table 3.4.
They are:

$$k = 1.3806 \times 10^{-16} \text{ erg/(molec} \cdot \text{K)}$$
$$T = 400 \text{ K}$$
$$P = 1 \text{ atm} = 1.01325 \times 10^6 \text{ g/(cm} \cdot \text{s}^2)$$
$$W_0 = 1$$
$$D_0 = 381.5 \text{ kcal/mol}$$
$$\Theta_v = 954 \text{ K, } 954 \text{ K, } 1890 \text{ K, } 3360 \text{ K}$$
$$\sigma = 2$$
$$\Theta_r = 0.561 \text{ K}$$
$$h = 6.626 \times 10^{-27} \text{ erg} \cdot \text{s}$$
$$m = 7.3062 \times 10^{-23} \text{ g/molec}$$

Using these values, we then calculate for the dimensionless chemical potential relative
to the separated atoms $\mu/kT = -503.05$. The largest contribution arises from the D_0
term. If we use the ground state of the molecule as the reference, rather than the separated
atoms, we obtain $\mu/kT = -23.06$.

PROBLEMS

ELECTRONIC STATES

1. In some cases, more than just the ground electronic state may be populated.[5] For
   example, consider the case where both the ground and first excited states are
   important; that is,

$$q_e = W_0 + W_1 e^{-\Theta_{el}/T}.$$

(a) Derive an expression for the probability of finding the atom in the first excited state: $\wp_1$.

(b) Determine the electronic contribution to the internal energy, U, and entropy, S, in terms of $\wp_1$ and Θ_{el} for this situation.

(c) Determine the limits of the electronic contribution to U and S as $T \to 0$ and as $T \to \infty$.

2. Calculate the population of the first few electronic energy levels of an oxygen atom at room temperature.[5]

3. Show that the contribution of the electronic degrees of freedom to the internal energy is small at ordinary temperatures.

VIBRATIONAL STATES

4. (a) Calculate the fraction of oxygen and iodine molecules that are in excited (above the ground level) vibrational states at 300 K.[5]

(b) Calculate the fraction of oxygen and iodine molecules that are in the lowest two vibrational states at 500 K.

5. Calculate the vibrational force constant f in dyne/cm, the frequency ν in s^{-1}, and the wave number in cm^{-1} for HCl, Cl_2, and I_2.

6. A more accurate expression for the vibrational energy of diatomic molecules is

$$\epsilon_n = \left(n + \frac{1}{2}\right)h\nu - x_e\left(n + \frac{1}{2}\right)h\nu$$

where x_e is called the anharmonicity constant. The additional term here represents the first deviations from strictly harmonic behavior. Treating x_e as a small parameter, calculate the anharmonic effect on the various thermodynamic functions to first order in x_e.

ROTATIONAL STATES

7. Calculate the rotational entropy of NH_3 at 400 K in $J/(mol \cdot K)$.

8. Determine the most probable rotational quantum energy level J^* and the fraction of molecules expected to be in that level for gas-phase N_2 at 300 K and 1 atm.

9. Locate the center of mass of the linear molecule HCN, given that the equilibrium internuclear distances are 1.157 Å for CN and 1.059 Å for HC. Calculate the moment of inertia about the center of mass and the characteristic rotational temperature Θ_r.

10. For a spherical top, the rotational energy levels are

$$\epsilon_j = \frac{j(j + 1)h^2}{8\pi^2 I_A}, \qquad j = 0, 1, \ldots$$

with degeneracy $W(j) = (2j + 1)^2$. Verify Equation (3.38) for the classical limit of the rotational partition function for a spherical top.

11. Calculate the moment of inertia of HI and the internuclear separation.

TRANSLATIONAL PARTITION FUNCTIONS

12. For an ideal binary mixture, write down the canonical partition function in terms of molecular partition functions and then show that

$$U = \frac{3}{2}(N_1 + N_2)kT$$

$$S = N_1 k \ln\left(\frac{Ve^{5/2}}{\Lambda_1^3 N_1}\right) + N_2 k \ln\left(\frac{Ve^{5/2}}{\Lambda_2^3 N_2}\right)$$

if internal modes are ignored. Then derive the standard thermodynamic formula for the entropy of mixing for an ideal gas mixture.

13. Derive the classical canonical partition function and the equation of state for an ideal monatomic gas contained within a cubic box of length L on a side if the particles experience a gravitational field in the z direction. That is, the potential energy of each particle is given by $U(z) = mgz$. Your equation of state should express P as a function of T, V, and m.

14. Consider an ideal gas of molecules with permanent electric dipole moments μ in an electric field $\mathscr{E}$.[2] Neglecting the polarizability of the molecules, the potential energy is $u = -\mu\mathscr{E}\cos\theta$ where θ is the angle between the vectors μ and $\mathscr{E}$. Using classical mechanics, derive an expression for the additional effect of $\mathscr{E}$ on the internal energy U and the heat capacity of the gas.

THERMODYNAMIC PROPERTIES OF IDEAL GASES

15. Calculate A, U, μ, C_V, and S for 1 mole of Kr at 25°C and 1 atm.

16. Calculate the entropy of ClO_2 at 298 K and 1 atm.[2] Compare this calculated value to the experimental value of 61 cal/(mol · K). *Note:* ClO_2 has a ground-state electronic degeneracy of 2.

17. Calculate the molar entropy of CH_4 at 25°C and 1 atm. The experimental value (corrected for nonideal gas behavior) is 44.5 cal/(mol · K).

18. Show that the molar heat capacity, C_v, for NH_3 at 300 K is 3.28R.[2]

19. Calculate the equilibrium constant for the water–gas shift reaction

$$CO_2 + H_2 \leftrightarrows CO + H_2O$$

at 1200 K.[2] The experimental value is 1.37.

20. Calculate the temperature at which molecular nitrogen is 5% dissociated at 100 atm.[2]

21. Calculate the enthalpy of reaction at 1000 K for the reaction:

$$CH_4 + Cl_2 \leftrightarrows CH_3Cl + HCl$$

22. Determine the equilibrium constant for the isotopic reaction

$$H_2 + D_2 \leftrightarrows 2HD$$

at temperatures such that rotation is classical and vibration is unexcited.[2] The Born-Oppenheimer approximation requires that the ground-state electronic energy must be the same for all three species. Also, $\Theta_r = 64$ K for HD.

23. Calculate the equilibrium constant for the reaction

$$\tfrac{1}{2}N_2 + \tfrac{1}{2}O_2 \leftrightarrows NO$$

at 1500 K. The experimental value is 2.4×10^{-3}.[2]

24. Calculate the equilibrium constant at 3000 K for the reaction[2]

$$CO_2 \leftrightarrows CO + \tfrac{1}{2}O_2.$$

4

THERMOPHYSICAL PROPERTIES
OF SOLIDS

4.1 CRYSTALLINE SOLIDS

4.1.1 Einstein Model

Strong interactions between particles is the most common difficulty encountered in computing the partition function and subsequently thermodynamic properties. Strong interparticle forces produce a coupling link between the positions of various particles that prevents factorization of the partition function. As we have seen, the factorization of the partition function into independent, single-particle partition functions was the key to calculating thermodynamic properties of ideal gases in the last chapter. In light of these observations, it is rather remarkable that the strong forces within the solid which lock atoms into their positions in the crystal lattice in fact facilitate the decoupling of the many-body problem for a crystalline solid. These forces cage each atom into a volume centered around a lattice site. This permits us, at least for the Einstein model first considered, to treat the atoms as independent particles moving within their own, fixed little cells.

In the Einstein model for monatomic crystals, we consider the crystal as a lattice of regularly spaced sites. Each molecule is confined to a cell or cage, centered at a lattice site, by the repulsive forces between its nearest neighbors, which are in turn caged by their neighbors. The lattice site represents the equilibrium position of the atom; that is, its location corresponds to the bottom of the potential well felt by the atom within the cage. Figure 4.1 illustrates, in one dimension, the potential well which an atom might feel as it moves about within its cage. To decouple the system, we assume that all other atoms are fixed at their lattice sites except the one of interest. Translational motion of this atom is confined within the potential well shown in Figure 4.1 and becomes simply an oscillatory motion about the lattice point. The translational motion in essence becomes equivalent to a vibrational mode. It is this modeling of the translational modes of the individual atoms as vibrational modes within a single crystalline entity which allows us to treat crystals much as we did ideal gases in the previous chapter. In this model, we view the atoms as though they are interconnected by springs as shown in Figure 4.2. At sufficiently low temperatures, the motions of the atoms appear as small vibrations about the equilibrium positions. As the temperature is increased, the vibrations become more violent, leading to lattice imperfections, migration of atoms from their cages, and ultimately melting.

We now make three assumptions about the model which allow us to simplify it sufficiently that a solution can be obtained.

1. First, we assume that the vibrations of the atoms about their lattice points are independent of the neighboring atoms. Obviously, this is a key assumption that changes the task at hand from a many-body problem to something manageable.

2. Next, we assume that the potential field for the central atom is found by fixing all other atoms are at their lattice sites. This simplification means that the potential felt by each atom in the model is a stable, mean-field value rather than the fluctuating potential that we would expect to occur in the actual crystal where neighbors also continuously move.

3. Finally, the vibrations are assumed to be relatively small.

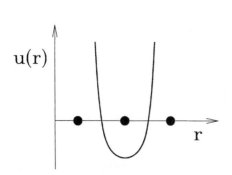

Figure 4.1 Potential well centered about each lattice site.

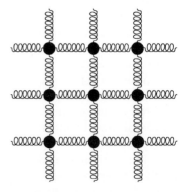

Figure 4.2 Interpretation of crystal as atoms joined by springs.

This last assumption permits us to construct a Taylor's series expansion for the potential energy felt by any particular atom as it oscillates about its lattice position:

$$u(r) = u_0 + \left.\frac{du}{dr}\right|_{r_0} (r - r_0) + \frac{1}{2}\left.\frac{d^2u}{dr^2}\right|_{r_0} (r - r_0)^2 + \ldots = u_0 + \frac{1}{2}f(r - r_0)^2. \tag{4.1}$$

Notice that the second equality results because the first derivative of the potential is zero at the lattice site. Lattice sites represent equilibrium positions where the potential energy is minimized as shown in Figure 4.1. We have also replaced the second derivative evaluated at the lattice site with a spring force constant, f, to obtain the last equality.

Equation (4.1) is the equation for a three-dimensional, *isotropic,* harmonic oscillator, and can therefore be decomposed into three one-dimensional harmonic oscillators. We have already seen the relationship between the vibrational frequency of an harmonic oscillator and its equivalent spring constant (see Example 1.6):

$$\upsilon = \frac{1}{2\pi}\sqrt{\frac{f}{m}}. \tag{4.2}$$

It should be mentioned that f is a function of density. Tighter packing reduces the spacing between the lattice sites, which is equivalent to increasing the spring constant.

If no vibrations were to occur, the problem would be trivial because the potential energy would be a constant, $u = u_0$, and the partition function would be

$$Q = \prod_{i=1}^{N} e^{-\beta u_0/2} = e^{-N\beta u_0/2}. \tag{4.3}$$

The factor of 1/2 in Equation (4.3) is required to prevent overcounting. The potential u_0 results from the spring connection between neighboring molecules on each side, but we only want to count each interaction once. When the vibrations are included, the partition function becomes

$$Q = e^{-N\beta u_0/2}q_{vib}{}^{3N}, \tag{4.4}$$

where the factorization results from the assumption of independence (assumption number 1). The one-dimensional atomic partition function, q, is simply that of the harmonic oscillator. We already know that the energy levels for the harmonic oscillator are $\epsilon_n/k = (n + 1/2)\Theta$, where $n = 0, 1, 2 \ldots$ As in Equations (3.21) to (3.23), the q can therefore be written as

$$q_{\text{vib}} = (e^{-\Theta/2T}) \sum_{n=0}^{\infty} e^{-n\Theta/T} = \frac{e^{-\Theta/2T}}{1 - e^{-\Theta/T}}.$$

(4.5)

Equations (4.4) and (4.5) can be combined, yielding

$$Q = \frac{e^{-N\beta u_0/2} \, e^{-3N\Theta/2T}}{(1 - e^{-\Theta/T})^{3N}}$$

(4.6)

for the total partition function of the crystal. The thermodynamic properties can then be obtained in the usual manner. A summary of some of the thermodynamic properties is contained in Table 4.1.

How good is this model of a crystalline substance? Certainly we expect the three assumptions made to limit the quantitative accuracy, but when is the model valid? We happen to know from experiment the actual behavior of the heat capacity of solids in the limit of both high and low temperatures and these limits make good points for checking the validity of the model. The Dulong and Petit law indicates that C_V approaches $3Nk$ in the limit of high temperatures. Likewise, it is known that C_V has a T^3 dependence in the limit as $T \to 0$ K. One can show (see Problem 1 at the end of the chapter) that the temperature limits of the heat capacity equation in Table 4.1 are given by

$$\lim_{T \to 0} \frac{C_V}{Nk} = 3 \left(\frac{\Theta}{T} \right)^2 e^{-\Theta/T}$$

(4.7)

and

TABLE 4.1 Thermodynamic Properties of Crystalline Solids in the Einstein Model

$$\frac{A}{NkT} = \frac{1}{2}\beta u_0 - 3\ln\left(\frac{e^{-\Theta/2T}}{1 - e^{-\Theta/T}} \right)$$

$$\frac{U}{NkT} = \frac{1}{2}\beta u_0 + \frac{3}{2}\left(\frac{\Theta}{T} \right) + \frac{3\Theta/T}{e^{\Theta/T} - 1}$$

$$\frac{C_V}{Nk} = 3 \left(\frac{\Theta}{T} \right)^2 \frac{e^{\Theta/T}}{(e^{\Theta/T} - 1)^2}$$

$$\frac{S}{Nk} = 3 \left[\frac{\Theta/T}{e^{\Theta/T} - 1} - \ln(1 - e^{-\Theta/T}) \right]$$

$$\lim_{T \to \infty} \frac{C_V}{NK} = 3 \ . \tag{4.8}$$

The high-temperature limit of the Einstein model agrees with the Dulong–Petit law, but C_V approaches zero too quickly at the 0 K limit as illustrated in Example 4.1. We next examine a more general treatment of the problem which corrects this default.

Example 4.1   In units of J/(mol·K), the heat capacities of copper, silver, and gold at various temperatures are[1]:

T (K)	Cu	Ag	Au
10	0.0555	0.183	0.431
50	6.154	11.66	14.29
100	16.01	20.10	21.44
200	22.63	24.16	24.41

Use the Einstein model to find characteristic lattice vibration temperatures and the corresponding force constants for the crystal.

Using the heat capacity equation in Table 4.1 and the data in the above table, we can regress a "best" value of θ to fit the data. A nonlinear least-squares fit of θ is shown below along with a linear estimate of its standard deviation, σ.

| | θ (K) | σ (K) | Calculated values of C_v in J/(mol·K) | | | |
			10 K	50 K	100 K	200 K
Cu	225.6	4.9	2×10^{-6}	5.70	16.59	22.46
Ag	157.3	2.8	9×10^{-4}	11.59	20.38	23.70
Au	132.9	2.7	0.007	14.28	21.57	24.04

As expected, the calculated values at 10 K are much too small, relatively speaking, while the other values are reasonably well represented by the model.

Next, we use the fact that $\upsilon = \theta k/h$ and the relation of f to υ given in Equation (4.2) to obtain the final results shown in the table below.

	θ (K)	υ ($10^{12}\,\mathrm{s}^{-1}$)	m (10^{-22} g)	f (10^4 g·s^{-2})
Cu	225.6	4.70	1.055	9.20
Ag	157.3	3.28	1.791	7.61
Au	132.9	2.77	3.271	9.91

4.1.2 More General Treatment

We might expect that the biggest problem with the above model is the assumption that all of the modes are independent, yet this was the feature that made solution of the Einstein model possible. Let us look at a more general treatment in which neighboring molecules are also allowed to move from their lattice sites. Because neighbors move, we cannot completely decouple the various vibrations of the particles, but we can still retain solvability with the appropriate assumptions. For simplicity, we will illustrate the methodology with the one-dimensional crystal lattice shown in Figure 4.3 and assume that the influence of the molecule extends only to the second neighbor. The procedure is similar for longer range interactions and for three-dimensional crystals, but certainly not as clear from a pedagogical viewpoint.

In Figure 4.3, the distance between atom i and $i + 1$ can be written in terms of the lattice spacing a and the distances relative to the lattice points at which the atoms are found, namely, $a + x_{i+1} - x_i$. Therefore, the potential energy is now

$$u(x) = u_0 + \sum_{i=1}^{N} [u(a + x_{i+1} - x_i) + u(2a + x_{i+2} - x_i) + ...]. \quad (4.9)$$

This obviously complicates the problem because the Hamiltonian,

$$H = \frac{1}{2} \sum_i m_i \dot{x}_i^2 + \sum_{i=1}^{N} [u_0 + u(x_i, x_{i+1}, x_{i+2}, ...)], \quad (4.10)$$

is no longer separable and solvable for each mode independently. All is not lost, however. Without going into the mathematical details, an equation in quadratic form, such as Equation (4.10), can always be put in a form that eliminates cross terms (see Appendix 4). A linear transformation of the coordinate system is always possible which orients the axes so that all cross terms

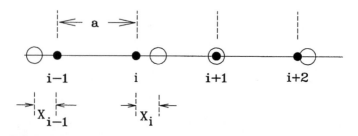

Figure 4.3 All atoms (*open circles*) may move from their lattice sites (*filled circles*) in the more general treatment.

disappear. This is similar to the transformation mentioned in Chapter 3 that produces only the principal moments of inertia for the description of rotational motion. This coordinate transformation removes all of the off-diagonal elements in the potential energy term, again reducing the problem to one of N independent atoms. Unfortunately, we can no longer use the atomic masses and vibrational constants to compute characteristic vibrational temperatures, because the coordinate transformation also operates on them. The masses and force constants in the equation are now "effective" values. In these normal coordinates the Hamiltonian becomes

$$H_i = \frac{1}{2}M_i\dot{\xi}_i^2 + \frac{1}{2}f_i\xi_i^2 + \frac{1}{2}NU_0 \,, \tag{4.11}$$

and the solution is similar to that obtained before. In terms of these effective force constants, f_i, and effective masses, M_i, the vibrational frequencies are

$$\upsilon_i = \frac{1}{2\pi}\sqrt{\frac{f_i}{M_i}} \,. \tag{4.12}$$

Note the difference between Equation (4.4) and the new equation for the partition function

$$Q = e^{\beta N u_0/2} \prod_{i=1}^{3N} q_{\text{vib}}(\Theta_i) \,. \tag{4.13}$$

No longer is there a single vibrational frequency or characteristic vibrational temperature for the crystal. The frequencies are no longer equivalent because the atoms now behave as though they have an effective mass M_i and interact with effective force constants f_i, both of which depend on the positions of neighbors. The coupling of the frequency to the neighboring atoms in the more general model results in a whole distribution of Θ_i values. The large number of atoms in a macroscopic crystal in fact implies that the distribution of Θ_i values can be represented by a continuous distribution, $g(\Theta)$. That is, we let $g(\Theta)d\Theta$ represent the number of normal vibrational modes with characteristic temperatures between Θ and $\Theta + d\Theta$ subject to the constraint that the total number of modes is $3N$; that is,

$$\int_0^\infty g(\Theta)d\Theta = 3N \,. \tag{4.14}$$

Analogous to Equation (4.5), the logarithm of the partition function can now be written as

$$\ln Q = \frac{1}{2}N\beta u_0 + \int_0^\infty \ln\left(\frac{e^{-\Theta/2T}}{1 - e^{-\Theta/T}}\right)g(\Theta)\,d\Theta \,. \tag{4.15}$$

In principle, the thermodynamic properties of the crystal can now be formally

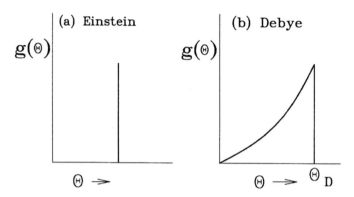

Figure 4.4 Characteristic temperature distribution assumed in the **(a)** Einstein and **(b)** Debye models.

determined from the formulas in Table 2.1. In practice, this procedure is not very useful until an expression for $g(\Theta)$ is postulated. Hence, much of the effort expended on the generalization of the Einstein model has focused on development of an appropriate representation for $g(\Theta)$. One such representation constitutes the basis of the Debye model.

4.1.3 Debye Model

As depicted in Figure 4.4a, the Einstein model can be thought of as the specific instance of the more general model when $g(\Theta)$ is given by the Dirac delta function. This is because fixing all neighboring atoms at their lattice sites restricts the vibrational modes to a single frequency. A more realistic approximation for $g(\Theta)$ was suggested by Debye. Elastic-wave theories in a continuum indicate that the low-frequency distribution must be of the form $g(\Theta) = \alpha\Theta^2$. Debye adopted this form for the crystal lattice frequencies over the entire range of permissible frequencies. The Debye distribution is pictured in Figure 4.4b. This form requires that there be a cutoff or maximum frequency in order to satisfy the conservation Equation (4.14). The characteristic temperature corresponding to this maximum allowed frequency is called the Debye temperature, Θ_D. One can in fact eliminate the proportionality constant α in the Debye distribution in favor of Θ_D by performing the integration indicated in Equation (4.14). Thus,

$$\int_0^{\Theta_D} g(\Theta)d\Theta = \int_0^{\Theta_D} \alpha\Theta^2 \, d\Theta = \frac{1}{3}\alpha\Theta^3 \bigg|_0^{\Theta_D} = \frac{1}{3}\alpha\Theta_D^3 = 3N \Rightarrow \alpha = \frac{9N}{\Theta_D^3}. \tag{4.16}$$

With this substitution for α, the Debye distribution can be written as

$$g(\Theta) = \begin{cases} \dfrac{9N\Theta^2}{\Theta_D^3} & 0 \le \Theta \le \Theta_D \\ 0 & \Theta > \Theta_D \end{cases}. \tag{4.17}$$

Table 4.2 contains values of the Debye temperatures for a few substances.

Once a distribution function has been defined, all of the thermodynamic properties can be calculated in the usual manner. For notational convenience we define the following:

$$X \equiv \frac{\Theta}{T} \qquad X_D \equiv \frac{\Theta_D}{T}. \tag{4.18}$$

Using the above definitions, we can substitute Equation (4.17) into Equation (4.15) to obtain an expression for $\ln Q$ for the Debye model

$$\ln Q = \frac{1}{2}N\beta u_0 - \frac{9N}{X_D^3}\left[\int_0^{X_D}\frac{X^3}{2}\,dX + \int_0^{X_D} X^2 \ln(1 - e^{-X})\,dX\right]. \tag{4.19}$$

The first integral can be performed immediately to yield,

$$\ln Q = \frac{1}{2}N\beta u_0 - \frac{9N}{8}X_D - \frac{9N}{X_D^3}\int_0^{X_D} X^2 \ln(1 - e^{-X})\,dX. \tag{4.20}$$

The internal energy is readily derived from the partition function with the usual identity. By switching the order of differentiation and integration, one can write

$$\frac{U}{NkT} = \frac{1}{2}\beta u_0 + \frac{9}{8}X_D + 3I, \tag{4.21}$$

where I is the integral

TABLE 4.2   Debye Temperatures for Several Metals

Element	Θ_D (K)	Element	Δ_D (K)
Li	430	Pt	225
Na	160	W	315
K	199	Hg	90
Au	185	Be	980
Pb	68	Mg	330
Cr	405	Zn	240
Ca	230	Cd	165
Mo	375		

$$I(X_D) = \frac{3}{X_D^3} \int_0^{X_D} \frac{X^3 dX}{e^X - 1} . \tag{4.22}$$

This integral can only be evaluated numerically. Note, however, that I is only a function of X_D (i.e., Θ_D/T).

As before, we will want to compare predictions of the model to experimental results and the heat capacity serves this purpose nicely. We find the heat capacity in the usual manner:

$$\frac{C_V}{Nk} = \left(\frac{\partial U/Nk}{\partial T}\right)_V = 3Nk\left(\frac{\partial TI}{\partial T}\right)_V = 12I - \frac{9X_D}{\exp(X_D) - 1} . \tag{4.23}$$

Example 4.2 illustrates the use of this equation.

It is again interesting to compare the high- and low-temperature limits of the derived expression to that of the known behavior for C_V. To do so, we need to evaluate the temperature extremes of the integral I. At low temperatures,

$$\lim_{T\to 0} X \to \infty \qquad \text{and} \qquad \lim_{T\to 0} X_D \to \infty$$

$$\therefore \lim_{T\to 0} I = \frac{3}{X_D^3} \int_0^{\infty} \frac{X^3 \, dX}{e^X - 1} . \tag{4.24}$$

There is an analytical solution for this definite integral, namely,

---

Example 4.2   Calculate and plot C_V for Fe from 32 to 42 K.

We use Simpson's rule to integrate I in accordance with Equation (4.22) using 0 as the lower limit and X_D as the upper limit. These values can then be used in conjunction with Equation (4.23),

$$\frac{C_V}{Nk} = 12I - \frac{9X_D}{e^{X_D} - 1} ,$$

to obtain the following data:

T	X_D	$I \times 10^3$	C_V/Nk
32	14.16	6.86	0.082
34	13.32	8.24	0.099
36	12.58	9.77	0.117
38	11.92	11.48	0.137
40	11.33	13.35	0.159
42	10.79	15.42	0.183

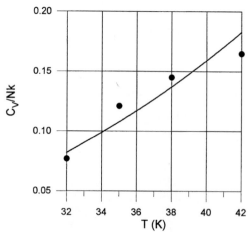

The data in the table are plotted in the figure along with some experimental data.

$$\int_0^\infty \frac{X^s \, dX}{e^X - 1} = s! \, \zeta(s + 1) \,, \tag{4.25}$$

where ζ is the zeta function. The first few terms of the zeta function are $\zeta(2) = \pi^2/6$, $\zeta(3) = 1.202$, and $\zeta(4) = \pi^4/90$. Thus,

$$\lim_{T \to 0} I = \left(\frac{3}{X_D^3}\right)\left(\frac{\pi^4}{15}\right) = \frac{\pi^4}{5X_D^3} \,. \tag{4.26}$$

With this result, one can show the low-temperature limit of Equation (4.23) to be

$$\lim_{T \to 0} \frac{C_V}{Nk} = \frac{12\pi^4}{5}\left(\frac{T}{\Theta_D}\right)^3 \,. \tag{4.27}$$

Unlike the Einstein model, the Debye model contains the correct T^3-dependence in the low-temperature limit.

At high temperatures,

$$\lim_{T \to \infty} X \to 0 \qquad \text{and} \qquad \lim_{T \to \infty} X_D \to 0 \,,$$

and the exponential e^x can be expanded. Thus,

$$\lim_{T \to \infty} I = \frac{3}{X_D^3} \int_0^{X_D} \frac{X^3 \, dX}{X + \frac{1}{2}X^2 + \ldots} = 1 \,. \tag{4.28}$$

Using this result in Equation (4.23), we see that the high-temperature limit of the heat capacity equation is

$$\lim_{T \to \infty} \frac{C_V}{Nk} = 3 \,, \tag{4.29}$$

which is still in agreement with the Dulong–Petit law.

Obviously, agreement at the high- and low-temperature limits is comforting, but by no means a guarantee of the model's accuracy at intermediate temperatures. One way to test the efficacy of the Debye model is to calculate Θ_D from experimental C_V data at various temperatures. In the Debye model, Θ_D is a constant, but the value obtained from experimental data[1] for silver does vary by up to 5% over a 100 K range as shown in Figure 4.5. Actually, in light of the assumptions inherent in the model, such consistency is really quite good. Other properties can also be calculated from the Debye partition function in the usual manner as illustrated in Example 4.3.

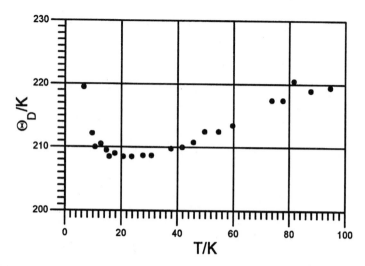

Figure 4.5 The Debye temperature for silver calculated from heat capacity data.

4.2 CRYSTAL DEFECTS

Two kinds of crystal defects can be rather easily treated within the framework of independent particles thus far developed. A Frenkel defect can be thought of as an atom removed from its lattice site into an interstitial site, as depicted in Figure 4.6a. Schottky defects also leave a hole at the lattice site, but the displaced atom is removed to the surface of the crystal, as depicted in Figure 4.6b. We will wish to determine the equilibrium number of such defects in the crystal.

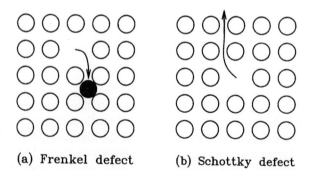

(a) Frenkel defect   (b) Schottky defect

Figure 4.6 Two common crystal defects are: (**a**) a lattice atom displaced to an interstitial site (Frenkel) and (**b**) a lattice atom removed from the crystal (Schottky).

Example 4.3   Derive an expression for the chemical potential of a crystal at low temperatures in terms of the heat of sublimation at 0 K and the Debye temperature.

The (dimensionless) chemical potential may be found from the identity

$$\frac{\mu}{kT} = \beta \left(\frac{\partial A}{\partial N} \right)_{T,V} = -\left(\frac{\partial \ln Q}{\partial N} \right)_{T,V}$$

Using Equation (4.20), we obtain upon differentiation

$$\frac{\mu}{kT} = \frac{1}{2}\beta u_0 + \frac{9}{8}X_D + \frac{9}{X_D^3} \int_0^{X_D} X^2 \ln(1 - e^{-X}) \, dX.$$

The first term represents the energy required to compress ideal gas molecules into the crystal lattice sites. The second term represents the ground-state vibrational energy in the crystal. Together these two terms represent the energy of the crystal at 0 K relative to the separated atoms or ideal gas state. We can therefore replace the first two terms with the negative of the energy of sublimation at 0 K (or *enthalpy* of sublimation in this case since PV is small for a solid).

The final term can be integrated in the limit of low temperature. As $T \to 0$, $\Theta_D \to \infty$ and the upper integration limit can be replaced with ∞. We may then integrate by parts,

$$\int_0^\infty X^2 \ln(1 - e^{-X}) \, dX = \frac{1}{3}X^3 \ln(1 - e^{-X}) \Big|_0^\infty - \frac{1}{3}\int_0^\infty X^3 \frac{e^{-X}}{1 - e^{-X}} \, dX.$$

The first term vanishes at both limits. The second term can be cast in the form of Equation (4.25) and immediately integrated in terms of the zeta function. Thus,

$$\int_0^\infty X^2 \ln(1 - e^{-X}) \, dX = \frac{1}{3} \int_0^\infty \frac{X^3}{e^X - 1} \, dX = \frac{3!}{3}\zeta(4) = \frac{\pi^4}{45}.$$

Finally, we obtain

$$\frac{\mu}{kT} = -\frac{\Delta H_{s,0}}{kT} + \left(\frac{9}{X_D^3} \right)\left(\frac{\pi^4}{45} \right) = -\frac{\Delta H_{s,0}}{kT} - \frac{\pi^4}{5}\left(\frac{T}{\Theta_D} \right)^3.$$

Let w be the energy required to remove an atom from its lattice site to an interstitial site in the case of Frenkel statistics or entirely from the crystal in the case of Schottky defects. Further, let N be the number of atoms in the crystal, I be the number of interstitial sites, and n be the number of defects. Now, we expect n to be much, much smaller than either N or I. The total energy due to defects (relative to a perfect crystal) is therefore nw. At this point, we need to treat the statistics of the two types of defects slightly differently.

4.2.1 Frenkel Defects

The partition function due to Frenkel defects relative to the perfect crystal is readily found. It is

$$Q_{def} = W(n) \, e^{-\beta nw} \, , \tag{4.30}$$

where the degeneracy is the number of different arrangements of n holes on N lattice sites and n displaced atoms in I interstitial sites; that is,

$$W(n) = (_N C_n)(_I C_n) = \frac{N! \, I!}{n! \, (N - n)! \, n! \, (I - n)!} \, . \tag{4.31}$$

As we have seen on several previous occasions, there are so many more ways to obtain the maximum term than any other configuration for large values of N and I that the maximum term totally dominates. Without loss of generality, we can replace the distribution with the maximum configuration which we represent as n^*. To find the maximum term, it is most convenient to first take the logarithm of the partition function, differentiate the general term with respect to n, set the derivative equal to zero, and finally solve for n^*. Sterling's approximation is used to expand the logarithm of factorial terms. Thus,

$$F = \ln Q = \ln\left(\frac{N! \, I!}{n! \, n! \, (N - n)! \, (I - n)!}\right) - \beta nw \tag{4.32}$$

$$= N\ln N + I\ln I - 2n\ln n - (N - n)\ln(N - n) - (I - n)\ln(I - n) - \beta nw \, .$$

As we did on several equations in Chapter 2, we again find the maximum term in the distribution by taking the derivative with respect to n and setting it equal to zero at the extremum. Thus,

$$\left(\frac{\partial F}{\partial n}\right) = 0 = -2\ln n^* + \ln(N - n^*) + \ln(I - n^*) - \beta w$$

$$\Rightarrow \frac{n^{*2}}{(N - n^*)(I - n^*)} = e^{-\beta w}. \tag{4.33}$$

Because $n << N$ and $n << I$, Equation (4.33) can be solved for the equilibrium number of defects. This simplification yields

$$<n> = \sqrt{NI} \, e^{-\beta w/2}. \tag{4.34}$$

To use this equation, one would first obtain N, I, and w from the characteristics and geometry of the crystal lattice.

Of course, the effects of defects on the thermodynamic properties of the crystal can be obtained in the usual way once the partition function has been

---

Example 4.4   Determine an expression for the additional entropy due to Frenkel defects.

Because $S/k = \beta(U - A)$, we may write for the defect entropy,

$$S/k = \beta nw + \ln Q = \beta wn + \ln W - \beta wn = \ln W .$$

This is identically the expression obtained from the microcanonical ensemble as shown in Table 2.3. The final answer could then be obtained by substituting Equation (4.34) for n in Equation (4.31). This provides an expression for the degeneracy which can be used in the preceding equation to obtain S.

---

determined. For example, the entropy due to the defects can be computed as illustrated in Example 4.4.

4.2.2 Schottky Defects

The procedure for calculating the equilibrium number of Schottky defects is very similar to that shown above. The main difference is in the calculation of the degeneracy, since we do not have to find interstitial locations for the displaced atoms. We retain the original definition of N as the number of atoms and n as the number of defects or holes. However, in this case, we have $N + n$ lattice sites. Thus,

$$W(n) = \frac{(N + n)!}{n! \, N!} . \tag{4.35}$$

The partition function is the same as before except for this new degeneracy. Simple calculations then yield,

$$\frac{S}{k} = \ln W = (N + n)\ln(N + n) - n\ln n - N\ln N , \tag{4.36}$$

$$U = nw , \tag{4.37}$$

and

$$\frac{A}{k} = \frac{U - TS}{k} = \frac{nw}{k} - T[(N + n)\ln(N + n) - n\ln n - N\ln N] \tag{4.38}$$

for the entropy, internal energy, and Helmholtz free energy, respectively. The equilibrium condition corresponds to a minimum in A (maximum in Q). Thus,

$$\left(\frac{\partial A}{\partial n}\right) = 0 = \frac{w}{k} - T[\ln(N + n) - \ln n] \Rightarrow \frac{n}{N + n} = e^{-\beta w}. \tag{4.39}$$

Again, at temperatures considerably below the melting point, $n << N$ and the equilibrium number of Schottky defects can be more simply written as

$$\langle n \rangle = N e^{-\beta w}. \tag{4.40}$$

4.3 SURFACE ADSORPTION

4.3.1 Langmuir Isotherm

The adsorption of a gas molecule onto fixed surface sites is another process which can be modeled using a solid lattice and the basic assumption of independent particles which we have focused on in this chapter. Despite the simplicity of the inherent assumption, such models have found widespread usage. We will use the adsorption model depicted in Figure 4.7 to examine the equilibrium states established between free, ideal gas molecules and molecules adsorbed at lattice sites on the surface of the solid. We will assume that only one gas molecule can be adsorbed per lattice site and that the relative energy of the adsorbed molecule is $-\epsilon_0$ relative to that in the free gas state. Thus, for N_1 molecules adsorbed, the total energy relative to the free state is $E = -N_1\epsilon_0$, and the partition function is

$$Q(N_1) = W e^{\beta N_1 \epsilon_0} = \frac{N!}{N_1! \, (N - N_1)!} \, e^{\beta N_1 \epsilon_0}. \tag{4.41}$$

To obtain the second expression, the degeneracy was replaced by the number of ways in which N_1 adsorbed particles can be distributed on N *equivalent* surface lattice sites. Here again is the assumption of independence between the sites. A more realistic model would take into account the change in adsorption energy associated with increasing surface coverage owing to the presence of neighboring adsorbed molecules. As might be expected, the final result for the Langmuir isotherm derived here on the basis of independent adsorbed molecules will be less accurate as the surface coverage increases, and the effects of interactions between adsorbed molecules on neighboring sites becomes more important.

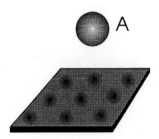

Figure 4.7 Depiction of a free gas molecule (*A*) which may adsorb on surface lattice sites (*darkened spots*).

Equation (4.41) is the canonical partition function for N_1 adsorbed molecules. However, a variable number of particles may adsorb on the surface, not just N_1. We must therefore use the grand canonical ensemble and permit N_1 to range from 0 (no surface coverage) up to N (complete surface coverage). The grand canonical ensemble partition function is

$$\Xi = \sum_{N_1=0}^{N} Q(N_1)e^{\beta N_1 \mu} = \sum_{N_1=0}^{N} \frac{N!}{N!\,(N-N_1)!}\left[e^{\beta(\mu+\epsilon_0)}\right]^{N_1}. \tag{4.42}$$

The sum in Equation (4.42) can be obtained directly using the standard summation trick with the binomial expansion. That is, we note that the summation is actually the binomial expansion for

$$\Xi = \left[1 + e^{\beta(\mu+\epsilon_0)}\right]^{N}.$$

Thermodynamic properties can be obtained from this partition function in the usual manner as shown in Example 4.5. Additionally, one is often interested in the surface coverage or covering ratio of adsorption sites $\Theta \equiv \langle N_1 \rangle / N$. The expected number of adsorbed sites is found from the partition function using the appropriate equation of Table 2.2,

$$\langle N_1 \rangle = kT\left(\frac{\partial \ln \Xi}{\partial \mu}\right)_{T,V} = N\left[1 + e^{-\beta(\mu+\epsilon_0)}\right]^{-1},$$

and the fraction of sites covered is therefore

$$\Theta = \left[1 + e^{-\beta(\mu+\epsilon_0)}\right]^{-1}. \tag{4.43}$$

This equation is of little value to us in its present form because it contains μ, the chemical potential of adsorbed molecules. As we have no chemical potential meters, an equation with μ as an independent variable is very difficult to use for property calculations. However, at equilibrium the chemical potential of the adsorbed species is equal to that of the free gas, which we have already expressed in terms of measurable variables. For an ideal, monatomic gas, the chemical potential can be written as (see Example 3.5)

$$e^{\beta \mu} = \beta P \Lambda^3. \tag{4.44}$$

By using Equation (4.44) to eliminate μ from the previous equations, we obtain the surface fraction of covered sites as

$$\Theta = \left[1 + \frac{e^{-\beta \epsilon_0}}{\beta P \Lambda^3}\right]^{-1}. \tag{4.45}$$

This is in fact the expression for a Langmuir isotherm, perhaps more easily recognized when written as

Example 4.5   Find expressions for U, S, A, and P for an adsorbed gas on a crystalline solid in terms of the fractional surface coverage.

The requested relationships can be readily derived from the equations in Table 2.2 for the grand canonical partition function. From the development in the text,

$$\ln\Xi = N\ln[1 + e^{\beta(\mu + \epsilon_0)}] \, .$$

The internal energy is found from

$$U = -\left(\frac{\partial\ln\Xi}{\partial\beta}\right)_V + N_1\mu = -\frac{N(\mu + \epsilon_0)}{1 + e^{-\beta(\mu+\epsilon_0)}} + N_1\mu \, .$$

We may eliminate the denominator by using Equation (4.43) to obtain the final expression for internal energy,

$$U = -N(\mu + \epsilon_0)\Theta + N\Theta\mu = -N\epsilon_0\Theta \, .$$

Similarly, A, S, and P may be found from their relationship to $\ln\Xi$. To obtain expressions in terms of Θ, we may eliminate exponential terms involving μ and ϵ by using Equation (4.43) in the form

$$e^{\beta(\mu+\epsilon_0)} = \frac{\Theta}{1 - \Theta} \, .$$

The resulting expressions are

$$S = k\ln(1 - \Theta) - Nk\Theta(\mu + \epsilon_0) \, ,$$

$$A = N\Theta\mu + NkT\ln(1 - \Theta) \, ,$$

and

$$P = \frac{kT}{V} \ln(1 - \Theta)^{-1}.$$

$$\Theta = \frac{KP}{1 + KP} \, , \tag{4.46}$$

where $K \equiv \beta\Lambda^3 e^{-\beta\epsilon_0}$.

4.3.2 Extension to Multiple Sites[2]

We might also derive a more general adsorption partition function by assuming that multiple binding sites occur on each molecule or location. An illustration of this situation is shown in Figure 4.8. This is also useful for molecules onto which multiple ligands or ions may attach, as in the case of a polybasic acid. The notation quickly becomes cumbersome, so we define the following terms up front and use them in the derivation:

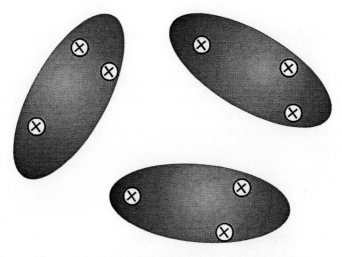

Figure 4.8   Molecules with multiple sites for binding.

M = number of molecules
m = number of binding sites on each molecule
s = number of ligands attached $(0 \leq s \leq m)$
N_s = number of molecules with s ligands attached
$q(s) = \exp(-\beta\epsilon_s)$ = molecular partition function for s attached ligands
q_i = individual site partition function for ligand attached at site i
$\lambda = \exp(\beta\mu)$
η = total number of sites bound with a ligand

General conservation equations can now be written for the number of molecules

$$M = \sum_{s=0}^{m} N_s \tag{4.47}$$

and the total number of sites bound with a ligand

$$\eta = \sum_{s=0}^{m} sN_s, \tag{4.48}$$

respectively. The generalization of Equation (4.42) to multiple sites is not too difficult, although somewhat notationally awkward. For a particular η and M,

$$Q(\eta,M,T) = \sum_{N_i} \left(\frac{M!}{N_0!N_1! \ldots N_m!} \right) q(0)^{N_0} q(1)^{N_1} \ldots q(m)^{N_m}, \qquad (4.49)$$

where the summation is over all possible partitions of N_i such that Equation (4.47) is satisfied. But, this canonical partition function is written for a specific number of bound sites η. The grand canonical partition function allows us to generalize the partitioning of bound sites over the entire possible range of η values, namely

$$\Xi = \sum_{\eta=0}^{mM} Q(\eta,M,T) \lambda^0 \lambda^{N_1} \lambda^{2N_2} \ldots \lambda^{mN_m}, \qquad (4.50)$$

where Equation (4.48) has been used to factor the λ^η term. Substitution of Equation (4.49) into Equation (4.50) yields

$$\Xi = \sum_{N_i} \left(\frac{M!}{N_0!N_1! \ldots N_m!} \right) q(0)^{N_0} [q(1)\lambda]^{N_1} [q(2)\lambda^2]^{N_2} \ldots [q(m)\lambda^m]^{N_m}, \qquad (4.51)$$

which is the multinomial expansion for

$$\Xi = [q(0) + q(1)\lambda + q(2)\lambda^2 + \ldots + q(m)\lambda^m]^M. \qquad (4.52)$$

This can be written more simply in terms of ξ, the molecular grand canonical partition function, as

$$\Xi = \xi^M, \qquad (4.53)$$

where

$$\xi = q(0) + q(1)\lambda + q(2)\lambda^2 + \ldots + q(m)\lambda^m = \sum_{s=0}^{m} q(s)\lambda^s. \qquad (4.54)$$

We can now use the relations in Table 2.2 to find expectation values. For example, the expected value for the total number of bound sites is

$$<\eta> = kT\left(\frac{\partial \ln\Xi}{\partial \mu}\right)_{T,M} = MkT\left(\frac{\partial \ln\xi}{\partial \mu}\right)_T = \frac{M\sum_{s=0}^{m} sq(s)\lambda^s}{\xi}, \qquad (4.55)$$

and the average number of filled sites per molecule is

$$<s> = \frac{<\eta>}{M} = \frac{\sum\limits_{s=0}^{m} sq(s)\lambda^s}{\xi} = \lambda\left(\frac{\partial\ln\xi}{\partial\lambda}\right)_T. \qquad (4.56)$$

An important application of this model is prediction of adsorption isotherms. For example, the Brunauer–Emmett–Teller or BET adsorption theory
can be based on this model. We assume zero energy for empty sites, so $q(0) =$
1. We also assume that the first layer of adsorbate is different than the remaining
layers owing to the surface interactions. The second, third, and subsequent layers
are considered more of a bulk phase because nearest interactions would be only
between adsorbed molecules as new layers stack on top of previously adsorbed
molecules. The BET model also assumes that the first and second layers are
uncorrelated or independent. This is an important simplifying assumption which
permits the two-site partition function to be factored as $q(2) = q_1q_2$. Finally,
the assumption is also made that the contribution to the partition function from
each additional layer is the same as the second layer; that is, that the second
layer is the clear demarcation point between the surface layer and the bulk
phase stacked atop it. Thus, $q(k) = q_1q_2^{k-1}$ and

$$\xi = 1 + q_1\lambda(1 + q_2\lambda + q_2^2\lambda^2 + \ldots) = 1 + \frac{q_1\lambda}{1 - q_2\lambda}, \qquad (4.57)$$

where the identity $(1 - x)^{-1} = 1 + x + x^2 + \ldots$ was used to obtain the final
equality. When Equation (4.57) is differentiated in accordance with Equation
(4.56) and the result simplified, we obtain

$$<s> = \frac{q_1\lambda}{(1 - q_2\lambda + q_1\lambda)(1 - q_2\lambda)}. \qquad (4.58)$$

Since the adsorbate phase is in equilibrium with the bulk (ideal) gas phase,
the chemical potential must be the same in each phase; that is, $\lambda_{ad} = \lambda_{gas} =
\beta P\Lambda^3$. Thus,

$$<s> = \frac{cx}{(1 - x - cx)(1 - x)}, \qquad (4.59)$$

where $c = q_1/q_2$ and $x = q_2\beta P\Lambda^3$. Equation (4.59) is the governing equation
for the BET isotherm. The assumptions involved in its derivation are of course
rather crude, but the general shape shown in Figure 4.9 does reproduce the basic
features observed experimentally. At low reduced pressures x, a monolayer
preferentially adsorbs on the solid surface for $c >> 1$. Only after that surface
is nearly full do other layers begin to build up significantly. As the reduced
pressure is further increased, more layers are added. Eventually a rapid increase
in $<s>$ is observed which indicates the onset of vapor condensation. Generally,

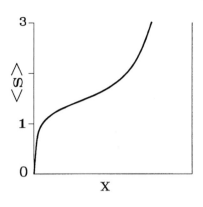

Figure 4.9 BET adsorption isotherm showing number of adsorbed species.

one treats c in Equation (4.59) as an adjustable parameter in fitting experimental data and the resultant correlation is often quite good. Nevertheless, one should exercise caution and not attach too much physical significance to the constants obtained from the model. While the model can reproduce the qualitative aspects observed experimentally, values of parameters regressed from experimental data will necessarily compensate for model inadequacies inherent in the assumptions and may not therefore be amenable to quantitative interpretations.

Often when this multiple-site ligand methodology is applied to molecules, an interaction energy w is assumed between molecules bound to the same molecule. For example, the binding of a second hydrogen ion onto a dibasic acid would presumably be influenced by the repulsion between the two bound hydrogens. Modification to the above theory can then be made by replacing the two-site partition function with $q(2) = q_1 q_2 e^{-\beta w}$. Note that allowing interactions between adsorbed molecules on a given adsorbent does not invalidate the basic assumption used in this chapter, namely no interactions between the substrate molecules themselves. Independent molecules allow us to factor the partition function as in Equation (4.49) even though interactions occur between the ligands on any one molecule. Example 4.6 illustrates this point. In addition to the application shown in Example 4.6, one could use this technique in development of a theory for correlation of successive dissociation (or association) equilibrium constants of ligands.[2]

4.4 SEMICONDUCTORS

The band theory[3] of electron conduction in metals and crystalline solids has been very effective in understanding electrical conductivity of materials and in designing semiconductor devices. Qualitatively, bands arise from the broadening influence of the relatively close, periodically spaced atoms in the crystal lattice. Electrons in isolated atoms have discrete energy levels, depicted with horizontal lines in Figure 4.10. In the crystal lattice, nuclei have a periodic and close

Example 4.6   Suppose attachment of a molecule can occur on either or both of two binding sites on a polymer molecule.[2] The two sites on the polymer are different. Also, when both sites of the polymer are occupied, there is a potential energy of interaction w between the two bound molecules. Derive an expression for the fractional coverage.

Because there is no interaction between molecules bound to different polymers, the introduction of w between bound pairs on the same site does not affect the assumption of independence used in obtaining Equations (4.54) to (4.56). Thus, a pair of sites is treated as an independent subsystem which can be vacant, singly occupied, or doubly occupied. From Equation (4.54),

$$\xi = q(0) + q(1)\lambda + q(2)\lambda^2.$$

We take as the reference the unbound polymer, so $q(0) = 1$. Then the partition functions for the singly and doubly occupied states can be written as

$$q(1) = q_1 + q_2 \qquad q(2) = q_1 q_2 e^{-\beta w},$$

where q_1 and q_2 are the partition functions for a molecule adsorbed on sites 1 and 2, respectively. Thus,

$$\xi = 1 + (q_1 + q_2)\lambda + q_1 q_2 \lambda^2 e^{-\beta \lambda}.$$

The average number of filled sites per molecule is given by

$$<s> = kT\left(\frac{\partial \ln \xi}{\partial \mu}\right)_T = \lambda\left(\frac{\partial \ln \xi}{\partial \lambda}\right)_T.$$

The second equality results from the chain rule and the identity $\lambda = \exp(\beta\mu)$. Differentiating, we finally obtain

$$<s> = \frac{(q_1 + q_2)\lambda + 2q_1 q_2 \lambda^2 e^{-\beta w}}{1 + (q_1 + q_2)\lambda + 2q_1 q_2 \lambda^2 e^{-\beta w}}.$$

The fraction of total *sites* would be half $<s>$.

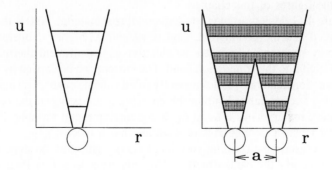

Figure 4.10   Schematic of electronic potential energy levels for separated atoms (*left*) and bands produced by atoms at regular lattice sites (*right*).

spacing denoted as *a* in Figure 4.10. The interactions between the electrons and these very closely spaced nuclei broaden and stabilize the energy levels available to the electron. Because the electron "feels" the influence of multiple nuclei simultaneously, the energy required to remove it from a nucleus is compensated for by the attraction between neighboring nuclei. This frees the electron to move relatively easily between nuclei. The higher electronic bands available to the electrons can therefore be associated more with the whole crystal than any one individual atom. This is depicted in the sketch on the right of Figure 4.10. Here, *a* is small enough that the potential wells for electronic transitions are close enough that the bands intersect and give rise to *conduction bands* in which electrons move relatively freely throughout the crystal. The potential field felt in these upper conduction bands is a mean field associated with multiple neighboring nuclei and shielded by inner shell electrons such that they are relatively free to move when a small electrical field is applied to them. Even below the conduction band, the narrowness of the potential barriers between the individual wells permits considerable quantum mechanical tunneling, and molecules can begin to move between nuclei. Because each atomic orbital contributes one level to a band, there are generally just enough lower levels to accommodate the number of available electrons. These lower or *valence* bands are therefore completely filled. Electrons in the conduction band carry the current in conductors and semiconductors.

It is convenient in developing the partition function for electrons to talk in terms of the density distribution of states available to the electron as a function of energy. Let $D(\epsilon)$ be a one-particle density distribution of states possessing energy ϵ. Although it is not obvious that $D(\epsilon)$ may be treated as a continuous distribution, quantum mechanical and classical derivations yield the same results for the densities dealt with in semiconductor materials. We will therefore use the classical or continuous representation of the distribution function derived in Example 4.7 to represent the closely spaced (but discontinuous) energy levels. We see from the final form of that distribution function that $D(\epsilon) \sim \sqrt{\epsilon}$, hence we will represent the distribution as a function of energy with a parabolic band shape in the figures of this chapter.

Figure 4.11 depicts an *intrinsic* semiconductor material. At 0 K the valence band is filled and the conduction band is vacant. At higher temperatures, the material may become a conductor as electrons gain sufficient thermal energy to be promoted into the conduction band. The current can be carried by electrons in the conduction band or by holes in nearly filled valence bands. The temperature at which this occurs depends upon the energy gap E_G between the two bands. An insulating material has a large E_G, a conducting metal virtually no energy gap, and an intrinsic semiconductor generally has a modest gap.

Some crystals with a relatively large energy gap may be doped with an impurity to modify the band structure. Dopants are selected by their ability to produce new bands within the energy gap of the undoped crystal structure as depicted in Figure 4.12. These so-called impurity semiconductors may be of

Example 4.7   Derive an expression for $D(\epsilon)$ considering electrons as an ideal gas with a spin degeneracy of 2.

This problem can be done quantum mechanically or classically. While it is perhaps not obvious that a classical treatment is justified, the same result is obtained,[4] and so we show only the classical method here.

We first find the volume of phase space accessible to the electrons at an energy ϵ. This means that $p^2/2m \leq \epsilon$. Thus,

$$\Gamma(\epsilon) = \int_V \int_{p^2 \leq 2m\epsilon} d\mathbf{p}d\mathbf{q} = V \int_{p^2 \leq 2m\epsilon} d\mathbf{p} = V \int_0^{2\pi} \int_0^{\pi} \int_0^{\sqrt{2m\epsilon}} p_r^2 \sin p_\theta \, dp_r dp_\theta dp_\phi$$

$$= \frac{4}{3}\pi V(2m\epsilon)^{3/2}.$$

The *density* of states is related to a small or differential phase space volume divided by the differential energy. Thus,

$$D(\epsilon) = \frac{2}{h^3} \frac{d\Gamma}{d\epsilon} = \frac{8m\pi V}{h^3}\sqrt{2m\epsilon}$$

where the factor of 2 was included as the degeneracy of each energy state and the factor of h^3 was divided out to prevent overcounting. Recall from Chapter 2 that a factor of h is obtained for each $dqdp$ integration in classical phase space because of the Heisenberg uncertainty principle.

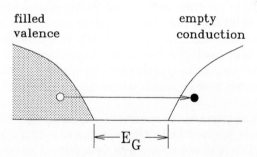

filled
valence

empty
conduction

$\longleftarrow E_G \longrightarrow$

Figure 4.11   Intrinsic semiconductor material with energy gap E_G.

two types. The first type occurs with dopants that contain a full complement of electrons. Electron-rich dopants fit into the crystal structure in such a way that the filled valence electrons contributed by the dopant fills a band intermediate in energy between the original valence and conduction bands. Because the new valence band lies in the original energy gap, the new energy gap E_D for promotion of electrons from this band to the conduction band is now smaller (Fig. 4.12A). Thus, the doped material will be a conductor at lower temperatures than the

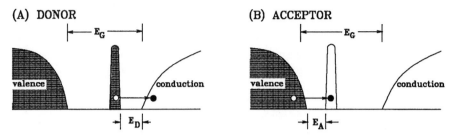

Figure 4.12   Impurity semiconductors: (**A**) N-type and (**B**) P-type.

pure material. These kinds of donor dopants produce **N-type** (emphasizing that the current carriers are negatively charged particles or electrons) semiconductors. The current is carried by electrons promoted to the conduction band in N-type conductors. The second type of impurity semiconductor is created by doping the crystal with an electron-deficient impurity. This produces new vacant acceptor bands within the energy gap of the pure material (Fig. 4.12B). The lower energy gap E_A between the valence band and this new conduction band makes it easier for a valence electron to be excited. This creates a hole in the valence band, and movement of the holes occurs as electrons fill into the holes leaving a hole at a new location. This movement of holes or positive current carriers characterizes the **P-type** semiconductors.

To a good approximation, conducting electrons may be modeled as an "ideal gas," free of interactions between themselves. Because no two identical electrons can exist in the same state (by the Pauli exclusion principle), a high-density system will fill many energy levels and the interactions between particles will be negligible. Free electrons can have only two possible quantum states designated as "spin up" and "spin down." We are primarily interested in computing the density of carriers in a semiconductor material. This property is the primary design criterion from which semiconductors are selected for particular applications.

Before we can calculate the number of current carriers in particular semiconductor materials, we must look at the statistics of the particles. The statistics of electrons is different than what we have encountered so far. To this point in the text, we have dealt with what are often called Bose–Einstein statistics. Bose–Einstein statistics are applicable to particles that may have a large number of quantum states, $j = 0, 1, 2, \ldots$ Often the particles that follow Bose–Einstein statistics are called bosons. On the other hand, electrons belong to a group of particles referred to as fermions. Fermions obey Fermi–Dirac statistics which permit only two possible quantum states, $j = 0, 1$.

The distribution functions for both kinds of statistics can be derived to provide us directly with the distribution of particles among the energy levels. We start with the grand canonical ensemble for N particles with n_j particles in state j. Of course,

$$N = \sum_{j=0}^{\infty} n_j . \tag{4.60}$$

Similar to the notation and development in the previous section, we write $\lambda = e^{\beta\mu}$, $q(j) = \exp(-\beta\epsilon_j)$, and

$$\Xi = \sum_{N=0}^{\infty} \lambda^N Q(N) = \sum_{N=0}^{\infty} \lambda^N \sum_{n_j}^{\infty} \prod_{j}^{m} e^{-\beta\epsilon_j n_j} = \sum_{N=0}^{\infty} \lambda^N \sum_{n_j}^{\infty} \prod_{j}^{m} q(j)^{n_j} , \tag{4.61}$$

where Q, which contained an exponential of a sum of particle energy levels, has been factored by energy level so that the remaining sum is over n_j. Here m is the maximum number of particles in state j. Substituting Equation (4.60) into (4.61), we obtain

$$\Xi = \sum_{n_j} \prod_{j} q(j)^{n_j} \lambda^{\Sigma n_j} = \sum_{n_j} \prod_{j} [q(j)\lambda]^{n_j} = \prod_{j} \sum_{n_j} [q(j)\lambda]^{n_j} = \prod_{j} \xi_j , \tag{4.62}$$

where

$$\xi_j \equiv \sum_{n_j}^{m} [q(j)\lambda]^{n_j} = \sum_{n_j}^{m} e^{n_j \beta(\mu-\epsilon_j)}. \tag{4.63}$$

As in the previous section on adsorption, the partition function ξ_j is just for one state (one energy level here), but it may be occupied by up to m particles. The assumption of independence has again been introduced in Equation (4.61) by assuming that the energy for level j is given by $n_j\epsilon_j$.

The sum indicated in Equation (4.63) can be performed for either Bose–Einstein or Fermi–Dirac statistics. Remarkably analogous forms of the equation result although the procedure to obtain a closed form for the summation is quite different in each case. For Bose–Einstein statistics, any number of particles may be in energy state j, that is, $m = \infty$. The identity $(1 - x)^{-1} = 1 + x + x^2 + \ldots$ can be used in this case to replace the infinite sum with a closed analytical expression. Thus,

$$\xi_j = \frac{1}{1 - e^{\beta(\mu-\epsilon_j)}} \quad \text{(bosons)} \tag{4.64}$$

and

$$\Xi = \prod_{j} (1 - \lambda e^{-\beta\epsilon_j})^{-1} \quad \text{(bosons)}. \tag{4.65}$$

For fermions, the sum is easily written out term by term because each state may have only zero or one particle in it by the Pauli exclusion principle, that is, $m = 1$. Consequently,

$$\xi_j = 1 + e^{\beta(\mu - \epsilon_j)} \quad \text{(fermions)} \tag{4.66}$$

and

$$\Xi = \prod_j (1 + \lambda e^{-\beta \epsilon_j}) \quad \text{(fermions).} \tag{4.67}$$

Having derived the grand canonical partition function for fermions, we may now calculate properties of interest for semiconductor materials. For example, the average occupation number for electrons in state j is

$$<n_j> = \frac{1}{\beta} \left(\frac{\partial \ln \xi_j}{\partial \mu} \right)_{V,T} = \frac{e^{\beta(\mu - \epsilon_j)}}{1 - e^{\beta(\mu - \epsilon_j)}} = [1 + e^{\beta(\epsilon_j - \mu)}]^{-1}. \tag{4.68}$$

The average total energy, the total number of particles, and the Helmholtz free energy are

$$E = \sum_j \epsilon_j <n_j> = \sum_j \frac{\epsilon_j}{1 + e^{\beta(\epsilon_j - \mu)}} \tag{4.69}$$

$$N = \sum_j <n_j> = \sum_j \frac{1}{1 + e^{\beta(\epsilon_j - \mu)}} \tag{4.70}$$

$$\beta A = \beta \mu N - \sum_j \ln[1 + e^{-\beta(\epsilon_j - \mu)}], \tag{4.71}$$

respectively.

Assuming that the one-particle energy levels are densely distributed, (i.e., that they are sufficiently close together that the previously derived continuous distribution function $D(\epsilon)$ represents the electronic energy bands), we may replace the sums in Equations (4.69) to (4.71) with integrals. The corresponding equations may therefore be written as

$$E = \int \epsilon f(\epsilon) D(\epsilon) \, d\epsilon \tag{4.72}$$

$$N = \int f(\epsilon) D(\epsilon) \, d\epsilon \tag{4.73}$$

$$\beta A = \beta \mu N - \int \ln[1 + e^{-\beta(\epsilon-\mu)}]D(\epsilon)\, d\epsilon , \qquad (4.74)$$

where

$$f(\epsilon) \equiv \frac{1}{1 + e^{\beta(\epsilon-\mu)}} . \qquad (4.75)$$

The function $f(\epsilon)$ is called the Fermi distribution function. Figure 4.13 shows the behavior of this function. At 0 K it is a step function with

$$f(\epsilon) = \begin{cases} 1 & \epsilon < \mu_o \\ 0 & \epsilon > \mu_o \end{cases} .$$

Thus the electrons are all in the valence bands and the material is insulating. At higher temperatures, some of the electrons can jump to the conduction band, thus broadening out the distribution of energies. Figure 4.13 also shows $f(\epsilon)$ at room temperature. The broadening of the distribution around μ at higher temperatures is still seen to be fairly small. Since μ is generally centered at or near the center of the energy gap, a material will only become a good conductor when the thermal energy produces a broad enough distribution to overlap the energy gap of the material E_G. Thus, choice of a semiconductor material for an application is made by matching the desired characteristics with a material of appropriate band gap. The band gap itself is a function of temperature, but not as strong of function as the distribution. Energy gaps for a few of the more important pure and compound semiconductor materials are shown at two temperatures in Table 4.3.

The primary quantity of interest in the design of semiconductor materials is the number of current carriers, either electrons in the conduction band, n, or holes in the valence band, p. Once these quantities are known, other properties, such as electrical conductivity and the Hall effect, can be computed. We will only discuss the computation of carrier populations here. Example 4.8 illustrates this kind of calculation for an intrinsic semiconductor and Example 4.9 treats an impurity semiconductor. Table 4.4 contains values for acceptor and donor levels for selected dopants of Si and Ge.

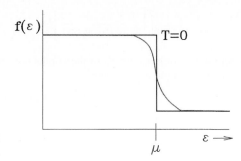

Figure 4.13   The Fermi distribution function at 0 K and room temperature.

TABLE 4.3 Energy Gaps of Selected Semiconductors

Material	E_G (300 K) (eV)	E_G (0 K) (eV)	Material	E_G (300 K) (eV)	E_G (0 K) (eV)
Si	1.12	1.17	Ge	0.67	0.75
PbS	0.37	0.29	PbSe	0.26	0.17
PbTe	0.29	0.19	InSb	0.16	0.23
GaSb	0.69	0.79	AlSb	1.5	1.6
InAs	0.35	0.43	InP	1.3	
GaAs	1.4		GaP	2.2	

TABLE 4.4 Energy Levels (in eV) of Group V (Donors) and Group III (Acceptors) Dopants in Silicon and Germanium

Group V	Si $(\epsilon_c - E_D)$	Ge $(\epsilon_c - E_D)$	Group III	Si $(E_A - \epsilon_v)$	Ge $(E_A - \epsilon_v)$
P	0.044	0.012	B	0.046	0.0104
As	0.049	0.0127	Al	0.057	0.0102
Sb	0.039	0.0096	Ga	0.065	0.0108
Bi	0.069	——	In	0.16	0.0112
			Tl	0.26	0.01

Example 4.8   Consider an intrinsic semiconductor which has an energy gap E_G = 0.7 eV, conduction electron density n, and valence hole density p. Find the density of carriers at 300 K and the chemical potential.

The number of carriers per unit volume can be written as

$$n = \int_{\epsilon_c}^{\infty} \frac{1}{e^{\beta(\epsilon-\mu)} + 1} \, D_c(\epsilon) \, d\epsilon$$

$$p = \int_{-\infty}^{\epsilon_v} \left[1 - \frac{1}{e^{\beta(\epsilon-\mu)} + 1} \right] D_v(\epsilon) \, d\epsilon = \int_{-\infty}^{\epsilon_v} \frac{1}{e^{\beta(\mu-\epsilon)} + 1} \, D_v(\epsilon) \, d\epsilon \, ,$$

where the subscript c refers to the conduction band and v refers to the valence band. We may generally assume that

$$e^{\beta(\epsilon_c-\mu)} \gg 1 \text{ and } e^{\beta(\mu-\epsilon_v)} \gg 1$$

because there will be a range of values of μ for which these inequalities hold for even quite narrow gaps, but we will check these assumptions at the end of the problem. This allows us to simplify the statistical factors:

Example 4.8 Continued

$$\frac{1}{e^{\beta(\epsilon-\mu)}+1} \simeq e^{-\beta(\epsilon-\mu)} \text{ (for } \epsilon > \epsilon_c)$$

$$\frac{1}{e^{\beta(\mu-\epsilon)}+1} \simeq e^{-\beta(\mu-\epsilon)} \text{ (for } \epsilon < \epsilon_v) \, .$$

Thus,

$$n = e^{-\beta(\epsilon_c-\mu)}\int_{\epsilon_c}^{\infty} D_c(\epsilon)e^{-\beta(\epsilon-\epsilon_c)}\, d\epsilon$$

$$p = e^{-\beta(\mu-\epsilon_v)}\int_{-\infty}^{\epsilon_v} D_v(\epsilon)e^{-\beta(\epsilon_v-\epsilon)}\, d\epsilon \, .$$

Using the distribution density $D(\epsilon)$ derived in Example 4.7 (divided by V to produce densities for n and p), we obtain for n

$$n = \frac{8m\pi\sqrt{2m}}{h^3}e^{-\beta(\epsilon_c-\mu)}\int_{\epsilon_c}^{\infty}(\epsilon-\epsilon_c)^{1/2}e^{-\beta(\epsilon-\epsilon_c)}\, d\epsilon \, .$$

This equation can be integrated analytically. Using the change of variables $x^2 = \beta(\epsilon-\epsilon_c)$ we may write the integral as

$$\int_{\epsilon_c}^{\infty}(\epsilon-\epsilon_c)^{1/2}e^{-\beta(\epsilon-\epsilon_c)}\, d\epsilon = \frac{2}{\beta^{3/2}}\int_0^{\infty}x^2 e^{-x^2}\, dx = \frac{1}{2}\sqrt{\frac{\pi}{\beta^3}}$$

which then yields

$$n = \frac{1}{4}\left(\frac{8m\pi kT}{h^2}\right)^{3/2}e^{-\beta(\epsilon_c-\mu)}.$$

A similar procedure yields

$$p = \frac{1}{4}\left(\frac{8m\pi kT}{h^2}\right)^{3/2}e^{-\beta(\mu-\epsilon_v)}.$$

In these equations we have assumed that m is the same mass for both n and p carriers. These population densities still depend upon μ, but their product does not

$$np = \frac{1}{16}\left(\frac{8m\pi kT}{h^2}\right)^3 e^{-\beta E_G}.$$

For intrinsic semiconductors, the number of holes created in the valence bands must equal the number of electrons donated to the conduction band, and we may write

$$n = p = \sqrt{np} = \frac{1}{4}\left(\frac{8m\pi kT}{h^2}\right)^{3/2}e^{-\beta E_G/2} = 3.3 \times 10^{13} \text{ cm}^{-3}.$$

Example 4.8 Continued

The chemical potential is also found from the restriction that $n = p$. This requires that

$$e^{-\beta(\epsilon_c - \mu)} = e^{-\beta(\mu - \epsilon_v)} \Rightarrow \mu = \epsilon_v + \frac{1}{2}E_G .$$

again for the case where the mass of both carriers is the same.

Finally, we may return and check the assumption upon which these calculations were based. Using the above values, we find that $\beta(\mu - \epsilon_v) = 1/2E_G = 13.54 > 1$ and $\beta(\epsilon_c - \mu) = 1/2E_G = 13.54 > 1$, validating the assumptions made.

Example 4.9 Consider an N-type semiconductor whose donor levels lie E_D below the bottom of the conduction band. Let N_D, n_D, and n be the number of donors, the number of electrons in the donor levels, and the number of conduction electrons, per unit volume, respectively. Determine a relationship between N_D, n_D, and n.

The possible microscopic states for a donor level are (1) empty, (2) occupied by an electron of spin up, and (3) occupied by an electron of spin down. The doubly occupied state would be of much higher energy and so is practically excluded from a donor level. The energies of either of the two occupied states is $-E_D$, and we may write out the grand canonical partition function in terms of these three states. Either Equation (4.67) or Equations (4.62) and (4.63) could be used. For example, using (4.63) we obtain

$$\xi_D = 1 + 2\lambda e^{\beta E_D}$$

since there are two singly occupied states of equal energy. This yields

$$\Xi_D = \left(1 + 2\lambda e^{\beta E_D}\right)^{N_D}$$

for the partition function. The same result is of course obtained directly from Equation (4.67) by including the level degeneracy of 2. To find the average number of electrons distributed over N_D donor levels we take the partial derivative

$$n_D = \lambda \left(\frac{\partial \ln \Xi_D}{\partial \lambda}\right)_{T,V} = \frac{N_D 2\lambda e^{\beta E_D}}{1 + 2\lambda e^{\beta E_D}} = \frac{N_D}{1 + \frac{1}{2}e^{-\beta(E_D + \mu)}}.$$

The number of conduction electrons is the same as in Example 4.9, but we set ϵ_c to zero since the energy of the conduction band was taken as zero in this problem. Thus,

$$n = \frac{1}{4}\left(\frac{8m\pi kT}{h^2}\right)^{3/2} e^{\beta\mu}.$$

Combining these two equations to eliminate μ, we obtain

$$\frac{n(N_D - n_D)}{n_D} = \frac{1}{8}\left(\frac{8m\pi kT}{h^2}\right)^{3/2} e^{-\beta E_D}.$$

Example 4.9   Continued

This is the desired relationship between these quantities. What does it mean? The above equation is really nothing but the law of mass action for the equilibrium condition of the electron dissociation reaction

$$D = D^+ + e^-,$$

where D is the donor, D^+ the ionized donor, and e^- the conduction electron.

4.5 FREELY JOINTED POLYMERS

There are many other systems that can be treated approximately with idealized, noninteracting models. Here we look at the expected length of freely jointed polymers as an archetype of the methodology used for a wide range of applications. Additional applications are illustrated in the problems at the end of the chapter.

While there are many properties of polymers that are important to process chemists and engineers that can be treated with statistical mechanics, most require models with interactions. This is also generally true for calculating polymer lengths, but we can learn quite a bit from trying to calculate the length of an idealized polymer whose monomer subunits do not interact. Consider an idealized polymer as consisting of M monomer units—an M-mer, if you will. We will assume that the M monomer units are linked end to end to create a chain. For example, we might think of very long n-alkanes as chains of polymethylene. Other common examples are:

$$- CH_2 - CH -$$

polystyrene

$$- CH_2 - CH_2 -$$

polyethylene

$$- CH - CH -$$

polyvinyl chloride

Typically polymers have hundreds or thousands of such monomer units connected together into very long chains. Nevertheless, the length of the chain is not the sum of the bond lengths, d. Because carbon–carbon bond angles are approximately 109°, the chains are not linear. As seen in Figure 4.14, there is a maximum length for the fully extended chain, but rotations about the carbon–carbon bond can reorient the next bond angle, producing many different configurations of length, L, where L is shorter than the maximum. A fundamental problem in polymer statistics which we address here is the determination of the expected end-to-end distance L of M-mers. One can imagine lengths continuously varying from zero to the maximum due to the combination of all the various bond directions in three dimensional space.

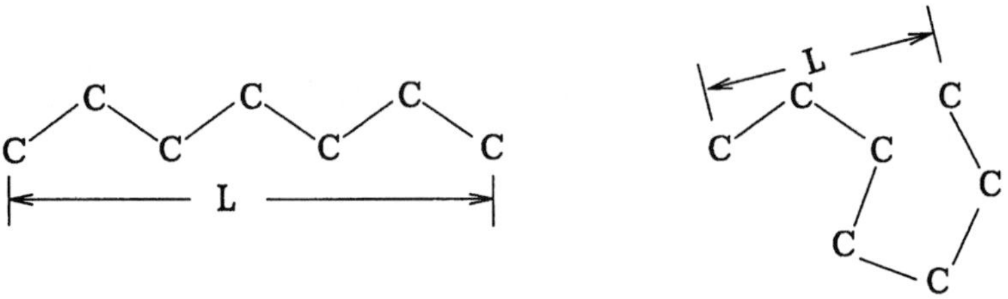

Figure 4.14 Two-dimensional projections of fully extended and alternative configurations.

Our model for the M-mer in this chapter is M end-to-end monomer units, each of length d, forming a chain. The chain is considered freely jointed; that is, the angle made by the junction of the two monomers may freely take on any value, and all orientations are equally likely because there are no interactions between segments. In this manner, we have introduced the assumption of independent subunits which has characterized the applications in this chapter. We will also implicitly assume that M is sufficiently large to allow treatment of the system thermodynamically.

As shown in the two-dimensional illustration of Figure 4.15, the polymer length, L, is the sum of the bond length projections onto the end-to-end vector $\mathbf{L}$ that is,

$$L = \sum_{i=1}^{M} l_i \, M_i .$$ (4.76)

Now let us assume an effective end-to-end force of τ pulling outward along the end-to-end vector. Obviously the length will be a function of this pulling force. The origin of the force is not important here, but can be considered a replacement for the interactions that will occur in real polymer systems that keep it from folding back on itself. In terms of these variables, the Helmholtz free energy can be written as

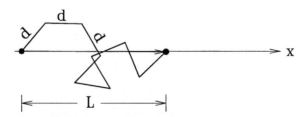

Figure 4.15 End-to-end length of polymer.

$$dA = -SdT + \tau dL + \mu dM .$$ (4.77)

We will use a new partition function here, one analogous to the isothermal–isobaric partition function introduced in Chapter 2. For the partition function

$$\Delta(\tau,M,T) = \sum_l Q(L,M,T)e^{\beta \tau l} ,$$ (4.78)

the thermodynamic connection equation is

$$G = -kT\ln\Delta ,$$ (4.79)

where the Gibbs free energy is related to the property variables by

$$dG = -SdT - Ld\tau + \mu dM .$$ (4.80)

To find Q for a particular length, consider that each monomer can exist in orientations $i = 1, 2, ..., n$ with partition function j_i and length l_i for each. Then,

$$Q(L,M,T) = \sum_{M_i} M! \prod_{i=1}^{n} \frac{j_i^{M_i}}{M_i!} .$$ (4.81)

Substituting this expression into Equation (4.78), we obtain

$$\Delta = \sum_{M_i} M! \prod_{i=1}^{n} \frac{\left(j_i e^{\beta \tau l_i}\right)^{M_i}}{M_i!} .$$ (4.82)

As in the previous sections of this chapter, we can immediately sum the partition function using the multinomial theorem to obtain

$$\Delta = \left(\sum_{i=1}^{n} j_i \, e^{\beta \tau l_i} \right)^M = \delta^M ,$$ (4.83)

where we have maintained the convention of using the lower case equivalent (in this case δ) of the total partition function to represent the single subunit partition function. The average end-to-end length is then readily found by using the appropriate thermodynamic identities,

$$<L> = -\left(\frac{\partial G}{\partial \tau}\right)_{M,T} = kT\left(\frac{\partial \ln\Delta}{\partial \tau}\right)_{M,T} = MkT\left(\frac{\partial \delta}{\partial \tau}\right)_{M,T} .$$ (4.84)

Consider for a moment the specialized case of a one-dimensional polymer. Each monomer can be oriented in either the $+x$ or the $-x$ direction. In this case, each monomer contributes only $+d$ or $-d$ to the length of the chain, and the chain itself resembles a folding ruler. There are only two possible states, each of equal probability. Thus, $j_1 = j_2 = j$, $l_1 = +d$ and $l_2 = -d$. As shown in Example 4.10, the expected length can be readily obtained for this specialized case as

$$<L> = Md \tanh(\beta\tau d) . \tag{4.85}$$

Or, if one prefers, the force acting between the ends can be found by inverting Equation (4.85):

$$\tau = dkT \tanh^{-1}\left(\frac{<L>}{md}\right) . \tag{4.86}$$

For the three-dimensional case, the contribution to L of each monomer

---

Example 4.10   Determine the temperature dependence of the end-to-end length of a one-dimensional, freely jointed polymer if the effective force pulling at the ends of the molecule is 1.04×10^{-7} dynes and the monomer lengths are 20 Å.

Because the polymer is one dimensional, each monomer can contribute $+d$ or $-d$ to the overall length. The maximum length of the polymer is therefore Md when it is fully extended with all monomers oriented in the same direction. It will be convenient to divide the length by this maximum length to look at the fractional extension of the polymer as a function of temperature. With no force on the molecule, the average length is zero because both orientations are equally probable, that is, $j_1 = j_2 = j$. Real polymers have steric and potential effects that can be modeled as a net or effective force stretching the molecule along the end-to-end vector. The probability of momoners adding to the length is then enhanced by the exponential term in Equation (4.83).

Because only two states are available to the system, we can readily obtain the partition function by direct enumeration. Equation (4.83) can be expanded as

$$\delta = je^{\beta\tau d} + je^{-\beta\tau d} = 2j \cosh(\beta\tau d) .$$

Using Equation (4.84), the expected length of the polymer is

$$<L> = kT\left(\frac{\partial\ln\Delta}{\partial\tau}\right)_T =$$

$$Md \tanh(\beta\tau d) .$$

And, the fractional extension is given by:

$$\frac{<L>}{L_{max}} = \tanh\left(\frac{\tau d}{kT}\right) .$$

By using the values given in the problem statement and assuming that the effective force is independent of the temperature, we can plot this function as shown in the diagram.

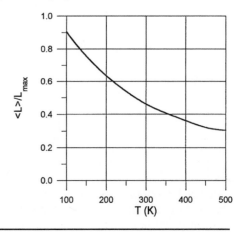

subunit can vary continuously between $-d$ and $+d$. Let x represent that variable. As in the one-dimensional case, j is the zero-force probability of length x, which is a uniform probability independent of x. We can then write,

$$\delta = \int_{-d}^{+d} je^{\beta\tau x}\,dx = 2jkT\,\sinh(\beta\tau d)\,.\tag{4.87}$$

Analogous to the procedure in Example 4.10, we find the expected length of the polymer from

$$<L> = kTM\left(\frac{\partial\ln\delta}{\partial\tau}\right)_T = Md\left[\coth(\beta\tau d) - \frac{1}{\beta\tau d}\right]\,.\tag{4.88}$$

Often a distribution is characterized by its moments (see Chap. 1, Sec. 5). Equation (4.88) gives the mean length, and we can also calculate the variance in length using the methods of Chapter 2. One can show that the fluctuation in L for a fixed τ is

$$<L^2> - <L>^2 = kT\left(\frac{\partial<L>}{\partial\tau}\right)_{M,T}\,.\tag{4.89}$$

The largest fluctuations occur when τ is very small. In the limit of small τ, $<L> = M\beta\tau d^2/3$, and

$$<L^2> - <L>^2 = \frac{1}{3}Md^2\,.\tag{4.90}$$

While there are many more systems that could be treated using the independent particle assumption, the ones dealt with in this chapter on solids serve to illustrate the techniques. We now turn to interacting systems where our prime concern is the evaluation of the configurational partition function. This is particularly important in dealing with liquid properties where the structure is neither random nor lattice-like.

REFERENCES

1. Weast, R.C., ed. *CRC Handbook of Chemistry and Physics,* 51st ed., The Chemical Rubber Company, 1970, p. D-74.

2. Hill, T.L. *An Introduction to Statistical Mechanics,* Addison-Wesley, Reading MA, 1960.

3. Ashcroft, N.W., and Mermin, N.D. *Solid State Physics,* Saunders College, Holt, Rinehart and Winston, Philadelphia, 1976.

4. Kubo, R. *Statistical Mechanics: An Advanced Course with Problems and Solutions,* North-Holland, Amsterdam, 1965.

5. McQuarrie, D.A. *Statistical Mechanics,* Harper & Row, New York, 1976.

PROBLEMS

CRYSTALLINE SOLIDS

1. Find the low- and high-temperature limits of the heat capacity of a crystal within the framework of the Einstein model; that is, prove Equations (4.7) and (4.8).

2. Derive equations for P and μ for the Einstein model, considering u_0 and Θ functions of V/N.

3. Derive an equation for the vapor pressure $P^*(T)$ of an Einstein crystal, assuming the vapor is an ideal gas. Recall that phase equilibrium requires that $\mu^{gas} = \mu^{adsorbed}$. You may make use of an approximate expression for μ of the crystal as simply A/N. The expression for μ^{gas} can be obtained from Example 3.5.

4. The vapor pressure of Ag is 10^{-5} mm Hg at 767°C. Use the results of Problem 3 and the data for Θ obtained in Example 4.1 to estimate a value of u_o for the crystal structure.

5. Calculate the heat capacity and entropy of Au and Cu from the Einstein model at 50 K given that C_V for Au and Cu are 0.108 J/g·K and 0.254 J/g·K, respectively, at 100 K.

6. Calculate the heat capacity and entropy of Au and Mg from the Debye model at 50 K.

7. The heat capacity of Al at 32 K is 0.254 cal/mol·K. Determine Θ_D.

8. Find the high- and low-temperature limits of Equation (4.23).

9. The heat capacity of a particular monatomic solid at 300 K is found to be $2R$ per mole. Use the Einstein theory to calculate the frequency of the crystal vibrations.

10. Equation (4.23) suggests that the heat capacity of crystals obeys a corresponding states relationship in which the dimensionless temperature T^+ is taken to be X_D^{-1}. Prepare a corresponding states plot of dimensionless heat capacity versus T^+ over a reduced temperature range from 0 to 2. Use your plot to obtain a value of the heat capacity of Au at 100 K and compare this with the experimental value of 21.44 J/mol·K.

11. The heat capacity of copper at 100 K is 3.85 cal/mol·K. Calculate Θ using the Einstein theory and Θ_D for the Debye theory. Then calculate the heat capacity of Cu at 25 K using both models and compare the resultant values to the experimental value of 0.23 cal/mol·K. Which model gives better results at low temperature?

CRYSTAL DEFECTS

12. Calculate the number of Schottky defects per mole of crystal at 300 K and 1000 K given that it takes 1.0 eV to bring an atom or ion from an interior lattice site to a surface lattice site.

13. Repeat Problem 12 for Frenkel defects assuming 0.2 eV to move an atom from a lattice site to an interstitial location. Assume that for the crystal in question, there are an equal number of lattice and interstitial sites.

14. Compute the molar entropy, internal energy, and Helmholtz free energy for the crystal of Problem 12 at 1000 K relative to the perfect crystal structure at the same temperature.

15. Compute the molar entropy, internal energy, and Helmholtz free energy for the crystal of Problem 13 at 1000 K relative to the perfect crystal structure at the same temperature.

16. Consider an ionic crystal of NaCl which primarily has Schottky defects.[5] If n_1 represents the number of single positive or negative ion vacancies and n_2 the number of ion-pair vacancies, derive an expression for the Helmholtz free energy and show by minimizing this with respect to n_1 and n_2 that

$$\frac{n_2}{n_1} = 6e^{\beta(\epsilon - \frac{1}{2}\phi)},$$

where ϵ is the binding energy of a pair of oppositely charged vacancies, and ϕ is the energy required to produce a single positive and negative ion vacancy.

ADSORPTION

17. Consider argon gas adsorbed on a solid at 200 K.[2] For this solid, ϵ_0 is 1500 cal/mol. Calculate Θ when the argon gas pressure is 1 atm.

18. For a system of adsorbent molecules each of which has m equivalent and independent sites for adsorption, show that $\xi = (1 + q\lambda)^m$ and that the adsorption isotherm is the same as the Langmuir equation.[2]

19. Show that the chemical potential of an adsorbed gas on the surface of a solid can be written as

$$\mu = kT\ln\frac{\Theta}{1 - \Theta} - \epsilon_0.$$

20. Apply the ξ-method to a two-component (A and B) ideal gas adsorbed on independent pairs of lattice sites. Let M represent the number of independent pairs of sites. Each site in the pair may be empty or have an A or B gas molecule adsorbed. But, only one molecule can adsorb per site and the two sites in the pair are equivalent. Then show that the expected number of type A molecules adsorbed per molecule (or pair of sites) is given by

$$\frac{\langle N_A \rangle}{M} = \frac{2q_A\lambda_A}{1 + q_A\lambda_A + q_B\lambda_B},$$

and therefore the fraction of total sites covered with an A molecule is

$$\frac{\langle N_A \rangle}{N} = \frac{q_A\lambda_A}{1 + q_A\lambda_A + q_B\lambda_B}.$$

21. Consider a system of adsorbent molecules, each with two adsorption sites. Let w

be the interaction energy when both sites of a pair are occupied. Let x_0, x_1, and x_2 be the fractions of adsorbent molecules with zero, one, and two adsorbed molecules, respectively. Strictly from a conservation equation, show that the number of sites occupied per molecule is given by

$$\frac{<N_1>}{N} = \frac{\dfrac{x_1}{x_0} + 2\dfrac{x_2}{x_0}}{1 + \dfrac{x_1}{x_0} + \dfrac{x_2}{x_0}}.$$

Apply the ξ method to show that

$$\frac{<N_1>}{N} = \frac{q_1\lambda + q_1^2\lambda^2 e^{-\beta w}}{1 + 2q_1\lambda + q_1^2\lambda^2 e^{-\beta w}}.$$

By comparing these two equations, identify two expressions for $q_1\lambda$ in terms of x_0, x_1, and x_2. Equate your two expressions to show that

$$x_1 = 2\sqrt{x_0 x_2}\, e^{\beta w/2}.$$

SEMICONDUCTORS

22. (a) Show that if the energy of a doubly occupied donor level is taken to be $2E_D + \Delta$, then

$$n_D = N_D \frac{1 + e^{-\beta(E_D - \mu + \Delta)}}{1 + \dfrac{1}{2}e^{-\beta(E_D + \mu)} + \dfrac{1}{2}e^{-\beta(E_D - \mu + \Delta)}}$$

(b) Verify that this reduces to the equation derived in Example 4.9 for n_D as Δ approaches infinity and that it reduces to the expected result for independent electrons as Δ approaches zero.[3]

23. Show that the equation of state of an ideal Fermi gas can be written as

$$PV = \frac{2}{3}U.$$

Hint: You should be able to deduce the form of $\ln\Xi$ from Equation (4.74). This expression can then be integrated by parts.

24. Using the results of Example 4.9, the condition of electroneutrality, and the equation

$$\sigma = \frac{e^2 n \tau}{m}$$

which relates the electrical conductivity, σ, to the relaxation time, τ, find the high- and low-temperature limits for the electrical conductivity. Note that at low temperatures the equilibrium expression derived in Example 4.9 implies very little dissociation while at high temperatures it implies nearly complete dissociation.

25. Consider a semiconductor which has N_A acceptors (per cm³) whose levels are E_A above the top of the filled band.[4] Find the temperature dependence of the density of holes which are created in the filled band. Here it is assumed that the density of acceptors is so small that the holes are not degenerate and that each acceptor level can accommodate only one electron. You may also assume that N_A is much greater than the number of holes in the filled band.

26. If one considers electron spin, an electron in a donor level may have two states. The Coulomb interaction between electrons, however, prevents a donor level from accommodating two electrons at the same time. The energy levels of electrons relative to the bottom of the conduction band are then $-E_D + \mu_B H$ and $-E_D - \mu_B H$ for the positive and negative spins, respectively. Here, μ_B is the Bohr magneton given by $\mu_B = eh/(4\pi mc)$ and H is the magnetic field strength. Show that the magnetization of the system of electrons in the donor levels is given by

$$M = N_D \mu_B \left[\frac{A\sinh(\beta\mu_B H)}{1 + A\cosh(\beta\mu_B H)} \right],$$

where $A = 2\lambda\exp(\beta E_D)$. Magnetization is defined in terms of the free energy as

$$M = \left(\frac{\partial A}{\partial H}\right)_{T,V}.$$

27. Consider a sample of Ge containing $N_D = 10^{15}$ cm⁻³ As donors.[4] Compute the density of conduction electrons n at 300 K. You should use the condition of electroneutrality.

FREELY JOINTED POLYMERS

28. A problem mathematically analogous to the freely jointed polymer problem is that of an ideal gas in an electric field. Let D be the applied electric field strength, M_1 be the average dipole moment of a single molecule, αD be the induced moment of a single molecule (independent of T), and μ_0 be the permanent dipole moment of the molecule. The total electrostatic potential energy U_1 of a molecule in electric field D is then given by

$$U_1 = -\frac{1}{2}\alpha D^2 - \mu_0 D\cos\theta,$$

where θ is the orientation angle of the dipole with respect to the applied field. The total canonical partition function is found by angle averaging over all possible angles. Thus,

$$q = \frac{q_0}{4\pi} \int_0^{2\pi}\int_0^{\pi} e^{-\beta U_1} \sin\theta \, d\theta \, d\phi,$$

where q_0 is the partition function with no applied field. The thermodynamic equation for this system is

$$dA = -S dT - P dV - M dD + \mu dN.$$

Thus, the expectation of the total electrical moment of the system can be found from

$$<M> = -\left(\frac{\partial A}{\partial D}\right)_{T,V,N}$$

(a) Show that the moment for a system of N molecules can be written as

$$<M> = N\alpha D + N\mu_0 \left[\coth(\beta\mu_0 D) - \frac{1}{\beta\mu_0 D} \right].$$

(b) In practice, $\beta\mu_0 D \ll 1$. Show that in this case,

$$<M> \simeq ND\left(\alpha + \frac{\mu_0^2}{3kT}\right).$$

29. When a particle with spin 1/2 is placed in a magnetic field of strength H, it can exhibit only two energy levels, $E = -\mu H$ and $E = +\mu H$. These energies correspond to a magnetic moment of $-\mu$ parallel to the applied magnetic field and $+\mu$ antiparallel to the field, respectively. Derive and simplify where possible the canonical partition function for N independent particles, the corresponding Helmholtz free energy, internal energy, and heat capacity, C_H. Your results should contain hyperbolic trigonometric functions.

30. A one-dimensional polymer comprised of 100 monomeric units, each of 15 Å length, is observed to have an average length in solution of 600 Å at 300 K. What is the effective end-to-end force on the polymer chain?

5

NONIDEAL FLUID PROPERTIES FROM THE CONFIGURATIONAL PARTITION FUNCTION

5.1 ORIGIN OF FLUID NONIDEALITIES

As we have seen, the canonical partition function is the key to the calculation of thermodynamic properties. It is conveniently factored into separate parts,

$$Q = \frac{Z \, Q_{int}}{N! \, \Lambda^{3N}}, \tag{5.1}$$

and we have seen how to calculate each part for an ideal gas. The configurational integral, Z, defined as

$$Z = \int \ldots \int e^{-\beta U} \, dq^{3N}, \tag{5.2}$$

contains all of the information about the location of the molecular centers of mass and is therefore the only density-dependent part of Q. Equations (5.1) and (5.2) are true for any system: solid, liquid, or gas. Only as further assumptions are made about the intermolecular potential, $U(q)$, are limitations imposed. For example, in the limit of very low densities molecules are sufficiently far apart that U is very small or nearly zero. Equation (5.2) is readily integrable in this ideal-gas limit and $Z = V^N$, as we saw in Chapter 3. This approximation is certainly not true at higher densities, and integration of Equation (5.2) must then be performed using a more appropriate potential energy function.

Because Z is the only density-dependent factor in Q, it contains all of the information about fluid nonidealities. Contributions to the thermodynamic properties that result from the translational and internal degrees of freedom are evaluated for real or nonideal fluids just as we did for ideal gases in Chapter 3. The nonidealities are then computed from the configurational partition function Z as *departure functions*. The sum of the departure function and the ideal-gas value yields the total property at the specified condition, although often only the departure function itself may be needed.

The only difference between the ideal gas and the real fluid is the value of Z. Evaluation of Z and the corresponding configurational properties will therefore be a central theme throughout the remainder of this book. Generally, a four-step procedure will be used to obtain a real-fluid property, J, from the configurational partition function:

1. Evaluation of the total potential energy U
2. Evaluation of the configurational contribution to the property, J_c, using Equation (5.2) with the relationships in Table 2.1
3. Evaluation of the translational J_t and internal J_i contributions as in Chapter 3
4. Summation of the various contributions,

$$J = J_c + J_t + \sum_{\text{int. modes}} J_i . \tag{5.3}$$

Step 1 is often the most crucial for reliable prediction of properties, and much current research focuses on development of the most appropriate and accurate potential models. Step 2 is often mathematically very difficult, and simplifying assumptions are often needed to develop analytical expressions for the properties. However, with today's computers, analytical methods are not always necessary and numerical methods can be used to obtain results that are independent of assumptions associated with step 2. For example, molecular dynamics (Chap. 8) is, in essence, a numerical method for completing step 2. Because simplifying assumptions are not used to obtain an analytical solution, molecular dynamics simulations are often used as "experimental data" against which theories may be checked. Both the theory and the molecular dynamic simulation can be based on the same model (step 1) so that only the assumptions used in step 2 to obtain the analytical theory are assessed by the comparison. On the other hand, if actual experimental data are used to check the predictions of theory, discrepancies might be due to the assumptions in either step 1 or step 2. In fact, to take an even more skeptical posture, we might argue that agreement of theory with experimental data over a limited range of conditions may not be a satisfactory validation of theory because of the possible cancellation of errors between the assumptions of steps 1 and 2. For these reasons, molecular dynamics simulations have become important test data for the assumptions of step 1.

Understanding the forces between molecules and quantitatively modeling those forces appears to be the last major hurdle in establishing accurate, universal prediction of fluid properties using statistical mechanics. This is not an easy problem, nor strictly a contemporary problem. In Chapter 1, we mentioned the often heated controversy between atomists and nonatomists near the turn of the century. In his 1873 thesis, van der Waals recognized that if both attractive and repulsive forces existed between molecules, then both the liquid and gas phases could be explained in terms of a single continuous equation of state. Furthermore, transition between phases could be readily explained in terms of these intermolecular forces. While there was much speculation at the time about the nature of these forces, real insight into the origin of the forces between molecules had to wait until the development of quantum mechanics. Even then, it wasn't until about 1970 that a precise description of the forces between even the simplest molecules was achieved.

What is the origin of intermolecular forces? There are very few fundamental forces in nature. Of these, one might expect gravitational forces to be a likely candidate for the attraction between molecules, but the very small masses of the molecules makes gravitational attraction insignificant in the calculation of thermophysical properties. In fact the magnitude of gravitational forces is about 10^{30} smaller than the dominant forces. The dominating forces are Coulombic in origin, accounting for both the attractions and repulsions. We can further break these Coulombic forces down into several different types of interactions. If the particles have a net charge, then the *electrostatic* forces that attract oppositely charged particles and repel like-charged particles have a very long range. Even if there is no net charge, the distribution of charge within the molecule may create localized regions of positive and negative charge in the molecule. This charge separation leads to *polar* interactions between positive and negative sites on the molecules. Furthermore, the charge distribution on one molecule may induce small changes in the electronic distribution of nearby molecules leading to *induction* interactions. *Dispersion* or van der Waal forces occur even between nonpolar, neutral molecules. The mathematical description of these forces arises from the quantum mechanical calculation of electron positions, but the physical interpretation roughly corresponds to small, rapidly fluctuating induction effects as the spatial location of electrons on one molecule polarizes neighboring molecules. Rapidly changing, instantaneous dipoles in one molecule correlate with those in another molecule. Crudely speaking, when an electron of molecule 1 is between the two nuclei, the electron on molecule 2 tends to have a higher probability of being on the other side of the nucleus. This reduced shielding of the Coulombic interaction between the nucleus of molecule 2 and the electron of molecule 1 creates a short-range attraction. Finally, when atoms or molecules approach close enough that substantial *overlap* of the charge clouds occurs, very strong repulsions result between the negatively charged electron clouds of the two molecules. Specific interactions involving charge transfer and hydrogen bonding between molecules with particular valence electron configurations may also be present.

We have been discussing intermolecular forces when actually it is the intermolecular potential energy that enters into the configurational partition function [cf. Equation (5.2)]. The two are related by

$$f = -\nabla u, \tag{5.4}$$

where f is the intermolecular force and u is the intermolecular potential between two molecules. If the potential is only a function of the distance between the particles, then the force between them is found from

$$f(r) = -\frac{du(r)}{dr}. \tag{5.5}$$

The potential energy required in Equation (5.2) is the total potential energy of the system. As mentioned above, the first step in obtaining departure function properties is calculating this total potential energy. To make the problem somewhat tractable, the total potential is often represented by

$$U = \sum_{i<j} u_{ij} + \sum_{i<j<k} \Delta u_{ijk} + \ldots + \Delta u_{123\ldots N}, \tag{5.6}$$

where u_{ij} is the pair potential energy between molecules i and j. It represents the potential energy of interaction between the two molecules independent of the other $N-2$ molecules surrounding them. It is referred to as the pair potential, meaning an isolated pair. The first summation in Equation (5.6) is over all such pairs. The term Δu_{ijk} is the *additional* contribution to the sum of pair potentials made by the presence of a third molecule. The presence of a third molecule distorts the electronic wave function from that for the isolated pair, and the change in the potential energy due to this effect is accounted for by these three-body terms. Thus, for a system composed only of three particles, the potential energy could be found from the sum of the isolated pair potentials u_{12}, u_{13}, and u_{23} plus the additional three-body effect u_{123}. Similarly, four- and higher-body effects are included in the summation shown in Equation (5.6). The obvious intent of writing the potential energy in this form is that higher order terms may become rapidly small and that the summation will therefore converge. However, Equation (5.6) written out to the final term, which is a correction for any additional effects from all N molecules not accounted for in lower order terms, is in fact exact.

The degree to which Equation (5.6) can be truncated depends on the density of the system. Currently, most applications of statistical mechanics assume that multibody effects on thermophysical properties are negligible; that is, only pair interaction energies are required so that

$$U = \sum_{i<j} u_{ij} \, . \tag{5.7}$$

This assumption is known as pairwise additivity for obvious reasons. While not exact, it yields good results under many normal conditions. It is expected to become progressively worse at higher densities. However, some properties are more sensitive to higher order terms than others. For example, the effect of three-body terms on the internal energy of a liquid is small even at the triple point where it is only a few per cent of the total configurational energy.[1] But, the neglect of three-body terms leads to a 25% error in the surface tension and a 10% error in surface energy for liquid argon at the triple point.[1] The contribution of Δu_{ijk} may be as high as 50% of the third virial coefficient for dense argon.[1] There is evidence, however, that even at relatively high densities pairwise additivity may yield better estimates of properties than we have any reason to expect a priori. There appears to be some cancellation in higher order terms, making pairwise additive results applicable at higher densities than one might otherwise expect. While methods for evaluating multibody effects are available in rudimentary forms (see Appendix 5), use of the pairwise additivity assumption is still somewhat of a computational necessity. Therefore, we will use it throughout the remainder of the book. Generally results based on it are adequate at most densities.

In the next two sections, we discuss in more detail pair potential models used for dispersion forces and direct electrostatic forces (including induction and polar interactions), respectively. All of the models presented are based on spherical symmetry. That is, the pair potential is assumed to be only a function of intermolecular separation, $u = u(r)$, and not orientation of the molecules. Often the distance between the interaction centers r is taken to be the distance between the centers of mass, but this is not necessary. Spherically symmetrical potentials would be expected to represent adequately the interactions between simple, monatomic molecules such as the inert gases, but they obviously lack the spatial specificity that is required to describe actual potentials between polyatomic molecules. Nevertheless, these spherically symmetrical models are extremely important in property calculations of real fluids as well as in calculating the properties of model fluids. For example, spherical potentials can be used as approximate or average potentials to determine properties to first order. That is, the real potential may be thought of as an expansion about the spherical potential with this first term being the primary contributor to the main features of the desired properties. Spherical potentials may also be used as "effective" potentials with parameters regressed from experiment to correlate properties reasonably accurately over a limited range of conditions. Most importantly, we will see that multiple spherical potential sites can be used in a single molecule to produce a quite accurate model for the actual potential. We will have more to say about the use of these models for polyatomic molecules in Section 4.

5.2 DISPERSION FORCES

All molecules, whether polar or nonpolar, whether charged or neutral, experience dispersion forces. These relatively short-ranged forces have the general shape shown in Figure 5.1. As mentioned above, the models described here are a function of intermolecular separation only. Generally the parameter σ represents the closest separation distance at which the potential between the molecules is zero, that is, where the attractive and repulsive forces just balance. The parameter ε represents the maximum depth of the potential. The close-range repulsive forces when $r < \sigma$ are due to the strong Coulombic repulsion that occurs when the electron clouds of two approaching molecules begin to overlap. The longer-range attractive forces for $r > r_0$ are due to the instantaneous polarizations set up by electron positions which we previously described. The minimum in the potential well at r_0 is where the intermolecular force becomes zero as a result of competing repulsions and attractions.

Quantum mechanics and molecular beam-scattering experiments indicate that the short-range repulsions can generally be effectively represented by[2]

$$u_{ij}^{\text{rep}} = Be^{-br}, \tag{5.8}$$

where r is intermolecular separation. Direct quantum mechanical evaluation of the potential between model molecules which can experience instantaneous dipoles indicates that the dispersion forces of an isolated pair might well be represented by the form[2]

$$u_{ij}^{\text{disp}} = -\frac{C_{6ij}}{r^6}\left[1 + \left(\frac{C_8}{C_6}\right)_{ij}\frac{1}{r^2} + \left(\frac{C_{10}}{C_6}\right)_{ij}\frac{1}{r^4} + \dots \right], \tag{5.9}$$

where an integer subscript, say k, designates the coefficient, C_k, of the r^{-k} term in a series solution of the Schrödinger equation. We will now look at several

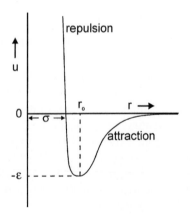

Figure 5.1 General characteristics of the dispersion potential energy function in terms of common model parameters.

empirical models that are much simpler than the above two equations, yet retain to varying degrees the essential features suggested by these results.

5.2.1 Pair-Potential Models for Dispersion Forces Between Like Molecules

Many empirical models much simpler in form than Equations (5.8) and (5.9) have been proposed for the spherical potential of nonpolar molecules. Generally, the repulsion and dispersion forces are modeled together in a mathematical form that attempts to maintain simplicity without loss of the main features suggested by these equations. A few of the more important and common models are shown in Figure 5.2.

Model *a* represents the intermolecular potential as strictly repulsion between the point centers of the molecules. We have mentioned the fact that van der Waals found that inclusion of both attractive and repulsive forces was necessary for his equation of state to represent a continuity of liquid and gas states. Model *a* is therefore not useful for modeling properties of fluids with a phase transition. Rather, the model is primarily used for theoretical studies to understand the contribution that repulsions make to properties. Interestingly, this model can provide reasonable results for simple dense liquids because repulsions tend to dominate the behavior of liquids.

Model *b*, perhaps the simplest one both from a mathematical and a physical perspective, treats the molecules as hard spheres. Within the framework of this model, molecules feel no forces at a distance owing to the presence of other molecules. They behave like billiard balls with infinite repulsion at the point of contact during physical collisions. This model is particularly popular for theoretical use. Its mathematical simplicity and segmented nature are convenient for development of theories which can serve as a reference in development of more sophisticated theories or as the reference portion of perturbation theories. The hard-sphere model retains much of the correct coarse features of liquid behavior in spite of the extreme simplicity of the model. This is again because molecules in liquids are packed so tightly that repulsions dominate the other influences on the properties of the fluid. Some effective hard-sphere parameters are given in Appendix 5.

The square-well model retains the mathematical simplicity of constant potential segments while including an attractive region. This permits development of analytical theories that include some modeled effects due to attractive forces. Like the hard-sphere model, it is widely used in development of theory and as a reference fluid in perturbation techniques. Because it contains both attractive and repulsive potentials, it can be used to roughly model the properties of both gases and liquids as well as phase transitions. But, its calculational simplicity for development of theory is its main asset. Hard-sphere parameters are conveniently obtained from second virial coefficient data, and some values obtained from this source are given in Appendix 5.

(a) point of repulsion at molecular centers

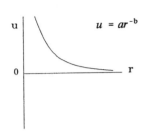

$$u = ar^{-b}$$

(d) Sutherland

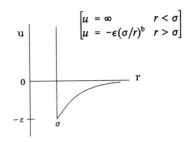

$$\left[\begin{array}{ll} u = \infty & r < \sigma \\ u = -\epsilon(\sigma/r)^b & r > \sigma \end{array}\right]$$

(b) hard sphere

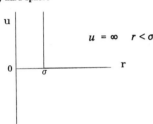

$$u = \infty \quad r < \sigma$$

(e) Lennard-Jones

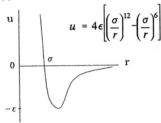

$$u = 4\epsilon\left[\left(\frac{\sigma}{r}\right)^{12} - \left(\frac{\sigma}{r}\right)^{6}\right]$$

(c) square well

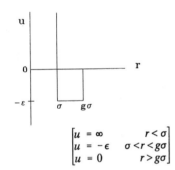

$$\left[\begin{array}{ll} u = \infty & r < \sigma \\ u = -\epsilon & \sigma < r < g\sigma \\ u = 0 & r > g\sigma \end{array}\right]$$

(f) Kihara

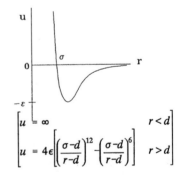

$$\left[\begin{array}{ll} u = \infty & r < d \\ u = 4\epsilon\left[\left(\frac{\sigma-d}{r-d}\right)^{12} - \left(\frac{\sigma-d}{r-d}\right)^{6}\right] & r > d \end{array}\right]$$

Figure 5.2 Commonly used intermolecular potential models for dispersion forces.

The Sutherland potential, model d, compromises the computational convenience of constant potential segments found in the square-well potential for a more realistic attractive potential. It still retains the hard-core representation of a physically well-defined molecule characteristic of the hard-sphere and square-well models, but focuses on a continuous attractive force. Sutherland model molecules are attracted toward one another until the center-to-center distance σ is reached at which point they bounce off each other like billiard balls because of the infinite repulsion at the hard surface.

The Lennard-Jones potential,

$$u = 4\epsilon \left[\left(\frac{\sigma}{r}\right)^{12} - \left(\frac{\sigma}{r}\right)^{6} \right], \qquad (5.10)$$

is the most widely used empirical potential model for calculation of thermophysical properties. This is because it is still reasonably simple, having only two parameters, yet it models both the attractive and repulsive features of real potentials quite well. Many effective Lennard-Jones (LJ) parameters for real fluids have been regressed from experimental data. The behavior of "Lennard-Jones fluids" have been widely modeled and studied for theoretical purposes and for use as a model of real fluids. Carefully constructed equations of state have even been developed for the LJ fluid from compilations of previous results.[3,4] Appendix 5 contains LJ parameters regressed from viscosity and virial coefficient data.

Because of the relatively common use of the LJ potential model, it is interesting to take a closer look at it in dimensionless form. In terms of dimensionless potential, $u^+ \equiv u/\epsilon$, and intermolecular separation, $r^+ \equiv r/\sigma$, the LJ potential can be written as

$$u^+ = 4[(r^+)^{-12} - (r^+)^{-6}]. \qquad (5.11)$$

In this form it is easily seen that the potential is zero at $r^+ = 1$. The minimum in the potential well where the attraction is strongest can be located by setting to zero the derivative of Equation (5.11) with respect to r. Doing so yields a value of $r^+ = 1.1225$ for the location of the point of maximum attraction, $u^+ = -1$. The potential is also seen to be of quite short range since u^+ diminishes to -0.001, 0.1% of its maximum attractive value, by $r^+ = 3.98$. These features are shown in Figure 5.3 where the LJ potential is drawn to scale. Example 5.1 illustrates the shapes of the Lennard-Jones potential and force in actual units for models of two real fluids.

Once values of the two parameters in the Lennard-Jones model have been chosen, the shape of the intermolecular potential is completely specified. Like the LJ model, most other continuous empirical models can be expressed in the general form

$$u(r) = \epsilon \Phi(r/\sigma), \qquad (5.12)$$

where the well depth multiplies the shape function Φ. We will see in Chapter 11 that such a functionality leads to a very important generalized method for property prediction. The LJ model contains the two scale parameters σ and ϵ in a nonparametric shape function. There are more complex models that contain shape parameters in addition to the two scale parameters. The addition of shape parameters provides parametric flexibility in the shape of the potential well itself for different fluids.

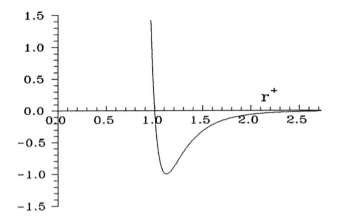

Figure 5.3 Lennard-Jones potential in dimensionless energy and distance coordinates.

A modified form of the Lennard-Jones potential is the exp-6 model

$$u(r) = Ae^{-Br} - \frac{C}{r^6} = \frac{\epsilon}{(1 - 6/\alpha)}\left\{\exp \alpha\left[\left(1 - \frac{r}{\sigma}\right)\right] - \left(\frac{\sigma}{r}\right)^6\right\}. \quad (5.13)$$

In addition to the two scaling parameters, this potential has a third parameter α which defines the steepness of the repulsive interaction. The Kihara potential (model f in Fig. 5.2) also has three parameters. It can also be written in the form of Equation (5.11) as

$$u = 4\epsilon\left[\left(\frac{1 - d'}{r/\sigma - d'}\right)^{12} - \left(\frac{1 - d'}{r/\sigma - d'}\right)^6\right], \quad (5.14)$$

where $d' = d/\sigma$. Physically this model is very similar to the Lennard-Jones model except that it contains a hard core inside the softer repulsive region that exists for $d < r < \sigma$.

Another three-parameter model which has one adjustable shape parameter is

$$u(r) = \epsilon\left[\frac{m}{n - m}\left(\frac{\sigma}{r}\right)^n - \frac{n}{n - m}\left(\frac{\sigma}{r}\right)^6\right], \quad (5.15)$$

where $n = 13.0 + \gamma(r/\sigma - 1)$. This model has been widely used for accurate representation of inert gas potential functions.

There are also models that include slightly more flexibility in the shape function at the expense of additional parameters and more complexity. For example the Hartree–Fock potential

Example 5.1   Plot the intermolecular potential and force between two Lennard-Jones molecules out to a separation of 10 Å for representations of argon and ethane molecules.

From Appendix 5.4, $\sigma_{Ar} = 3.428$ Å, $(\epsilon/k)_{Ar} = 121.85$ K, $\sigma_{C2H6} = 3.428$ Å, and $(\epsilon/k)_{C2H6} = 121.85$ K. These values can be used immediately in Equation (5.16) to obtain the potential curves shown in the figure.

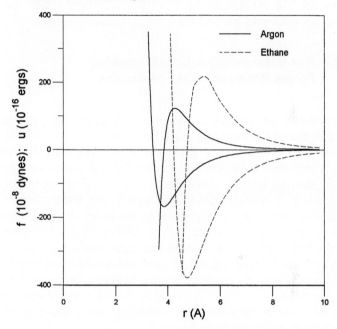

Any intermolecular potential can be differentiated with respect to separation distance in accordance with Equation (5.5) to obtain the intermolecular force. For the Lennard-Jones potential,

$$f = -\frac{du}{dr} = -\frac{24\epsilon}{r}\left[2\left(\frac{\sigma}{r}\right)^{12} - \left(\frac{\sigma}{r}\right)^{6}\right].$$

The force curves for the two model fluids obtained from this equation are also shown in the figure.

$$u(r) = A\exp\left(-\frac{\alpha r}{\sigma}\right) + F\left(\frac{c_6}{r^6} + \frac{C_8}{r^8} + \frac{C_{10}}{r^{10}}\right) \tag{5.16}$$

with the damping function

$$F = \left\{ \begin{array}{ll} \exp\left[-D\left(\dfrac{\sigma - r}{r}\right)^2 \right] & r \leq D\sigma \\ \\ 1 & r > D\sigma \end{array} \right\} \tag{5.17}$$

contains six shape parameters and can introduce a great deal of realism into the model. The penalty for this flexibility is of course the need for some way to regress the model parameters from experimental data.

5.2.2 Pair-Potential Models for Dispersion Forces Between Unlike Molecules

The situation for mixtures is complicated by the presence of cross-interactions. In addition to a potential function between like molecules *A-A* and *B-B,* one must also have a model for the unlike *A-B* interactions. For simplicity's sake, one would hope to be able to ascertain the *A-B* interactions from the *A-A* and *B-B,* then no mixture experimental data would be required. Yet, upon careful reflection, it appears unlikely that there is any information in the pure-component interactions that predicts how unlike molecules will interact. There seems to be no accurate, general way to predict cross-terms from like-like interactions. Nevertheless, approximate empirical *combining rules* for the pure potentials have been devised as ad hoc estimates for the cross-terms. These are used when approximations are required sans mixture information. Generally the combining rules are based on the assumption that the potential due to dispersion forces between unlike molecules lies somewhere intermediate to those of the pure components as illustrated in Figure 5.4.

An exact combining rule has been obtained only for the hard-sphere model. Because the molecules are hard spheres, the distance between centers of unlike molecules at contact is given by

$$\sigma_{12} = \frac{1}{2}(\sigma_1 + \sigma_2) \quad \text{(hard spheres)} \tag{5.18}$$

as shown in Figure 5.5. Because of the rigorous base for σ_{12} in the hard-sphere model, the same combining rule for σ is usually retained for other models. One should realize, however, that the combining rule is no longer rigorous when applied to more complex models and polyatomic species. In many of the above models, there is a rather steep repulsive core with a thin, softer region of repulsion outside that core. While σ is still spoken of as a molecular diameter in these models, it is really only a parameter in the potential model because there is no clear physical boundary of the molecule. Thus, one should remember that σ describes a distance in terms of a field, not a distinct physical boundary of mass in these models.

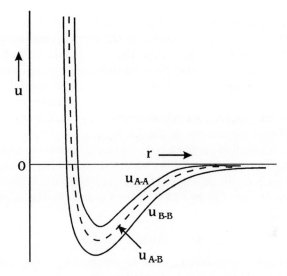

Figure 5.4 Expected relationship between like and unlike molecular interactions.

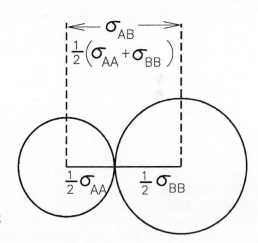

Figure 5.5 Hard-sphere combining rule for σ.

The most popular combining rule for the Lennard-Jones potential is that due to Lorentz and Berthelot (LB),

$$\sigma_{12} = \frac{1}{2}(\sigma_1 + \sigma_2) \quad \text{and} \quad \epsilon_{12} = \sqrt{\epsilon_1 \epsilon_2}. \qquad (5.19)$$

Theoretical calculations indicate that the geometric combining rule for ϵ expressed in this equation is appropriate when the unlike molecules are about the same size and have about the same ionization potential. This is generally not true, and the LB combining rule serves only as a first guess for the cross-interactions. While it is fairly common to see the LB combining rule used in the literature to calculate mixture properties, one would do well to remember that actual cross-interactions may be quite different, perhaps even outside the domain bracketed by the two pure fluids.[5] You should be careful not to attribute deviations between mixture predictions which use Equation (5.19) and experimental data to the potential model itself when in fact the LB combining rule may account for the biggest part of the discrepancy. Better accuracy is obtained when the cross-interaction parameters σ_{12} and ϵ_{12} are treated as adjustable parameters. Generally the approximation for ϵ_{12} is worse than that for σ_{12}, so one may want to only treat ϵ_{12} as an adjustable parameter. Equivalently, an adjustable parameter close to zero can be added to the Lorentz–Berthelot combining rule for ϵ

$$\epsilon_{12} = \sqrt{\epsilon_1 \epsilon_2} \left(1 - k_{12}\right), \tag{5.20}$$

where the adjustable parameter k_{12} must be obtained by fitting property predictions using the model to experimental data.

The combining rules for ϵ and σ used in three-parameter models, such as the Kihara potential, are generally the same as those used for the Lennard-Jones model. The combining rule for d is often analogous to that used for σ,

$$d_{12} = \frac{1}{2}(d_1 + d_2). \tag{5.21}$$

For lack of better information, combining rules for additional parameters are often taken as arithmetic averages.

Again we emphasize that combining rules are not necessary in calculating thermophysical properties. For example, to use the LJ potential for unlike interactions, one must simply have the unlike pair parameters σ_{ij} and ϵ_{ij}. These can be obtained in exactly the same way as the like interactions σ_{ii} and ϵ_{ii}, except that some mixture data must be used to regress values for the cross-interactions. As there is nothing inherent in the pure-component interaction parameters that infers anything about the cross-interactions, this is by far the safest mode in which to make mixture calculations. On the other hand, the possibility of predicting mixture properties from pure-component data provides considerable incentive toward continual development of approximate combining rules. Properties predicted using empirical combining rules on effective, spherical-potential parameters are particularly inaccurate when the molecules have nonspherical shapes.

5.3 DIRECT ELECTROSTATIC INTERACTIONS

Charge separation in molecules results in local positive and negative regions of the molecule. These localized partial charges can then interact with other molecules creating temporary charge separations in them. This may occur even in unpolarized molecules. Polar molecules have permanent, but partial, charge separations usually written in terms of moments. An ion has a complete charge separation and can be viewed as a zero-order moment, or monopole, with respect to the charge distribution within the molecule, q_i, since the net charge is given by

$$q = \sum_i q_i .$$ (5.22)

Water molecules are dipolar. Although a water molecule is neutral, one end is slightly positive, the other slightly negative owing to the difference in hydrogen and oxygen electronegativities. This is pictorially represented in Figure 5.6. As shown in this schematic, dipole moments are vectors having both magnitude and orientation. They may be represented by a vector $\mathbf{\mu}$ extending from the center of negative charge to the center of positive charge. If these two centers coincide, the dipole moment is zero. The dipole vector is the first moment of the charge distribution. The x component is given by

$$\mu_x = \sum_i q_i x_i ,$$ (5.23)

and similar relations can be written for the y and z components.

Carbon dioxide has neither a zeroth nor a first moment of charge distribution, but it does have a nonzero second moment. Although it is neutral and has no dipole moment, it is *quadrupolar*. In the case of CO_2, the charge separation is such that the four regions of partial charge spatially cancel to eliminate any dipole moment. This is viewed pictorially as two mutually compensating dipoles in Figure 5.7. In general, the molecules have quadrupole moments when there are four regions of partial charge separation. This does not mean that the molecule doesn't also have lower order moments. For example, HCl is one of the simplest dipolar substances with a dipole moment of 1.08 D (10^{-18} erg$^{1/2}$ cm$^{3/2}$) and a sizeable quadrupole moment of 3.8×10^{-26} erg$^{1/2}$·cm$^{5/2}$. The quadrupole moment is a tensor with coordinates xy given by

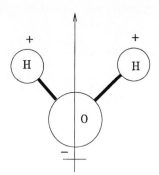

Figure 5.6 Partial charge separation in H_2O molecule creates dipole.

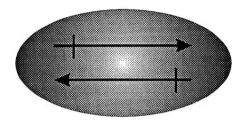

Figure 5.7 Schematically, two compensating dipoles constitute a quadrupole.

$$Q_{xy} = \sum q_i x_i y_i . \tag{5.24}$$

Higher moments are also found in real molecules. Multipole moments with localized charges of 2^n ($n = 0, 1, 2, 3 \ldots$) are all possible. A few illustrations are shown in Figure 5.8 for $n = 0$, 1, 2, and 3 (octopole). All of these moments in the molecule affect the properties of the fluid. For example, HCl remains a liquid over 166 K temperature range because of the dipole and quadrupole moments. There is a tendency to focus on the lower moments of a molecule, but higher order moments can have considerable influence on the intermolecular interactions.

Some confusion arises when we talk about polar and nonpolar molecules. Often the distinction between these two groups is made based on the magnitude of the dipole moment regardless of whether higher order moments exist or not. It is perhaps equally correct to use the term *polar* for molecules with a nonzero dipole moment or for molecules with some nonzero moment. Where the distinction is important, we intend the latter meaning.

In addition to permanent charge separations within a molecule, partial charge separation can be induced by the presence of a neighboring polar molecule. A dipole can distort or polarize the electron cloud of even a nonpolar neighbor molecule from its normal configuration. A molecule's propensity for this type of polarization is characterized by the scalar polarizability factor, α.

As we have seen, multipolar moments are vectors and tensors. Spatial orientation is important in determining multipole and polarization interactions. The complexity of even a pair potential becomes quite unwieldy as the number of

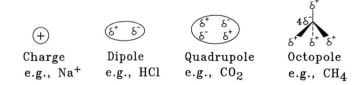

| Charge | Dipole | Quadrupole | Octopole |
| e.g., Na^+ | e.g., HCl | e.g., CO_2 | e.g., CH_4 |

Figure 5.8 Representation of the lowest nonzero moment in some multipole molecules.

separated charges increases. To illustrate this, consider the case of dipole–dipole, dipole–quadrupole, and quadrupole–quadrupole interactions between two linear molecules. Figure 5.9 depicts this situation and serves to define the angles necessary to describe the interactions. The intermolecular separation is assumed here to be large relative to interatomic distances (bond lengths) so that r can be taken as the separation of the molecular centers of mass. In terms of the angles defined in this figure, the electrostatic portion of the pair potential can be written as

$$u_{AB} = \frac{\mu_A \mu_B}{r^3} f_1(\theta_A, \theta_B, \phi) + \frac{\mu_A Q_B}{r^4} f_2(\theta_A, \theta_B, \phi)$$
$$- \frac{\mu_B Q_A}{r^4} f_2(\theta_B, \theta_A, \phi) + \frac{Q_A Q_B}{r^5} f_3(\theta_A, \theta_B, \phi) \,, \tag{5.25}$$

where the angle dependencies of the interaction energies are given by

$$f_1(\theta_A, \theta_B, \phi) = \sin\theta_A \sin\theta_B \cos\phi - 2\cos\theta_A \cos\theta_B \tag{5.26}$$

$$f_2(\theta_A, \theta_B, \phi) = \frac{3}{2} [\cos\theta_A (3\cos^2\theta_B - 1) - 2\sin\theta_A \sin\theta_B \cos\theta_B \cos\phi] \tag{5.27}$$

$$f_3(\theta_A, \theta_B, \phi) = \frac{3}{4} [1 - 5\cos^2\theta_A - 5\cos^2\theta_B - 15\cos^2\theta_A \cos^2\theta_B \tag{5.28}$$
$$+ 2(4\cos\theta_A \cos\theta_B - \sin\theta_A \sin\theta_B \cos\phi)^2] \,.$$

The angle dependence of these interactions is obviously very important. Consider for example f_1. If the dipoles are aligned such that $\phi = 0$ and $\theta_A = 0 = \theta_B$, then $f_1 = 1$. If instead $\theta_A = 0$ and $\theta_B = \pi$, then $f_1 = -1$. Finally, if

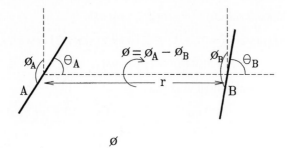

Figure 5.9 Definition of the angles used to describe the interactions between two linear molecules.

$\theta_A = 0$ and $\theta_B = 1/2\pi$, then $f_1 = 0$. The importance of orientation is further illustrated in Example 5.2.

It is usually quite complicated to develop the total potential between molecules with oriented interactions. However, one can simplify the process by averaging the vector dipole and tensor quadrupole moments over all angles between the pair of interacting molecules. This produces an effective, spherically symmetric dipole and quadrupole interaction. If all angles of the dipole–dipole interaction were equally weighted in this averaging process, the net dipole and quadrupole interactions would be zero. This is clearly not appropriate. Instead, ensemble averages are computed using Boltzmann weighting factors for each angle. Orientations that are energetically more favorable are thus weighted more heavily than those that are repulsive in nature. For instance, the $\uparrow \downarrow$ configuration of Example 5.2 is considerably more favored than the $\uparrow \uparrow$ configuration at higher densities and would receive a correspondingly higher weight. This averaging procedure rapidly becomes mathematically complex as the structural complexity of the molecules increases. We list here only the final results for linear molecules. Even in this case, the mathematical details become somewhat messy. We summarize here only the final results, but the derivations are available elsewhere.[6,7] The angle-averaged potentials for linear molecules can be written as

---

Example 5.2 Compute the electrostatic portion of the pair potential for two HCl molecules as a function of separation distance of the centers of mass. Plot the functionality for two orientations, one in which the dipole moments are aligned parallel and one in which they are antiparallel. The dipole moment of HCl is 1.08 D and the quadrupole moment is 3.8×10^{-26} erg$^{1/2}$·cm$^{5/2}$.

Let $\uparrow$ represent the dipole moment of the HCl molecule along the molecular axis. The head of the arrow represents the partial positive charge on the H atom while the tail represents the partial negative charge on the Cl atom. In this notation, the two requested configurations can be schematically represented by $\uparrow \uparrow$ and $\uparrow \downarrow$.

For the parallel configuration, $\uparrow \uparrow$, the angles defined in Figure 5.10 are $\theta_A = \pi/2 = \theta_B$ and $\phi = 0$. Using these values in Equations (5.26)–(5.28), we find

$$f_1 = \sin(\pi/2) \sin(\pi/2) \cos(0) - 2 \cos(\pi/2) \cos(\pi/2) = 1$$

$$f_2 = 3/2\{\cos(\pi/2) [3 \cos^2(\pi/2) - 1] - 2 \sin(\pi/2) \sin(\pi/2) \cos(0)\} = 0$$

$$f_3 = 3/4[1 - 0 - 0 - 0 + (2)(4 \cdot 0 - 1)^2] = 9/4 .$$

Equation (5.25) can then be used to obtain

$$u_{AB} = \frac{\left(1.08 \times 10^{-18} \text{ erg}^{1/2}\text{cm}^{3/2}\right)^2}{r^3} + \frac{9}{4} \frac{\left(3.8 \times 10^{-26} \text{ erg}^{1/2}\text{cm}^{5/2}\right)^2}{r^5} ,$$

which is plotted in the figure.

The antiparallel configuration, $\uparrow \downarrow$, is characterized by $\theta_A = \pi/2$, $\theta_B = 3\pi/2$, and $\phi = 0$. Equations (5.26)–(5.28) yield $f_1 = -1$, $f_{2,} = 0$, and $f_3 = 9/4$ for this

Example 5.2   Continued

case. The electrostatic portion of the pair potential for ↑ ↓ is therefore

$$u_{AB} = -\frac{\left(1.08 \times 10^{-18}\ \text{erg}^{1/2}\text{cm}^{3/2}\right)^2}{r^3} + \frac{9}{4}\frac{\left(3.8 \times 10^{-26}\ \text{erg}^{1/2}\text{cm}^{5/2}\right)^2}{r^5}.$$

This function is also plotted in the figure. Note the difference between the two potentials. In particular, the potential is everywhere repulsive for ↑ ↑ and everywhere attractive for ↑ ↓.

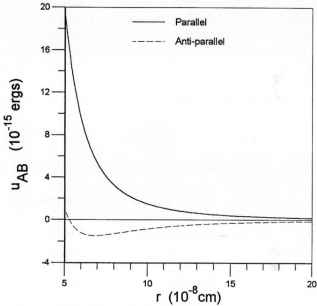

$$<u^{qq}>_{\text{ang}} = \frac{q_a q_b}{r} \quad \text{(charge–charge interactions)} \tag{5.29}$$

$$<u^{\mu\mu}>_{\text{ang}} = -\frac{1}{3kT}\cdot\frac{\mu_a^2\mu_b^2}{r^6} \quad \text{(dipole–dipole interactions)} \tag{5.30}$$

$$<u^{\mu\alpha}>_{\text{ang}} = -\frac{\mu_a^2\alpha_b + \mu_b^2\alpha_a}{r^6} \quad \text{(dipole–polarization interactions)} \tag{5.31}$$

$$<u^{\mu Q}>_{\text{ang}} = -\frac{1}{kT}\frac{[\mu_a^2\,Q_b^2 + \mu_b^2\,Q_a^2]}{r^8} \quad \text{(dipole–quadrupole interactions)} \tag{5.32}$$

$$<u^{QQ}>_{\text{ang}} = -\frac{14}{5kT}\frac{Q_a^2\,Q_b^2}{r^{10}}\,, \qquad \text{(quadrupole–quadrupole interactions)} \qquad (5.33)$$

where μ_a is the scalar value of the dipole moment for molecule a and Q_a is the scalar quadrupole moment. Values for μ_a and Q_a are listed in Appendix 5 for selected molecules.

We will use the angle-averaged equations for problems done in this text. Simplicity in calculating properties is the primary justification for such a procedure, but simplicity is justification enough. When done appropriately (with the appropriate ensemble weighting for the various interaction orientations), the angle-averaged pair-energy does yield the correct configuration integral, and the true pair potential function $u(r, \theta_a, \theta_b, \phi)$ can be replaced in the configurational integral with the angle-averaged potential function $<u>_{\text{ang}}$ which is only a function of intermolecular separation r. Thus Equation (5.2) can be written as

$$Z = \int \ldots \int e^{-\beta<U>\text{ang}}\, \mathbf{d}r^N = \int \ldots \int e^{-\beta\Sigma<u>\text{ang}}\, \mathbf{d}r^N \qquad (5.34)$$

under the assumption of correct angle averaging and pairwise additivity. Because of the consistency in form between Equations (5.2) and (5.34), we will drop the $<\ >_{\text{ang}}$ notation. This should not lead to confusion since the same results are obtained when either the true potential is substituted into the equation and integrated over all angles, or the angle-averaged potential is used and integrated over all positions.

5.4 TOTAL INTERMOLECULAR POTENTIAL ENERGY

We have grouped the repulsive forces of electron cloud overlap with the dispersion forces in pair potential models and simply called them dispersion-force models. (Strictly speaking, the repulsive forces are not part of the dispersion forces.) We have also looked at direct electrostatic forces, both permanent and induced electrostatic forces, and have grouped them together. The total spherical pair potential necessary for Equation (5.34) is then found by adding together the electrostatic and dispersion potentials:

$$u_{ij} = u_{ij}^{\text{disp}} + u_{ij}^{\text{el}}\,. \qquad (5.35)$$

All potential terms involved in the interaction between two specific molecules must therefore be summed into the total pair potential for use in the configurational partition function. Alternatively, one can use each of the individual potentials to calculate the configurational partition function and the corresponding properties for each potential. The contributions from the various kinds of interaction can then be identified or summed to give the total property. Example 5.3 illustrates the relative significance of the various dispersion and electrostatic potentials in the total potential for the case of HCl.

As mentioned earlier in this chapter, there are additional potentials that one must consider when dealing with specific classes of molecules. *Association* occurs when attractions are sufficiently strong that some empirical evidence of the formation of a new molecular species exists. For example, absorption peaks in the IR or UV spectrum for a pair of molecules that are not present for an isolated molecule indicate that association occurs. In terms of interaction strength, associations involve energies on the order of 10^{-13} erg per pair while

---

Example 5.3   Use the angle-averaged formulas of Equations (5.29)–(5.33) and the potential parameters of Appendix 5 to compute and display the various contributions to the total pair potential for two HCl molecules at 300 K.

From Appendix 5, we have LJ parameters and electrostatic constants of $\sigma^{\circ} = 3.458$ Å, $\epsilon^{\circ}/k = 274.6$ K, $\mu = 1.08$ D, $\alpha = 2.63$ Å^3, and $Q = 3.8 \times 10^{-26}$ erg$^{1/2}$cm$^{5/2}$ for HCl. The individual contributions to the total pair potential are then readily obtained from the equations mentioned above:

dispersion:

$$u^{\mathrm{d}} = 4\epsilon^{\circ}\left[\left(\frac{\sigma^{\circ}}{r}\right)^{12} - \left(\frac{\sigma^{\circ}}{r}\right)^{6}\right] = 1.517 \times 10^{-13} \text{ erg}\left[\left(\frac{\sigma^{\circ}}{r}\right)^{12} - \left(\frac{\sigma^{\circ}}{r}\right)^{6}\right]$$

qq:

$$u^{qq} = 0$$

μμ:

$$u^{\mu\mu} = -\frac{1}{3kT}\frac{\mu^4}{r^6} = -\frac{1.094 \times 10^{-59} \text{ erg}\cdot\text{cm}^6}{r^6}$$

μα:

$$u^{\mu\alpha} = -\frac{2\mu^2\alpha}{r^6} = -\frac{6.135 \times 10^{-60} \text{ erg}\cdot\text{cm}^6}{r^6}$$

μQ:

$$u^{\mu Q} = -\frac{2}{kT}\left(\frac{\mu Q}{r^4}\right)^2 = -\frac{8.133 \times 10^{-74} \text{ erg}\cdot\text{cm}^8}{r^8}$$

QQ:

$$u^{QQ} = -\frac{14}{5kT}\frac{Q^4}{r^{10}} = -\frac{1.41 \times 10^{-88} \text{ erg}\cdot\text{cm}^{10}}{r^{10}}$$

Example 5.3 Continued

These contributions and the total potential are shown on the following plot.

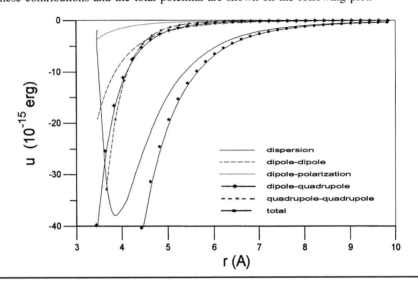

chemical bonds and dispersion energies are on the order of 10^{-12} erg and 10^{-14} erg per pair, respectively. Associations can be made and broken by physical processes rather than chemical, and in this sense resemble the physical attractions of electrostatic and dispersion forces more than chemical bonding. Nevertheless, such distinctions are sometimes difficult to make because associations really fill in a continuum of energies that range from physical to chemical attractions. Hydrogen bonding is a common example of such associations. Likewise, charge-transfer complexes fall into this category. Because of the specific orientational nature of these interactions and their dependence upon particular atoms within the molecule, spherically symmetric approximations and angle averaging do not work well in modeling them. They can be treated by the addition of a particular oriented force model added to the previous model. Calculations of the thermo-physical properties can then be done using molecular dynamics simulations[8] or using Wertheim's theory.[9] For example, the interaction between two molecules capable of forming hydrogen bonds might be represented by the model

$$u = u^{LJ}(r) + u^{assoc}(r, \theta_{A1}, \theta_{B2}) ,$$

where u^{LJ} is the Lennard-Jones potential acting between the centers of the molecules and u^{assoc} is the association interaction. This latter term is a function of the relative orientation angles between the molecules as defined in Figure 5.10. One might choose another simple potential model to represent the association interactions. For example, a simple anisotropic square-well model,

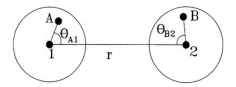

Figure 5.10 Association model between attractive site A on molecule 1 and site B on molecule 2.

$$u^{\text{assoc}} = \begin{bmatrix} -\epsilon_{AB}, & \text{for } r < r_c, \, \theta_{A1} < \theta_c, \, \theta_{B2} < \theta_c \\ 0, & \text{otherwise} \end{bmatrix},$$

has been used quite effectively.[8] The attractive association potential in this case "turns on" only when the relative angles between the attractive sites are within a certain critical angle θ_c. Treating associations in this manner is an example of using multiple interaction sites, an important technique which we will discuss further in the discussion below on polyatomic molecules. Associations can also be treated by using a full quantum mechanical potential to describe the potential in three-dimensional space.

Before further discussing polyatomic molecules, we note that the electrostatic interaction potentials that we have listed in this chapter all assume point location of the partial charges when in actuality the charge is a distribution. This causes a problem only when r is less than the outer edge of the charge distribution. We do not know the form of the potential for values of r less than this outer edge and can not therefore integrate with respect to r to obtain the configurational partition function. This is often not a problem. In fact, we usually regress the interaction parameters from experimental data, a procedure which hides this slight complication by using "effective" parameters. This can be seen by using the case of a dipolar Lennard-Jones fluid. Because Equations (5.30) and (5.31) have the same spatial dependence as the attractive term in the LJ potential, r^{-6}, a convenient factorization occurs when they are combined with the LJ potential. If ϵ° and σ° are the values of the LJ potential for the nonpolar, dispersion forces, then Equation (5.35) becomes

$$u_{ab} = 4\epsilon_{ab}^{\circ}\left[\left(\frac{\sigma_{ab}^{\circ}}{r}\right)^{12} - \left(\frac{\sigma_{ab}^{\circ}}{r}\right)^{6}\right] - \frac{1}{r^6}\left(\frac{\mu_a^2\mu_b^2}{3kT} + \mu_a^2\alpha_b + \mu_b^2\alpha_a\right), \quad (5.36)$$

which can be rewritten in the same form as the original LJ potential

$$u_{ab} = 4\epsilon_{ab}\left[\left(\frac{\sigma_{ab}}{r}\right)^{12} - \left(\frac{\sigma_{ab}}{r}\right)^{6}\right], \quad (5.37)$$

but now the ϵ and σ values contain polar information in the form

$$\epsilon = \epsilon^{\circ} F^2 \quad \text{and} \quad \sigma = \sigma^{\circ} F^{-1/6} \quad (5.38)$$

with

$$F = 1 + \frac{\frac{1}{3}\beta\mu_a^2\mu_b^2 + \mu_a^2\alpha_b + \mu_b^2\alpha_a}{4\epsilon^\circ\,(\sigma^\circ)^6}. \tag{5.39}$$

In this form, electrostatic contributions to the pair potential pose no additional problems in obtaining thermodynamic properties. If thermodynamic properties can be obtained for the LJ fluid, then the same equations and functionalities apply for polar and/or polarizable fluids, although the LJ parameters are no longer purely dispersion parameters but effective potential parameters containing the polar effects. In fact, because the shape function Φ in Equation (5.12) is the same in Equation (5.37) as for a nonpolar LJ fluid, corresponding states can be applied to this model of polar fluids using correlations developed for nonpolar fluids. We will elaborate on this point in Chapter 11.

   In simulations, where the relative orientations of the molecules are known (i.e., molecular dynamics simulations), we do not have to use an angle-averaged value of the dipole potential. In this case the pair potential is given by[10]

$$u = -\frac{\mu^2}{r^3}\left[\frac{3(e_1 \cdot r)(e_2 \cdot r)}{r^2} - e_1 \cdot e_2\right], \tag{5.40}$$

where e_i is the unit vector along the direction of the dipole moment in molecule i, r is the vector between the dipole centers, and μ is the scalar dipole moment.

   Note that when the full orientational implementation of dipole–dipole interactions is used, the potential is independent of temperature. This of course must be true for conservative systems for which $u = u(r)$. In the angle-averaged implementation, Equation (5.30) has an inverse temperature dependence introduced through the Boltzmann weighting factor. This makes the potential dependent upon the particle velocities through the temperature and the mechanics of the system are nonconservative. One should therefore not use the angle-averaged relations in molecular dynamics simulations (Chapter 8) based on the microcanonical or NVE ensemble.

5.5 POTENTIALS OF POLYATOMIC MOLECULES

Most molecules are not spherical. Molecules of practical interest are generally polyatomic and the potential is not spherically isotropic. Several approaches can be taken to calculate the thermophysical properties of real, polyatomic fluids.

   The most accurate method of dealing with real fluids is also, unfortunately, the most difficult. In this approach, one uses the actual molecular interaction potential parameterized in three-dimensional space. Generally one uses ab initio quantum mechanics calculations to generate the required data in three-dimensional space. These values can then be used directly in a molecular dynamics simulation or regressed using complex models with many parameters. Of course, obtaining the intermolecular potential is just the beginning of property calculation; the configurational partition function must still be calculated. This may be quite difficult to do analytically, and molecular dynamics is a more practical approach. With current technology, it is now possible to start with quantum mechanics, do the ab initio calculations, and feed that information directly to a molecular dynamics program to calculate thermophysical properties. Indeed, some commercial software is now available that handles this process for some molecules. This will probably become a more common approach as software development continues and computer speeds increase.

The second approach uses multiple interaction sites to model the full molecular potential. It is currently very popular because of the simplicity of the models that can be used for each interaction site, the general compatibility with codes developed for spherical potentials, and the accuracy that can be obtained. Basically, one constructs the more complex potential of the polyatomic molecule using simpler potential models, such as the previously mentioned spherical models, placed at strategic sites on the molecule. A simple illustration of constant potential lines in two dimensions obtained from a two-site model is shown in Figure 5.11. The sites can be located at atomic centers, but need not be. For example, benzene has been modeled with six equivalent CH sites located at the carbon centers, six equivalent CH sites located equidistant between C and H centers, and 12 sites (six H sites and six C sites) located at atomic centers.[11] All three of these models produced about the same thermophysical property predictions. The net effect of the multicenter site method is replacement of a single, complex, anisotropic potential function with multiple, simple, isotropic

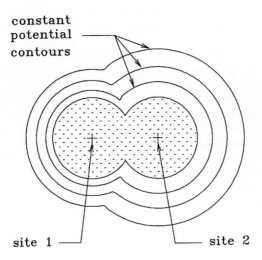

Figure 5.11   The use of site–site spherical potentials to model asymmetric potential functions.

sites within the molecule, as illustrated in Example 5.4. The convenience of using simple models for the sites is somewhat diminished by an increase in the number of interactions that must be computed to obtain the total intermolecular potential. Because we now deal with site–site interactions rather than molecule–molecule interactions, the summation in Equation (5.7) must run over all pairs of sites rather than pairs of molecules. Each site in the molecule interacts with all sites in all the other molecules as illustrated in Figure 5.12. Consider then a molecular dynamics simulation that uses a six-site model for each of 500 benzene molecules. Now instead of 500^2 (250 thousand) pair interactions, there are 3000^2 (9 million) interactions at each time step. We shall see in Chapter 8 that there are ways to reduce this number significantly, but the point is the same: the simplicity of site–site potential models is bought partially at the expense of larger numbers of interactions. Appendix 5 contains a table of site–site model potential parameters.

Example 5.4   Consider a three-site model for propane. Each of the $-CH_2$ and $-CH_3$ groups are to be represented by a square-well potential model with the distance parameters $\sigma = 2.9$ Å and $g = 1.79$. The bond lengths are 1.53 Å and the bond angle is 109°. Draw a schematic figure for the model by drawing the two lines of constant potential where the attraction and repulsion begin.

In the square-well potential, σ is the distance of closest approach between two molecules, each molecule contributing $\sigma/2$. For this three-site model, an infinite repulsion potential occurs at distances less than $\sigma/2$ from each site. The attractive well begins a distance $g\sigma/2$ from each site. We can construct the molecule by placing the three sites a distance 1.53 Å from each other such that they form an angle of 109°. We can then draw circles of radius 1.45 Å ($\sigma/2$) around each site. When we erase the regions interior to the intersection of the circles, we have a contour for the hard-sphere repulsive part of the potential.

Similarly, we can draw a circle of radius 2.6 Å ($g\sigma/2$) around each site and erase the region interior to the overlap of the circles to find the contour for the edge of the attractive well for the molecule as a whole. The results are shown as the solid lines of the figure.

It is interesting to overlay on the same figure the potential contours for a spherical square-well potential applied to the whole molecule. We use the values $\sigma = 4.316$ Å and $g = 1.46$ from Appendix 5 to draw in the spherical potential contours shown with dashed lines in the figure.

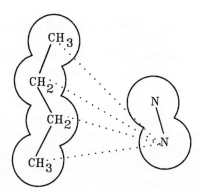

Figure 5.12 Site–site interactions between one of the two sites of a N_2 molecule and the sites of a four-site model for n-butane.

   The easiest method of calculating properties of polyatomic molecules is to assume a spherically averaged potential for the molecule. That is, one assumes that the simple spherical potential models of Figure 5.2 are adequate to describe the interactions between the molecules if spatially averaged or "effective" parameters are used in the model. Of course, to apply the method, you do not actually perform the spatial average, you simply assume that the spherical potential model applies to the molecule and regress the effective parameters from experimental data.

   There is considerable loss of fundamental information when this is done. If an exact potential model is available, all properties can be calculated from a particular set of potential parameters. Moreover, the same potential parameters can be used at virtually all conditions for any phase. When a spherical potential model is used instead, the parameters may influence various properties differently. Normally, effective parameters are obtained by fitting the model's predictions to experimental data. Deficient or incomplete representation of the potential by the model is often manifest in poor predictions of properties other than those from which the parameters were obtained. Worse yet, the effective parameters become state dependent and can only be used to calculate values over a small range of conditions, even for the property from which the parameters were regressed. This is not to say that spherical potential models should not be used to compute thermophysical properties of polyatomic molecules. Indeed, most polyatomic potentials can be idealized as a base spherical portion plus orientation-specific perturbation terms, and the spherical base term is often the most significant in thermophysical property prediction. A spherical model may therefore provide reasonably good engineering data, predictions from which trends can be analyzed, approximate predictions at new conditions, and approximate properties for new fluids. One should simply realize the limitations of the model and the predictions obtained from them. Additionally, the simplicity of spherical potential models permits closed-form, sometimes analytical, descriptions of properties, while retaining the essence of the interactions. Appendix 5 contains some effective potential parameters regressed from selected properties for the models shown in Figure 5.2.

In addition to intermolecular interactions, polyatomic molecules also have intramolecular interactions. We have already discussed in Chapter 3 how to handle intramolecular rotations, and Appendix 3 contains constants for a few molecules. Bond distances within a molecule are generally shorter than σ. Therefore, one does not include dispersion interactions between bonding neighbors when using the site–site approach. However, one does include intramolecular dispersion interactions between sites on the same molecule for distances larger than σ_{ij}. These are in addition to the intramolecular potential model. Inclusion of intermolecular interactions permits accurate modeling of molecular configurations and increases the accuracy of the predicted properties.[12]

5.6 CONFIGURATIONAL PARTITION FUNCTION APPROACH

Equations (5.1) through (5.3) form the basis for calculation of thermodynamic properties from the canonical partition function. Thermodynamic properties are often expressed as departure or residual functions, values of the property for the actual system minus that for the ideal gas at some fixed reference condition. If the reference condition is chosen as the same temperature and volume as the real system, departure functions are obtained directly from the configurational partition function. The departure function at constant T and V for the Helmholtz free energy is

$$\frac{(A^* - A)}{kT} = -\ln Q^* + \ln Q = \ln\frac{Q}{Q^*}, \qquad (5.41)$$

where the superscript * indicates the ideal-gas value at the system T and V. Other departure functions can be readily derived from Equation (5.41) using standard thermodynamic identities. The ratio Q/Q^* is found from Equation (5.1) to be

$$\frac{Q(N,V,T)}{Q^*(N,V,T)} = \frac{Z}{V^N}. \qquad (5.42)$$

It is apparent from Equation (5.42) that the nonidealities expressed as a departure function in Equation (5.41) are all contained in the configurational partition function. Ideal-gas properties can be computed as in Chapter 3; we only need to learn to evaluate Z to obtain the complete thermodynamic description of real systems. This is done using Equations (5.2) and (5.7) in conjunction with an appropriate pair-potential model.

Configurational properties, represented by J_c, in Equation (5.3) may be computed using the same relationships between J and $\ln Q$ expressed in Table 2.1. For example,

$$P_c = kT\left(\frac{\partial \ln Z}{\partial V}\right)_{T,N}$$ (5.43)

and

$$A_c = -kT\ln Z .$$ (5.44)

The relationship between the departure functions commonly used in thermodynamics and the configurational functions is obvious from Equation (5.42). The difference between the real and ideal configuration functions is the departure function:

$$J^r = J_c - J_c^* .$$ (5.45)

The configurational approach to calculating thermodynamic properties is thus based on the following assumptions:

1. Validity of the semiclassical partition function
2. Independence of the various energy modes
3. Independence of internal modes on density
4. Validity of factorization of Q^{int} into $(q^{int})^N$

5.7 PAIR CORRELATION FUNCTION APPROACH

The configurational integral contains information about the loci of molecules and their interactions within the system. The same information can be reexpressed in terms that provide physically meaningful information about the structure of the fluid. This provides an equivalent but alternative path to the thermodynamic properties. This latter method, the pair correlation method, involves the probability of finding pairs of molecules a particular distance from each other. Either method is fraught with the difficulties attendant with $3N$ integrations over a complicated function of molecular positions, but there are conveniences obtained in using the pair correlation method. We will not derive the basic equations associated with this approach.

The probability of finding molecule 1 at r_1 in volume element dr_1, molecule 2 at r_2 in volume element dr_2, and so forth, is the joint probability,

$$\rho^{(N)}(r_1, r_2 \ldots r_N) \, dr_1 \, dr_2 \ldots dr_N = \frac{e^{-\beta U} \, dr_1 \, dr_2 \ldots dr_N}{Z}, \tag{5.46}$$

where r_i is the vector position of molecule i consisting of the three components q_{1i}, q_{2i}, and q_{3i}. Recall from Chapter 1 that we can find the joint probability for h of N particles being located at positions $r_1, r_2 \ldots r_h$, independent of the positions of the other N-h particles, by integrating Equation (5.46) over all possible positions for the N-h particles. Thus the probability density function for h of N particles located at positions 1 through h, respectively, independent of the positions of the other N-h particles, is given by

$$\rho^{(h)}(r_1, r_2 \ldots r_h) = \frac{\int\limits_{h+1} \ldots \int\limits_{N} e^{-\beta U} \, dr_{h+1} \, dr_{h+2} \ldots dr_N}{Z}. \tag{5.47}$$

If the particles are indistinguishable, then the joint probability density function for *some* particle located at position 1, another at 2, and on through position h (not necessarily 1 at r_1, 2 at r_2, and on through h at r_h) independent of the positions of the other N-h particles is the physically important quantity. Equation (5.47) does not include the $_NP_{(N-h)}$ ways of arranging N *indistinguishable* particles h at a time. We must therefore multiply by this factor for indistinguishable particles, that is,

$$\rho^{(h)}(r_1, r_2 \ldots r_h) = \frac{N!}{(N-h)!} \frac{\int\limits_{h+1} \ldots \int\limits_{N} e^{-\beta U} \, dr_{h+1} \, dr_{h+2} \ldots dr_N}{Z}. \tag{5.48}$$

We mentioned earlier that pairwise additivity was usually used in the evaluation of the configurational integral. If three-body and higher order effects are ignored, only $\rho^{(1)}$ and $\rho^{(2)}$ need be evaluated. The singlet distribution function $\rho^{(1)}$ is the probability of finding a single particle at any given location irrespective of the other particle positions. The pair density function $\rho^{(2)}$ represents the probability of finding a second particle at a particular location relative to a given position of the first particle. $\rho^{(1)}$ is quite easily evaluated. Since we want the probability of finding a particle at a fixed location *independent* of the positions of the other particles, U cannot be a function of the positions of the other N-1 molecules. Thus,

$$\rho^{(1)} = \frac{N!}{Z(N-1)!} e^{-\beta U} \int\limits_{(N-1)} \ldots \int dr_2 \ldots dr_N = \frac{N}{\int dr_1} = \frac{N}{V} = \rho, \tag{5.49}$$

where ρ is the number density (not to be confused with the mass density). In simplifying Equation (5.49), the exponential term in Z is also independent of particle positions and cancels with the same term in the numerator. Likewise, N-1 integrals over position appear in both the numerator and in Z, and they therefore cancel. The equality $\rho^{(1)} = \rho$ physically implies that all locations are equally probable; the likelihood of finding a molecule at a particular position is just the number of molecules divided by the volume of the system.

It is difficult to evaluate $\rho^{(2)}$, but we do know that if the two particles are totally uncorrelated the exponential term factors from the integrals, and an analysis similar to that above for $\rho^{(1)}$ yields

$$\rho^{(2)} = \frac{N(N-1)}{V^2} \simeq \rho^2, \text{ (2 uncorrelated particles and large } N) \qquad (5.50)$$

where for large N, $N(N-1)$ is approximated as N^2. We can then define a very useful structural factor as the ratio of the actual pair distribution function to the uncorrelated value, namely,

$$g(\boldsymbol{r}_1, \boldsymbol{r}_2) = \frac{\rho^{(2)}}{\rho^2}. \qquad (5.51)$$

This ratio is called the pair correlation function (pcf). If two molecules interact with spherical potentials then g depends only on the distance between the two molecules, $|\boldsymbol{r}_1 - \boldsymbol{r}_2|$, and in this case g is called the radial distribution function (rdf). Spherically symmetrical potentials are used so often that the names are often used interchangeably, but the rdf is actually a subset of the more general pcf. The rdf tells us the *relative* structure of the fluid due to correlations between pairs of molecules. Physically, it corresponds to the probability (relative to the bulk number density) of finding a second molecule a distance r from the center of a molecule. If molecules are uncorrelated, $g = 1$, as can be easily seen from Equations (5.50) and (5.51). This means that the local number density is the same as the overall or bulk density; there is no effect upon the position of the second particle due to the presence of the first. If $g > 1$ then the presence of the first molecule enhances the probability of finding the second molecule in that region, while values less than one indicate a smaller than average probability of finding the second molecule in that region.

A typical rdf for the Lennard-Jones potential is shown in Figure 5.13. The characteristic peaks and valleys are easily explained. At distances closer than σ ($r < \sigma$), there is zero probability of finding a second molecule because of the infinite repulsion of the overlapping hard cores. At distances just further than σ, there is an attraction between the two molecules corresponding to the negative region in the potential well. At these distances there is a higher than normal (normal referring to the bulk number density) probability of finding the second molecule. Neighboring molecules that "fall" into this attractive well form a first coordination shell or cluster of nearest neighbors around the central molecule. The physical presence of the first coordination shell diminishes the probability of finding another molecule in the vicinity immediately outside this coordination shell. This effect continues to cause g to oscillate about unity, but each successive peak in a liquid would be considerably attenuated due to the

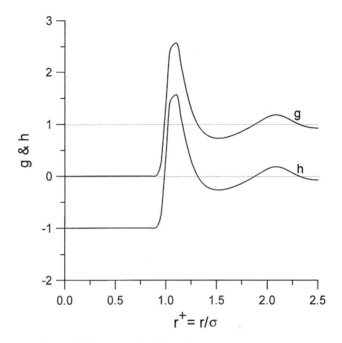

Figure 5.13   Typical rdf for Lennard-Jones potential.

more diffuse nature of each coordination shell. Eventually these correlations completely damp out and molecules quite far away are uncorrelated with the central molecule. Thus, g must become unity at large values of r.

The rdf for a crystalline solid would be considerably different than that of the fluid shown in Figure 5.13. Because molecules in the solid are at fixed, regular, or periodic intervals, the rdf would have sharp peaks at each lattice site and there would be very little attenuation of the peaks at larger distances. That is, all of the peaks would be approximately the same height. This is illustrated in Example 5.5.

Sometimes it is convenient to introduce a function known as the total correlation function, $h(r)$, defined in terms of $g(r)$ as

$$h(r) \equiv g(r) - 1. \tag{5.52}$$

Whereas $g(r)$ is a *relative* correlation function between two molecules separated by a distance r, $h(r)$ is an *absolute* correlation; whereas $g(r)$ represents the correlation relative to the bulk probability, $h(r)$ tracks the correlations relative to the isolated molecule. A typical behavior of $h(r)$ is also depicted in Figure 5.13.

As can be seen in Figure 5.13, effects due to dispersion forces are quite localized. Often g decays to unity in three to five molecular diameters. Long-

Example 5.5   Consider a face-center cubic crystal lattice of lattice spacing a in two dimensions for which only very small vibrations of the atoms about the lattice site occur. Construct $g(r)$ for this crystalline solid.

This is essentially an exercise in trigonometry. One simply needs to determine the relative locations of the lattice sites with respect to a selected particle. If we select the particle shown in the diagram as a solid circle, we can find the location of the first coordination shell by constructing a 45°–45°–90° triangle as shown. The second coordination shell is seen to be a distance of a from the central atom. Each consecutive coordination shell can be determined by using right triangles. For example, the third shell would be $a(2)^{0.5}$, and the fourth shell can be found from the hypotoneuse of a right triangle with sides $3a/2$ and $a/2$, or $(10)^{0.5}a/2$.

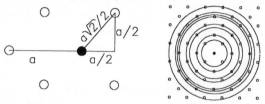

The radial distribution function $g(r)$ is then constructed from the distances of the coordination shells. The peaks will be spikes, only slightly broadened by the small vibrations. We cannot say much about the width or height of the peaks because we don't know anything about the size of the particles or the distances from the lattice sites that the vibrations will carry them. We do know that the smaller the particles and the more fixed are their positions, the narrower and taller the peaks. In the limit of point particles fixed at lattice sites, the peaks are infinite lines.

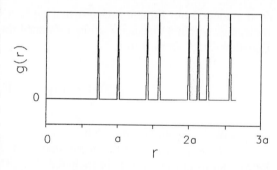

range interactions are important for ionic species and long-range correlations become important near the fluid critical point, but the correlation or structure of fluids is generally a short-ranged effect. Nevertheless, this correlation is the essence of the difficulty in calculating thermodynamic properties. Properties of fluids would actually be quite easy to compute were it not for these short-range correlations, and it is this local structure that determines the uniqueness of the thermodynamic properties for a particular fluid.

As mentioned, the same information is contained in the configurational partition function Z or the radial distribution function g, and the problem of thermodynamic property calculation can be formulated in terms of either one. Sometimes we can calculate properties directly from Z, but often we find it more convenient to formulate the problem in terms of g. In the next few pages, we derive the relationships between the thermodynamic properties and the local structure of the fluid in terms of $g(r)$.

The local, differential number of molecules in a shell a distance r from the center of a reference molecule is

$$dN_r = \rho g \, d\mathbf{r} = 4\pi \rho g r^2 \, dr , \tag{5.53}$$

where the second equality results from the conversion of the differential vector position of the molecule $d\mathbf{r}$ to the scalar distance of the shell dr using spherical coordinates; that is,

$$d\mathbf{r} = \int_0^{2\pi} \int_0^{\pi} r^2 \sin\theta \, d\theta \, d\phi \, dr = 4\pi r^2 \, dr . \tag{5.54}$$

It is evident from Equation (5.53) that ρg is a local density. The number of molecules within a distance r of the reference molecule is found by integrating Equation (5.53) from 0 to r,

$$N(r) = 4\pi\rho \int_0^r g r^2 \, dr . \tag{5.55}$$

This is illustrated in Example 5.6.

If the upper limit for the above integral is set to ∞, then all molecules of the system would necessarily be included (except for the reference molecule) and

$$4\pi\rho \int_0^\infty g r^2 \, dr = N - 1 \simeq N . \tag{5.56}$$

The configurational internal energy, U_c, is found from the relationship for U in Table 2.1, using Z in place of Q. Thus,

$$U_c = \frac{kT^2}{Z} \left(\frac{\partial Z}{\partial T} \right)_{N,V} = \frac{\int \cdots \int U e^{-\beta U} \, d\mathbf{r}_1 \cdots d\mathbf{r}_N}{Z} . \tag{5.57}$$

For pairwise additivity, the preexponential U can be replaced by the sum over all pair potentials u_{ij}. We therefore obtain $_N C_2$ indistinguishable pair interactions which we label as u_{12}. Equation (5.57) then becomes

Example 5.6   Calculate the number of particles from the central one out to each of the coordination shells drawn in Example 5.5. Compare these values with the value obtained by assuming uniform density.

The uniform density is found by drawing a square enclosing the unit lattice. This line encloses two particles, one at the center and one-fourth of each of the particles at the four corners. The area is a^2. Therefore the (two-dimensional) density is $2/a^2$. The number of particles within each coordination shell is therefore $2\pi r^2/a^2$. We can find the actual number of particles by counting from the figure, but we only count one-half for each of the particles through whose center the line for the coordination shell is drawn. The results are shown in the table below.

	Shell number							
	1	2	3	4	5	6	7	8
r	$0.719a$	$1.0a$	$1.41a$	$1.58a$	$2.0a$	$2.13a$	$2.28a$	$2.57a$
$\rho\pi r^2$	3.14	6.28	12.6	15.7	25.1	28.4	32.1	41.5
N_{actual}	3	7	11	17	23	27	33	41

$$U_c = \frac{N(N-1)}{2Z} \int \cdots \int u_{12} e^{-\beta U} \, d\mathbf{r}_1 \cdots d\mathbf{r}_N$$

$$= \frac{N(N-1)}{2} \iint u_{12} \left(\frac{\int \cdots \int e^{-\beta U} d\mathbf{r}_3 \cdots d\mathbf{r}_N}{Z} \right) d\mathbf{r}_1 \, d\mathbf{r}_2 \qquad (5.58)$$

$$= \frac{1}{2} \iint u_{12} \rho^{(2)} \, d\mathbf{r}_1 \, d\mathbf{r}_2 = \frac{4\pi N^2}{2V} \int u(r) g(r) r^2 dr \; .$$

The last step in the above derivation is a common integration procedure in statistical mechanics which deserves further comment. By vector addition, $\mathbf{r}_2$ can be written as $\mathbf{r}_1 + \mathbf{r}_{12}$ as shown in Figure 5.14. A change of reference from an arbitrary origin to the center of molecule 1 as the origin will therefore permit us to locate molecule 2 with the relative coordinate $\mathbf{r}_{12}$ instead of the absolute

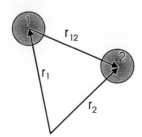

Figure 5.14   The relationship of $\mathbf{r}_{12}$ to $\mathbf{r}_1$ and $\mathbf{r}_2$.

coordinate r_2. Similarly the differential quantity dr_2 can be replaced with dr_{12} for any fixed position of the first molecule. The integral over dr_1 is easily performed to obtain a factor of V, because it does not matter where the first particle is located. Because u_{12} and g (or $\rho^{(2)}$) depend only on the relative positions of the two particles, r_{12}, not the absolute positions of the pair, the integral over dr_1 can be performed separately, and the differential vector r_{12} can be converted to the scalar dr as we did in Equation (5.54). Thus,

$$\iint u_{12}\rho g \, dr_1 \, dr_2 = \left(\int dr_1\right)\int u_{12}\rho g \, dr_{12} = 4\pi V\int u_{12}\rho g r^2 \, dr . \qquad (5.59)$$

We now drop the superfluous subscript on u_{12}, recognizing the lower case u as the pair potential between any two molecules to obtain the connection between the rdf and the configurational internal energy,

$$U_c = 2\pi N\rho \int_0^\infty u(r)g(r)r^2 \, dr . \qquad (5.60)$$

This equation is entirely equivalent to the relation developed in Chapter 2 between the configurational partition function Z and U_c, but Equation (5.60) directly shows the relationship between the local fluid structure and the thermodynamic properties. The total internal energy is the sum of the different modes, or

$$U = 3NkT/2 + U_i + U_c . \qquad (5.61)$$

The pressure can also be related to the rdf. We could also derive this expression in the manner above, but we choose here a method of obtaining the pressure equation that is perhaps more physically intuitive. Since the force between molecular pairs is $-du/dr$, the force between a molecule and dN_r other molecules in a shell at a distance r must be $-[4\pi\rho g r^2(du/dr)]dr$. The pressure increment is the force divided by the area of the shell, $4\pi r^2$, or $P = -[\rho g(du/dr)]dr$. Finally, the pressure-volume product for the central molecule interacting with all molecules in the shell a distance r from its center must therefore be

$$(PV)^r = -\frac{4\pi\rho g r^3}{3}\frac{du}{dr} \, dr . \qquad (5.62)$$

The superscript r designates the quantity as a residual property—Equation (5.62) only contains the contribution due to the nonzero pair potential u. We have already calculated the ideal case to be $(PV)^* = \rho kT$ when $u = 0$. To find the total PV contribution due to local structuring around one central molecule, we must integrate Equation (5.62) over the whole range of r values. We can then sum the $(PV)^r$ contribution of all N molecules. This result must be divided by 2 to eliminate the overcounting caused by treating the 1-2 and 2-1 contributions separately. That is, when molecule 1 was the central molecule we counted its interaction with all other N-1 molecules. When each of those molecules is in turn treated as the central molecule we would again count their interaction with molecule 1, and this factor of 2 must be divided out. Finally, the total $(PV)^r$ is

$$(PV)^r = -\frac{2\pi N}{3} \int_0^\infty \frac{du}{dr} \rho g r^3 \, dr \,, \tag{5.63}$$

and the total pressure, found from $P^r + P^*$, is

$$P = \rho kT - \frac{2\pi\rho^2}{3} \int_0^\infty \frac{du}{dr} g r^3 \, dr \,. \tag{5.64}$$

Other thermodynamic properties can be derived from the above equations using standard thermodynamic identities. For example, the Helmholtz free energy is obtained from

$$\left(\frac{\partial A}{\partial V}\right)_{T,N} = -P \,. \tag{5.65}$$

Integration of Equation (5.65) from a virtually infinite volume (corresponding to an ideal gas) to the system volume V yields $A - A^*$, the residual Helmholtz free energy. Thus,

$$A^r = \frac{2\pi N^2}{3} \int_\infty^V \left(\int_0^\infty \frac{du}{dr} g r^3 \, dr \right) \frac{dV}{V^2} \,. \tag{5.66}$$

A summary of the relationships between the thermodynamic properties and g is provided in Table 5.1.

Equation (5.64) is called the *pressure equation*. It represents the equation of state for any real material in terms of the pcf. The only assumption in its derivation is that of pairwise additivity. Actually, an alternative to this form of the equation of state that does not contain the assumption of pairwise additive potentials can be derived from the grand canonical ensemble. Agreement between the two equations can then be used as a check on the efficacy of the pairwise additivity assumption. We will briefly consider the derivation of this alternative equation, the *compressibility equation*.

The probability that the system contains N particles is related to the N-particle canonical partition function by

$$\wp_N = \frac{e^{\beta \mu N} Q_N}{\Xi} \,. \tag{5.67}$$

The h-particle distribution function $\hat{\rho}^{(h)}$ for finding h particles at specific locations 1 through h *regardless* of the total number of particles N is

TABLE 5.1 Relationship Between Thermodynamic
Properties of Pure Fluids and Pair Correlation Function

$$U = U^* + 2\pi\rho N \int_0^\infty u g r^2 \, dr$$

$$P = \rho kT - \frac{2\pi\rho^2}{3} \int_0^\infty \frac{du}{dr} g r^3 \, dr$$

$$A = A^* + \frac{2\pi N^2}{3} \int_\infty^V \left[\int_0^\infty \frac{du}{dr} g r^3 \, dr \right] \frac{dV}{V^2}$$

$$S = \frac{U - A}{T}$$

$$G = A + PV$$

$$\mu = \left(\frac{\partial A}{\partial N} \right)_{T,V}$$

$$\hat{\rho}(h) = \sum_{N \geq h} \rho_N^{(h)} \, \wp_N = \frac{1}{\Xi} \sum_{N \geq h} \frac{e^{\beta\mu N} Q_N N!}{Z(N-h)!} \int \cdots \int e^{-\beta U} \, d\mathbf{r}_{h+1} \cdots d\mathbf{r}_N , \quad (5.68)$$

where $\rho_N^{(h)}$ is the N-particle distribution function defined in Equation (5.48). The distinction between $\hat{\rho}^{(h)}$ and $\rho_N^{(h)}$ is that the former is the h-particle distribution function for all $N > h$ while the latter pertains to a particular N. We set $h = 1$ (since we have shown that the singlet distribution function is equivalent to ρ) and take the derivative with respect to μ at constant T and N to obtain

$$\left(\frac{\partial \rho}{\partial \mu} \right)_{T,N} = \frac{\beta}{\Xi} \sum_{N \geq 1} \frac{N e^{\beta\mu N} Q_N N!}{Z(N-1)!} \int \cdots \int e^{-\beta U} \, d\mathbf{r}_2 \cdots d\mathbf{r}_N$$

$$- \frac{1}{\Xi^2} \left(\sum_{N \geq 1} \frac{e^{\beta\mu N} Q_N N!}{Z(N-1)!} \int \cdots \int e^{-\beta U} \, d\mathbf{r}_2 \cdots d\mathbf{r}_N \right) \left(\frac{\partial \Xi}{\partial \mu} \right)_{T,N}.$$

We can replace the complicated sum enclosed in parentheses in the above equation with ρ. Similarly, we can introduce ρ and $\rho^{(2)}$ in place of the first summation in the above equation if we first replace the N that appears there with $(N - 1) + 1$. This trick yields

$$\left(\frac{\partial\rho}{\partial\mu}\right)_{T,N} = \frac{\beta}{\Xi}\sum_{N\geq 1} e^{\beta\mu N}Q_N \int\left[\frac{N!}{Z(N-1)!}\int\cdots\int e^{-\beta U}\,d\mathbf{r}_3\cdots d\mathbf{r}_N\right]d\mathbf{r}_2$$

$$+\frac{\beta}{\Xi}\left(\sum_{N\geq 1} e^{\beta\mu N}\,Q_N\left[\frac{N!}{Z(N-1)!}\int\cdots\int e^{-\beta U}\,d\mathbf{r}_2\cdots d\mathbf{r}_N\right]\right) - \rho\left(\frac{\partial\ln\Xi}{\partial\mu}\right)_{T,N}.$$

The first term in square brackets is $\rho^{(2)}$, the second is ρ, and the partial derivative of Ξ with respect to μ is βN. Thus,

$$\left(\frac{\partial\rho}{\partial\mu}\right)_{T,N} = \beta\int_0^\infty \rho^{(2)}\,d\mathbf{r}_2 + \beta\rho - \beta\rho N. \tag{5.69}$$

From thermodynamics, $Nd\mu = -SdT + VdP$ and

$$\left(\frac{\partial\mu}{\partial\rho}\right)_{T,N} = \frac{V}{N}\left(\frac{\partial P}{\partial\rho}\right)_{T,N} = \frac{1}{\rho}\left(\frac{\partial P}{\partial\rho}\right)_{T,N} \Rightarrow \left(\frac{\partial\rho}{\partial\mu}\right)_{T,N} = \rho\left(\frac{\partial\rho}{\partial P}\right)_{T,N}. \tag{5.70}$$

Substitution of Equation (5.70) into (5.69) yields

$$kT\left(\frac{\partial\rho}{\partial P}\right)_{T,N} = \int_0^\infty \frac{\rho^{(2)}}{\rho}\,d\mathbf{r}_2 + 1 - N. \tag{5.71}$$

Finally, we may use Equations (5.51) and (5.52), the usual conversion from absolute to relative coordinates [cf. Equation (5.59)], and the now familiar change to scalar distances [cf. Equation (5.54)] to put Equation (5.71) into its final form

$$\boxed{kT\left(\frac{\partial\rho}{\partial P}\right)_{T,N} = 1 + 4\pi\rho\int_0^\infty (g-1)r^2\,dr = 1 + 4\pi\rho\int_0^\infty hr^2\,dr.} \tag{5.72}$$

Equation (5.72) is the desired *compressibility equation*. Both the pressure and compressibility equations are equations of state relating P, ρ, and T in terms of the pcf. If the total potential energy is in fact pairwise additive, the two equations are equivalent because the only difference involved in their derivation was the assumption of pairwise additive potentials for the pressure equation. We will use both forms later as a consistency check for theories of liquids and dense gases based on the rdf.

We will find ways to determine g in later chapters. If $g(r)$ is known then thermodynamic properties can be determined from the relationships of Table 5.1. This is illustrated in Problem 18 in which you are to use the tabulated values of g given in Table A5.6. A general problem with this method is the sensitivity of the thermodynamic property to the integrand. To obtain accurate values, one must know g quite accurately, particularly in the region of the first peak.

The equations relating mixture thermodynamic properties to the rdf are similar to those derived above, except that molecules of different components are distinguishable. The singlet distribution functions are again easily shown to be

$$\rho_i^{(1)} = \rho_i = \frac{N_i}{V}. \tag{5.73}$$

The pair probability distribution function for a mixture $\rho_{ij}^{(2)}$ represents the probability of finding a molecule of type i located at r_1 *and* a molecule of type j located at r_2. Similarly,

$$g_{ij} = \frac{\rho_{ij}^{(2)}}{\rho_i \rho_j}. \tag{5.74}$$

There are three separate rdf's for mixtures:

1. g_{11}, the relative probability of finding a molecule of type 1 a distance r from a central molecule of type 1,

2. g_{12} (equivalent to g_{21}), the relative probability of finding a molecule of type 1 a distance r from a central molecule of type 2, and

3. g_{22}, the relative probability of finding a molecule of type 2 a distance r from a central molecule of type 2.

Values as a function of r must be available for all three g_{ij} in order to compute thermophysical properties. We will see in later chapters how to obtain g_{ij} from integral equations and from molecular dynamics simulations. The relationships between thermodynamic properties of mixtures and the g_{ij} are summarized in Table 5.2.

We will return periodically throughout the text to methods developed in this chapter for the computation of thermodynamic properties of liquids and dense gases. Before extending these ideas further, however, we will examine the properties of low-density gases. In this case, we do not need to calculate an rdf nor use the equations of Table 5.1 because the configurational partition function can be expanded as a function of density and the terms evaluated directly. The expansion converges rapidly only for the low-density gas case. On the other hand, the formulation of thermophysical properties in terms of the pcf is a more general approach which is applicable for dense gases and liquids. We will therefore return to it after the brief interlude on low-density gases in the next chapter.

TABLE 5.2   Relationship Between Thermodynamic
Properties of Mixtures and Pair Correlation Function

$$U = U^* + 2\pi\rho N \sum_i \sum_j x_i x_j \int_0^\infty u_{ij} g_{ij} r^2 \, dr$$

$$P = NkT - \frac{2\pi\rho^2}{3} \sum_i \sum_j x_i x_j \int_0^\infty \frac{du_{ij}}{dr} g_{ij} r^3 \, dr$$

$$A = A^* + \frac{2\pi N^2}{3} \sum_i \sum_j \int_\infty^V \left[\int_0^\infty \frac{du_{ij}}{dr} g_{ij} r^3 \, dr \right] \frac{dV}{V^2}$$

$$S = \frac{U - A}{T}$$

$$G = A + PV$$

$$\mu_i = \mu_i^* + \frac{2\pi}{3} \left(\frac{\partial}{\partial n_i} \left\{ \sum_i \sum_j n_i n_j \int_\infty^V \left[\int_0^\infty \frac{du_{ij}}{dr} g_{ij} r^3 \right] \frac{dV}{V^2} \right\} \right)_{T,V,n_{k \ne i}}$$

REFERENCES

1. Gray, C.G., and Gubbins, K.E., *Theory of Molecular Fluids. Vol. 1: Fundamentals,* Oxford Press, New York, 1984.

2. Rigby, M., Smith, E.B., Wakeham, W.A., and Maitland, G.C., *The Forces Between Molecules,* Oxford Press, New York, 1986.

3. Nicolas, J.J., Gubbins, K.E., Streett, W.B., and Tildesley, D.J., "Equation of state for the Lennard-Jones Fluid," *Mol. Phys.* **1979,** *37,* 1429.

4. Adachi, Y., Fijihara, I., Takamiya, M., and Nakanishi, K., "Generalized equation of state for Lennard-Jones fluids—I. Pure fluids and simple mixtures," *Fluid Phase Equilib.* **1988,** *39,* 1.

5. Rowley, R.L., Oscarson, J.L., and Giles, N.F., "Experimental and molecular-dynamics simulated excess enthalpies and solubilities of neopentane in supercritical carbon dioxide," *Fluid Phase Equilib.* **1990,** *60,* 143.

6. Reed, T.M., and Gubbins, K.E., *Applied Statistical Mechanics,* McGraw-Hill, New York, 1973.

7. Hill, T.L., *Statistical Mechanics,* McGraw-Hill, New York, 1956.

8. Chapman, W.G., "Prediction of the thermodynamic properties of associating Lennard-Jones fluids: Theory and simulation," *J. Chem. Phys.* **1993,** *93,* 4299.

9. Wertheim, M.S., *J. Stat. Phys.* **1984,** *35,* 19; **1984,** *35,* 35; **1986,** *42,* 459; **1986,** *42,* 477.

10. Lee, L.L., *Molecular Thermodynamics of Nonideal Fluids,* Butterworths, Boston, 1988.

11. Rowley, R.L., and Ely, J.F., "Non-equilibrium molecular dynamics simulations of structured molecules. II. Isomeric effects on the viscosity of models for *n*-hexane, cyclohexane and benzene," *Mol. Phys.* **1992,** *75,* 713.

12. Rowley, R.L., and Ely, J.F., "Non-equilibrium molecular dynamics simulations of structured molecules. Part I. Isomeric effects on the viscosity of butanes," *Mol. Phys.* **1991,** *72,* 831.

PROBLEMS

PAIR POTENTIALS

1. **(a)** Plot in dimensionless units $u^+ = u/\epsilon$ versus $r^+ = r/\sigma$ for a Lennard-Jones potential.

   (b) Determine how to make the force dimensionless and then plot the dimensionless force as a function of r^+ on the same graph.

   (c) Suppose two identical particles are constrained to move in one dimension. Further suppose that they have zero velocity relative to each other at a point where they are separated by $r^+ = 2.5$. Write down the classical differential equation and appropriate initial conditions that could be used to numerically solve for r^+, the distance between the particles, as a function of time. Without solving the equation, sketch in phase space the expected trajectory of the two-particle system.

2. Find r^+ at which the Lennard-Jones potential exhibits a minimum and at which the potential is only 0.1% of the minimum value.

3. In the hard-sphere theory, the molecular diameter is a rigorous physical concept. It is often convenient to retain the concept of a molecular diameter even for soft-sphere models, but in this case, the diameter becomes a function of temperature. For example, the relative kinetic energy of two molecules at infinite separation has a mean value of kT in one dimension. As the molecules approach one another along the line connecting their centers, the kinetic energy is exchanged for potential energy. The distance at which a molecule of average kinetic energy (kT) comes to rest and then begins to move in the opposite direction can be thought of as the molecular diameter. It is the point at which the kinetic energy has been completely converted to potential energy. Find an expression for the temperature dependence of the diameter of Ar using the Lennard-Jones potential.

4. Use the potential parameters for water given in Table A5.5 of Appendix 5 to plot on the same graph over the range $0 < r < 3\sigma$ (a) the potential due just to dispersion forces, (b) the potential due to dipole forces, (c) the potential due to polarization effects, and (d) the total potential.

5. Using the model parameters in Appendix 5, plot on the same graph $\mu(r)$ for methane as calculated from the (a) square-well, (b) Sutherland, (c) Lennard-Jones, and (d) Kihara potential models.

6. The LJ potential is consistent with the principle of corresponding states which means that there is a relationship between the LJ parameters and critical properties. Suppose one were to correlate the LJ parameters as $\epsilon/k = AT_c$ and $\sigma^3 = BkT_c/P_c$. Determine appropriate values of A and B in these correlations from some of the LJ parameters in Appendix 5.

ELECTROSTATIC POTENTIALS

7. One can show from first principles that an equation of state can be derived directly from a knowledge of forces between molecules and their relative positions. The virial theorem can be written as

$$PV = NkT + \frac{1}{3}\left\langle \sum_i \mathbf{F}_i \cdot \mathbf{r}_i \right\rangle,$$

where the second term on the right is called the virial. Long-range interactions between ions obey a central forces potential of the form

$$U(r) = \frac{a}{r},$$

where r is the distance between any pair of atoms. Suppose the spatial distribution of ions in such a system is given by the Boltzmann factor

$$\rho(r) = \frac{N}{V} e^{-U(r)/kT},$$

where N is the total number of ions per volume V. Compute the resultant equation of state.

8. Compute the electrostatic portion of the pair potential for two HCl molecules whose centers are separated by 10 Å for the following alignments of dipole moments: (a) $\rightarrow\leftarrow$, (b) $\nearrow\searrow$, and (c) $\rightarrow\rightarrow$.

9. Compute the electrostatic portion of the pair potential for two SO_2 molecules that are aligned parallel ($\uparrow\uparrow$) and antiparallel ($\uparrow\downarrow$).

10. Compute the various angle-averaged contributions to the pair potential of two SO_2 molecules whose centers are separated by a distance of 6 Å at 300 K.

11. Calculate from values of ϵ^0, σ^0 and electrostatic parameters given in Appendix 5 the values of the effective LJ parameters ϵ and σ that would equivalently model SO_2. Then, on the same graph, plot the actual LJ portion of the potential and the effective total potential.

12. Compute the force acting between the center of two ammonia molecules separated by a distance of 8 Å at 300 K.

POLYATOMIC MOLECULES

Alkanes are often effectively represented by equivalent methylene/methyl LJ sites located at the carbon centers. Bond distances can be taken as 0.153 nm, bond angles as 109.47°, $\epsilon/k = 72$ K, and $\sigma = 0.3923$ nm. Use these values in the problems below.

13. If the force on one site of an ethane molecule oriented with the bond along the x axis is 3×10^{-7} dynes in the $+z$ direction and the force on the other site is 4×10^{-7} dynes in the $-z$ direction, compute the torque on the molecule.

14. Calculate the total force between two propane molecules that are oriented parallel in the same plane, as shown in the figure at the right, such that each of the three sites in one molecule is separated from the corresponding site in the other molecule by a distance of 0.6 nm.

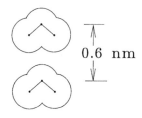

0.6 nm

all sites coplanar

15. Draw a constant potential curve where $u = 0$ for the representation of a two-site model if the site parameters on the one end are those described above but σ for the other site is 50% larger than that given above.

RADIAL DISTRIBUTION FUNCTION

16. Often in molecular dynamics simulations interactions are cut off when molecules exceed a separation of 2.5σ. Cutting the potential off does affect the properties and so a correction is usually made by integrating the relationship between the property and the rdf from the cutoff distance to infinity assuming that $g = 1$ in this region. Use this procedure to evaluate the long-distance corrections to the dimensionless properties U^+, P^+, and μ^+ for a LJ fluid. The reduced properties are defined by $U^+ = U/\epsilon$, $P^+ = P\sigma^3/\epsilon$ and $\mu^+ = \mu/\epsilon$. Your final equations for these properties should be entirely in terms of the dimensionless number density $\rho^+ = \rho\sigma^3$.

17. From classical thermodynamics, one can show that

$$\left(\frac{\partial S}{\partial V}\right)_T = \left(\frac{\partial P}{\partial T}\right)_V.$$

Use this relationship to derive an equation relating S to $g(r)$, and describe the type of information needed to use your equation to calculate S.

18. Table A5.6 in Appendix 5 contains tabulated values of the rdf as a function of r for $T^+ = kT/\epsilon = 1.0843$ and $\rho^+ = 0.8054$. Using this data and the Lennard-Jones potential, numerically evaluate the dimensionless configurational internal energy and pressure.

19. Write a computer program that generates 500 random real numbers between 1 and 5, but devise a method for weighting the uniform random number generator such

that numbers between i and $i + 0.5$ are three times as likely as numbers between $i-0.5$ and i where i represents the integers 1, 2, 3, 4, and 5. Suppose these numbers represent the positions of particles relative to a reference particle in a fluid. Have your program group the numbers into boxes of width 0.2 to produce and plot the radial distribution function for the generated numbers.

PRESSURE EQUATION

20. Suppose a gas obeys the virial expansion truncated at second order in density,

$$P = kT(\rho + B\rho^2) \,.$$

   (a) What is the relationship of the second virial coefficient B to the radial distribution function?

   (b) If the truncated virial equation holds for a binary mixture where now $\rho = \rho_1 + \rho_2$, then determine the relationship between the mixture rdf's and the virial coefficients B_{ij}.

   (c) What is the mixing rule for the mixture virial coefficient B in terms of these B_{ij}.

21. Rederive the pressure equation, this time using the method used in the text to obtain U_c.

22. Starting with

$$P = kT\left(\frac{\partial \ln Z}{\partial V}\right)_{N,T} ,$$

derive the pressure equation. *Hint:* Since the pressure is independent of the shape of the container, assume a cubical box and use Cartesian coordinates. Then do a change of variables.

6

THERMOPHYSICAL PROPERTIES
OF LOW-DENSITY GASES

Sections 5.5 and 5.6 of Chapter 5 identify two equivalent ways of computing thermophysical properties of nonideal fluids. Looking at the relative simplicity of the pcf equations in Tables 5.1 and 5.2, compared to the $3N$ integrals indicated in Equation (5.2), might lead you to think that the best route to thermophysical properties is always through the pcf. While the pcf approach is the easiest approach for some fluid conditions, it is not the best approach for some other conditions. In fact, the pcf formulas for thermodynamic properties are deceptively simple in the closed, analytical forms shown in these tables. Although the two methods are equivalent, some of the computational difficulties are hidden in the definition of the pcf. The pcf itself requires $N-2$ integrations over molecular positions, as seen from Equations (5.48) and (5.51). For values of N approaching the thermodynamic or macroscopic limit, it is impossible to carry out all of the integrations of either method and simplifying assumptions must be used. Therefore, which approach is easiest depends upon the conditions and, more particularly, to which approach the simplifying assumptions valid for those conditions appropriately pertain.

In this chapter, we shall examine low-density gases, which we shall define as fluids with densities less than about 60% of their critical density. Because the density is relatively low, the assumption of pairwise additivity should be quite good. Furthermore, we shall see that we can expand the configurational partition function in a density expansion which will converge for low-density expansions. The lower order terms in the expansion involve fewer integrations than the expression for Z, and so the approach has considerable practical appeal. This is only one of several possible approaches, but it is one of considerable importance because of its direct relation to the virial equation of state. At higher densities, simplifying assumptions related to the pcf are more applicable, and we shall see in later chapters that powerful methods for calculating the pcf have been developed.

6.1 MAYER f FUNCTIONS

In the configurational partition function approach (Z formalism), the troublesome feature of the equations is the exponential term $\exp(-\beta U)$. It is this term that can be successfully expanded in a series to facilitate calculations of low- to moderate-density properties. If pairwise additivity is assumed (Equation 5.7), then the exponential can be written as

$$e^{-\beta U} = e^{-\beta \sum_i \sum_j u_{ij}} = \prod_{i<j} e^{-\beta u_{ij}} = \prod_{i<j} (1 + f_{ij}) \,, \tag{6.1}$$

where f_{ij} is called Mayer f function and is defined by

$$f_{ij} = e^{-\beta u_{ij}} - 1 \,. \tag{6.2}$$

The behavior of the Mayer f function is shown in Figure 6.1. Note that it goes

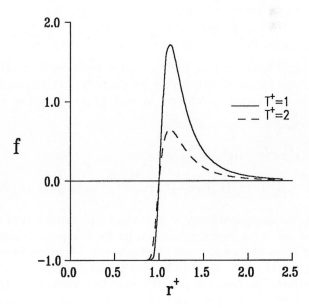

Figure 6.1 The dependence of f on dimensionless distance and temperature for a LJ fluid.

to zero at larger intermolecular separation distances as the pair potential drops off. It is in this respect a measure of the correlation between the particles.

By converting the exponential of the total potential to a product of terms in Equation (6.1), we can rewrite the resultant product of terms as a series. To do so, visualize the product shown in Equation (6.1) written out as

$$\prod_{i<j} (1 + f_{ij}) = (1 + f_{12}) (1 + f_{13})...(1 + f_{23})(1 + f_{24})...(1 + f_{N-1,N}) . \quad (6.3)$$

Then imagine multiplying all of the terms together and rearranging the product into groups of like power in the f functions. We will shortly develop a nomenclature that allows us to succinctly write down this expansion, but for now let's write out explicitly the terms for a three-particle system to illustrate the idea. For three particles,

$$e^{-\beta U} = (1 + f_{12})(1 + f_{13})(1 + f_{23})$$

$$= 1 + (f_{12} + f_{13} + f_{23}) + (f_{12}f_{13} + f_{12}f_{23} + f_{13}f_{23}) + f_{12}f_{13}f_{23} , \quad (6.4)$$

and the partition function is given by

$$Z = \int e^{-\beta U} \, d\mathbf{r}^3 = \int d\mathbf{r}^3 + \int (f_{12} + f_{13} + f_{23}) \, d\mathbf{r}^3$$

$$+ \int (f_{12}f_{13} + f_{12}f_{23} + f_{13}f_{23}) \, d\mathbf{r}^3 + \int f_{12}f_{13}f_{23} \, d\mathbf{r}^3 , \quad (6.5)$$

where the short-hand notation $\int d\mathbf{r}^N$ is used to represent N integrals over the vector positions for the N particles (or $3N$ integrals over $3N$ coordinates for N particles). In the example given here, $N = 3$. In general, let us represent this equation by

$$Z = \int [1 + (f_{12}+f_{13}+f_{14}+...+f_{N-1,N})$$

$$+ (f_{12}f_{13}+f_{12}f_{14}+...+f_{N-2,N-1}f_{N-1,N}) + ...] \, d\mathbf{r}^N. \quad (6.6)$$

A shorter, more convenient way to write this equation is to use graphs[1-4] to represent the terms in the expansion. In this notation, an integral over N coordinates is an N-particle graph, depicted with N circles. Lines are drawn connecting circles i and j when i and j are linked through a Mayer f function in the integrand. The same two circles cannot be connected by more than one line. Two N-particle graphs are different if their circles are connected differently. Consider for example two six-particle graphs. The integrals $\int\int f_{24}f_{25}f_{36} d\mathbf{r}^6$ and $\int\int f_{14}f_{35} d\mathbf{r}^6$ can be represented in this graph notation as

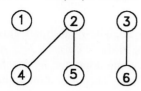 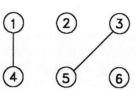

respectively. Such integrals are also called *cluster integrals* because the connections between the circles represent Mayer f functions in the integrand between particles that are close enough together for the pair interactions between the designated molecules to be of significance. Thus the first term in Equation (6.5) represents a three-particle cluster integral with none of the particles interacting; the second group of terms represents three-particle clusters with interactions between pairs; and so on. There are only two possible $N = 2$ clusters,

and eight three-particle graphs,

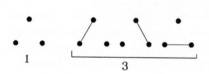 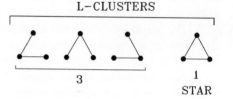

In this new notation, the configurational partition function for three particles given in Equation (6.5) can be conveniently represented by

$$Z = \overset{\circ}{\underset{\circ\;\circ}{}} + \overset{\circ}{\underset{\circ}{}} + \overset{}{\underset{\circ}{}} + \overset{\circ}{\underset{\circ-\circ}{}} + \wedge + \overset{}{\underset{\circ}{}} + \overset{}{\underset{\circ}{}} + \triangle \qquad (6.7)$$

The general expression for the expansion of N particles, Equation (6.6), can be simply represented in graphical notation as

$$Z = \sum \text{(all } N\text{-particle graphs)} . \qquad (6.8)$$

It is evident from the above pictures that there is more than one type of graph for $N \geq 3$. The distinction between types of graphs will be important in relating the expansion to thermophysical properties. We define an L cluster as an N-particle graph in which all the particles are interconnected; that is, there are no particles disconnected or isolated from the cluster. If a group is an L cluster, you can start at any point and travel to all other points in the graph via the connecting lines. The last four graphs shown above for $N = 3$ fit this description and are therefore also $L = 3$ graphs. Even among the $L = 3$ graphs there are two different kinds of connectivity displayed. The final graph shown above in the $N = 3$ sequence is called a star graph; in this case an $S = 3$ star.

Star graphs are so tightly connected that if any one point and its attached lines are removed, an L-1 graph (still connected) results. This definition implies that each point in a star graph can be reached from any other point by at least two independent paths (except for the trivial case of $S = 2$). For this reason star graphs are sometimes called doubly connected graphs. However, be aware that a doubly connected graph may mean more than double connections at each point. In Table 6.1,[1] which tabulates L graphs for $L = 2$ through 4, the top graph in the third column has at least two connections at each point, but it is not a star. This can be seen by removing the top vertex which then separates the remaining graph into two pieces. Such a point, whose removal disconnects the graph into two separate graphs, is called an *articulation point*.[4] Double connection at each point is certainly a necessary, but not a sufficient, condition for double connectivity of the whole cluster. Also shown in Table 6.1 are the number of L graphs of each type that can be drawn and the identification of the graphs as stars $(+)$ or nonstars $(-)$. Example 6.1 further illustrates the difference between the N, L, and S classifications of graphs.

The purpose of using this graphical notation is the convenience associated with both representation of the integrals over f functions that appear in expansions of Z such as Equation (6.5) and simplification of the integrals using convenient properties of the graphs. Some of the properties and features of graphs useful in simplification of these complex integrals are stated below and illustrated for the case of $N = 4$:

TABLE 6.1   The $L = 2, 3, 4,$ and 5 Graphs with k Lines[1]

L	k	#	S	type	L	k	#	S	type	L	k	#	S	type
2	1	1	+	—	5	4	5	−	⋀	5	6	15	−	⋔
					5	4	60	−	⋂	5	6	60	+	⬠
3	2	3	−	⋀	5	4	60	−	⋃	5	6	10	+	⧖
3	3	1	+	△	5	5	60	−	⋒	5	7	20	−	⧖
4	3	12	−	⊔	5	5	60	−	ℕ	5	7	10	+	⧖
4	3	4	−	∨	5	5	30	−	⧸	5	7	60	+	⬠
4	4	12	−	ℕ	5	5	60	−	⬠	5	7	30	+	⧖
4	4	3	+	□	5	5	12	+	⬠	5	8	30	+	⧖
4	5	6	+	⊠	5	6	60	−	⬠	5	8	15	+	⧖
4	6	1	+	⊠	5	6	60	−	⧖	5	9	10	+	⧖
										5	10	1	+	⧖

The number of topologically equivalent graphs are indicated under # and $S = +$ indicates a star configuration.

Example 6.1   Sketch the graphs for the following cluster integrals: (a) $\int\int f_{12}f_{14}f_{15}f_{23}d\mathbf{r}^5$, (b) $\int\int f_{12}f_{13}f_{35}f_{25}f_{24}d\mathbf{r}^5$, (c) $\int\int f_{13}f_{14}f_{15}f_{23}f_{24}d\mathbf{r}^5$, (d) $\int\int f_{23}f_{24}f_{15}f_{34}d\mathbf{r}^5$, (e) $\int\int f_{12}f_{23}f_{24}f_{45}f_{15}f_{35}d\mathbf{r}^5$. Classify each by its highest order designation as an N, L, or S graph.

(a)   Classification: L graph

(b)   Classification: N graph

(c)   Classification: L graph

(d)   Classification: N graph

(e)   Classification: S graph

---

1. Each unconnected particle results in a factor of V to the integral.

$$\substack{\circ\circ\\\circ\circ} = \int\int\int\int d\mathbf{r}_1 d\mathbf{r}_2 d\mathbf{r}_3 d\mathbf{r}_4 = V^4$$

$$\substack{\circ\circ\\\circ\!-\!\circ} = \left(\int d\mathbf{r}_1\right)\left(\int\int\int f_{23}f_{34}d\mathbf{r}_2 d\mathbf{r}_3 d\mathbf{r}_4\right) = V(\,\circ\!\!-\!\!\circ\,)$$

2. If two parts of a graph are not connected by a line, the integral can be factored.

$$\substack{\circ\circ\\\circ\circ} = \int\int\int\int f_{12}f_{34}\, d\mathbf{r}_1 d\mathbf{r}_2 d\mathbf{r}_3 d\mathbf{r}_4$$

$$\substack{\circ\circ\\\circ\circ} = \left(\int\int f_{12}\, d\mathbf{r}_1 d\mathbf{r}_2\right)\left(\int\int f_{34}\, d\mathbf{r}_3 d\mathbf{r}_4\right) = (\,\S\,)(\,\S\,)$$

3. Each completely connected part of a cluster is proportional to V and an integral over *relative* distances. This is the usual trick of integrating with respect to the first particle because the cluster integral depends only on interactions between the particles, not the location of the first point.

$$\text{88} = V^2 \left(\int f_{12} \, d\mathbf{r}_{12} \right)\left(\int f_{34} \, d\mathbf{r}_{34} \right)$$

Example 6.2 further illustrates the use of these rules for simplifying cluster integrals.

We can now use these rules to evaluate expansions such as that shown in Equation (6.5). For example, the first integral on the right side of Equation (6.5) just yields a factor of V^3 (V^N for N molecules) by rule 1. We have in fact already seen how to evaluate this integral before. This is just the ideal-gas contribution to the configurational partition function. The fact that there is no connectivity in the cluster integral in fact tells us that it represents the ideal or no-interaction portion of the function. Similarly, the next group of terms involves singly connected cluster integrals which physically represent interactions between isolated pairs. Higher order terms represent successively higher order interactions. We can simplify these terms still further by using the rules enumerated above, but we will not do so at this point. We simply comment here that lower order terms involve relatively simple integrals, and, for regions in which the series converges, we have a tractable method for evaluating Z and the corresponding thermodynamic properties. The added advantage of the expansion method is the physical significance that can be attached to each term. Because the integrals vanish for all r larger than the effective distance of the intermolecular forces, they contribute to Z only when the molecules are "clustered" close enough to interact, and the effects of different clusters are explicitly observable in the expansion.

6.2 VIRIAL EQUATION OF STATE

As mentioned, the virial equation of state

$$\frac{P}{kT} = \rho + \sum_{i=2}^{\infty} B_i(T)\rho^i \tag{6.9}$$

is a density expansion and is therefore closely related to Equation (6.6). In fact, it can be shown that virial coefficients $B_i(T)$ can be conveniently written in terms of the corresponding $L = i$ star graphs. Thus,

$$B_i = -\frac{i-1}{i!V} \sum_i S_i , \tag{6.10}$$

where ΣS_i is the sum of all $L = i$ star graphs. The complete proof[2] of this

Example 6.2   Write the following cluster integral in graph notation and simplify it as much as possible using the rules stated above:

$$I \equiv \iiiint\!\!\iiint f_{23} f_{45} f_{56} f_{67} f_{47} \, d\mathbf{r}_1 \, d\mathbf{r}_2 \, d\mathbf{r}_3 \, d\mathbf{r}_4 \, d\mathbf{r}_5 \, d\mathbf{r}_6 \, d\mathbf{r}_7$$

If we write the above integral in graph notation, we see that there are three fragments to the cluster. The fragments can be factored and one integration can be performed immediately for each piece. Thus,

$$I = \circ\, 8\, 88 = V^3 \left(\int f_{23} \, d\mathbf{r}_{23} \right) \left(\iiint f_{45} f_{56} f_{67} f_{47} \, d\mathbf{r}_{45} \, d\mathbf{r}_{46} \, d\mathbf{r}_{47} \right)$$

relationship is beyond the scope of this book, but we do sketch out the expansion procedure below, without the mathematical details.

The N-particle canonical partition function (omitting internal modes for the sake of convenience) is given by Equation (5.1) as

$$Q(N) = \frac{Z_N}{N!\, \Lambda^{3N}}. \tag{6.11}$$

For $N = 1$, there are no other neighbors with which the particle can interact and so Z must be the ideal-gas value $Z_1 = V^1$. Therefore, Equation (6.11) becomes

$$Q(1) = \frac{V}{\Lambda^3}. \tag{6.12}$$

Replacement of Λ in Equation (6.11) using Equation (6.12) yields

$$Q(N) = \frac{Z_N}{N!} \left(\frac{Q(1)}{V} \right)^N. \tag{6.13}$$

The grand canonical partition function is related to $Q(N)$ in the usual way,

$$\Xi = \sum_N Q(N) \lambda^N = \sum_{N=0}^{\infty} \frac{Z_N}{N!} \left(\frac{Q(1)\lambda}{V} \right)^N = 1 + \sum_{N=1}^{\infty} \frac{Z_N}{N!} \zeta^N, \tag{6.14}$$

where λ has the usual definition of $e^{\beta\mu}$ and ζ, sometimes called the activity, is just the term in parentheses above,

$$\zeta \equiv \frac{Q(1)\lambda}{V} = \frac{e^{\beta\mu}}{\Lambda^3}. \tag{6.15}$$

In the last equality expressed in Equation (6.14), the first term of the sum is unity because $Z_0 = 1$ (there is only the zero energy state available if there are no particles), $0! = 1$, and $(Q(1)\lambda/V)^0 = 1$.

Equation (6.14) is an expansion for Ξ in terms of the activity. If we also assume that the pressure of a gas can be expanded in terms of the activity

$$\frac{P}{kT} = b_1\zeta^1 + b_2\zeta^2 + b_3\zeta^3 + \dots , \tag{6.16}$$

then we can make a direct comparison between the b coefficients and the Z_i terms in Equation (6.14) by matching coefficients of equal power in ζ. Thus substituting Equation (6.16) into the grand canonical expression for pressure yields[3]

$$\Xi = \exp\left(\frac{PV}{kT}\right) = \exp\left[V\left(b_1\zeta + b_2\zeta^2 + b_3\zeta^3 + \dots\right)\right]. \tag{6.17}$$

The exponential term in the above equation can be expanded and then terms of like power in ζ collected to obtain[3]

$$\Xi = 1 + V(b_1\zeta + b_2\zeta^2 + \dots) + \frac{1}{2}V^2(b_1\zeta + b_2\zeta^2 + \dots)^2 + \dots \tag{6.18}$$

$$= 1 + \frac{b_1V}{1}\zeta + \left(\frac{b_2V}{1} + \frac{b_1V^2}{2}\right)\zeta^2 + \left(\frac{b_3V}{1} + \frac{2b_1b_2V^2}{2} + \frac{b_1V^3}{6}\right)\zeta^3 + \dots \tag{6.19}$$

We may now equate the coefficients of Equations (6.14) and (6.19) term by term. For $i = 1$,

$$Z_1 = b_1V \Rightarrow b_1 = \frac{Z_1}{V} = \frac{V}{V} = 1$$

and $b_1 = 1$. For $i = 2$,

$$\frac{Z_2}{2} = b_2V + \frac{1}{2}b_1V^2 \Rightarrow b_2 = \frac{Z_2 - V^2}{2V} = \frac{Z_2 - Z_1^2}{2V},$$

and so forth.

This process can be continued for higher order terms. A summary of these coefficients through b_4 is sufficient to illustrate the point:

$$b_1 = \frac{Z_1}{1!V}$$

$$b_2 = \frac{Z_3 - Z_1^2}{2!V} \tag{6.20}$$

$$b_3 = \frac{Z_3 - 3Z_1Z_2 + 2Z_1^3}{3!V}$$

$$b_4 = \frac{Z_4 - 4Z_3Z_1 - 3Z_2^2 + 12Z_2Z_1^2 - 6Z_1^4}{4!V}$$

The general form for successive b_i may not be apparent from these equations, but the important physical feature which they contain is evident. Notice that b_1 contains only the single-particle partition function Z_1, b_2 contains only one- and two-particle partition functions, b_3 contains only one-, two-, and three-particle partition functions, and so forth. To relate the b coefficients to the viral coefficients one must now relate ζ to ρ. We will do this through the standard relations

$$P = \frac{kT}{V}\ln\Xi \qquad (6.21)$$

$$N = kT\left(\frac{\partial\ln\Xi}{\partial\mu}\right)_{V,T} = \lambda\left(\frac{\partial\ln\Xi}{\partial\lambda}\right)_{V,T}. \qquad (6.22)$$

Combination of these two equations yields

$$\rho = \frac{N}{V} = \frac{\lambda}{V}\left(\frac{\partial\ln\Xi}{\partial\lambda}\right)_{V,T} = \frac{\zeta}{V}\left(\frac{\partial\ln\Xi}{\partial\zeta}\right)_{V,T} = \frac{\zeta}{kT}\left(\frac{\partial P}{\partial\zeta}\right)_{V,T}, \qquad (6.23)$$

and differentiation of Equation (6.16) in accordance with Equation (6.23) yields

$$\rho = \sum_{j=1}^{\infty} jb_j\zeta^j. \qquad (6.24)$$

Now that we have both P and ρ as power series in ζ, the final challenge is to invert Equation (6.24) and substitute into Equation (6.19) to get back a ρ expansion. This can be done by expanding ζ in powers of ρ and matching coefficients as we have done above. The final result of this somewhat arduous algebra is the remarkable relation given in Equation (6.10). Using this equation, one can calculate the ith virial coefficient B_i directly from the sum of all ith star-graph integrals. It is physically quite interesting and enlightening that this procedure identifies the second virial coefficients as the sum of two-body star clusters, the third virial coefficient as the sum of all three-body star clusters, and so forth.

6.3 SECOND VIRIAL COEFFICIENTS

The computational advantage gained by this expansion technique is that lower order terms involve integrals over only a few particle positions. The second virial coefficient is obtained from Equation (6.10) as

$$B_2 = -\frac{1}{2V} S_2 . \tag{6.25}$$

There is only one two-body star (see Table 6.1) which when substituted into Equation (6.21) yields

$$B_2 = -\frac{1}{2V} \int f_{12}\, d\mathbf{r}_1 d\mathbf{r}_2 = -\frac{1}{2}\int f_{12}\, d\mathbf{r}_{12} = 2\pi \int_0^\infty (1 - e^{-\beta u})r^2\, dr . \tag{6.26}$$

Notice how the rules for evaluating L graphs and Equation (5.54) have been applied to simplify the expression. Further evaluation of the integral requires specification of a pair potential u. Segmented potentials are particularly nice for illustrating the procedure because of the mathematical simplification that occurs. We illustrate, therefore, application of Equation (6.26) first for segmented potentials and then for the LJ potential.

6.3.1 Hard-Sphere Fluid

Equation (6.26) can be readily evaluated for the hard-sphere potential model. Because $u = 0$ for values of $r > \sigma$ and $u = \infty$ for values of $r < \sigma$, the integral between 0 and ∞ is conveniently split into two parts:

$$B_2 = 2\pi \left[\int_0^\sigma (1 - e^{-\beta u})r^2\, dr + \int_\sigma^\infty (1 - e^{-\beta u})r^2\, dr \right]. \tag{6.27}$$

Thus,

$$B_2 = 2\pi \left(\int_0^\sigma r^2\, dr + 0 \right) = \frac{2\pi r^3}{3}\bigg|_0^\sigma = \frac{2\pi\sigma^3}{3} . \tag{6.28}$$

Notice that the hard-sphere second virial coefficient is actually independent of temperature. It only takes a cursory glance at second virial coefficient data (for example in the Appendix 6 material on the diskette) to see that this is inconsistent with experimental values. The inadequate temperature dependence results from the lack of a soft repulsive term that allows deeper penetration into the potential for molecules with higher kinetic energy. It will be convenient to scale the second virial coefficient obtained from more realistic models with the hard-sphere result. To this end, the hard-sphere value, $2\pi\sigma^3/3$, is often given the symbol b_0 and the dimensionless virial coefficient, $B_2^+(T)$ is defined relative to this value by

$$B_2^+(T) = B_2(T)/b_0 , \tag{6.29}$$

where $b_0 = 2/3\pi\sigma^3$. Obviously, $B_2^+ = 1$ for the hard-sphere fluid.

6.3.2 Square-Well Fluid

The square-well model, like the hard-sphere potential model, is constant in distinct regions of r. This again allows separation of the integral into regions over which the potential is constant. Because

$$u(r) = \begin{bmatrix} \infty & r < \sigma \\ -\epsilon & \sigma < r < g\sigma \\ 0 & r > g\sigma \end{bmatrix} , \tag{6.30}$$

the integral is conveniently split into three parts

$$B_2 = 2\pi \int_0^\sigma r^2 \, dr + 2\pi \int_\sigma^{g\sigma} (1 - e^{\beta\epsilon}) r^2 \, dr + 0 . \tag{6.31}$$

The last term is zero because the potential is zero for distances larger than $g\sigma$. The first term is the same as that obtained for the hard-sphere potential, b_0. The second term is readily integrated to obtain

$$2\pi \int_\sigma^{g\sigma} (1 - e^{\beta\epsilon}) r^2 \, dr = \frac{2\pi\sigma^3}{3} (1 - e^{\beta\epsilon})(g^3 - 1) . \tag{6.32}$$

Finally, the dimensionless second virial coefficient for the square-well model is given by

$$B_2^{+\,sw} = 1 + (1 - e^{\beta\epsilon})(g^3 - 1) . \tag{6.33}$$

While the emphasis in this text is generally the calculation of thermophysical properties from potential parameters, equations such as (6.33) can be used in just the reverse manner. That is, one can use the theory in conjunction with experimental thermophysical property values to probe the nature of the intermolecular interactions. In fact, quite often second virial coefficient data are used to obtain values for the parameters in a potential model. The inverse problem, as this regression of potential parameters from experimental data is called, is particularly convenient for the square-well model because of the simple analytical expression given in Equation (6.33). One can obtain the three square-well parameters σ, ϵ, and g using three or more experimental values of B_2^{sw} at different temperatures. Example 6.3 illustrates this procedure.

6.3.3 Lennard-Jones Fluid

The Lennard-Jones potential is a more realistic potential than the segmented hard-sphere and square-well models. However, this continuous behavior makes it considerably more difficult to obtain an analytical expression for the second virial coefficient. The equation

Example 6.3   Second virial coefficients for a fluid were measured at various temperatures and found to be:[5]

$T(K)$	360	450	540
$10^6 B_2 (m^3/mol)$	-25.45	-17.68	-12.96

Determine the square-well potential parameters that are in best agreement with this data. The equation

$$B_2 = \frac{2\pi N_o \sigma^3}{3}[1 + (g^3 - 1)(1 - e^{\epsilon/kT})]$$

is more simply written as

$$B_2 = b_o[1 + x(1 - e^{y/T})] \, .$$

Substitution of the three data pairs into this equation produces three equations and three unknowns. The equations are nonlinear, but any convenient method such as Newton–Raphson, trial-and-error, and so on, may be used to obtain the solution:

$$b_o = 6.0365 \times 10^{-6} \qquad x = 7.0097 \qquad y = 200.25 \text{ K}.$$

Change of variables back to the square-well potential parameters yields

$$\sigma = \left(\frac{3b_o}{2\pi N_o}\right)^{1/3} = \left[\frac{(3)(6.0365 \times 10^{-6})}{(2\pi)(6.023 \times 10^{23})}\right]^{1/3} = 1.682 \text{ Å}$$

$$\frac{\epsilon}{k} = y = 200.25 \text{ K}$$

and

$$g = (1 + x)^{1/3} = 2.001.$$

$$B_2(T) = -2\pi \int_0^\infty \exp\left[4\beta\epsilon\left(\left(\frac{\sigma}{r}\right)^6 - \left(\frac{\sigma}{r}\right)^{12}\right) - 1\right]r^2 \, dr \qquad (6.34)$$

does have an analytical solution,

$$B_2^{LJ} = -\frac{2\pi\sigma^3}{3}\sum_{n=0}^{\infty} \frac{2^{\frac{2n+1}{2}}}{4\,n!}\left(\frac{\epsilon}{kT}\right)^{\frac{2n+1}{4}}\Gamma\left(\frac{2n-1}{4}\right), \qquad (6.35)$$

where Γ is the gamma function given in Appendix 2. In terms of reduced or dimensionless variables, this equation can be written more simply as

$$B_2^{+ \, \text{LJ}} = - \sum_{n=0}^{\infty} \frac{2^{\frac{2n+1}{2}}}{4n!} (T^+)^{-\frac{2n+1}{4}} \Gamma\left(\frac{2n-1}{4}\right). \qquad (6.36)$$

Second virial coefficients for more complicated potential functions are usually evaluated numerically.

Figure 6.2[5] illustrates the dependence of B_2^+ on temperature as predicted with the three models discussed in this section. Notice again that the hard-sphere model predicts that B_2^+ should be independent of temperature. This is contrary to experimental fact, but the hard-sphere value does appear to be a high-temperature limit approached by the real virial coefficient and more sophisticated models. Figure 6.3[6] shows that the agreement between $B_2^+(T)$ predicted by the Lennard-Jones potential and that measured for simple gases is quite good.

The ability of the Lennard-Jones potential to predict $B_2^+(T)$ for more complex molecules is obviously limited by the spherical symmetry of the model itself. Nevertheless, *effective* Lennard-Jones parameters can be regressed from experimental data for $B_2^+(T)$ even for nonspherical molecules. These effective or spherically averaged parameters may or may not be applicable to other properties and conditions considerably removed from those at which the parameters were determined. For a more detailed analysis, the discussion in Appendix 5 on effective model parameters should be consulted. The point is, a consistent

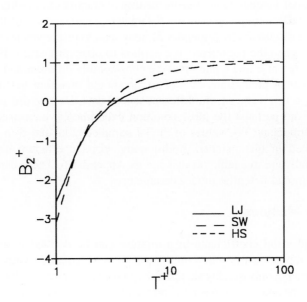

Figure 6.2 B_2^+ for the hard-sphere (HS), square-well (SW), and Lennard-Jones (LJ) potentials. For SW, g was taken to be 1.5.[5]

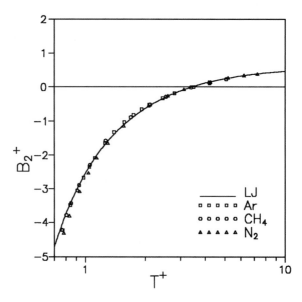

Figure 6.3   Comparison of B_2^+ for Ar, CH_4, and N_2 to the Lennard-Jones value as a function of dimensionless temperature.[6]

set of potential parameters can be obtained from experimental data only if the potential model adequately represents the true interactions occurring in the fluid. Even then, the nonuniqueness of the parameters, characteristic of the inversion problem (see discussion in Appendix 5), may lead to discrepancies with experimental data when the parameters are applied to other properties. For example, two quite different σ and ϵ pairs may be considerably different and yet produce nearly equivalent predictions of $B_2(T)$. One should therefore be careful not to interchange σ or ϵ values from different sets of data. Despite this caveat, virial coefficients are perhaps the most common experimental data used to regress potential parameters. The values of the LJ parameters tabulated in Appendix 5 were obtained in this manner. Additionally, virial coefficient data of some selected fluids[7] are available on diskette as Appendix 6. These can be used to regress additional potential model parameters.

6.3.4 Mixtures

Second virial coefficients in a mixture can be derived in an analogous manner by replacing the pure-component pressure equation with that for the mixture. We shall only quickly sketch through the procedure for a binary mixture, pointing out the analogy between the pure and mixture equations as we proceed.[3]

The grand canonical partition function for a binary mixture analogous to Equation (6.14) is

$$\Xi = e^{(PV/kT)} = \sum_{N_1>0} \sum_{N_2>0} \frac{Z_{N_1 N_2}}{N_1! N_2!} \zeta^{N_1} \zeta^{N_2} ,$$ (6.37)

or written in a form analogous to Equation (6.17),

$$\Xi = 1 + V(\zeta_1 + \zeta_2) + \frac{1}{2}Z_{20}\zeta_1^2 + Z_{11}\zeta_1\zeta_2 + \frac{1}{2}Z_{02}\zeta_2^2 + \dots .$$ (6.38)

We may take the logarithm and expand this series to obtain

$$\frac{P}{kT} = \zeta_1 + \zeta_2 + b_{20}\zeta_1^2 + b_{11}\zeta_1\zeta_2 + b_{02}\zeta_2^2 + \dots ,$$ (6.39)

where

$$b_{10} = b_{01} = 1 \qquad b_{11} = \frac{Z_{11} - V^2}{1!1!V}$$
$$b_{20} = \frac{Z_{20} - V^2}{2!0!V} \qquad b_{02} = \frac{Z_{02} - V^2}{0!2!V} .$$ (6.40)

Note from this development that b_{20} involves only the configurational partition function Z_{20}. The subscripts indicate that it involves pair interactions between type 1 molecules, but no interactions involving type 2 molecules. Thus the pair potential function used in the exponential term involves only pair potentials between molecules of type 1,

$$Z_{20} = \int e^{-\beta u_{11}} \, d\mathbf{r}^2 .$$ (6.41)

Note that only the pair potential u_{11} appears. Because $\int d\mathbf{r}^2 = V^2$, we can transform the expression for b_{20} given in Equation (6.40) into one that we immediately recognize, namely

$$b_{20} = \frac{1}{2V} \int_0^\infty \left(e^{-\beta u_{11}} - 1 \right) d\mathbf{r}^2 = -B_{2,11} .$$ (6.42)

Here, we use the notation $B_{2,11}$ to indicate the pure-component 1 second virial coefficient. The double 1 subscript emphasizes that only like interactions between type 1 molecules are involved in its evaluation. Likewise, we can easily show that $B_{2,22} = -b_{02}$ and that $B_{2,12} = -1/2b_{11}$. While $B_{2,11}$ and $B_{2,22}$ depend on only pure-component potential parameters, $B_{2,12}$ contains information about the cross-interactions between components 1 and 2. To calculate $B_{2,12}$ explicitly, one must use the cross-potential between particles 1 and 2,

$$B_{2,12} = -\frac{1}{2V} \int_0^\infty \left(e^{-\beta u_{12}} - 1 \right) d\mathbf{r}^2.$$ (6.43)

The cross-virial term contains the information about unlike interactions between the two components. As was discussed in Chapter 5, there is no rigorous way to obtain u_{12} from the pure-component values except in the case of hard spheres. Approximations such as the Lorentz–Berthelot combining rule can be used to obtain ϵ_{12} from ϵ_{11} and ϵ_{22} and σ_{12} from σ_{11} and σ_{22}, but the approximate nature of such relationships should always be kept in mind.

On the other hand, one can turn the equations around and regress from a combination of mixture and pure-component virial data both the like- and unlike-interaction parameters. To do so, we need to first identify the relationship between the mixture virial coefficient B_2 and the individual terms $B_{2,11}$, $B_{2,22}$, and $B_{2,12}$ shown above. We will follow the same procedure used in the previous section for identifying the pure virial coefficients in terms of the density expansion of the pressure equation. Again, the derivation is not the important point here, so we simply state the results:

$$B_2(T,x_1) = B_{2,11}(T)x_1^2 + 2B_{2,12}(T)x_1x_2 + B_{2,22}(T)x_2^2 . \qquad (6.44)$$

This equation is an exact relation. It does not depend on any assumptions about the cross-interactions. Therefore, one can use the pure-component second virial coefficients and values of $B_{2,12}$ obtained from experiments to regress the unlike pair potential in Equation (6.43). Example 6.4 illustrates the calculation of the second virial coefficient and the partial fugacities of the components in a mixture of hard spheres, while Example 6.5 illustrates the reverse process of calculating potential parameters from experimental data for an LJ mixture.

The extension of Equation (6.44) to multicomponent mixtures can also be made, its form being intuitive:

$$B_2(T,x) = \sum_{i=1}^{n} \sum_{j=1}^{n} B_{2,ij}(T)x_ix_j . \qquad (6.45)$$

6.4 HIGHER ORDER VIRIAL COEFFICIENTS

Higher order virial coefficients can be obtained in a manner analogous to that for second virial coefficients. Because there is only one three-body star, Equation (6.10) becomes

$$B_3(T) = -\frac{2}{6V} S_3 = -\frac{1}{3} \int\int f_{13} f_{23} f_{12} \, d\mathbf{r}_{12} \, d\mathbf{r}_{13} . \qquad (6.46)$$

This equation must be numerically integrated even for hard spheres because of the product of terms. Likewise, the fourth virial may be written down in terms of its 10 constituent stars

Example 6.4 Determine the second virial coefficient and partial fugacities of a 50 mol% mixture of $CO_2(1)$ and $CH_4(2)$ at 100°C and 10 atm. Assume a hard-sphere model for both components with values for σ_1 and σ_2 of 4.416 Å and 4.010 Å, respectively.

For hard spheres, the combining rule for σ_{12} is exact and yields

$$\sigma_{12} = 1/2(\sigma_1 + \sigma_2) = 4.213 \text{ Å}.$$

For two components, the second virial coefficient is given in Equation (6.44) by

$$B_2 = x_1^2 B_{2,11} + 2x_1 x_2 B_{2,12} + x_2^2 B_{2,22}.$$

For the hard-sphere model, the individual $B_{2,ij}$ are found from Equation (6.28). Substitution of the appropriate σ values into Equation (6.28) and conversion of the results to units of cm^3/mol yields

$$B_{2,11} = 108.62 \text{ cm}^3/\text{mol} \qquad B_{2,12} = 94.31 \text{ cm}^3/\text{mol} \qquad B_{2,22} = 81.30 \text{ cm}^3/\text{mol}.$$

For the mixture we have

$$B_2 = 0.25 B_{2,11} + 0.5 B_{2,12} + 0.25 B_{2,22} = 94.64 \text{ cm}^3/\text{mol}.$$

The partial fugacity coefficients are easily derived from the virial equation of state using classical thermodynamics. They are

$$\ln\phi_i = \left(\frac{P}{kT}\right)\left(2\sum_j x_j B_{2,ij} - B_2\right) = \left(\frac{P}{kT}\right)(2x_1 B_{2,i1} + 2x_2 B_{2,i2} - B_2).$$

For this case $x_1 = 0.5 = x_2$, so

$$\ln\phi_1 = \left(\frac{P}{RT}\right)(B_{2,11} + B_{2,12} - B_2) = \frac{(108.29 \text{ cm}^3/\text{mol})(10 \text{ atm})}{(82.06 \text{ cm}^3/\text{mol})(373 \text{ K})} = 0.0354,$$

and

$$\ln\phi_2 = (B_{2,22} + B_{2,12} - B_2)(P/kT) = 0.0264.$$

Finally, the partial fugacities can be obtained as:

$$f_1 = \phi_1 P = 10.36 \text{ atm} \qquad f_2 = \phi_2 P = 10.27 \text{ atm}.$$

$$B_4(T) = -(3\,\square + 6\,\boxtimes + \boxtimes)/(8V) \qquad (6.47)$$

$$B_3^{hs} = 0.6250 b_0^2 \qquad B_4^{hs} = 0.2869 b_0^3 \qquad B_5^{hs} = 0.1097 b_0^4$$
$$B_6^{hs} = 0.0386 b_0^5 \qquad B_7^{hs} = 0.0138 b_0^6$$

The complexity and the number of integrals involved in calculating virial coeffi-

Example 6.5   Determine the LJ cross-interaction parameters ϵ_{12} and σ_{12} that best fit the cross-virial data reported by Holste et al.[8] for CO_2–C_2H_6 mixtures.

T (K)	$B_{2,12}$(cm³/mol)
250	−181.0
260	−167.0
270	−154.4
280	−142.9
290	−132.5
300	−122.9

Equations (6.26) and (6.43) reveal that the cross-virial coefficient is related to the cross-potential parameters in the same way that the pure-virial coefficients are related to the pure-potential parameters. Therefore, Equation (6.35) can be used to regress the potential parameters. A nonlinear least-squares regression program can be used to obtain the "best-fit" values of ϵ_{12} and σ_{12}. Here, we have used KINFIT and programmed Equation (6.35) as a subroutine. The results of the fit are:

T (K)	$B_{2,12}^{exp}$(cm³/mol)	$B_{2,12}^{calc}$(cm³/mol)
250	−181.0	−180.8
260	−167.0	−167.1
270	−154.4	−154.5
280	−142.9	−143.0
290	−132.5	−132.5
300	−122.9	−122.8

with regressed values for the parameters of σ_{12} = 4.879 ± 0.014 Å and $(\epsilon/k)_{12}$ = 169.6 ± 6.9 K. (The uncertainties were calculated by the parameter regression program.)

It is of interest to compare these values to those that would have been obtained based on the Lorentz–Berthelot (LB) combining rule. From Appendix 5, we find that σ_{CO2} = 4.416 Å, $(\epsilon/k)_{CO2}$ = 192.25 K, σ_{C2H6} = 5.220 Å, and $(\epsilon/k)_{C2H6}$ = 194.14 K. The LB combining rule approximates σ_{12} as 4.818 Å and $(\epsilon/k)_{12}$ as 193.19 K.

cients diverges very rapidly. For example, in going from B_3 to B_4 the number of stars increases from one to 10. The calculation of B_7 involves 468 integrals. No one has even tabulated the star graphs for B_8.[1]

While third virial coefficients can be measured experimentally, the resultant accuracy is generally considerably less than for second virial coefficients. A few values are reported on the diskette under Appendix 6 along with the second virial coefficients.[7] Extremely accurate PVT data are required to obtain fourth virial coefficients, and only a few data points have been reported. The agreement between experimental data and predictions based on the LJ potential are reasonably good for fluids of simple, spherical molecules as shown in Figure 6.4.[8] Values for B_3 for less spherical molecules are expected to deviate more from experimental data. More complicated, nonspherical potentials would be required for more complex molecules. Three-body effects may also play an important role in B_3.

As is the case for mixture second virial coefficients, a mixture virial coefficient can be obtained from the above equations with an appropriate combining rule for the intermolecular potential parameters. For B_3,

$$B_3 = \sum_i \sum_j \sum_k x_i x_j x_k B_{3,ijk} \,, \tag{6.48}$$

and analogous expressions also hold for the higher virial coefficients.

We have seen in this chapter that at reasonably low densities the configurational partition function can be expanded in terms of density. This simplifies the number of integrals that must be performed, at least for the lower order virial coefficients, and has the added benefit of providing physical insight into the virial coefficients themselves. In the next two chapters we look at solving the problem head-on. In essence, we solve the problem exactly using numerical techniques. In Chapter 7 we use Monte Carlo methods to sample phase space and find ensemble averages of properties, while in Chapter 8 we use molecular dynamics methods to trace out the time-dependent path of the system through phase space.

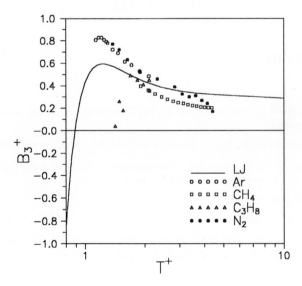

Figure 6.4 Comparison of $B_3^+(T)/b_0^2$ for the LJ potential and several simple molecules.[8]

REFERENCES

1. McQuarrie, D.A., *Statistical Mechanics,* Harper & Row, New York, 1976.

2. Reed, T.M., and Gubbins, K.E., *Applied Statistical Mechanics,* McGraw-Hill, New York, 1973.

3. Hill, T.L., *An Introduction to Statistical Thermodynamics,* Addison-Wesley, Reading MA, 1960.

4. Friedman, H.L., *A Course in Statistical Mechanics,* Prentice-Hall, Englewood Cliffs, NJ, 1985.

5. Walas, S.M., *Phase Equilibria in Chemical Engineering,* Butterworth, Boston, 1985.

6. Hirschfelder, J.O., Curtiss C.F., and Bird, R.B., *Molecular Theory of Gases and Liquids,* Wiley, New York, 1954.

7. Dymond, J.H., and Smith, E.B., *The Virial Coefficients of Gases. A Critical Compilation,* Clarendon, Oxford, 1969.

8. Holste, J.C., Young, J.G., Eubank, P.T., and Hall, K.R., "Interaction second virial coefficients and binary interaction parameters for the CO_2–C_2H_6 systems between 250 and 300 K," *AIChE J.* **1982,** *28,* 807.

9. Bird, R.B., Spotz E.L., and Hirschfelder, J.O., "The third virial coefficient for nonpolar gases," *J. Chem. Phys.* **1950,** *18,* 1395.

10. Patel, M.R., Holste, J.C., Hall K.R., and Eubank, P.T., "Thermophysical properties of gaseous carbon dioxide–water mixtures," *Fluid Phase Equilib.* **1987,** *36,* 279.

PROBLEMS

GRAPH THEORY

1. (a) Write down an expression for B_5, the fifth virial coefficient, in terms of cluster graphs.

   (b) Write down an expression for B_4 in terms of the appropriate Mayer f functions.

2. Sketch the six-cluster diagrams corresponding to integrals over the following f functions and state whether they are N, L, or S graphs.

   (a) $f_{12}f_{23}f_{34}f_{45}f_{51}f_{14}f_{25}$

   (b) $f_{12}f_{23}f_{13}f_{34}f_{45}f_{46}f_{56}$

3. Write the following integrals in graph notation and simplify the integrals as much as possible using the rules for graphs mentioned in the text.

   (a) $\int\int f_{23}f_{45}f_{56}f_{67}f_{47}\ d\mathbf{r}^7$

   (b) $\int\int f_{12}f_{23}f_{24}f_{25}f_{34}f_{35}f_{15}\ d\mathbf{r}^7$

   (a) $\int\int f_{16}f_{17}f_{23}f_{45}f_{34}\ d\mathbf{r}^7$

SECOND VIRIAL COEFFICIENTS

4. Second virial coefficients of perfluorohexane, n-C_6F_{14}, are

T (K)	B_2(L/mol)
395.56	-1.051
415.48	-0.920
432.68	-0.818
451.55	-0.725

Determine square-well parameters for perfluorohexane and plot $B_2^{sw}(T)$ between 300 K and 500 K and put the experimental values on the same plot.

5. Using the Lennard-Jones potential and the virial equation truncated after the second virial coefficient, calculate (a) the heat capacity difference $C_P - C_V$ for benzene at 400 K and 0.6 atm, and (b) the speed of sound in benzene at the same conditions as in part (a) if $C_V = 103.74$ J/mol.

6. For a fluid with a dipole moment, we might choose to model the pair interaction energy as a hard-core contribution for the dispersion forces plus a polar portion; that is, $u = u^{hs} + u^{dipole}$. Using this concept, calculate the second virial coefficient for acetone at 500 K using $\sigma = 5.1$ Å and $\mu = 2.88$ D. *Hint:* Use the expansion of the exponential

$$e^x = 1 + x + x^2/2 + x^3/3! + \dots .$$

7. It has been suggested that the triangular potential

$$\left[\begin{array}{ll} u(r) = \infty & r < \sigma_0 \\ u(r) = -\epsilon \dfrac{r - \sigma_1}{\sigma_0 - \sigma_1} & \sigma_0 < r < \sigma_1 \\ u(r) = 0 & r > \sigma_1 \end{array} \right]$$

may provide adequate second virial coefficients. Using this model, derive an equation for B_2 in terms of the model parameters σ_1, σ_0, and ϵ. Your equation should be fully integrated.

8. Show that the second virial coefficient for the Sutherland potential is

$$B_2(T) = -\frac{2\pi\sigma^3}{3} \sum_{j=0}^{\infty} \frac{1}{j!} \left(\frac{3}{j\gamma - 3} \right) \left(\frac{c}{\sigma^\gamma kT} \right)^j .$$

The parameter γ is usually taken to be 6.

9. Derive an expression for the first nonideal correction to the speed of sound in a gas. Calculate this quantity for N_2 at STP.

10. Calculate the compressibility factor for argon at 10 atm and 0°C.

11. Use the $B_2(T)$ data from the diskette (Appendix 6) for cyclohexane to regress values for the LJ ϵ and σ parameters.

12. Show that the virial expansion for the thermodynamic energy is

$$\frac{U}{NkT} = \frac{3}{2} - T\sum_{j=1}^{\infty} \frac{1}{j}\frac{dB_{j+1}}{dT}\rho^{j}$$

and that for the entropy is

$$\frac{S}{Nk} = \frac{S^*}{Nk} - \sum_{j=1}^{\infty} \frac{1}{j}\left(\frac{\partial TB_{j+1}}{\partial T}\right)\rho^{j}.$$

MIXTURES

13. Using the LB combining rule and virial-derived LJ parameters from Appendix 5, calculate the second virial coefficient for a 50 mol% mixture of CO in C_3H_8 at 300 K. Then determine the mixture density at 1.5 atm assuming that the virial expansion truncated after the second virial term is adequate.

14. Compute the second virial coefficient for a mixture containing 25 mol% Ar, 50 mol% Kr, and 25 mol% CH_4 by treating the components as hard-sphere fluids. You may use the square-well values of σ as approximate hard-sphere diameters.

15. Patel et al.[10] report the following cross-interaction second virial coefficients for CO_2 + H_2O mixtures:

T (K)	348.15	398.15	448.15	498.15
$B_{2,12}$ (cm³/mol)	−125.2	−82.8	−63.4	−46.4

Determine ϵ_{12}/k and σ_{12} assuming the molecules interact through LJ potentials; then compare the resultant values with those predicted by the LB combining rule.

7

MONTE CARLO SIMULATIONS OF THERMOPHYSICAL PROPERTIES

Methods that extensively use random numbers to sample phase space are called Monte Carlo (MC) simulations, because of their kinship to the games of chance and probability in the casino of Monte Carlo. Monte Carlo simulation methods generate large quantities of possible state points in proportion to the probability of their actual occurrence. This density of points in phase space is then used as a probability density function in the calculation of properties using ensemble averages. As you will soon see, computer simulations of phase space points is a powerful technique for calculating thermophysical properties. The Metropolis[1] algorithm is practically the universal algorithm used to carry out the simulations. But, before exploring the Metropolis algorithm, we first examine the basic principles of the MC method with a simpler application, that of numerical integration. The insight gained about importance sampling from a desired distribution will make the rationale behind the Metropolis algorithm much clearer. We will also use MC simulations to investigate fluid phase transitions and cooperative phenomena using the Ising model.

7.1 MONTE CARLO INTEGRATION

To begin our study of the underpinnings of MC simulations, let us develop the basic simulation procedures within the framework of MC integration of arbitrary functions.[2-4] Suppose you wish to know the surface area of the irregularly shaped, small pond shown in Figure 7.1. There are many ways that could be devised to estimate the surface area. As an example of an MC approach, one could try throwing a large number of rocks to land randomly within a rectangular area

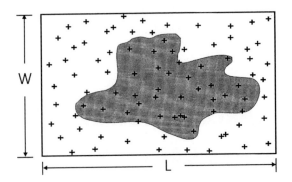

Figure 7.1 Estimation of a pond's surface area with an MC technique.

of width W and length L and counting the number of splashes or "hits" within the boundary of the pond. If indeed the rock throwing was random, then the fraction of "hits" should equal the ratio of the surface area of the pond to the rectangle. Let n_h be the number of "hits," n be the total number of rocks thrown, A_r be the area of the rectangle ($L \times W$), and A_p be the area of the pond. Then

$$A_p = \frac{n_h}{n} A_r . \tag{7.1}$$

Finding an area bounded by a curve, as in the above example, is an integration procedure. MC integration is one of several numerical techniques that can be used to obtain the integral of a function over a complex boundary. Example 7.1 is an illustration of a simple and straightforward integration technique. Often there are better numerical methods (i.e., more accuracy per CPU time) available for integration, but the method is of pedagogical interest and can still be quite useful for complex integration problems. The accuracy of such methods is poor for small n (number of trials), but the methods become exact as $n \to \infty$. Only for relatively large values of n can the simple MC method be expected to generate good estimates of integrals.

Another MC procedure is based on the mean-value theorem of calculus. The mean-value theorem states that the integral of a function $f(x)$ from a to b is approximated by the area of the rectangle of height $<f(x)>$ and width $(b-a)$, where $<f(x)>$ is the mean value of the function between the limits; that is,

$$\int_a^b f(x) \, dx = (b-a) <f>. \tag{7.2}$$

You should realize that this also results directly from our definition of expectation values, because

Example 7.1   Use the MC integration technique to estimate the value of π.

A simple procedure is to use a random number generator to obtain a set of N random (x,y) coordinates in the range $-1 \le x \le 1$ and $-1 \le y \le 1$. The distance from the origin for each point is obtained from $r = (x^2 + y^2)^{1/2}$. If $r \le 1$ for a randomly chosen coordinate (x,y), the point is contained within a circle of radius 1 centered at the origin and is considered a "hit"; values outside the circle ($r > 1$) are misses. The area of the circle is $A_c = \pi r^2 = \pi$, and the area of the square is $A_s = 2 \times 2 = 4$.

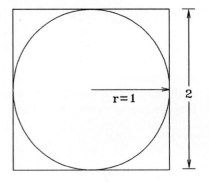

Thus, from Equation (7.1), $\pi = 4n_h/n$. Shown below is a calculation from a MC run of 10 shots:

x	y	r	n_s
0.411	0.067	0.416	1
0.159	−0.421	0.450	1
−0.396	0.549	0.677	1
−0.972	0.521	1.103	0
0.629	0.418	0.755	1
−0.909	−0.172	0.925	1
0.725	0.581	0.929	1
−0.253	0.924	0.958	1
0.743	−0.888	1.157	0
0.899	−0.272	0.939	1
			8

which yields $\pi = (4)\cdot(8/10) = 3.2$.

As $n \to \infty$ the approximate value obtained from this method should approach the correct value $\pi = 3.14159$. Extended results of the simulation as a function of n are:

n	π
10	3.2 − (somewhat lucky with only 10 samples)
100	3.28
1000	3.204
10,000	3.16
100,000	3.139

$$<f> = \int_a^b f(x)\,\wp(x)\,dx = \frac{1}{b-a}\int_a^b f(x)\,dx\,, \qquad (7.3)$$

where $\wp(x)$ is the *normalized* probability distribution function. Because the x values are equally probable over the whole domain, $\wp(x) = (b-a)^{-1}$ in the above equation. One can use Equation (7.2) in a Monte Carlo procedure by evaluating $f(x)$ at random x values between a and b in order to numerically find the average value of f. Thus,

$$\int_a^b f(x)\,dx = \frac{(b-a)}{n}\sum_{i=1}^{n} f(x_i)\,. \qquad (7.4)$$

Note that if equally spaced x values between a and b are selected instead of random values, the trapezoidal rule results. The trapezoidal rule is in general more accurate for smaller values of n, but the MC method yields better accuracy for very large values of n. Even so, one would probably not use the MC method for a single integral; its most important application to integration is for multidimensional integrals as illustrated in Example 7.2.

We used uniformly distributed random numbers to estimate the integrals in Examples 7.1 and 7.2. All numbers from the domain are equally probable if obtained from a uniform distribution. These are the kind of random numbers commonly generated by computer random number generators. A large number of trials is generally required for MC methods based on random numbers from a uniform distribution, especially for rapidly varying functions. We can minimize the number of trials required and improve accuracy at the same time by sampling more often in regions of x where $|f(x)|$ is large or rapidly varying. For example, suppose we wish to find the area under the curve shown in Figure 7.2. If we sample uniformly over the range a to b, we waste considerable time sampling in regions of little importance to the overall area of the function. By sampling more frequently in the more important regions of the function, the fraction of "hits" is greatly increased. This is analogous to choosing a box in Example 7.1 which just inscribes the circle rather than one of width much larger than the diameter of the circle. The results will be the same in both cases, but the efficiency is dramatically better for the smaller box. This technique, called *importance sampling,* uses a biased sample to compute the average value of f and therefore requires a nonuniform probability distribution biased in the same manner as the sampling in order to obtain correct averages.

Again let $\wp(x)$ be the probability distribution function of x, normalized over the domain. The integral of a function $f(x)$ can be written in terms of this probability distribution as

Example 7.2　Consider the two-dimensional square, shown below, which has sides of length $L = 4$ and a circular hole of radius $r = 1$, centered a distance of 1 in the x direction from the center of the square. If the disk has a uniform density of 1 per unit thickness, determine the mass of the disk per unit thickness and the center of mass coordinates (X, Y).

The mass of the disk per unit thickness is

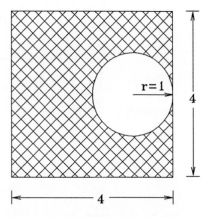

$$M = \int_{-2}^{2} \int_{-2}^{2} \rho \; dx \; dy = \frac{16}{n} \sum_{i=1}^{n} \rho(x_i, y_i)$$

and the center of mass is given by

$$X = \frac{1}{M} \int_{-2}^{2} \int_{-2}^{2} x\rho \; dx \; dy = \frac{16}{Mn} \sum_{i=1}^{n} x_i \rho(x_i, y_i)$$

$$Y = \frac{1}{M} \int_{-2}^{2} \int_{-2}^{2} y\rho \; dx \; dy = \frac{16}{Mn} \sum_{i=1}^{n} y_i \rho(x_i, y_i)$$

　　In the MC procedure, a set of coordinates (x,y) in the domain $-2 \le x \le 2$ and $-2 \le y \le 2$ is randomly chosen. The local density of the chosen point is set to $\rho = 1$ if it lies within the square and outside the hole, or to $\rho = 0$ if it falls within the hole. Thus,

$$\rho = 1 \quad \text{whenever} \quad \sqrt{(x - 1)^2 + y^2} \ge 1.$$

Results for 20 trials are:

i	x_i	y_i	ρ	i	x_i	y_i	ρ
1	0.822	0.134	0	11	0.099	1.068	1
2	0.318	−0.842	1	12	−1.786	0.370	1
3	−0.792	1.099	1	13	−0.125	−0.807	1
4	−1.944	1.043	1	14	0.491	0.591	0
5	1.258	0.836	0	15	−0.945	−0.883	1
6	−1.819	−0.344	1	16	1.319	1.298	1
7	1.450	1.162	1	17	0.357	1.944	1
8	−0.506	1.848	1	18	1.644	−1.093	1
9	1.486	−1.775	1	19	0.780	1.920	1
10	1.798	−0.544	0	20	−1.024	0.135	1

From these results, we find $M = 16 \cdot (16/20) = 12.8$. This can be compared to the exact answer $M = \rho[4^2 - \pi(1)^2] = 16 - \pi = 12.858$. For longer simulations, we obtain:

$n = 1000$	$M = 12.896$	$X = -0.27$	$Y = -0.01$
$n = 10,000$	$M = 12.886$	$M = -0.26$	$Y = -0.01$.

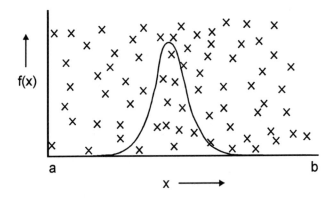

Figure 7.2   Random sampling is not very efficient for many functions.

$$F = \int_a^b f(x)\,dx = \int_a^b \left[\frac{f(x)}{\wp(x)}\right]\wp(x)\,dx = \left\langle\frac{f(x)}{\wp(x)}\right\rangle. \qquad (7.5)$$

As can be seen from this equation, the integral can be found numerically by computing the average of $f/\wp$,

$$F = \frac{1}{n}\sum_{i=1}^{n}\frac{f(x_i)}{\wp(x_i)}, \qquad (7.6)$$

for any desired $\wp(x)$ if $\wp(x)$ is used to compute the average. Of course if x is a uniformly distributed random variable, then $\wp(x) = (b-a)^{-1}$ and Equation (7.3) is recovered. We can minimize the variance of the result if we use a nonuniform probability distribution function which mimics the function $f(x)$ because the sampling from $\wp(x)$ will then match the regions of most importance in the function. We still obtain an unbiased estimator of the mean, as implied in Equation (7.5), because the x values are chosen from the same probability distribution used in the denominator of Equation (7.6). The two biases cancel out, so to speak, and the result remains unaffected if x is sampled from the same distribution used in the denominator of the integrand. The difficulty of making an appropriate choice for $\wp(x)$ is generally more than compensated for by the large reduction in CPU time that can be achieved without loss of accuracy. This time savings results from the more efficient sampling of the function with fewer trials.

    Two key problems are associated with this method: 1) choosing the probability distribution function and 2) generating random numbers from that distribution. The most common method of picking $\wp(x)$ is to choose a function that mimics $f(x)$ over the domain such that it minimizes the variance. There are procedures for this, but we will not address them here. Rather, we will simply try to find a function that mimics $f(x)$, without worrying about whether it optimizes the variance. The second issue, sampling from a particular probability distribution function, is easily handled once the function $\wp(x)$ has been chosen. Let $Q(x)$ represent the cumulative probability from the lower limit a to x; that is,

$$Q(x) = \int_a^x \wp(x')\,dx'. \tag{7.7}$$

Then for any random number r generated from a uniform distribution, the random number obtained from the $\wp(x)$ distribution can be found from the relation

$$x = Q^{-1}(r). \tag{7.8}$$

The manner in which the nonuniform distribution is generated is illustrated in Figure 7.3. Suppose that we choose a linear probability distribution function, $\wp = cx$, to perform importance sampling on the function f over the domain 0 to 1 shown in graph a on the left. Using the linear relation for $\wp(x)$ in Equation (7.7), one obtains $Q = cx^2/2$. This has the general shape shown in graph b on the right. In this figure, the y intervals are regularly spaced indicating that any $r = Q(x)$ is equally probable because the distribution is uniform, while the x intervals are nonlinear representing the fact that the probability of sampling larger x values is increased. Thus, the mapping in Equation (7.8) allows us to take uniformly distributed random numbers from the y axis and convert them to random numbers x_i which sample the $\wp$ distribution. Illustration of the use of this method to integrate a function is illustrated in Example 7.3.

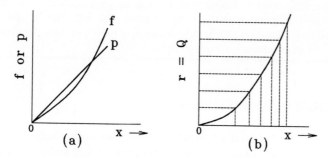

Figure 7.3   A function f to be integrated with a distribution $\wp$ (**a**) requires sampling from the nonuniformly distributed random numbers x obtained from $x = Q^{-1}(r)$ (**b**).

Example 7.3   Using importance sampling, evaluate the integral

$$F = \int_0^1 e^{-x^2}\, dx\, .$$

A reasonable choice of the weighting function is $\wp(x) = Ae^{-x}$, where A is chosen such that $\wp(x)$ is normalized over the domain. In this case the domain is 0 to 1, and

$$\int \wp(x)\, dx = 1 = -Ae^{-x}\Big|_0^1 \quad\Rightarrow\quad A = \left(1 - \frac{1}{e}\right)^{-1} = 1.582.$$

We thus generate n random numbers and distribute the n trials according to Equation (7.7); that is,

$$Q(x) = \int_0^x Ae^{-x'}\, dx' = -Ae^{-x'}\Big|_0^x = A(1 - e^{-x})\, .$$

Thus, for a random number r generated from a uniform distribution, we may find an x value from

$$r = A(1 - e^{-x}) \quad\Rightarrow\quad x = -\ln\left(1 - \frac{r}{A}\right)$$

which samples the distribution $\wp(x_i)$.

The integral is computed using Equation (7.6) where

$$\sum_i \frac{f(x_i)}{\wp(x_i)} = \sum_i \frac{e^{-x_i^2}}{Ae^{-x_i}} = 0.632 \sum_i e^{x_i(1-x_i)}.$$

For 15 trials, the importance sampling method yields $F = 0.7509$ while uniformly distributed sampling yields $F = 0.700$. These values may be compared with the actual value of 0.7468. Obtaining such a close value with only 15 trials is rather fortuitous, but even with 500 trials, $F = 0.7469$ with importance sampling and 0.758 without. One must sample on the order of 10,000 trials from an uniform distribution to obtain about the same degree of accuracy that can be obtained with less than 50 trials from the nonuniform distribution. With 10,000 trials, sampling from a uniform distribution yields $F = 0.7458$ while importance sampling yields 0.7468.

7.2 RANDOM WALK METHODS

A more general way to produce an arbitrary nonuniform probability distribution is with a particular kind of importance sampling procedure introduced by Metropolis et al.[1] in 1953. Let us first examine random walk methods in general. The methods themselves are useful for calculating diffusion coefficients, polymer configurations, defect migration in crystal lattices, and so forth. Then, we will show how to use a random walk method to generate random variables from any desired nonuniform probability distribution. Being able to generate nonuniform random numbers is necessary to apply the Metropolis algorithm for calculating thermodynamic properties because it uses importance sampling.

Consider now a one-dimensional example of a random walk model. A drunkard beginning at $x = 0$ repetitively takes steps either to the right or left on the sidewalk shown in Figure 7.4. Each step taken is of uniform length L, and the direction of the step is independent of the previous step. This latter requirement stretches the credibility of the analogy because the momentum of the previous step would in reality tend to cause the drunk to stumble along in the same direction for more than one step. We shall see that this step independence is necessary to generate a Markov chain of events for which the Metropolis method is applicable. It does not mean, however, that steps to the right and left are equally probable. Presumably the drunk has a preferred direction. A step in the intended direction would have a probability of one for a completely sober walker, but this probability would decrease toward 0.5 with increasing levels of inebriation. Let us denote the probability of a step to the right as p and that of a step to the left as $q = 1 - p$. We are interested in the probability of finding the drunk at position x after N total steps. The domain of x is $-NL \le x \le NL$; these limits corresponding to the cases of all steps during the walk being taken in the same direction.

A Monte Carlo solution of the random walk problem is done by multiple simulations of the walk, starting each time from $x = 0$ and recording the final position. Each move is done by choosing a random number and moving to the right if the random number is less than p, or to the left if it is greater than p. The average displacement, $<x>$, is found by taking the average of the final positions of the many simulations. Likewise, the variance or mean square displacement, $V(x) = <x^2> - <x>^2$, can be determined directly from the final positions and the average position. Alternatively, one could determine the probability of any location x after N steps, $\wp_N(x)$, by dividing the number of times x is the final position by the total number of simulations. The corresponding values of the mean displacement and the mean-square displacement are then found from the generated probabilities using,

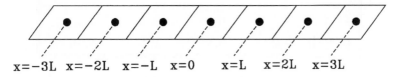

$$x=-3L \quad x=-2L \quad x=-L \quad x=0 \quad x=L \quad x=2L \quad x=3L$$

Figure 7.4   One-dimensional walk of a drunkard on a sidewalk.

$$<x> = \sum_{x=-NL}^{+NL} x\, \wp_N(x)$$

$$V(x) = \sum_{x=-NL}^{+NL} x^2\, \wp_N(x) .$$

For small N, direct enumeration of the probabilities can be made as in Figure 7.5. Notice from the enumeration that the random walk probabilities are related to the binomial coefficients. We can in fact solve this particular random walk problem analytically by making use of the binomial theorem as in Example 7.4. The analytical results for the above quantities are $<x> = (p - q)NL$ and $<x^2> - <x>^2 = 4NpqL^2$. Notice that if $p = q = 1/2$ then the mean displacement is zero, but the dispersion about the starting point is NL^2.

Of course, we are more interested in the motion of molecules in a fluid than a drunk on a sidewalk. The positional dispersion noted in this problem is suggestive of, in fact analogous to, diffusional dispersion in a fluid. The self-diffusion coefficient relates the flux of particles past a plane under equilibrium conditions, that is, when there is no driving force due to macroscopic gradients of temperature, pressure, or chemical potential. The Einstein relation

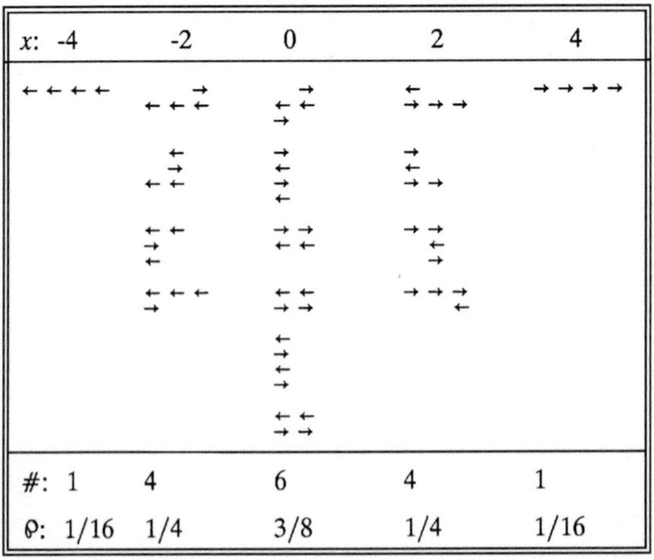

Figure 7.5 Direct enumeration of one-dimensional random walk after four steps.

Example 7.4   Consider the one-dimensional walk of a drunk along the sidewalk of Figure 7.4. Derive analytical expressions for the mean and mean-square displacement in terms of the step length L, the number of steps N, the probability of a step to the right p and the probability of a step to the left q. For the case of $p = q = 1/2$, $L = 2$ ft and $N = 1000$, determine $<x>$, $<x^2> - <x>^2$, and the self-diffusion coefficient D of the drunk assuming each step takes 1 s.

It is convenient in this problem to work with the number of steps taken to the right N_+ and the number taken to the left N_-. Of course the total number of steps is N, so $N_- = N - N_+$. We can then express the desired quantities in terms of these directional steps. Thus,

$$<x> = (<N_+> - <N_->)L$$

and

$$x = (N_+ - N_-)L = (2N_+ - N)L \quad \Rightarrow \quad x - <x> = 2(N_+ - <N_+>)L \,,$$

which yields for the mean-square displacement or dispersion term

$$<x^2> - <x>^2 = \langle x - <x> \rangle^2 = 4 \langle N_+ - <N_+> \rangle^2.$$

We can now proceed to find the expectation values of the directional steps. The probability of taking N_+ steps to the right is given by the usual binomial expression

$$\wp_N(N_+) = \frac{N!}{N_+!(N - N_+)!} \, p^{N_+} \, q^{N-N_+} \,.$$

The first and second moments are given by

$$<N_+> = \sum_{N_+=0}^{N} N_+ \, \wp_N(N_+)$$

$$<N_+^2> = \sum_{N_+=0}^{N} N_+^2 \, \wp_N(N_+) \,.$$

The binomial theorem is a useful trick for evaluating these sums. Note that if the N_+ terms did not appear in the above moments, the sum over $\wp_N$ would simply be $(p + q)^N$. We can use derivatives of $\wp$ with respect to p to transform the terms in the sum to expressions that can be summed via the binomial theorem. By differentiating $\wp_N(N_+)$ with respect to p once, we obtain

$$p\left(\frac{\partial \, \wp_N(N_+)}{\partial p}\right) = N_+ \, \wp_N(N_+) \,.$$

Thus,

Example 7.4   Continued.

$$<N_+> = \sum_{N_+=0}^{N} N_+ \wp_N(N_+) = p\left(\frac{\partial \sum \wp_N(N_+)}{\partial p}\right)$$

$$= p\left(\frac{\partial(p + q)^N}{\partial p}\right) = pN(p + q)^{N-1} = pN.$$

By a similar analysis, one can show that $<N_-> = qN$. Therefore we obtain

$$<x> = (p - q)NL .$$

The mean-square deviation is found by applying the derivative trick twice. Thus,

$$N_+^2 \wp_N(N_+) = p\left[\frac{\partial}{\partial p}\left(p\frac{\partial \wp_N}{\partial p}\right)\right] .$$

Using this relationship, one can show with some simple algebra that

$$<N_+^2> - <N_+>^2 = Npq ,$$

or

$$<x^2> - <x>^2 = 4NpqL^2.$$

After 1000 steps, the expected position of the drunk is $<x> = (1/2 - 1/2)\cdot200$ ft $= 0$. The variance is given by $<x^2> - <x>^2 = (4)(1000)(1/2)(1/2)(4\ ft^2) = 4000$ ft^2. This dispersion is directly related to a self-diffusion coefficient through the Einstein Equation (7.9); that is,

$$D = \frac{4000\ ft^2}{(2)(1000\ s)} = 2\ ft^2/s.$$

$$D(t) = \frac{1}{2dt}<\Delta R^2(t)> \tag{7.9}$$

relates the self-diffusion coefficient to the mean-square displacement at time t. In Equation(7.9), d is the dimensionality of the system. We should remind ourselves at this point that MC simulations statistically sample phase space; they are not intended to actually follow the trajectory of a particle. Although the random walk simulation is analogous to the diffusional process, it is not to be taken as the time history of the system. In the next chapter, molecular dynamics simulations, which do follow the transient behavior of the model system, are introduced. We will find that Equation (7.9) is valid only at times long relative to molecular collisions.

Random walks can of course be done in more than one dimension and with more than one walker. For example, we might place c walkers on a three-dimensional lattice of empty sites. Each site is either vacant or occupied by a molecule. Each particle's initial position is recorded in an array. At each step, a particle is chosen at random and a neighboring site is randomly selected. If the neighboring site is empty, the molecule is moved to the new site, otherwise the original position is retained. The simulation mimics the idealized view of diffusion as random molecular jumps to thermal vacancies. Such *lattice gas* models have received considerable attention (see Problems 25–27).

Many applications of random walk simulations exist. One can easily imagine using such procedures to model Brownian motion, surface diffusion, absorption, and so forth. A very important application of random walk methods is in investigation of polymer physics. Polymers consist of repeated chemical units. Because of bond rotational degrees of freedom, a long polymer can be quite flexible and take on a number of different geometrical shapes in dilute solutions. The end-to-end length of the polymer can be used as a measure of the degree to which the polymer kinks and bends in the solution. If we view the polymer as equal-length segments linked together at flexible joints, we can easily perform MC simulations on a lattice of points spaced equally in all directions by the length of the monomeric segments. We then pick an arbitrary lattice point to start the walk. The walk from node to node represents the addition of monomer segments to the polymer as shown in Figure 7.6. For an N-mer, a polymer of N segments, we repeatedly take N-step random walks, calculate the end-to-end distance R_D of each resultant polymer, and use the results to find the expectation value of R_D.

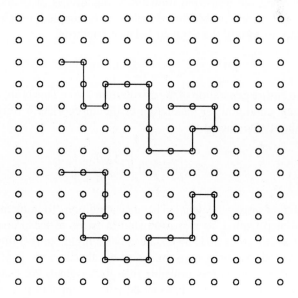

Figure 7.6   Depiction of polymer with random walk on a lattice.

A physical constraint in generating the polymer is that two monomers cannot occupy the same location in space. Many methods of incorporating this constraint into the simulation have been developed. The easiest, but least efficient, method is a self-avoiding walk. In the self-avoiding walk, one continues taking steps until either all N segments have been generated or the molecule intersects with itself. In the latter case, the random walk is terminated, the configuration is discarded and a new walk is begun from the origin. Example 7.5 employs such a method to generate sample configurations and obtain $<R_D>$. Obviously, this method becomes very inefficient for large N when most of the simulations will self-intersect prior to placement of all N segments on the lattice. More efficient methods are available[4] to handle the self-intersection problem.

Our short excursis into the subject of random walks has laid the foundation for a very important use of random walks: generating random variables from a nonuniform distribution for use in importance sampling techniques. The key to random walk simulations is the transition probability that connects the new and old locations. It is obvious from Example 7.4 that accepting moves to the right or left in accordance with a uniform random number generator produces a binomial distribution. By changing the transition probability function, we can generate points from any distribution we choose. To generate a set of nonuniformly distributed points $[x_i]$, selection is made during a random walk from one point x_i to the next x_j, accepting or rejecting possible steps in accordance with a transition probability function, $w(x_i \rightarrow x_j)$. This function is chosen so that the distribution of points $x_0, x_1, x_2 \ldots$ converges (after a considerable number of steps) to $\wp(x)$. Choosing the transition probability function is of course the key to ensuring that the correct probability distribution is sampled. Forcing the transition probability to satisfy the detailed balance condition

$$\wp(x_i) \cdot w(x_i \rightarrow x_j) = \wp(x_j) \cdot w(x_j \rightarrow x_i)$$

is sufficient to ensure generation of the distribution $\wp(x)$. This is only a sufficient, not a necessary, condition for generation of the appropriately weighted points. While not unique, the choice

$$w(x_i \rightarrow x_j) = \min\left[1, \frac{\wp(x_j)}{\wp(x_i)}\right] \tag{7.10}$$

is simple and does satisfy the detailed balance condition. To implement Equation (7.10), a trial step from x_i to x_j is evaluated in terms of the probability of the two states. If $\wp(x_j)/\wp(x_i) > 1$, then state x_j has a higher probability than x_i and the step is favored. All such steps are accepted; that is, $w = 1$. If $\wp(x_j)/\wp(x_i) < 1$ then the final state is less probable than the original. We cannot reject all such steps, but such unfavored steps can only be accepted in proportion to their relative probability in the desired distribution. Thus the transition probability for an unfavorable step is set to $\wp(x_j)/\wp(x_i)$. If the step is rejected due to

Example 7.5   Write a simple self-avoiding walk program that will generate various configurations for a two-dimensional, 10-mer molecule and compute the expected R_D in monomer-length units. Use a regular square lattice.

A sample QUICKBASIC subroutine that would perform the random walk is shown below. This code is similar to the routine used in the simulation Example 7.5 on disk. It first uses the random number generator to choose a direction (ndirec) between 1 and 4 (1 = up, 2 = right, 3 = down, and 4 = left). If the new direction is exactly opposite that of the previous direction (direc), then that back-track choice is excluded and a new random number is selected. A check is then performed to exclude self-intersection. The array variable "dot" is changed from 0 to 1 when a walk has arrived at the corresponding site. If the value of "dot" at the new position is already 1, then the walk is aborted and a new one started. This would be handled in the subroutine called "restart" in the code below.

```
SUB walk
'---------------{ Select move }----------
count = count + 1
DO
    ndirec = 1 + INT (4 * RND)
    change = ABS(ndirec - direc)
LOOP WHILE (change = 2)
direc = ndirec
SELECT CASE direc
CASE IS = 1
    y = yold + 1      '------{ Move up }----------
CASE IS = 2
    x = xold + 1      '------{ Move right }-------
CASE IS = 3
    y = yold - 1      '------{ Move down }-------
CASE IS = 4
    x = xold - 1      '------{ Move left }-------
CASE ELSE
    STOP
END SELECT
IF dot(x, y) = 1 THEN      '------{ Intersection occurred }-------
    CALL restart
ELSE
    dot(x, y) = 1      '------{ New position is OK }-------
    IF count >= nmer THEN CALL madeit '------{ Walk is complete }
END IF
END SUB
```

The code on disk yielded $<R_D>$ = 4.8 for the 10-mer case after 100 successful generations of configurations.

unfavorable probabilities, x_i is retained for that step and the procedure continues to the next trial step. In this manner, the more probable states are sampled more often.

Implementation of this procedure to generate a set of $[x_i]$ conforming to the distribution $\wp(x)$ is generally done with the following algorithm (where x_i is the current point, x_t is the trial point, and x_j is the next point to be calculated):

1. Choose a trial position $x_t = x_i + n$ where n is a random number in the interval $[-\delta, \delta]$.
2. Calculate $w = \wp(x_t)/\wp(x_n)$.
3. If $w \geq 1$, accept the change and let $x_j = x_t$.
4. If $w < 1$, generate a random number r and accept the change ($x_j = x_t$) if $r \leq w$, otherwise reject the step.
5. If x_t is rejected, then $x_j = x_i$.

A couple of tricks help speed up the sampling procedure and optimize its efficiency. Because we want to obtain the asymptotic distribution as rapidly as possible, the first value x_0 is generally chosen at or near the maximum of $\wp(x)$ where sampling will be most heavily performed. If we choose too large of a step size (δ), most of the steps will be rejected making the generation of $\wp(x)$ inefficient. On the other hand, if δ is too small, it will take too many steps to sample the distribution adequately, and again the procedure will be inefficient. A rough guideline for an optimized value of δ is one for which an acceptance ratio of approximately 0.3 to 0.5 is generated. An example of the application of this method to the generation of a Gaussian distribution is given as Example 7.6.

The importance of generating states or trials with the appropriate probability distribution is obviously an essential part of importance sampling, and the Metropolis algorithm has become almost synonymous with MC molecular simulations. The Metropolis method generates a *Markov chain* of states, a sequence of trials that have the appropriate limiting distribution and satisfy two conditions: 1) the outcome of each trial belongs to a finite set of permissible outcomes, and 2) the outcome of each trial depends only on the outcome of the trial that immediately precedes it. In calculating accurate thermophysical properties using MC simulations, generation of a Markov chain is essential to ensure proper sampling of phase space. Only as phase space points are generated with the proper probability will ensemble averaging yield appropriate properties.

7.3 FLUID SIMULATIONS

The calculation of fluid thermophysical properties from MC simulations is based on generation of sufficient ensemble members that statistically accurate properties can be calculated. We can never hope to generate all states but must

Example 7.6   Using the Metropolis algorithm, generate the Gaussian distribution

$$\wp(x) = A\exp(-x^2/2).$$

That is, generate a set of random numbers that obeys a Gaussian or normal distribution instead of the uniform set of random numbers generated by computers.

To generate $\wp(x)$ we will start at $x_0 = 0$ where the distribution is at a maximum and use a step size of $\delta = 3.5$. Each step is made by choosing a random number between $-\delta$ and δ and comparing it to the ratio $\wp(x_j)/\wp(x_i)$ in accordance with the acceptance–rejection criteria given in the algorithm on page 230. The first few steps using the accompanying QUICKBASIC code yields:

Step	x_i	x_j	$\wp(x_j)$	$\wp(x_i)$	$\dfrac{\wp(x_j)/}{\wp(x_i)}$	r	Accept
1	0	1.439	0.36	1.00	0.36	0.53	−
2	0	0.557	0.86	1.00	0.86	0.29	+
3	0.557	−0.830	0.71	0.86	0.83	0.77	+
4	−0.830	−4.232	0.0001	0.71	0.00	0.76	−
5	−0.830	1.372	0.39	0.71	0.55	0.71	−

A histogram formed by collecting the results in 0.3-width bins is shown below for a 2000-step simulation.

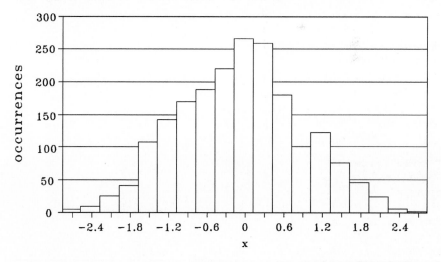

QUICKBASIC CODE:

```
REM**********************************************
REM**    METROPOLIS RANDOM WALK              **
REM** Use random walk to generate random numbers**
REM** from a Gaussian distribution           **
REM**********************************************
DECLARE SUB metropolis(x)
```

Example 7.6   Continued

```
DECLARE FUNCTION p(x)
DIM bin (-9 TO 9)
CLS
ntry = 2000                                   :REM Number of steps in simulation
x = 0                                         :REM Initial location
del = 3.5                                     :REM Step size
naccept = 0
FOR k = -9 TO 9                               :REM Zero histogram bins
   bin(k) = 0
NEXT
FOR try = 1 TO ntry                           :REM Perform random walk
   CALL metropolis(x)
   FOR k = -9 TO 9                            :REM Put step into histogram bin
   IF x >= k*.3-.15 AND x < (k+1)*.3-.15 THEN bin(k) = bin(k) +1
   NEXT
NEXT
FOR i = -9 TO 9                               :REM Print out histogram
     PRINT USING "### ";bin(i)
NEXT
PRINT "Acceptance ratio="; naccept / ntry
PRINT
END


SUB metropolis(x)
SHARED naccept, del
  xt = x + del * (2 * RND - 1)
  test = RND
  w = p(xt) / p(x)
  PRINT USING "###.#### ";x; xt; p(xt); p(x); w; test
  IF test < = w THEN
    x = xt
    naccept = naccept + 1
  END IF
END SUB

FUNCTION p(y)
p = EXP(-y * y / 2)
END FUNCTION
```

be content with generating a representative, but considerably smaller, sample of M states that appropriately span and represent the region of phase space available to the system. For the canonical ensemble, the expectation value of some property J is then obtained from

$$<J> = \frac{\sum\limits_{i}^{M} J_i e^{-\beta E_i}}{\sum\limits_{j}^{M} e^{-\beta E_j}} . \tag{7.11}$$

A crude MC procedure would be to generate a configuration at random; calculate E_i, J_i, and the product $A_i \exp(-\beta E_i)$ for this state; and evaluate its contribution to the sums in Equation (7.11). Such randomly chosen configurations would include many fairly improbable states which would contribute little to the sums. As previously discussed in this chapter, a much more efficient technique is to use importance sampling and generate M configurations in accordance with the probability distribution function $\wp_i$. Because we will use a biased sample to obtain the average, each configuration must be divided by $\wp_i$ to remove the bias. Thus,

$$<J> = \frac{\sum\limits_{i=1}^{M} \frac{J_i}{\wp_i} e^{-\beta E_i}}{\sum\limits_{j=1}^{M} \frac{1}{\wp_j} e^{-\beta E_j}} . \tag{7.12}$$

From the form of Equation (7.12), it appears that a reasonable choice, and the one made by Metropolis, for $\wp_i$ that would make the sampling reasonably efficient is the Boltzmann probability function itself,

$$\wp_i = \frac{e^{-\beta E_i}}{\sum\limits_{j} e^{-\beta E_j}} = \frac{e^{-\beta E_i}}{Q} . \tag{7.13}$$

Substitution of Equation (7.13) into Equation (7.12) shows that no bias is introduced by this approach as the expectation value can be simplified to

$$<J> = \frac{1}{M} \sum\limits_{i} J_i . \tag{7.14}$$

Thus, using a Markov chain distributed according to the Boltzman probability function allows expectation values to be obtained from simple averages of the property values sampled at the weighted configurations.

MC simulations of fluids are considerably simplified by the fact that momentum variables are irrelevant to the configurational properties. Table 5.1 indicates that configurational contributions to thermodynamic properties can be computed from just the radial distribution function, that is, structural or positional information.

The Metropolis procedure for generating a Markov chain for molecular positions is:

1. Establish an initial configuration.
2. Make a random trial change in the position of a random molecule.
3. Compute ΔE, the change in energy of the system due to the trial change. Fortunately, for pairwise additive potentials only the energy between the moved molecule and neighbors within the distance of the potential interaction need be recalculated for this step since all other pair interactions will not change.
4. If $\Delta E \leq 0$, accept the new configuration.
5. If $\Delta E > 0$, compute the transition probability $w = e^{-\beta \Delta E}$, generate a random number r in the interval $[0,1]$, and accept the move if $w \geq r$ or retain the previous configuration if $w < r$.
6. Determine the value of the physical property J_i for this configuration.
7. Repeat the moves over a sufficient number of trials.
8. Find averages of the properties from Equation (7.14).

Actual implementation of the MC method to thermophysical property prediction obviously depends on the chosen intermolecular potential. We will first look at its use to calculate hard-sphere properties and then identify the changes in the approach that must be made for continuous potential functions. In both cases, we will concentrate on obtaining the radial distribution function as the property of interest. As discussed in Chapter 5, most other properties can be readily calculated from a knowledge of $g(r)$. However, many properties can be conveniently calculated from a direct ensemble average of the appropriate mechanical variables. We will wait and introduce those methods in the next chapter on molecular dynamics, but one should realize that most are also applicable to MC. Because the two simulation methods have much in common, we will focus more on simulation methodology in this chapter and the actual thermophysical property calculations in the next.

7.4 MC SIMULATION OF HARD-SPHERE FLUIDS

MC simulation of fluid properties is relatively easy, and the coding involved is straightforward. As mentioned, a number of properties can be obtained from the simulations, but we will focus primarily on calculation of the rdf in this chapter. Formulas in Tables 5.1 and 5.2 can then be used to readily calculate thermodynamic properties from a knowledge of the spatial dependence of the rdf. In this section we illustrate simulation of hard spheres; in the following section we provide a subroutine that can be added to the basic code to simulate soft potentials. PROGRAM *mc_hs* written in QUICKBASIC, serves as a procedural example or focal point for discussion of several common techniques used in MC simulations of fluids. In it, only dimensionless quantities are utilized so that box length, positions, and move distances are all scaled with respect to σ; that is, all lengths are in units of σ and the program is independent of the actual size of the particles.

```
REM ****************************************
REM ** PROGRAM mc_hs.bas                 **
REM ** MC simulation of hard-sphere fluids **
REM ****************************************
DECLARE SUB initial ()
DECLARE SUB move ()
DECLARE SUB finish ()
DECLARE SUB check (particle)
DECLARE SUB g ()
DIM x(3, 64), xnew(64), gsum(50), rslot(50)
RANDOMIZE (TIMER)
CLS
INPUT "Number of dimensions"; nd
INPUT "Dimensionless number density"; rho
INPUT "Maximum move distance"; delta
INPUT "Number of equilibration steps"; equil
INPUT "Number of MC steps"; nstep
n = 4 ^ nd: REM ** 4 particles per dimension **
v = n / rho: REM ** box volume **
L = v ^ (1 / nd): REM ** box length **
L2 = L / 2
nbins = 30: REM ** set up 30 bins for histogram **
delr = L2 / nbins
pi = 3.14159
CALL initial: REM ** set up initial configuration **
REM ** Do equilibration before finding g **
PRINT "equilibrating. . ."
FOR i = 1 TO equil
    CALL move
NEXT
REM ** Now do actual simulation **
accept = 0
PRINT USING "Of total ### steps, now doing step:"; nstep;
FOR i = 1 TO nstep
    LOCATE , 36: PRINT i;
    CALL move
    CALL g
NEXT
```

```
CALL finish
END
```

7.4.1 Initial Configuration

To begin the simulation, an arbitrary initial configuration must be chosen. Yet, the simulation must be independent of the starting configuration if the calculated properties are to be meaningful. This is enforced by running the simulation sufficiently long to "equilibrate" the fluid before information is collected for property calculations. This provides a sufficient number of collisions to occur to eliminate any "memory" of the initial configuration before beginning to find property averages. Generally, a relative invariance of the system energy with respect to averages taken at different times is assumed to be an indication of proper equilibration.

The initial configuration may be generated in several ways. A "cold" start may be used in which the molecules are assigned to regular lattice positions as shown in Figure 7.7. The most easily programmed configuration is a regular lattice of particles in rows and columns, but this starting configuration is impractical at high densities because the extra space trapped between stacked molecules precludes a sufficiently dense packing to initiate the simulation. The body-centered cubic lattice is a more tightly packed lattice suitable for high-density

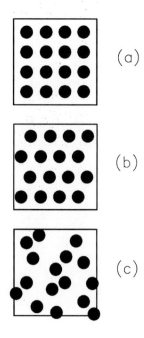

Figure 7.7 Possible starting configurations for two-dimensional simulations: (**a**) regular lattice, (**b**) triangular lattice, and (**c**) hot start.

simulations in three dimensions. The triangular lattice shown in Figure 7.7 serves a similar purpose for two dimensions.

Starting a simulation from a "cold" start requires considerable time for equilibration in order to dissipate the initial structure artificially introduced into the system. In essence one must allow the initial crystal to melt or sublime, as the case may be, and then continue to equilibrate until the fluid represents a phase-space point actually accessible to the equilibrium fluid. "Hot" starts, initial configurations where the particle positions are chosen at random, can be used to reduce the amount of equilibration time for low-density simulations. As shown in Figure 7.7, the hot-start configuration is random and therefore much more likely to be close to or within the volume of phase-space accessible to the equilibrium fluid. To generate a hot initial configuration, particles can be placed sequentially by assigning coordinates with a random number generator and checking for overlap with previously placed particles. This kind of a "hot" start also tends to fail at higher densities because it becomes more and more time consuming to insert a particle randomly into a void as the final particles are added to a nearly full box. The method becomes quite inefficient for high-density liquids.

The most efficient starting configuration is a configuration from a previous simulation. Usually the final configuration of a simulation is saved and used to start the next simulation. If the conditions of the new simulation are the same as in the previous run, then no equilibration steps are required because the initial configuration is itself a bona fide phase point. If the conditions for the new run are different, the final configuration from the previous simulation may still be useable as the initial configuration, but equilibration must be used. Generally the equilibration time is still much less from this kind of start than any of the others.

For the illustration code discussed here, SUBROUTINE *initial* generates a cold-start configuration. First, the number of particles per unit length per dimension is computed and the distance between centers of molecules required for the desired density is calculated. A triangular lattice for two dimensions, or a body-centered cubic lattice for three dimensions, is next generated by shifting every other row one half position. In a more sophisticated MC program one would also want available an option to begin the simulation by reading in a previous configuration. One might also program the code to choose a "hot" or "cold" starting option based on the desired density.

```
SUB initial
SHARED n, nd, x(), L
   REM ** compute number of particles required per side **
   nlin = INT(n ^ (1 / nd))
   IF nlin ^ nd <> n THEN
       PRINT "ERROR: n must be integer to nd power"
       STOP
```

```
            END IF
            dL = L / nlin:REM ** particle separation **
            particle = 0
            IF nd = 2 THEN
                FOR row = 1 TO nlin
                    IF (row MOD 2) = 0 THEN
                        offset = .5
                    ELSE
                        offset = 0
                    END IF
                    FOR col = 1 TO nlin
                        particle = particle + 1
                        x(1, particle) = (col - .75) * dL + offset
                        x(2, particle) = (row - .5) * dL
                    NEXT
                NEXT
            ELSEIF nd = 3 THEN
                FOR layer = 1 TO nlin
                    IF (layer MOD 2) = 0 THEN
                        offset = .5
                    ELSE
                        offset = 0
                    END IF
                    FOR row = 1 TO nlin
                        IF (row MOD 2) = 0 THEN
                            offset1 = .5
                        ELSE
                            offset1 = 0
                        END IF
                        FOR col = 1 TO nlin
                            particle = particle + 1
                            x(1, particle) = (col - .75) * dL + offset1
                            x(2, particle) = (row - .75) * dL + offset
                            x(3, particle) = (layer - .5) * dL
                        NEXT
                    NEXT
                NEXT
            ELSE
                PRINT "ERROR: only 2 and 3 dimensions allowed"
                STOP
            END IF
        END SUB
```

7.4.2 The Simulation

An easy way to implement the Metropolis algorithm for a hard-sphere system is to choose a particle at random and move it to a new trial position. If the particle overlaps another particle in the new position, then the trial move

---

Example 7.7   Write a program that implements the Metropolis method for hard spheres in two dimensions. The example on disk illustrates the trial moves and the subsequent acceptance or rejection of the trial steps in two dimensions.

---

is rejected and the previous configuration is retained. This is easily implemented, although checking for overlap can be quite CPU intensive. Various bookkeeping tricks can be used to shorten the overlap check. For example, one can keep a neighborhood list, a list of particles in the immediate vicinity of each particle. Overlap need only be checked between particles in the neighborhood list of the particle moved. This of course also requires frequent update of the neighborhood list, but it can still be an effective time-saving device. For simplicity of discussion, the following program does not incorporate any such features. For large numbers of particles, this code would be rather inefficient and a neighborhood list would be important.

Periodic boundary conditions are implemented by checking the coordinates of the trial position. For example, if the x component of the trial position exceeds that of the box, then the particle has been moved through the right face of the box and must be reentered through the left face. Mathematically this can be done by subtracting the length of the box in the x direction, L_x, from the particle's x coordinate; that is,

$$x_{\text{actual}} = x_{\text{trial}} - L_x \; (x_{\text{trial}} > L_x). \tag{7.15}$$

If, on the other hand, $x_{\text{trial}} < 0$, then the particle has been moved through the left face and must be reentered through the right face of the cell:

$$x_{\text{actual}} = x_{\text{trial}} + L_x \; (x_{\text{trial}} < 0). \tag{7.16}$$

Similar arguments and equations apply for each of the other directions. Because numerical calculations are faster than logic tests, some improvement in efficiency may be obtained by eliminating the IF–THEN test in favor of subtracting the appropriate number of box lengths from all positions using the INT function; that is,

$$x_{\text{actual}} = x_{\text{trial}} - \text{L*INT}(x_{\text{trial}}/L). \tag{7.17}$$

In SUBROUTINE *move*, the Metropolis algorithm is implemented. Particles chosen at random are moved to trial locations, and periodic boundary conditions are enforced as previously described. The acceptance of each new move is checked in SUBROUTINE *check* by looking for overlap between the trial position and the other N-1 particles. If overlap occurs, the move is rejected and the previous configuration is preserved for that step, otherwise the move is accepted. Example 7.7 illustrates the method described here.

```
SUB move
SHARED n, L, x(), xnew(), nd, accept, delta
    REM ** Implement Metropolis algorithm **
    FOR i = 1 TO n
        particle = INT(n * RND + 1): REM choose particle to move
        FOR j = 1 TO nd
            xnew(j) = x(j, particle) + (2 * RND - 1) * delta
            REM ** apply periodic boundary condition **
            IF xnew(j) > L THEN
                    xnew(j) = xnew(j) - L
            ELSEIF xnew(j) < 0 THEN
                    xnew(j) = xnew(j) + L
            END IF
        NEXT
        CALL check(particle)
    NEXT
END SUB


SUB check (particle)
SHARED n, L, x(), xnew(), nd, accept, L2
REM ** check for overlap of new position with other molecules **
    FOR neighbor = 1 TO n
        IF particle <> neighbor THEN
            r2 = 0
            FOR k = 1 TO nd
                dx = ABS(xnew(k) - x(k, neighbor))
                IF dx > L2 THEN
                    dx = dx - L
                END IF
                r2 = r2 + dx * dx
            NEXT
            IF r2 < 1 THEN EXIT SUB: REM overlap - reject move
        END IF
    NEXT
    accept = accept + 1
    FOR k = 1 TO nd
        x(k, particle) = xnew(k)
    NEXT
END SUB
```

7.4.3 Calculation of Properties

Properties are calculated from the MC simulation using Equation (7.14). In this example, we calculate only the rdf from the simulation. The rdf is obtained in SUBROUTINE g, by generating a histogram for the ensemble average number of particles a distance r from the center of a reference particle.

The distance between all N-1 particles and the chosen particle is calculated for all N particles. Numbers of particles lying within certain r values of the reference particle are then accumulated in equal-sized bins throughout the duration of the simulation. In SUBROUTINE *finish*, the histogram is normalized, and the ensemble average is formed from the number of particles and the number of MC steps used in the simulation. The discrete form of g tells us the number of particles in a ring for two-dimensional (2-D) or in a narrow spherical shell for three-dimensional (3-D) simulations of thickness dr located a distance r from the central molecule, relative to the number of particles that theoretically would be in this band if the molecules were entirely randomly positioned. The area of the ring or volume of the spherical shell can be calculated from $A = 2\pi r$ dr or $V = 4\pi r^2$ dr, respectively. For the 3-D case, the expected number of particles in the spherical shell from the bulk density would be ρV. This factor is divided into the ensemble average of particles for that shell to obtain g. Note that in SUBROUTINE g, only 1/2N particle distances are used to avoid overcounting. The local number density $<\rho(r)>$ is thus found by dividing *gsum(bin)* by ($nstep*n/2*vol$). Finally, $g(r) = <\rho(r)>/\rho$. A similar procedure is used for the 2-D case. The results are then printed out.

```
SUB g
SHARED n, x(), gsum(), delr, L2, nd, nbins
    REM ** generate histogram for rdf **
    FOR particle = 1 TO n - 1
        FOR neighbor = particle + 1 TO n
            r2 = 0
            FOR k = 1 TO nd
                dx = ABS(x(k, neighbor) - x(k, particle))
                IF dx > L2 THEN
                    dx = dx - L
                END IF
                r2 = r2 + dx * dx
            NEXT
            bin = INT(SQR(r2) / delr + .5)
            IF bin <= nbins THEN gsum(bin) = gsum(bin) + 1
        NEXT
    NEXT
END SUB


SUB finish
SHARED pi, nstep, n, accept, rho, rslot(), gsum(), delr, nd, nbins
REM ** normalize histogram and print results**
    ntime = nstep * n
    accept = accept / ntime
    PRINT
    PRINT "RESULTS:"
```

```
PRINT "Acceptance ratio="; accept
sum = 0
FOR bin = 1 TO nbins
    sum = sum + gsum(bin)
NEXT
FOR bin = 1 TO nbins
    rslot(bin) = (bin - .5) * delr
    IF nd = 2 THEN
        vol = 2 * pi * rslot(bin) * delr
    ELSE
        vol = 4 * pi * rslot(bin) * rslot(bin) * delr
    END IF
    gsum(bin) = 2 * gsum(bin) / (ntime * vol * rho)
NEXT
bin = 0
FOR col = 1 TO 65 STEP 25
    LOCATE 12, col
    PRINT " #     r     g"
    FOR row = 13 TO 22
        bin = bin + 1
        LOCATE row, col
        PRINT USING "##"; bin;
        PRINT USING "   ##.##"; rslot(bin); gsum(bin)
    NEXT
NEXT
END SUB
```

In SUBROUTINE g, use is made of the periodic boundaries and the minimum image convention. Periodic boundary conditions are equivalent to wrapping the cell around on itself such that opposite cell sides are coincident. This may also be represented as a replication of the basic cell in all directions as in Figure 7.8. But, we must be careful, because particles that appear to be on opposite sides of the cell are actually much closer together than they appear in our simple diagram, because their minimum separation distance is really through the artificial cell wall. We must be careful not to include particles in our averages that are further than half a cell length ($L/2$) away from the central particle in any one direction or the same particle will be included twice, once directly and again in the opposite direction through the imaginary cell boundary. The use of periodic boundary conditions eliminates the need for physical boundaries that would impart undesired wall effects to a simulation of a macroscopic fluid. As such, the fluid is thought of as a continuum and the minimum separation distance between particles may be taken as the minimum distance between nearest images in the replicated cells as shown in Figure 7.8. For example, if the x distance between two particles in a cell is $0.8L_x$, measured from left to right, the minimum image x separation is $0.8L_x - L_x = -0.2L_x$, as measured

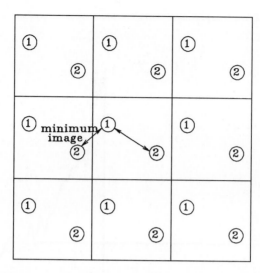

Figure 7.8   The periodic boundary condition and the minimum image convention.

through the left face and back through the right face of the cell. More is said in the next chapter about the minimum image convention.

Figure 7.9, generated using a 3-D simulation of 64 particles as described in Example 7.8, illustrates the fact that the rdf for a hard-sphere liquid contains the usual characteristics that we have come to expect for real fluids. Obviously no particles can be found in the simulation at $r^+ < 1$ because overlap is forbidden for hard spheres. The rdf peaks shortly beyond $r^+ = 1$ where the local probability of finding a particle is higher than the global probability. This may seem strange for a potential with no attractive region, but the exclusion of particles very near the central particle means that packing must be slightly higher than the bulk density in the accessible region just beyond the central particle. This enhanced probability of the first coordination shell decreases the number of molecules located in the region around $r^+ = 1.5$ relative to the bulk or average number density, producing an oscillating g similar to that obtained from potentials with attractive portions.

Values of g beyond about 2.0 have little meaning in this simulation. The minimum image convention permits accumulation of new information only out to a distance of $L/2$. Particles separated by a distance larger than $L/2$ have already been included through their minimum images; if these particles were again placed in bins for $r^+ > L/2$, an artificial and erroneous periodicity would be propagated in the calculation of g. Therefore, the maximum distance over which properties can be obtained from a simulation is $L/2$. For the density used in this simulation $L/2 = 2.52$, about 2.5 molecular diameters. This restricts the minimum size of the cell that can be used for simulations, but does not cause

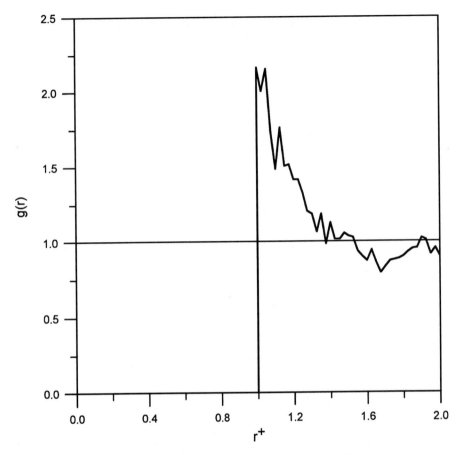

Figure 7.9   Radial distribution function at $\rho^+ = 0.5$.

Example 7.8   Using the MC method, compute $g(r)$ for a 64-particle system at a reduced density of $\rho^+ = 0.5$.

The example on disk is an example of this kind of a program. Figure 7.9 was generated with that program using 80 steps/particle. Twenty MC steps/particle were used to equilibrate the system before relative particle locations were used to increment the g histogram. With a maximum step size of 0.5σ, the acceptance ratio for this simulation was about 24%.

---

a big problem when simulating systems interacting through short-range interactions such as dispersion forces.

7.5 MC SIMULATIONS OF FLUIDS WITH CONTINUOUS POTENTIALS

Fluids interacting with other potentials can also be simulated with the Metropolis algorithm. We have already discussed all the principles necessary to implement the acceptance/rejection criteria for the Metropolis algorithm for such fluids. Whereas for hard spheres all trial moves resulting in overlap were rejected, the Metropolis algorithm for softer potentials determines the acceptance of energetically unfavorable steps by comparison of the transition probability to a random number. A sample subroutine employing the Metropolis algorithm that could be used in place of SUBROUTINE *check* in the hard-sphere program is shown below. This subroutine is written only as an example of how to implement the method for continuous potentials; it would need to be appropriately integrated into the main program if it were to be used. This would include writing a subroutine to compute the potential energy for the desired potential model and establishing appropriate variable transfer between this subroutine and the main program.

```
SUB check (particle)
REM *****************************************************
REM ** Metropolis algorithm for continuous potential **
REM *****************************************************
REM ** Calculate potential of new configuration **
unew = 0
FOR neighbor =1 to n
    If particle <> neighbor THEN
        r2 = 0
        FOR k=1 to nd
        dx = ABS(xnew(k) - x(k, neighbor))
        IF dx > L2 THEN
          dx = dx - L
        END IF
        r2 = r2 + dx * dx
        NEXT
        r = SQR(r2)
        CALL potential(r, u)
        REM *******************************************
        REM ** subroutine potential would evaluate the **
        REM ** potential energy, u, for the chosen    **
        REM ** model at the above value of r. Units of **
        REM ** u are assumed to be kT here.            **
        REM *******************************************
        unew = unew + u
    END IF
NEXT
```

```
REM ** Calculate potential of old configuration **
uold = 0
FOR neighbor =1 to n
   If particle <> neighbor THEN
         r2=0
         FOR k=1 to nd
         dx = ABS(x(k, particle) - x(k, neighbor))
         IF dx > L2 THEN
              dx = dx - L
         END IF
         r2 = r2 + dx * dx
         NEXT
         r = SQR(r2)
         CALL potential(r, u)
         uold = uold + u
   END IF
NEXT
REM ** Now do Metropolis algorithm **
de = unew - uold
IF de > 0 THEN
     IF EXP(-de) < RND THEN EXIT SUB: REM ** reject move **
END IF
accept = accept + 1:REM ** accept move **
FOR k = 1 TO nd
   x(k, particle) = xnew(k)
NEXT
END SUB
```

The accuracy of properties generated in simulations is primarily dependent upon the efficacy of the intermolecular potential model. We can, however, learn a great deal about fluid behavior from very simplistic models that are but analogous representations of fluids. In the next section, we discuss the Ising model, a simplistic model that can be used to study a wide range of phase equilibrium behavior.

7.6 MC SIMULATION OF COOPERATIVE PHENOMENA

7.6.1 Cooperative Phenomena

Phase equilibrium and phase transitions are extremely important in processing materials, particularly in separation processes. This is because phases can be separated from each other by mechanical means and because the distribution of a second component will generally be different in the two phases. Determination of phase boundaries is therefore an important industrial and engineering application of thermodynamics and statistical mechanics.

Let us consider the phase transition between liquid and vapor phases using the van der Waals equation of state

$$P = \frac{nRT}{V-b} - \frac{n^2a}{V^2} \tag{7.18}$$

as a pedagogical model. Because the equation of state is cubic in volume, there are ranges of values for T and P which produce three real roots for V. Figure 7.10 shows the shape of several isotherms, including two at lower temperatures where three real roots are observed. What can three values of V at the same T and P mean physically?

To answer this question, we first examine the question of phase stability. As we shall see, stability is different than equilibrium and refers to the resistance to changes in state due to small intrinsic fluctuations in the fluid. One can show from thermodynamics that a stable, single phase in a one-component fluid minimizes the Helmholtz free energy.[5] This mathematical stability criterion requires that the second derivative of A with respect to V be greater than zero. Thus,

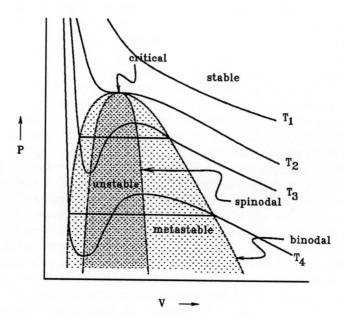

Figure 7.10   Isotherms and stability regions from the van der Waals equation of state.

$$\left(\frac{\partial^2 A}{\partial V^2}\right)_T = -\left(\frac{\partial P}{\partial V}\right)_T > 0 \quad \Rightarrow \quad \left(\frac{\partial P}{\partial V}\right)_T < 0. \tag{7.19}$$

In Figure 7.10, the densely dotted region represents unstable states where the isotherms are seen to have positive slopes, contrary to the stability conditions of Equation (7.19). The line separating this unstable region from the stable is called the *spinodal curve* and is mathematically given by

$$\left(\frac{\partial P}{\partial V}\right)_T = 0 \quad \text{(spinodal loci)}. \tag{7.20}$$

The spinodal line represents states of incipient stability dividing the stable and unstable regions. The presence of three real V roots then implies that there must be an unstable region between the outside two roots. Physically, the fluid splits into two coexisting phases when the system is placed in this unstable region. In this case, the two phases are vapor and liquid.

The condition for equilibrium, on the other hand, is equality of pressure in the two phases; that is, $P' = P''$. Graphically, the equilibrium condition is represented by the tie lines shown in Figure 7.10, the horizontal lines which connect the coexisting phase points of the isotherm. It is easy to show that the equilibrium condition requires that the tie lines be drawn such that the area enclosed by the isotherm below the tie line equals the area enclosed by the isotherm above the tie line. A line through the ends of these tie lines connects the *coexistence points* or *binodal points*. The lightly dotted area in Figure 7.10, between the binodal and spinodal curves, is the *metastable region*. Outside the binodal curve, the one-phase system is stable.

As we discovered in Chapter 2, there are local fluctuations in density and numbers of molecules in any fluid. The variance about the mean was shown to be quite small for these properties, but these fluctuations play an important role in phase transitions. In fact, it is the growth of these fluctuations that induces the onset of the phase separation.

Consider an experiment in which we very carefully decrease the pressure along the isotherm T_4 from the left in Figure 7.10. As the system enters the metastable region, its density is less than the equilibrium density and the system is overexpanded. Viewed relative to the equilibrium temperature rather than pressure, the state is superheated. As we carefully push the system further into the metastable region, we continue to overexpand (or superheat) the liquid considerably beyond the equilibrium phase transition pressure (or temperature) well into the metastable region. The word "carefully" implies that we minimize the external inducements to the localized fluctuations in density. In fact the region is stable only as long as the local density fluctuations are smaller than the distance (in density) to the spinodal. That is, when density fluctuations produce a local volume of the fluid that is in the unstable region, the second phase forms there. Moreover, the microscopic formation of the second phase due to this density fluctuation stabilizes the evaporation (or condensation, as the case may be) of other molecules into the new phase. The influence of the intermolecular potential in stabilizing the growing phase is the sense in which the phase transition is a *cooperative phenomenon*. A small fluctuation into the new phase stabilizes yet other molecules which cooperate in terms of the resulting potential, and the new phase grows. This precipitates a macroscopic change of phase as still other regions are induced through the intermolecular forces into the type of packing or density structure that is stable for the new phase.

Even if no external enhancements to the fluctuations occur during our hypothetical pressure reduction experiment, we eventually reach a point, the spinodal, at which even the normal, very small internal density fluctuations are large enough to precipitate the cooperative phase transition.

Notice in Figure 7.10 that at higher temperatures the binodal or coexistence points move closer together until they eventually merge into a single point. This point is also an inflection point on that particular isotherm. The two physical, real roots from the equation of state represent the binodal curve and at the *critical point* those roots converge. One obtains two equal real roots at that point. Likewise, the binodal and spinodal curves are coincident at the critical point. As we will see, the natural fluctuations grow rapidly in the near critical region as the critical point is approached and, in theory, become infinite at the critical point itself. This is equivalent to the metastable region rapidly diminishing to zero area relative to the natural fluctuations.

Figure 7.10 is a P-V projection of the fluid's PVT surface. The critical point is seen more clearly as the termination of the vapor pressure curve in Figure 7.11. At a condition above the critical (either $T > T_c$ or $P > P_c$), a

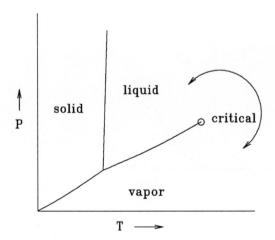

Figure 7.11   A P-T projection for a pure fluid.

continuous change in density can be achieved from clearly liquid-like densities to gas-like densities without ever crossing the phase boundary. Thus, if a process path circumvents the critical point as in Figure 7.11, one does not see the discontinuous phase transition associated with traversing the vapor pressure curve. There is no clear distinction between when the fluid is a liquid and when it is a vapor.

7.6.2 Critical Phenomena

The critical point and the behavior of properties in the critical region are of considerable importance in modern physics. Perhaps of most significance is the evidence of *universality* in the underlying physics of critical phenomena in systems that on the surface appear to be very different. Universality implies that exactly the same relations must apply at the critical point of these systems that appear widely disparate as long as the proper variables are compared in each case.

For example, the magnetic phase transition[6] in a ferromagnetic material is similar to the vapor–liquid transition when the appropriate field variables (intrinsically intensive properties) and the density variables (the ratio of two extensive properties) are substituted. In this case, $\mathscr{H}$, the magnetic field strength, takes the place of P; and M, the magnetization, replaces ρ. Representations of the $\mathscr{H}$-M and $\mathscr{H}$-T projections for a magnetic system are shown in Figures 7.12 and 7.13. As in the pure fluid case, there is a discontinuous phase transition from a spin-down to a spin-up phase when the magnetic field is increased from a negative to a positive value for temperatures below the critical or Curie temperature. On the other hand, a continuous change in magnetization occurs as the field is changed for $T > T_c$. One can change from a spin-down to a spin-

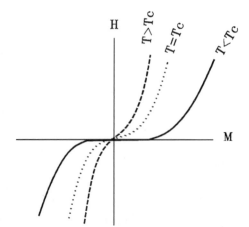

Figure 7.12 $\mathscr{H}$-M projection for a ferromagnetic substance.

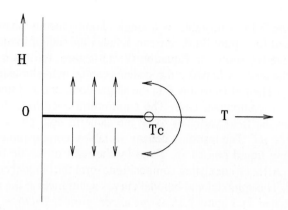

Figure 7.13 *M-T* projection for a ferromagnetic substance.

up state without crossing the phase boundary by manipulating the field and temperature such that the critical point is circumvented.

As another example, consider the phase split into two liquid phases which can occur in partially miscible liquid mixtures. In this case, the field variable is chemical potential of component 1 (for example) and the density variable is composition (usually x_1). The isotherm shown in the μ_1-x_1 projection of Figure 7.14 is similar to that observed in Figure 7.10 for a pure fluid. If $\ln(x_1)$ is chosen as the density variable, the analogy becomes even more striking. The condition for stability for this kind of system,

$$\left(\frac{\partial \mu_1}{\partial x_2}\right)_{T,P} < 0, \tag{7.21}$$

indicates that the region between the minimum and the maximum in the isotherm

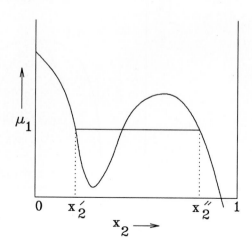

Figure 7.14 μ-x projection for a liquid–liquid phase transition.

shown in Figure 7.14 is unstable as a single, homogeneous phase. Similar to the analysis used for a pure fluid, one can connect the loci of incipient stability, where the derivative shown in Equation (7.21) is zero, to obtain the spinodal curve. Again the analogy between the systems can be made by using the appropriate variables. The field variable P in the single-component system is replaced by μ_i in the two-component case. The equilibrium conditions for the binary mixture require the field variables to be the same in both phases; that is, $\mu_1' = \mu_1''$ and $\mu_2' = \mu_2''$. The resulting density variables, compositions in this case, of the coexisting liquid phases are given by the ends of the tie line as shown in Figure 7.14. All such coexisting compositions form the binodal curve sketched in Figure 7.15. The spinodal and binodal curves again meet at the critical point. The case sketched in Figure 7.15 is *an upper critical solution temperature.* Above the upper critical solution temperature, the two components are completely miscible in all proportions. At temperatures below the critical, the mixture splits into two liquid phases in the region enclosed by the binodal curve. Upper critical solution temperatures are the most common, but some liquid mixtures also exhibit lower solution temperatures below which complete miscibility occurs. Some solutions have a completely enclosed miscibility gap, the two-phase region being bounded at the top by the upper critical solution temperature and on the bottom by the lower critical solution temperature.[7]

Universality implies that the behavior of properties near the critical point is the same for the above three examples, as well as for other phase transitions, because the underlying physics which lead to the phase transition are similar. This concept is perhaps most easily examined in terms of critical exponents.

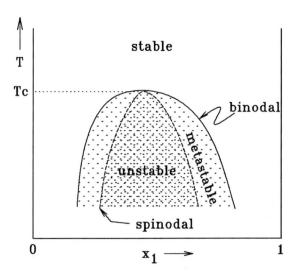

Figure 7.15   *T-x* projection for a liquid–liquid phase transition.

Critical exponents are used to characterize the behavior of variables (generally density variables) as the critical point is approached (generally as a field variable approaches the critical value). Consider, for example, the now classic plot by Guggenheim[8] reproduced in Figure 7.16, which shows the temperature dependence of $\rho_L - \rho_G$ for eight fluids. The difference $\rho_L - \rho_G$ is called the *order parameter* because it is nonzero only in the more ordered phase. Notice how rapidly $\rho_L - \rho_G$ goes to zero in this figure as the critical temperature is approached from below; that is, $T \to T_c$. This behavior can be represented in the form

$$\rho_L - \rho_G = (-\epsilon)^\beta [1 + B(-\epsilon)^x + \dots] , \qquad (7.22)$$

where

$$\epsilon \equiv \frac{T - T_c}{T_c} . \qquad (7.23)$$

In the near critical region as $\epsilon \to 0$, the leading term in the above expansion dominates and

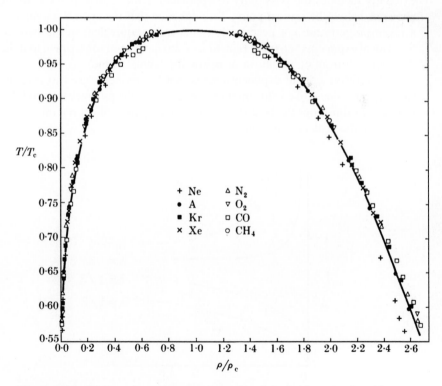

Figure 7.16 Measured coexistence curves for eight fluids and a fit with $\beta = 1/3$. (Adapted, with permission, from Guggenheim, E.A., *J. Chem. Phys.* **1945**, *13*, 257.)

$$\rho_L - \rho_G \sim (-\epsilon)^\beta. \tag{7.24}$$

The exponent β is the critical exponent for the order parameter.

Other properties can also be described in terms of critical exponents. In general, we define the critical exponent, λ, as $T \to T_c$, analogous to the above equation for the order parameter, namely,

$$\lambda \equiv \begin{cases} \lim\limits_{\epsilon \to 0} \dfrac{\ln J}{\ln \epsilon} & \text{for } \epsilon > 0 \\[2ex] \lim\limits_{\epsilon \to 0} \dfrac{\ln J}{\ln(-\epsilon)} & \text{for } \epsilon < 0 \end{cases}, \tag{7.25}$$

such that in the critical region,

$$J \sim \epsilon^{\lambda_+} \quad \text{or} \quad J \sim (-\epsilon)^{\lambda_-}. \tag{7.26}$$

While λ is intended to represent critical exponents in general, Equation (7.26) explicitly includes the possibility of approaching the critical point from either above or below the critical point. To emphasize that the critical exponents for a given property are not necessarily numerically equivalent in the two cases, the critical exponents shown in Equation (7.26) have been subscripted to indicate the approach from either above or below the critical point.

A positive critical exponent means that the property goes to zero at the critical point; a negative value implies divergence of the property toward infinity. Figure 7.17 illustrates the behavior of properties in the critical region as characterized by the critical exponent.

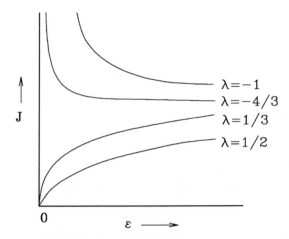

Figure 7.17 Behavior of functions near the critical temperature as represented by the critical exponent.

Universality has a much more encompassing implication than just what is illustrated in Figure 7.16. In that figure, different fluids are observed to have the same critical exponent for the order parameter of the vapor–liquid phase transition. This, in and of itself, is important and gives rise to the concept of corresponding states, the concept that all fluids behave similarly when scaled with respect to the liquid–vapor critical point. Corresponding states has been and continues to be one of the most important methods for thermophysical property prediction, and it is further discussed in Chapter 11. But, universality is more than the concept of corresponding states. It implies that exactly the same critical exponent used for the vapor–liquid phase transition also describes the liquid–liquid and ferromagnetic phase transitions, if proper correspondence between the variables is made. For example, the order parameter for a spin transition is M; for a liquid–liquid system it is $x_1' - x_1''$. Universality asserts that the same value for β applies to all three phenomena, namely,

$$\rho_L - \rho_G \sim (-\epsilon)^\beta \qquad \text{(vapor–liquid)}$$

$$x_l' - x_l'' \sim (-\epsilon)^\beta \qquad \text{(liquid–liquid)} \tag{7.27}$$

$$M \sim (-\epsilon)^\beta \qquad \text{(magnetic).}$$

Table 7.1 summarizes the corresponding variables for these three kinds of phase transformations and some recent best estimates of the critical exponents.[9] In this table, χ is the susceptibility defined by

$$\chi = -\frac{1}{V}\left(\frac{\partial V}{\partial P}\right)_T = \frac{1}{\rho}\left(\frac{\partial \rho}{\partial P}\right)_T \qquad \text{(vapor–liquid)}$$

$$\chi = x_2\left(\frac{\partial x_1}{\partial \mu_1}\right)_{T,P} \qquad \text{(liquid–liquid)} \tag{7.28}$$

$$\chi = \left(\frac{\partial M}{\partial \mathscr{H}}\right)_T \qquad \text{(magnetic),}$$

and ξ is the correlation length or the distance over which the local fluctuations

TABLE 7.1   Current Values of Some Common Critical Exponents

Exponent	Value	Vapor–Liquid	Liquid–Liquid	Magnetic
α	-0.110 ± 0.003	$C_V \sim \epsilon^\alpha$	$C_{p,x} \sim \epsilon^\alpha$	$C_H \sim \epsilon^\alpha$
β	0.326 ± 0.002	$\rho_L - \rho_G$ $\sim (-\epsilon)^\beta$	$x_1' - x_1''$ $\sim (-\epsilon)^\beta$	$M \sim (-\epsilon)^\beta$
γ	-1.239 ± 0.002	$\chi \sim \epsilon^\gamma$	$\chi \sim \epsilon^\gamma$	$\chi \sim \epsilon^\gamma$
ν	-0.630 ± 0.001	$\xi \sim \epsilon^\nu$	$\xi \sim \epsilon^\nu$	$\xi \sim \epsilon^\nu$

are correlated. We will have more to say about ξ in the next section as we see how to use the Monte Carlo method to simulate phase transitions and critical phenomena.

7.6.3 The Ising Spin Model

Universality implies that we can study phase transitions and critical phenomena in the most convenient system and extend the results to other systems. The Ising model is a simple, pedagogical interacting spin model that can be conveniently used to study cooperative phenomena. We will use it to study the paramagnetism–ferromagnetism transition, realizing that the study of critical exponents in this model system can then be used directly in the vapor–liquid or liquid–liquid fluid systems. In the Ising model, a fixed lattice is constructed, and spins are placed at each lattice point. The assumptions of the Ising model are:

1. Each site may only have one of two spin values associated with it, $+1$ for an "up" spin and -1 for a "down" spin.
2. Only nearest neighbors may interact.
3. The kinetic energy of the particles themselves is neglected.

If s_i represents the value of the spin on site i, then the net scaled magnetic moment or magnetization, M, is given by

$$M = \sum_{i=1}^{N} s_i .$$

(7.29)

The state of the system is specified when values are given for each of the spins.

The Hamiltonian for a spin system in a magnetic field of strength $\mathscr{H}$ directed upward is given by

$$H = -J \sum_{<i,j>} s_i s_j - \mathscr{H} \sum_{i=1}^{N} s_i ,$$

(7.30)

where the index $<i,j>$ represents the sum over all different nearest neighbor pairs and J is the *exchange constant*, a measure of the strength of the interaction between nearest neighbor spins. For example if $J = 0$, then there is no interaction between spins. For $J > 0$, neighboring states in which the spins are aligned ($\uparrow\uparrow$ and $\downarrow\downarrow$) are energetically favorable. Ferromagnetic substances would be expected to have positive J values because the most energetically favorable state is one with a net imbalance of spins. On the other hand, if $J < 0$ then neighboring oppositely aligned spins $\uparrow\downarrow$ and $\downarrow\uparrow$ are favored and the substance is expected to be antiferromagnetic. In the presence of the magnetic field, $\mathscr{H}$, directed upward, the spins ↑ and ↓ possess an additional energy of $-\mathscr{H}$ and $+\mathscr{H}$, respectively.

Consider first the case of a one-dimensional lattice of N sites. The Hamiltonian shown in Equation (7.30) can be simplified for the one-dimensional case to

$$H = -J\sum_{i=1}^{N} s_i s_{i+1} - \mathscr{H}\sum_{i=1}^{N} s_i . \tag{7.31}$$

Simulation of a macroscopic system with only a small number of particles would introduce spurious end effects because there would be an unrealistic fraction of the molecules in end positions. To avoid such effects, periodic boundary conditions are introduced. For the one-dimensional lattice shown in Figure 7.18, the two end spins are considered nearest neighbors. This is equivalent to arranging the spins in a ring so that there are no ends. Similar boundary conditions can be used in two- and three-dimensional models. Pictorially, the two-dimensional periodic boundary is equivalent to considering the lattice to be on the surface of an ellipsoid since the top lattice sites interact with those on the bottom, and the right lattice sites interact with those on the left.

It is instructive to simulate first the one-dimensional case because the results can be checked against rigorous analytical solutions. Example 7.9 illustrates calculation of the thermodynamic properties of a one-dimensional system with no interparticle interactions ($J = 0$), the "ideal" case. Because the spins can only be ± 1, $e^{-\beta H}$ can be directly enumerated in terms of the field strength as $e^{-\beta\mathscr{H}}$ and $e^{\beta\mathscr{H}}$. As shown in the example, this conveniently simplifies the partition function to a hyperbolic function from which explicit expressions for the thermodynamic properties can be readily derived.

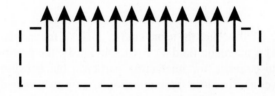

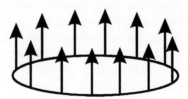

Figure 7.18   Periodic boundary conditions wrap the system back on itself so that end spins are neighbors.

Example 7.9   Develop an expression for the free energy, internal energy, and magnetization of noninteracting spins in a magnetic field of strength $\mathscr{H}$.

For this case $J = 0$ and Equation (7.30) reduces to

$$H = -\mathscr{H} \sum_i s_i .$$

There are only two spin states, $+1$ and -1, and each is independent of the other so the canonical partition function can be written as

$$Q = (e^{\beta \mathscr{H}} + e^{-\beta \mathscr{H}})^N = [2\cosh(\beta \mathscr{H})]^N.$$

The Helmholtz free energy is therefore

$$A = -NkT \ln[2\cosh(\beta \mathscr{H})]$$

and the internal energy is

$$U = NkT^2 \left(\frac{\partial \ln[2\cosh(\beta \mathscr{H})]}{\partial T} \right)_{\mathscr{H}}$$

$$= -N\mathscr{H} \tanh(\beta \mathscr{H}).$$

The magnetization is found from

$$M = -\left(\frac{\partial A}{\partial \mathscr{H}} \right)_T = N \tanh(\beta \mathscr{H}).$$

This relationship is shown in the figure.

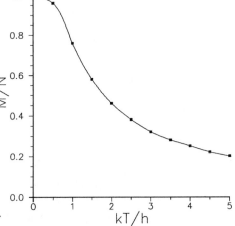

Example 7.10 illustrates the same kind of analysis for an interacting system in the absence of a magnetic field ($\mathscr{H} = 0$). Obviously, the partition function is more difficult to evaluate for interacting particles, but because only nearest neighbors interact and because the interaction is only two-valued, the partition function can again be simplified through direct enumeration.

We wish to develop now an MC simulation to study this one-dimensional Ising model. We will compute the same properties obtained via analytical methods in Examples 7.9 and 7.10 and compare the results as a check on the simulation. This should be standard procedure in benchmarking any new simulation code. Once the results have been verified for a known situation, the code can then be more reliably used to study models and systems for which no analytical solution is available. Molecular simulations are conveniently performed in dimensionless units. This makes the coding simpler, removes specificity from the code, and usually makes the results more general and meaningful. In this case, we use dimensionless energy, E/J, and dimensionless temperature,

Example 7.10   Derive an expression for the free energy, internal energy, and magnetization of the Ising model with $\mathscr{H} = 0$.

From Equation (7.31) with $\mathscr{H} = 0$ we obtain

$$H = -J\sum_i s_i s_{i+1} .$$

The exponential term in the partition function will therefore be

$$\exp\left(\beta J\sum_i s_i s_{i+1}\right) = \begin{cases} \prod e^{\beta J} & \text{for } s_i s_{i+1} = 1 \\ \prod e^{-\beta J} & \text{for } s_i s_{i+1} = -1 \end{cases} = \prod(\cosh\beta J + s_i s_{i+1}\sinh\beta J) .$$

When substituted into the partition function, this yields

$$\sum_{s_i=\pm 1} \cdots \sum_{s_N=\pm 1} \prod(\cosh\beta J + s_i s_{i+1}\sinh\beta J) .$$

This equation can be expanded for the case of $N \gg 1$ to yield

$$Q = [2\cosh(\beta J)]^N.$$

This partition function is exactly analogous to that derived in Example 7.9 and so A, U, and M can be written down immediately by inspection; that is,

$$A = -NkT \ln[2\cosh(\beta J)],$$
$$U = -NJ \tanh(\beta J), \text{ and}$$
$$M = N \tanh(\beta J).$$

kT/J, as the main simulation variables. The QUICKBASIC PROGRAM *Ising_1d*, shown below, performs the simulation. We present the code here as a means of discussing the methodology involved in the simulation itself.

```
REM ****************************************
REM ** PROGRAM Ising_1d                 **
REM ** MC simulation of Ising 1-d model **
REM ****************************************
DECLARE SUB neighbor (ispin!, n!, s!(), left!, right!)
DECLARE SUB answers (n!, nstep!, ecum!, mcum!, ratio!)
DECLARE SUB metropolis (n!, s!(), e!, m!, w(), ratio!)
DIM s(500), w(-2 TO 2)
RANDOMIZE (TIMER)
REM ** input values
REM ** energy is a reduced energy, e/J **
REM ** temperature is a reduced T, kT/J **
```

```
INPUT "Number of spins"; n
INPUT "Number of steps per spin"; nstep
INPUT "Equilibration steps"; equil
INPUT "Reduced temperature (kT/J)"; t
REM ** set up initial configuration **
FOR i = 1 TO n
   IF RND < .5 THEN
      s(i) = 1
   ELSE
      s(i) = -1
   END IF
NEXT
REM ** set up appropriate transition factors, w=exp(-de/kt) **
w(-2) = EXP(4 / t)
w(2) = EXP(-4 / t)
REM ** Equilibrate **
FOR i = 1 TO equil
   CALL metropolis(n, s(), e, m, w(), ratio)
NEXT
REM ** initialize magnetization and energy **
e = 0
m = 0
FOR i = 1 TO n
   m = m + s(i)
   CALL neighbor(i, n, s(), left, right)
   e = e - s(i) * right: REM ** only use right to not overcount
NEXT
REM ** Now do MC simulation **
ratio = 0
ecum = 0
mcum = 0
FOR i = 1 TO nstep
   CALL metropolis(n, s(), e, m, w(), ratio)
   ecum = ecum + e
   mcum = mcum + m
NEXT
CALL answers(n, nstep, ecum, mcum, ratio)
END
```

First, an initial configuration is chosen. In *Ising_1d* a random configuration is chosen to minimize the number of equilibration steps required. Next, the proper Boltzmann transition values are set up so that they only need be calculated once. In the one-dimensional case, flipping a spin from up to down between two neighbors can only change the energy in three ways:

$$\uparrow\uparrow\uparrow \rightarrow \uparrow\downarrow\uparrow \quad \Delta(E/J) = -4$$
$$\uparrow\uparrow\downarrow \rightarrow \uparrow\downarrow\downarrow \quad \Delta(E/J) = 0$$

$$\downarrow\uparrow\downarrow \rightarrow \downarrow\downarrow\downarrow \quad \Delta(E/J) = 4.$$

The transition probabilities for these cases are tabulated at the beginning of the above code, but the energy changes at each step could just as easily be calculated at each step as illustrated in the SUBROUTINE *metropolis*. Because we started with an arbitrary initial configuration, we next run the Metropolis algorithm to equilibrate the system; that is, we want the system to forget the intial state so that the results will be independent of any configuration from which the simulation is initiated. In SUBROUTINE *metropolis*, a random spin is chosen to flip and the energy change which would result from this step is computed. If $\Delta E \leq 0$ then the step is accepted, otherwise the Boltzmann probability for that step is compared to a random number and the step is accepted only if the probability is greater than the random number. This could be done in a single step, but this would require generating a random number for each trial which might require more CPU time. Finally the energy and magnetization of the new configuration are calculated.

```
SUB metropolis (n, s(), e, m, w(), ratio)
FOR spins = 1 TO n
    i = INT(RND * n + 1): REM ** select random spin **
    CALL neighbor(i, n, s(), left, right)
    de = s(i) * (left + right): REM ** energy change for this trial **
    IF de <= 0 THEN
        REM ** accept all favorable energy changes **
        s(i) = -s(i)
        ratio = ratio + 1
        m = m + 2 * s(i)
        e = e + 2 * de
    ELSE
        IF w(de) > RND THEN
        REM ** apply acceptance criteria for unfavorable changes **
            s(i) = -s(i)
            ratio = ratio + 1
            m = m + 2 * s(i)
            e = e + 2 * de
        END IF
    END IF
NEXT
END SUB

SUB neighbor (ispin, n, s(), left, right)
REM ** Apply periodic BC and find sign of neighbor spins
    IF ispin = 1 THEN
        left = s(n):      REM left neighbor of spin 1 is n
    ELSE
        left = s(ispin - 1)
    END IF
    IF ispin = n THEN
```

```
        right = s(1):        REM right neighbor of spin n is 1
    ELSE
        right = s(ispin + 1)
    END IF
END SUB
```

The periodic boundary conditions are applied in SUBROUTINE *neighbor*, and the sum of the energies and magnetizations for each MC step are accumulated in SUBROUTINE *answers*. The accumulated E and M values are normalized with respect to the total number of MC steps (*nstep*) and the total number of spins (n) in order to obtain intensive results independent of the number of spins. The acceptance ratio is also accumulated and printed with the results. Recall that acceptance ratios around 1:3 are desirable for efficient importance sampling.

```
            SUB answers (n, nstep, ecum, mcum, ratio)
            norm = 1 / (n * nstep)
            e = ecum * norm
            m = mcum * norm
            ratio = ratio * norm
            PRINT "Final energy="; e
            PRINT "Final magnetization ="; m
            PRINT "Acceptance ratio ="; ratio
            END SUB
```

Example 7.11 uses a code much like that outlined above to illustrate graphically the Metropolis moves and to calculate energy and magnetization

---

Example 7.11   Perform simulations on the one-dimensional Ising model at reduced temperatures from 0.5 to 5.0 in 0.5 increments. Use the simulations to determine the expectation value of the energy per MC spin.

The program on disk for this example computes both the energy and magnetization per spin. Running the simulation for 500 steps per spin after 100 equilibration steps produces the results shown at the right.

Note how the acceptance ratio increases with increasing temperature. We expect the simulations to be most accurate at about $kT/J = 1$ where the sampling is seen to be most efficient.

kT/J	$<E>$	Ratio
0.5	−0.998	0.002
1.0	−0.764	0.225
1.5	−0.585	0.415
2.0	−0.466	0.535
2.5	−0.382	0.624
3.0	−0.335	0.679
3.5	−0.275	0.732
4.0	−0.258	0.754
4.5	−0.226	0.782
5.0	−0.207	0.804

---

values. We can check the simulation of Example 7.11 by comparing the energy with the analytical solution obtained in Example 7.10. Figure 7.19 shows such a comparison. At $kT/J = 1$ where the acceptance ratio in Example 7.11 was optimum, the simulation results are seen to be virtually exact. Slightly larger deviations are observed in regions where the sampling is less efficient. This problem can be corrected by longer runs over more spins and by modifying the transition factor for the higher temperatures.

While the one-dimensional Ising model does not exhibit phase transitions, the two-dimensional model does. PROGRAM *ising1_d* is easily modified to a two-dimensional lattice of length L and total lattice sites $N = L^2$. Each spin now has four neighbors, one to the north, south, east, and west (up, down, right, and left). There are five different energy changes that can occur by flipping a spin from up to down (or vice versa) corresponding to $\Delta(E/J) = -8, -4, 0, 4,$ and 8. Again the periodic boundary conditions must be applied, this time at all four boundaries. It is also convenient to calculate the variance of the magnetization and energy during the simulation because the specific heat and the magnetic susceptibility are readily related to these fluctuation values by

$$C = (<E^2> - <E>^2)/kT^2 \qquad (7.32)$$

and

$$\chi = (<M^2> - <M>^2)/kT. \qquad (7.33)$$

With the following PROGRAM *ising2_d*, we can study the phase transition

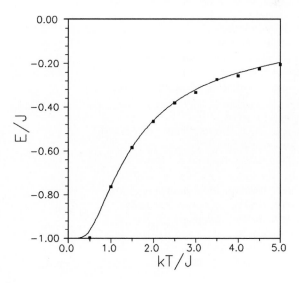

Figure 7.19   Comparison of simulated results (points) to the analytical solution for the 1-D Ising model.

from ferromagnetism to paramagnetism. As in the one-dimensional case the initial configuration is created by placing random "up" and "down" spins at the L^2 lattice sites. After the simulation has been run for a period of time to equilibrate the system, the properties are reinitialized to zero for the start of property calculations. Boltzmann distribution factors are calculated at the beginning of the program and stored since there are only a relatively small number of discrete energy levels that are available to the system.

```
REM *******************************
REM ** PROGRAM ising2_d        **
REM ** 2-Dimensional Ising Model **
REM *******************************
DECLARE SUB initial (L, spin(), e, m)
DECLARE SUB metropolis (N, L, spin(), e, m, w(), ratio)
DECLARE SUB ave (N, nmcs, ecum, e2cum, mcum, m2cum, ratio)
DECLARE SUB add (e, m, ecum, e2cum, mcum, m2cum)
DECLARE SUB periodic (x, y, L, spin(), sum)
DECLARE SUB accept (x, y, m, e, sum, spin(), ratio)
DECLARE SUB setup (N, L, t, nmcs, spin(), e, w(), equil)
DIM spin(32, 32), w(-4 TO 4)
CALL setup(N, L, t, nmcs, spin(), e, w(), equil)
REM ** equilibrate **
FOR imcs = 1 TO equil
    CALL metropolis(N, L, spin(), e, m, w(), ratio)
NEXT
REM ** get initial energy and magnetization **
CALL initial(L, spin(), e, m)
FOR imcs = 1 TO nmcs
    CALL metropolis(N, L, spin(), e, m, w(), ratio)
    CALL add(e, m, ecum, e2cum, mcum, m2cum)
NEXT
CALL ave(N, nmcs, ecum, e2cum, mcum, m2cum, ratio)
END


SUB setup (N, L, t, nmcs, spin(), e, w(), equil)
    RANDOMIZE (TIMER)
    INPUT "linear dimension of lattice ="; L
    N = L * L
    INPUT "number of MC steps/spin ="; nmcs
    INPUT "equilibration steps ="; equil
    INPUT "reduced temperature ="; t
    FOR y = 1 TO L
        FOR x = 1 TO L
            IF RND < .5 THEN
                spin(x, y) = 1
            ELSE
                spin(x, y) = -1
```

```
            END IF
        NEXT
    NEXT
    e4 = EXP(-4 / t)
    e8 = e4 * e4
    w(4) = e8
    w(-4) = 1/e8
    w(2) = e4
    w(-2) = 1/e4
    w(0) = 1
END SUB


SUB initial (L, spin(), e, m)
    e = 0
    m = 0
    FOR y = 1 TO L
        IF y = L THEN
            up = 1
        ELSE
            up = y + 1
        END IF
        FOR x = 1 TO L
            IF x = L THEN
                right = 1
            ELSE
                right = x + 1
            END IF
            sum = spin(x, up) + spin(right, y)
            e = e - spin(x, y) * sum
            m = m + spin(x, y)
        NEXT
    NEXT
END SUB


SUB metropolis (N, L, spin(), e, m, w(), ratio)
    FOR i = 1 TO N
        x = INT(L * RND + 1)
        y = INT(L * RND + 1)
        CALL periodic(x, y, L, spin(), sum)
        de = spin(x, y) * sum
        IF de <= 0 THEN
            CALL accept(x, y, m, e, sum, spin(), ratio)
        ELSEIF RND < w(de) THEN
            CALL accept(x, y, m, e, sum, spin(), ratio)
        END IF
    NEXT
END SUB
```

```
SUB accept (x, y, m, e, sum, spin(), ratio)
   spin(x, y) = -spin(x, y)
   ratio = ratio + 1
   m = m + 2 * spin(x, y)
   e = e - 2 * spin(x, y) * sum
END SUB


SUB add (e, m, ecum, e2cum, mcum, m2cum)
   ecum = ecum + e
   e2cum = e2cum + e * e
   mcum = mcum + m
   m2cum = m2cum + m * m
END SUB


SUB periodic (x, y, L, spin(), sum)
   IF x = 1 THEN
      left = spin(L, y)
   ELSE
      left = spin(x - 1, y)
   END IF
   IF x = L THEN
      right = spin(1, y)
   ELSE
      right = spin(x + 1, y)
   END IF
   IF y = 1 THEN
      down = spin(x, L)
   ELSE
      down = spin(x, y - 1)
   END IF
   IF y = L THEN
      up = spin(x, 1)
   ELSE
      up = spin(x, y + 1)
   END IF
   sum = left + right + up + down
END SUB


SUB ave (N, nmcs, ecum, e2cum, mcum, m2cum, ratio)
   norm = 1 / (nmcs * N)
   ratio = ratio * norm
   eave = ecum * norm
   e2ave = e2cum * norm
   mave = mcum * norm
   m2ave = m2cum * norm
   PRINT "E/spin ="; eave; "  E^2/spin ="; e2ave / N
   PRINT "M/spin ="; mave; "  M^2/spin ="; m2ave / N
   PRINT "acceptance ratio ="; ratio
```

```
END SUB
```

With the preceding code, we can use MC simulations to examine phase transitions more closely. Example 7.12 uses a similar code to do two-dimensional simulations of the Ising model. The example on diskette illustrates graphically the growth of domains and the onset of the phase transition as the temperature is lowered. We can use the numerical results of Example 7.12 to check what we have already learned about critical phenomena.

In Figure 7.20, values of the magnetization have been plotted as a function of temperature. Precision in the calculations is low because of the relatively small size of the lattice chosen, but clearly a phase transition takes place somewhere between the temperatures of 2.2 and 2.3. Analytical determination of T_c fixes its value at approximately 2.269, which is in good agreement with the results of this simulation. Values of the magnetization obtained from this simulation are seen to be somewhat erratic for $T > T_c$. Actual values are of course zero because the thermal energy is sufficient to overcome the interactions between spins thereby randomizing the orientations. Again, improvement in these high-temperature values could be obtained with larger lattice sizes and more MC steps/spin.

Example 7.12   Use a simulation of the two-dimensional Ising model to calculate expectation values for the energy, magnetization, squared energy, squared magnetization, and the fluctuations in energy and magnetization. Do your simulation on an $L = 8$ lattice, using an initial equilibration of 100 steps/spin and compute properties from subsequent simulations of 400 MC steps/spin. Tabulate results over the temperature range $T^+ = 1.5$ to 3.3.

The following results were obtained using the code on the diskette:

T^+	$-<E>$	$<M>$	$<E^2>/N$	$<M^2>/N$	Ratio	$<E^2>-<E>^2$	$<M^2>-<M>^2$
1.5	1.94	0.984	3.77	0.969	0.023	0.003	0.001
1.7	1.90	0.972	3.63	0.946	0.036	0.007	0.001
1.9	1.82	0.947	3.36	0.900	0.084	0.013	0.002
2.0	1.72	0.901	3.01	0.822	0.095	0.013	0.005
2.1	1.65	0.891	2.77	0.804	0.149	0.011	0.006
2.2	1.52	0.681	2.40	0.671	0.172	0.019	0.094
2.3	1.45	0.277	2.20	0.527	0.245	0.018	0.264
2.5	1.12	0.152	1.27	0.436	0.306	0.018	0.171
2.7	0.974	0.124	1.03	0.237	0.479	0.013	0.082
2.9	0.889	0.057	0.840	0.190	0.502	0.010	0.063
3.1	0.758	$-.003$	0.633	0.132	0.595	0.006	0.040
3.3	0.740	$-.019$	0.603	0.112	0.654	0.005	0.022

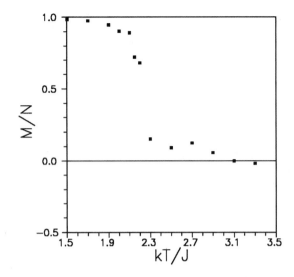

Figure 7.20   Magnetization near T_c in a 2-D Ising model.

   Note how rapidly the magnetization drops off very near the critical point. A plot of $\ln M$ versus $-\epsilon$ would yield the critical exponent β for this system in accordance with Equation (7.27). This particular simulation is not accurate enough to produce quantitative values of the critical exponents. Moreover, one would want to use a 3-D Ising model to study the actual values of the critical exponents for comparison with those listed in Table 7.1. However, the qualitative features are certainly well represented even in this simple simulation as shown in Figures 7.20 to 7.22.

   In Figure 7.21, the magnetic susceptibility is plotted as a function of temperature and the very rapid divergence close to the critical point, characterized by Equations (7.28) and the value of γ given in Table 7.1, is distinctly observed. The heat capacity in Figure 7.22 is observed to diverge more slowly than the susceptibility, also consistent with the values of α and γ given in Table 7.1. According to Equations (7.28), the susceptibility indicates how the order parameter changes with changes in the corresponding field variable. The divergence of χ as T_c is approached therefore indicates that the local fluctuations in the order parameter become very large for a small change in the field variable. For example, near the liquid–vapor critical point, large density fluctuations occur. In this region, a small change in pressure can cause a large change in density. Supercritical extraction processes take advantage of these density changes. A small increase in pressure can greatly enhance solute solubility while a small decrease in pressure decreases the solvent density, hence solute solubility, for efficient solvent recovery. The divergence of the fluctuations near the critical point also accounts for the convergence of the spinodal and binodal lines. Near

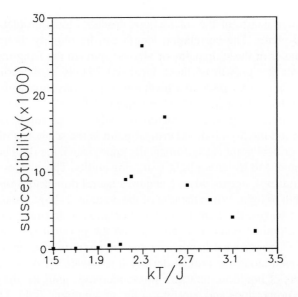

Figure 7.21   Magnetic susceptibility, χ, of the 2-D Ising model.

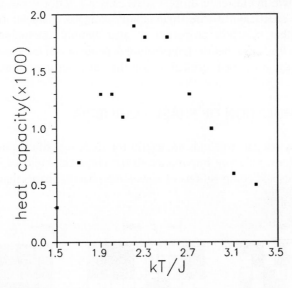

Figure 7.22   Heat capacity of the 2-D Ising model.

the critical point, even very small variations in P within the fluid produce large-density fluctuations, which in turn induce the cooperative phase transition.

Finally, let us mention again the correlation length ξ. As we perform the MC simulations at various temperatures, we see the growth of local phases.

The cooperative nature of the interactions produces local droplets or domains of correlated phase. The correlation length can be roughly thought of as the average diameter of these domains of aligned spin (in the Ising model). Figure 7.23 illustrates the growth of these localized islands as the critical point is approached. This corresponds to a divergence in ξ consistent with the value of ν shown in Table 7.1 for the critical exponent of ξ.

A very interesting and characteristic behavior of fluids near both the liquid–vapor and the liquid–liquid critical point is the scattering of light by the fluid. As the critical point is experimentally approached, the fluid becomes quite milky looking due to its strong light-scattering ability. This phenomenon, called *critical opalescence,* occurs when ξ acquires lateral dimensions on the order of the wavelength of light. When the size of the domains is large enough to interact with the light waves, the light is scattered creating a striking indication of the presence of a critical point. It is easy to see the physical significance of this growth in ξ. Consider what happens as the temperature of a single-component vapor is lowered along the critical density line toward T_c. As $T \to T_c$, the size of the droplets of liquid in the vapor phase increases until the droplets take on macroscopic proportions and separate in the gravitational field. The growth of ξ also dramatically affects other properties in the critical region. For example, the rapid growth in cluster or droplet sizes causes a "critical slowing down" of the diffusion coefficient as the fluid rapidly changes character from a gas to a liquid.[10] Other transport properties[10,11] also exhibit "anomalous" behavior, anomalous in the sense that the temperature dependence of the property behaves very differently in the near critical region than at other conditions.

7.7 MC SIMULATION OF PHASE EQUILIBRIA

We have seen that MC methods are useful for studying critical phenomena and phase transitions. Of more importance to the chemical engineer is knowledge of the densities and compositions of coexisting phases, phases that are in stable

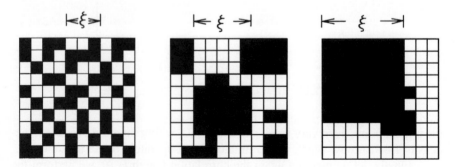

Figure 7.23   Growth of ξ as T_c is approached from above (left to right).

equilibrium. Equilibrium compositions are essential in design of separation trains, and these often constitute a large fraction of the energy and cost of the overall process. Despite the importance of this information, prediction of the equilibrium phases is quite difficult because one must find the compositions at which the chemical potentials of each component is the same in the two coexisting phases at the same temperature and pressure. Chemical potentials are not directly measurable and so one must use information about mixture nonidealities in the form of activity coefficients or partial fugacity coefficients to perform the calculation. Classical thermodynamics yields no rigorous information about the calculation of these nonidealities in different mixtures because no information about the constituency of matter is included in its development. On the other hand, because these nonidealities are a direct result of the intermolecular interactions, it seems reasonable that MC simulations of interacting particles can be used directly to establish phase equilibrium and to obtain the desired properties of the phases in equilibrium.

Earlier, MC methods were used to determine phase equilibrium by sampling from the μVT ensemble. Unfortunately the method was not very efficient. One performed the simulation at a specified chemical potential, but numerous simulations at different chemical potentials were required in order to find and determine the phase envelope. More recently, a method called the Gibbs ensemble[12] has become the most popular method of calculating phase equilibrium using MC simulations. Its popularity is due to its direct generation of the equilibrium phases. The two simulated phases are coupled in a way that assures the equality of component chemical potentials without requiring their initial specification. It combines elements of the NVT, NPT, and μVT ensembles to guarantee equality of the temperature, pressure, and component chemical potentials in the coexisting phases.

We will not discuss the theory of the Gibbs ensemble here, but only provide a prescription of its implementation. We will illustrate the method for one-component, vapor–liquid equilibrium, primarily for simplicity sake, but the method is general and can be applied to multicomponent systems. When mixtures are involved, the required CPU time becomes an issue, as does specification of cross-interaction parameters. In the one-component illustration used here, the desired thermophysical properties are the densities of the liquid and vapor phases that are in equilibrium. The implementation involves three different MC moves to establish: first, local equilibrium within the phase; second, mechanical equilibrium or constant pressure between the phases; and third, chemical or diffusional equilibrium between the particles in the two phases. These three steps are illustrated in Figure 7.24. To begin the simulation, one defines two separate boxes of particles. For convenience, we take both boxes to contain the same number of particles occupying equivalent volumes. This is a one-phase starting condition. The three types of moves are then carried out successively.

1. *Local particle moves within each phase.* First, the normal Metropolis

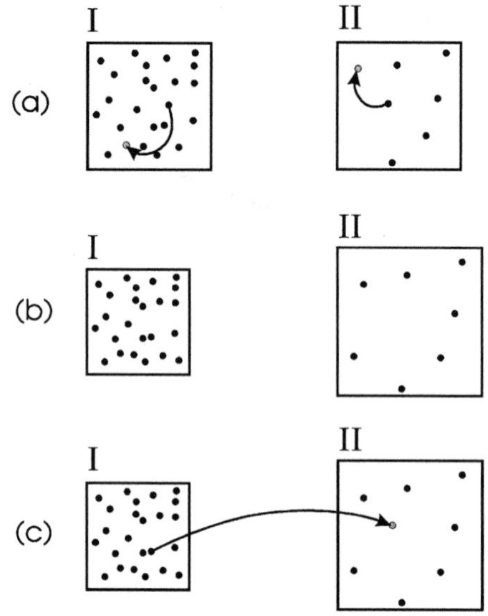

Figure 7.24　The three parts of the Gibbs ensemble: (**a**) internal moves, (**b**) volume displacements, and (**c**) particle transfers.

algorithm is implemented separately on each box. Particles are moved randomly within their own box and the usual acceptance criterion is applied for the transition probability:

$$w = \min[1, \exp(-\Delta E/kT)]. \qquad (7.34)$$

These moves are illustrated in (**a**) of Figure 7.24. They clearly constitute an ordinary *NVT* simulation for each phase. Many of these local displacements are performed before proceeding to the next step. One tries to choose a step size that produces an acceptance ratio of about 0.5.

2. *Volume displacement.* Next, we perform a single volume displacement, ΔV, chosen randomly between $-\Delta V_{max}$ and $+\Delta V_{max}$, such that on the average the acceptance ratio for the volume changes is about 0.5. One then adds this volume displacement to the box on the left and subtracts it from the box on the right. Thus, the overall density is preserved because there is no change in the number of particles or volume of the combined (including both phases) system. The positions of the particles in both boxes are then scaled with the new dimensions of the box and the new interaction energies are computed. The transition probability is once again given by Equation (7.34), but the energy change for the volume displacement is found from

$$\Delta E = \Delta E_{\mathrm{I}} + \Delta E_{\mathrm{II}} - N_{\mathrm{I}}kT\ln\frac{V_{\mathrm{I}} + \Delta V}{V_{\mathrm{I}}} - N_{\mathrm{II}}kT\ln\frac{V_{\mathrm{II}} - \Delta V}{V_{\mathrm{II}}}. \qquad (7.35)$$

This step, represented as (**b**) in Figure 7.24, is similar to the displacements used to perform *NPT* simulations.

3. *Particle phase transfers.* Finally, one does MC exchanges of particles between the two phases. At random and with equal probability, one of the boxes is chosen as the receiving box. A test particle is then chosen at random in the donating box and a random position chosen in the receiving box. Such particle transfers are then evaluated in terms of the transition probability, Equation (7.34), where now ΔE is calculated from

$$\Delta E = \Delta E_{\text{I}} + \Delta E_{\text{II}} + N_{\text{I}}kT\ln\frac{N_{\text{I}} + 1}{N_{\text{I}}} + N_{\text{II}}kT\ln\frac{N_{\text{II}} - 1}{N_{\text{II}}} \qquad (7.36)$$

$$+ kT\ln\frac{V_{\text{II}}}{V_{\text{I}}} + kT\ln\frac{N_{\text{I}} + 1}{N_{\text{II}} - 1}.$$

Generally, several of these particle transfers are attempted before continuing on to the next full cycle of steps.

Many of these cycles are required to establish equilibrium between the phases. Once equilibrium is established, properties can be obtained directly from the simulations. If the conditions were not in the two-phase region, then a single phase results and new conditions can be selected until the phase envelope is obtained. The speed and simplicity associated with direct determination of equilibrium phases, as opposed to chemical potential calculations, make the Gibbs ensemble very valuable for determining fluid equilibrium. A microcomputer illustration of the method is provided in Example 7.13. Appendix 7 on diskette contains sample code in QUICKBASIC that illustrate the three different types of perturbations.

Monte Carlo techniques are indeed powerful and versatile simulation methods with which the physics of matter can be studied and from which thermophysical properties can be calculated. They are easily programmed and can be used

---

Example 7.13   Using the Gibbs ensemble, determine the liquid and vapor densities that are in equilibrium for an LJ fluid at $T^+ = 1.15$ and an overall density (of the two phases combined) of $\rho^+ = 0.25$.

The code on the accompanying diskette is designed to give the user a feel for how the method works and provide a simple representation of the three different types of moves that are performed and their effect on the density of the two phases. It is too slow to include enough steps to obtain accurate quantitative results. Nevertheless, it is interesting to run the simulation and compare the simulation to values given in the literature for this problem. Accurate values of $\rho^+_L = 0.6$ and $\rho^+_V = 0.05$ were obtained for the liquid and vapor densities at this condition by Panagiotopoulos[12] after 1.2 million configurations on a supercomputer.

for a variety of different ensemble types, although only a method for the canonical ensemble has been illustrated here. Accurate results are dependent upon correct formulation of the transition probability function to implement the importance sampling technique and generation of sufficient quantities of phase space points to sample the distribution adequately. The importance sampling method conserves CPU time, making the requisite extensive simulations of phase space feasible.

While Monte Carlo methods sample a static density of states in phase space and use ensemble averages to obtain expectation values, molecular dynamics simulations sample phase space along a particular system's time trajectory and use time averages to compute properties. These simulation techniques are discussed in the next chapter.

REFERENCES

1. Metropolis, N., Rosenbluth, A.W., Rosenbluth, M.N., Teller A.H., and Keller, E., "Equation of state calculations for fast computing machines," *J. Chem. Phys.* **1953**, *21*, 1087.

2. Kalos, M.H., and Whitlock, P.A., *Monte Carlo Methods. Vol. I: Basics,* Wiley, New York, 1986.

3. Rubinstein, R.Y., *Simulation and the Monte Carlo Method,* Wiley, New York, 1981.

4. Gould, H., and Tobochnik, J., *An Introduction to Computer Simulation Methods. Applications to Physical Systems. Part 2,* Addison-Wesley, Reading, MA, 1988.

5. Modell, M., and Reid, R.C., *Thermodynamics and Its Applications,* 2nd ed. Prentice-Hall, Englewood Cliffs, NJ, 1983.

6. Stanley, H.E., *Introductions to Phase Transitions and Critical Phenomena,* Oxford University Press, New York, 1971.

7. Rowlinson, J.S., and Swinton, F.L., *Liquids and Liquid Mixtures,* 3rd ed. Butterworths, London, 1982.

8. Guggenheim, E.A., *J. Chem. Phys.* **1945**, *13*, 253.

9. Sengers, J.V., "Thermodynamic behavior of fluids near the critical point," *Ann. Rev. Phys. Chem.* **1986**, *37*, 189.

10. Sengers, J.V., "Transport processes near the critical point of gases and binary liquids in the hydrodynamic regime," *Ber. Bunsenges. Phys. Chem.* **1972**, *76*, 234.

11. Rowley, R.L., "Critical exponent of the heat of transport of water-isobutyric acid mixtures," *J. Chem. Phys.* **1979**, *71*, 3841.

12. Panagiotopoulos, A.Z., "Direct determination of phase coexistence properties of fluids by Monte Carlo simulation in a new ensemble," *Molec. Phys.* **1987**, *61*, 813.

13. Clark, W.M., and Rowley, R.L., "The mutual diffusion coefficient of methanol-*n*-hexane near the consolute point," *AIChE J.* **1986**, *32*, 1125.

PROBLEMS

MC INTEGRATION

1. Use an MC method to compute a value for π.
2. Use an MC method to compute the area of a regular hexagon inscribed in a circle of radius 5.
3. (a) Estimate the integral[4]

$$F = \int_0^1 xe^{-x}\,dx$$

using the sample mean MC method and 4000 trials. Your program should also compute the standard deviation from

$$\sigma = \sqrt{<f^2> - <f>^2}\,,$$

where

$$<f> = \frac{1}{n}\sum_{i=1}^n f(x_i) \quad \text{and} \quad <f^2> = \frac{1}{n}\sum_{i=1}^n f^2(x_i)\,.$$

   (b) The standard deviation computed above does not decrease with increasing n. Another estimate of the reliability of the MC-estimated value of F is from a standard deviation of mean values obtained from multiple simulations. Repeat the simulation of part a 19 more times and average the resultant values of F. From these 20 mean values compute σ_m, the standard deviation of the means. σ_m can be estimated from a single run with the approximate relation

$$\sigma_m \simeq \frac{\sigma}{\sqrt{n}}\,.$$

Compare the value of σ_m computed above with the value estimated from only the first run.

   (c) Analytically determine the integral in part a and compare the exact result to the simulated result. Do you feel σ or σ_m is a better estimator of the standard deviation of a simulation run?

4. Using importance sampling, compute the integral[4]

$$F = \int_0^1 xe^{-x}\,dx$$

using 500, 1000, 5000, and 10,000 trials. Use

$$\wp(x) = a\sqrt{x}\,,$$

for the probability distribution function.

5. Using importance sampling, compute the integral[2]

$$F = \cos\left(\frac{\pi x}{2}\right)$$

on the interval [0,1] (a) using a uniform random number generator and (b) using importance sampling with

$$\wp(x) = \frac{3}{2}(1 - x^2)$$

for the probability distribution. Use the same number of trials in the two cases and compare the variances.

6. Consider the object shown below which has been machined from a piece of material of uniform density. Find the center of mass of the object.

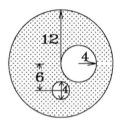

RANDOM WALKS

7. Write a program and use it to generate random, Gaussian, one-dimensional velocities in the range $-4 \leq v_{max} \leq 4$. Plot a histogram of your velocities to show that they are indeed Gaussian and determine the mean velocity and σ.

8. Simulate a swarm of bees around a central hive with a two-dimensional random walk.[4] Start with 50 bees. At each time step, each bee moves at random with equal probability in all four directions. Compute the expected mean position and the net mean square displacement of the bees after 100 steps.

9. The random walk of Example 7.4 can be modified to a "persistent" random walk. Instead of randomly choosing the direction at each step, one chooses the *same direction as the previous step* if the random number is less than a probability factor p and the opposite direction if the random number is greater than p. Set up a one-dimensional persistent random walk for the drunk of Example 7.4 and compute $<x>$ and D after 1000 steps.

10. Consider a two-dimensional lattice of 100 equally spaced sites (a 10×10 lattice). This represents the surface of a catalyst. Further suppose that at equilibrium, there is 10% coverage of the sites by adsorbed molecules of component A. The adsorbed molecules have a surface diffusion coefficient of 1 site per MC step. It is assumed that the production of the dimer A_2 is surface diffusion controlled on the catalyst surface. That is, when two A molecules are on adjacent sites, they react immediately. The dimer is immediately desorbed and two A molecules are immediately adsorbed

at random vacant sites to maintain the equilibrium coverage ratio. Determine the reaction rate of $A \rightarrow A_2$ in the presence of this heterogeneous catalysis surface.

11. In a "restricted" random walk, the particle moves through the lattice until it reaches a site which serves as a trap.[4] The trap prevents the particle from moving further. Consider the classical "gambler's ruin problem" in which two card players of equal skill each begin with $10. The result of each hand is the loss of $1 by one gambler and the gain of $1 by the other. How long, on the average, can they play before one of the gamblers is broke?

12. Another example of a restricted walk (see Problem 11) is the simulation of an annealing process. To anneal a crystalline material, the temperature is raised and maintained long enough that the Schottky defects or vacancy imperfections can diffuse to the surface. This produces a more perfect crystal structure. The surface of the solid acts as the trap for the random walk. Set up a simulation for a square two-dimensional lattice of size 51×51. The length of time required to anneal the material can be estimated by simulating a crystal with the vacancy located furthest from the surface, at the center of the lattice in this square case. Model the diffusion process as the interchange of a neighboring particle with the vacancy, and compute the expected number of steps for the vacancy to reach the surface of the crystal.

FLUIDS

13. Compute $g(r)$ for a hard sphere fluid over the range $0 \le r^+ \le 2$ for the three densities $\rho^+ = 0.1$, $\rho^+ = 0.5$, and $\rho^+ = 0.95$. Plot the functions obtained and comment on the differences observed.

14. Set up a two-dimensional MC simulation of hard-triangles. Each molecule is an equilateral triangle of unit side length that does not rotate. Compute $g(r)$ for this fluid at $\rho^+ = 0.5$.

15. Compute $g(r)$ for a Lennard-Jones fluid over the range $0 \le r^+ \le 2$ for $T^+ = 1.0843$ and $\rho^+ = 0.8054$ and compare to the values obtained from the approximate integral-equation solution given in Table A5.6.

16. Simulate and plot $g_{11}(r)$ and $g_{22}(r)$ for a binary mixture of Ar and Ne at $T^+ = 1$ and $\rho^+ = 0.6$.

COOPERATIVE PHENOMENA

17. Smoothing of the liquid–liquid separation temperatures, measured in methanol(1) + n-hexane(2) mixtures by Clark and Rowley,[13] indicate the following data for the coexistence curve:

$T(°C)$	x_1'	x_1''	$T(°C)$	x_1'	x_1''
25	0.244	0.790	32	0.336	0.696
27	0.263	0.774	33	0.365	0.655
29	0.288	0.755	33.5	0.396	0.625
30	0.300	0.740	33.6	0.42	0.59
31	0.317	0.722			

Determine a value for β, the critical exponent for the order parameter if $T_c = 33.84°C$.

18. Using the van der Waals equation of state, plot the binodal and spinodal curves.

19. Classical equations of state do not correctly reproduce the near critical region. The critical exponent obtained from them are not consistent with the values shown in Table 7.1. Determine a value of β for the classical van der Waals equation of state.

20. Clark and Rowley,[13] report the following values for the mutual diffusion coefficient in mixtures of methanol(1) + n-hexane(2) at temperatures near T_c. The critical temperature for this system is 33.84°C and the critical mole fraction is $x_1 = 0.523$.

$T - T_c(°C)$	$D (10^{-10} \text{ m}^2/\text{s})$
4.100	1.406
2.792	1.053
1.310	0.632
1.057	0.546
0.937	0.456
0.368	0.274
0.105	0.111

Determine the critical exponent for the mutual diffusion coefficient.

ISING MODEL

21. (a) Using the one-dimensional Ising model, start a simulation with all spins up and observe the approach to equilibrium by watching the value of the magnetization. Qualitatively estimate the number of MC steps required to equilibrate at three different temperatures.

   (b) Without including initial nonequilibrium configurations in your results, determine $<E>$, $<M>$, and $<M^2>$ for $N = 100$, $J = 1, \mathcal{H} = 0$, and 100 MC steps/spin at any value of T selected in part a.

22. (a) Using a two-dimensional Ising model, start a simulation with all spins up and determine how long it takes the system to equilibrate at $T^+ = 3$. Determine the equilibrium values of $<M>$ and $<E>$ for this temperature.

(b) Repeat part *a* starting from a random or "hot" start. Are the values of $<E>$ and $<M>$ the same?

23. Use the two-dimensional Ising model to determine as best you can the critical exponent for the magnetization and the susceptibility.

24. There are no exact results available for the three-dimensional Ising model. Write an MC code to simulate the Ising model on a simple cubic lattice (coordination number for each spin is six). With your code determine the heat capacity and susceptibility in the critical region. From the maximum in these values, estimate as best you can kT_c/J and compare with the best known value of 4.5108.[4] Note that the estimate of the critical point will be strongly dependent upon size, and the best value would be obtained from an infinitely large lattice.

25. An important application of the Ising model is simulation of a "lattice gas." In this model, we interpret an "up" spin as a site occupied with a gas particle and a "down" site as a vacancy. Each site is either occupied by one atom or vacant. Nearest neighbors interact just as in the spin simulations, but with one essential difference. In the spin system, there is no conservation of "up" or "down" spins, while there must be a conservation of gas particles in the lattice gas model. To handle this constraint, we use *spin exchange dynamics* rather than *spin flip dynamics*. A trial *interchange* between two nearest neighbor spins is made and acceptance or rejection of the trial is based on the same criterion for the change in energy as before. Set up a simulation for a square lattice gas of 64 sites, half of which are initially occupied. Compute and plot the energy of the system as a function of T^+ from 1.0 to 4.0.

26. Use the lattice-gas simulator developed in Problem 25 to plot the mean energy as a function of T^+ from 1.0 to 4.0 at the higher density of 44 of the 64 sites occupied. Unlike Problem 25, the energy will not vary continuously and you should see evidence of a first-order, liquid–vapor phase transition.

27. Use the lattice-gas simulator of Problems 25 and 26 to compute a dimensionless diffusion coefficient at $T^+ = 2.0$ for the 44/64 and 32/64 densities.

8

MOLECULAR DYNAMICS
SIMULATIONS OF
THERMOPHYSICAL PROPERTIES

The approach to calculating thermophysical properties presented thus far has been based on calculating ensemble averages. Methods introduced in Chapters 3 through 6 focused on analytical solutions, while Chapter 7 introduced numerical simulation of thermophysical properties. In this chapter, we continue our study of the numerical simulation approach, but the macroscopic properties are calculated from time averages of the instantaneous molecular momenta and positions as the system naturally evolves in time subject to Newton's laws of motion.

In years past, the principal purpose of simulation data was to provide "experimental" data on model systems to test theories developed with the analytical approach. The direct analytical approach requires a postulate about the intermolecular potential model and simplifying mathematical assumptions. For example, even when applied to the Lennard-Jones potential, the configurational integral or, equivalently, integrals involving the pcf contain complexities that require simplification before thermophysical properties can be calculated. It is of course difficult to separate the effects of the mathematical simplifications from those of the chosen potential model. Computer simulations, on the other hand, can be performed with the same potential model used in the theory, but without the additional restrictive assumptions. In this sense, the simulations can serve as "experimental" data for the model fluid and comparison of theory with these data provides a test of the theory and the efficacy of the mathematical simplifications.

Today, molecular dynamics simulations are not only used to test theory, but to compute thermophysical properties of real fluids and to investigate molecular phenomena. The increasing role of simulations in thermophysical property prediction is due to increasing computational capacity per unit cost and additional research in realistic description of intermolecular potentials.

Monte Carlo techniques generate large numbers of phase points which represent the system. However, there is no temporal relationship between the ensemble members. Thermophysical properties are computed using ensemble averages. An alternative simulation or numerical technique is to track the trajectory of the system through phase space from a single initial starting phase point. In so doing, one solves the equations of motion for all the particles to obtain new positions and velocities from the previous location in phase space. Hence the name molecular dynamics (MD). Time averages are then used to obtain property values. While the algorithms used to find phase points are completely different, the MC and MD techniques are similar in many other respects and much of the computer implementation is the same. Thus the methods introduced in Chapter 7 that apply directly to molecular dynamics are used here without further elaboration, so some review of Chapter 7 may be helpful.

MD simulations use a small representative model of the system involving a relatively few number of particles (on the order of 100 to 10,000). An initial starting configuration must be chosen for both the positions and velocities of the particles. Subsequent motion of the interacting particles is obtained from numerical integration of the classical equations of motion. Four basic issues are important in obtaining properties from the MD simulation:

1. The most appropriate intermolecular potential model
2. Elimination of any dependency on the initial starting configuration
3. An efficient way to perform the simulations
4. The correct way of extracting properties from the dynamics of the simulation

The first issue is not unique to molecular dynamics; it is in fact the quintessential problem of all statistical mechanics calculations of nonideal systems. Molecular dynamics can, in fact, be used as an effective probe to study molecular interactions by comparison of simulated and experimental values. We have already discussed the first issue in Chapter 5. The issue of the starting configuration is handled much as it is with MC simulations. Basically, we run the simulation long enough that the particles "forget" their initial relative positions and velocities. That is, after an adequately long "equilibration" time, the particles will have bounced around enough that positions and velocities will be independent of the starting configuration. The system will have evolved to a *bona fide* point in phase space. Much effort has been spent in developing time-saving techniques to address the third issue. The decreased CPU time is often paid for in code complexity. Our approach will be to introduce a basic code that is simple and emphasizes fundamentals of MD simulations. The code illustrated in this chapter is basically that of Gould and Tobochnik,[1] with some minor modifications. We will comment on some of the more important time-saving techniques and integration methods, but the treatment will be only a basic introduction of essentials without concern for efficiency. The book *Computer Simulation of Liquids* by Allen and Tildesley[2] is currently the premiere reference for the serious user of MD techniques, and it should be consulted for additional techniques that are commonly used to make production codes efficient. Once the basic simulation is set up, nearly any desired property can be extracted from the positions and velocities of the particles as a function of time. We will illustrate this for a few properties and again refer the serious MD student to the much more complete treatise by Allen and Tildesley.

For the pedagogical purposes of this chapter, the MD method will be developed using nonpolar molecules interacting only through spherical dispersion forces, but other potentials may be used to represent polar, associating, and electrolyte fluids, generally without major modifications to a generalized MD code. The development will also be based on the assumption of pairwise additivity. While production runs often simulate NVT or NPT ensembles, we will introduce the code with the NVE or microcanonical ensemble. This is the most natural ensemble for MD simulations because the chosen box size fixes the volume and the conservative equations of motion fix the energy. We will conclude the chapter by discussing one method to sample the NVT ensemble.

8.1 THE BASIC SIMULATION CODE

As in the case of MC simulations, an initial configuration must be generated for the desired density. As before, a hot start (Fig. 7.7c) can be used at lower densities to minimize equilibration time, or a cold start (Fig. 7.7a or 7.7b) may be used at higher densities in order to pack the molecules more efficiently into the required volume. As in the MC simulations, dependence of the positions and velocities upon the initial configuration must be eliminated before any information is saved for property calculations. This is done by letting the system evolve over a considerable number of equilibration steps. As the length of the phase-space trajectory increases, the large number of collisions effectively obscures the system's "memory" of the starting configuration, and the results are decoupled from the artificial initial state. In SUBROUTINE *initial* in the illustrative code below, the initial configuration is a regularly spaced lattice. Lattice spacing between molecular centers (dL) is obtained from the length of the cubic cell (L) and the number of molecules per dimension (nn) required to achieve the desired density. This subroutine could be easily modified to provide a triangular or face-centered cubic lattice starting configuration similar to that used as SUBROUTINE *initial* for the MC program of Chapter 7. In production runs generating accurate values of the thermophysical properties, it is customary to save the final configuration (as arrays of particle positions and velocities) in a file. This file can then be used to provide the starting configuration for subsequent runs. Because the starting configuration is already a member of the system's phase space, this method eliminates the need for long equilibration times. The following code could be readily modified to permit use of a hot start or a configuration saved from a previous run.

```
SUB initial
SHARED vmax, v(), nn, n, xo(), x(), L, nd, rd
REM ****************************************************************
REM ** Initialize positions and velocities                    **
REM ** Positions are assigned based on a normal square lattice **
REM ** Velocities are assigned as a random fraction of a maximum **
REM **    vamx=maximum velocity to select velocities from,      **
REM **    v=velocity array, nn=# molecules in a row,            **
REM **    n=total # particles, xo=array of old coordinates,     **
REM **    x=array of new coordinates, L=box length,             **
REM **    nd=dimensionality of system (i.e., 3), rd=radius to   **
REM **    be used for graphical representation                  **
REM****************************************************************
DIM vcum(3)
FOR i = 1 TO 3:    REM ** initialize velocity accumulators
  vcum(i) = 0
NEXT
dL = L / nn:    REM ** dL is interparticle linear spacing
particle = 0
REM ** set up crystal with regular spacing **
IF nd = 2 THEN
  REM ** 2-dimensional option for graphics purposes
  FOR i = 1 TO nn
    FOR j = 1 TO nn
      particle = particle + 1
      x(1, particle) = (i - rd) * dL: REM ** x coordinate
      x(2, particle) = (j - rd) * dL: REM ** y coordinate
    NEXT
  NEXT
ELSEIF nd=3 THEN
  REM ** 3-dimensional option for calculation purposes
  FOR i = 1 TO nn
    FOR j = 1 TO nn
      FOR k = 1 TO nn
        particle = particle + 1
        x(3, particle) = (i - rd) * dL: REM ** z coordinate
        x(2, particle) = (j - rd) * dL: REM ** y coordinate
        x(1, particle) = (k - rd) * dL: REM ** x coordinate
      NEXT
    NEXT
  NEXT
ENDIF
REM ** Assign random velocities from uniform distribution **
```

```
FOR k = 1 TO nd
  FOR particle = 1 TO n
    v(k, particle) = vmax * (2 * RND - 1)
    vcum(k) = vcum(k) + v(k, particle)
  NEXT
  REM ** Normalize velocities so the net velocity is zero **
  vcum(k) = vcum(k) / n:    REM ** average velocity
  FOR particle = 1 TO n
    v(k, particle) = v(k, particle) - vcum(k)
  NEXT
NEXT
END SUB
```

Unlike MC simulations, *initial velocities* must also be assigned to the molecules in MD simulations. However, velocities cannot be assigned totally arbitrarily, since collectively they determine the energy at which the simulation is run; that is, they fix the average temperature of the run. We must therefore generate velocities that will match the constraint which we desire to impose on the energy (for NVE simulations) or on the temperature (for NVT simulations). The kinetic energy for each translational or rotational mode is $1/2kT$. Considering only the translational modes for a d-dimensional ($d = 2$ or 3) simulation, the relationship between the mean particle velocities and the temperature is,

$$\frac{d}{2}NkT = \frac{1}{2}\sum_{i=1}^{N} \text{m}<v_i^2>, \qquad (8.1)$$

where the $<...>$ notation indicates a time average. One could also formulate the temperature in terms of a rotational or vibrational temperature, but because energy continually redistributes among the various modes, the temperatures calculated from vibrational, rotational, and translational motion must all be equivalent.

In the above sample subroutine, initial values of velocity between $-v_{max}$ and v_{max} are generated for each coordinate using a random number generator. Programming for this method is convenient, but generated velocities are uniformly distributed and more equilibration steps are required than if a Gaussian velocity distribution had been generated. Methods for generating random numbers conforming to a desired distribution were discussed in Chapter 7, and an algorithm based on Example 7.6 could be used to replace the uniform generator in the above subroutine with a Gaussian velocity generator. This would decrease the equilibration time, although the relaxation of uniformly distributed velocities to a Gaussian distribution occurs quite rapidly in an MD simulation.

There are two problems with initial velocities generated in this manner. First, because they were generated randomly from either a uniform or Gaussian distribution, there is no guarantee that the center of the velocity distribution for each coordinate axis is zero. Thus there may be a net velocity of the simulation box in one or more of the three coordinate directions. Usually we do not want the system itself to be moving, and so velocities relative to a stationary system can be obtained by subtracting the mean velocity in each direction from the molecular velocity components. This is illustrated in the preceding subroutine. Second, the velocities generated may not, and probably will not, yield the desired run temperature from Equation (8.1). Generally an estimate of the average desired velocity is obtained from Equation (8.1) from which the velocity distribution is generated. Even so, after equilibration the resultant velocities usually yield a temperature from Equation (8.1) different from that desired. The usual procedure for eliminating this problem is a repeated sequence of rescaling the velocities followed by an equilibration period until the desired temperature and the generated equilibrium velocity distribution match. From Equation (8.1) the rescaled velocities are related to the previous velocities by

$$v_{i,\text{new}} = v_{i,\text{old}} \sqrt{\frac{T_{\text{obs}}}{T_{\text{old}}}}, \tag{8.2}$$

where T_{obs} is the desired temperature for the simulation and T_{old} is the temperature calculated from current velocities, $v_{i,\text{old}}$. While temperature rescaling is an important feature of research MD programs, it has not been included in the above subroutine to keep it simple.

Equilibration involves running the simulation for a considerable number of time steps. The simulation is run by solving Newton's equations of motion. We assume pairwise additivity so that the total potential is given by

$$U = \sum_{j>i}^{N} \sum_{i}^{N-1} u_{ij}, \tag{8.3}$$

and the force acting on any one particle is the sum of the individual forces

$$F_i = -\sum_{j=i} \nabla u_{ji}. \tag{8.4}$$

For a Lennard-Jones fluid, the magnitude of the dimensionless force directed between two interacting particles is

$$F^+ \equiv \frac{F\sigma}{\epsilon} = 24(2r^{+^{-13}} - r^{+^{-7}}). \tag{8.5}$$

Solution of Newton's equations must be done numerically in MD because the force on a particle involves the other N-1 particles:

$$m_i \, \ddot{\boldsymbol{r}}_i = \sum_{j \neq i}^{N} \boldsymbol{F}_{ji} \, . \tag{8.6}$$

There are several finite-difference numerical algorithms that can be used to integrate Equation (8.6) numerically. A fifth-order predictor-corrector method is commonly employed. Some research has been done on the accuracy and speed of various methods, but it appears that the integration method generally has very little effect on the calculated thermophysical properties. Here, for simplicity sake, we choose to illustrate two very simple algorithms based on a method due to Verlet.[3] The Verlet algorithms have been widely adopted because of their simplicity and the ease with which they can be programmed. The predictor-corrector requires slightly more programming, but provides faster integration than Runge–Kutta methods. The latter methods require two evaluations of the force at each time step. The predictor-corrector methods are particularly convenient if derivatives of positions and velocities are desired (to impose bond constraints for example) because they are already determined at each step.

The first of the Verlet methods is often called the Verlet "leapfrog" method. To advance from time step k to $k + 1$, an advance in time of Δt, the algorithm uses

$$\boldsymbol{r}_{k+1} = \boldsymbol{r}_k + \boldsymbol{v}_{k+1/2} \Delta t \tag{8.7}$$

$$\boldsymbol{v}_{k+1/2} = \boldsymbol{v}_{k-1/2} + \boldsymbol{a}_k \Delta t \, . \tag{8.8}$$

The procedure is diagrammatically sketched in Figure 8.1. Knowing the positions at time step k, one computes all of the forces, hence accelerations, using Equation (8.4). Equation (8.8) is then used with the known accelerations at step k and the known velocities at step $k-1/2$ to advance the velocity to the next half-step, $k+1/2$. As depicted in Figure 8.1, the velocity "leapfrogs" over the coordinates and accelerations to give the next midstep value. Generally the velocities are needed at integral step values and so one obtains them from

$$\boldsymbol{v}_k = \frac{\boldsymbol{v}_{k+\frac{1}{2}} + \boldsymbol{v}_{k-\frac{1}{2}}}{2} \, . \tag{8.9}$$

Once the velocity is known at $k+1/2$, Equation (8.7) can be used to find the positions at the next time step. The whole process can then be repeated, working step-by-step through time.

The second Verlet method is known as the velocity form of Verlet's algorithm. Its advantage over the leapfrog method is the direct determination of the velocity at integral time steps. The form of this algorithm is

$$\boldsymbol{r}_{k+1} = \boldsymbol{r}_k + \boldsymbol{v}_k \Delta t + \frac{1}{2} \boldsymbol{a}_k (\Delta t)^2 \tag{8.10}$$

$$\boldsymbol{v}_{k+1} = \boldsymbol{v}_k + (\boldsymbol{a}_{k+1} + \boldsymbol{a}_k) \frac{\Delta t}{2} \, . \tag{8.11}$$

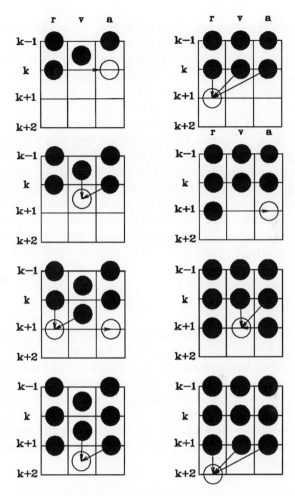

Figure 8.1   Diagram of integration procedure for leapfrog (*left*) and velocity form (*right*) of Verlet algorithm.

As shown in Figure 8.1, values of *r, v,* and *a* are known at step k. This allows the positions to be advanced to $k + 1$ using Equation (8.10). Obviously, once the new positions are known, the forces (hence accelerations) can be computed at the new time step using Equation (8.4). Equation (8.11) can then be used to move the velocity up to step $k + 1$, and the procedure can be repeated to continue to advance the system in time.

Because these algorithms perform a discrete integration of a continuous function, care must be taken to select an appropriate time step size. MD simulations can be quite time consuming so choosing a large value for Δt has the obvious advantage of decreasing the CPU time required for a particular trajectory length in phase space. However, if Δt is too long, the displacement during one time step may result in an erroneous particle overlap. The LJ potential is so steep that a large distance covered in a single step may cause abnormally high repulsions. Because the equations are discrete, two particles may find themselves severely embedded in their repulsive cores after a long time step, something that would not have occurred if they had felt the potential continuously as they approached each other. If this occurs, the next time step sends the two molecules flying apart at huge velocities. Evidence of too long of a time step is usually found in large fluctuations of the total energy of the system, a very large rise in the velocity (temperature) of some of the particles, or a code crash representing an explosion as the particles fly apart. At the other end of the spectrum, infinitely small time steps would conserve energy exactly but take infinite amount of computer time. One therefore tries to use time steps as large as possible without increasing the fluctuations in the energy beyond a desired tolerance. As a rule of thumb, a step size of $t^+ = 0.005$ is often chosen, where the reduced time is given by

$$t^+ \equiv \frac{t}{\sqrt{m\sigma^2/\epsilon}}. \qquad (8.12)$$

For Ar, this reduced step size corresponds to about 0.01 ps actual time.

In SUBROUTINE *move*, the velocity form of the Verlet algorithm is implemented. Given the current acceleration of the particles and their velocities, new positions of the molecules are determined from Equation (8.10). Next, periodic boundary conditions are applied just as they were in the MC simulations. If the move would take the particle out of the cell, the cell length for that coordinate is subtracted from the new position to bring the particle in through the opposite face of the cell. Then the velocities are updated for each particle (i) and dimension (k).

```
SUB move
REM ************************************************************
REM ** Verlet velocity algorithm                            **
REM **   dt=time step size, dt2=dt*dt, v=velocity array     **
REM **   a=acceleration array, ke=kinetic energy sum,       **
REM **   xnew=test array of part. positions before pbc      **
REM ************************************************************
SHARED n, nd, dt, dt2, x(), v(), a(), L, ke, virial, xnew()
FOR i = 1 TO n
  FOR k = 1 TO nd
    xnew(k) = x(k, i) + v(k, i) * dt + a(k, i) * dt2 / 2
    CALL periodic(k)
    x(k, i) = xnew(k)
    v(k, i) = v(k, i) + a(k, i) * dt / 2: REM Half update velocity
  NEXT
NEXT
```

```
CALL accel
FOR i = 1 TO n
  FOR k = 1 TO nd
    v(k, i) = v(k, i) + a(k, i) * dt / 2: REM finish velocity update
    ke = ke + .5 * (v(k, i) * v(k, i)): REM kinetic energy sum
  NEXT
NEXT
END SUB


SUB periodic (k)
REM **********************************************************
REM ** Apply Periodic Boundary Conditions              **
REM **********************************************************
SHARED nd, xnew(), L
WHILE xnew(k) < 0
  xnew(k) = xnew(k) + L: REM left of cell, add cell length
WEND
WHILE xnew(k) > L
  xnew(k) = xnew(k) - L: REM right of cell, subtract cell length
WEND
END SUB
```

With the new positions now located, new forces and accelerations can be computed. In SUBROUTINE *accel* the distance between each molecule and the other N-1 neighboring molecules is computed. To avoid computing each pair of interactions twice, only neighbors not previously used as the central molecule are included in the summations; that is, 3-2 and 4-2 interactions need not be calculated if 2-3 and 2-4 already have been. The sum shown in Equation (8.3) utilizes this concept to prevent overcounting. From the calculated intermolecular separations the force acting on each of the particles can be determined using an intermolecular potential model as in Equation (8.6). In the case of SUBROUTINE *LJ* shown below, the Lennard-Jones potential is used to obtain the force in accordance with Equation (8.4).

```
SUB accel
REM **********************************************************
REM ** Acceleration calculated from F = ma             **
REM **     pe=potential energy accumulator             **
REM **     virial=pressure accumulator                 **
REM **********************************************************
SHARED n, nd, a(), x(), L, pe, virial
DIM dx(3)
FOR i = 1 TO n
  FOR k = 1 TO nd
    a(k, i) = 0:                REM ** Initialize accelerations
  NEXT
```

```
NEXT
FOR molec = 1 TO n - 1:          REM ** Loop over central molecule
  FOR neighbor = molec + 1 TO n:   REM ** Loop over unique neighbors
    r2 = 0
    FOR k = 1 TO nd
      dx(k) = x(k, molec) - x(k, neighbor): REM coordinate distances
      REM ** Apply minimum image convention **
      IF ABS(dx(k))>.5*L THEN dx(k) = dx(k) - SGN(dx(k))*L
      r2 = r2 + dx(k) * dx(k):        REM ** nearest image distance
    NEXT
    r = SQR(r2)
    CALL LJ(r, force, potential):    REM ** calculate the pair force
    virial = virial + force * r:     REM ** vector add virial term
    pe = pe + potential:             REM ** sum potential energy
    FOR k = 1 TO nd:   REM ** vector add accel. to part. & neighbor
      a(k, molec) = a(k, molec) + force * dx(k)/r
      a(k, neighbor) = a(k, neighbor) - force * dx(k)/r
    NEXT
  NEXT
NEXT
END SUB


SUB LJ (r, force, potential)
REM ***********************************************
REM ** Compute force and potential from LJ model **
REM ***********************************************
ri = 1 / r
ri6 = ri ^ 6
force = 24 * ri * ri6 * (2 * ri6 - 1)
potential = 4 * ri6 * (ri6 - 1)
END SUB
```

The separation distance used in computing forces is the minimum separation between the particles, remembering that opposite faces are equivalent. This is the minimum image convention discussed in Chapter 7. Because the cell wraps around onto itself, each particle actually "sees" multiple images of itself and each of its neighbors as depicted in Figure 8.2. We do not want to count interactions with a neighbor more than once, so particles are permitted to interact only with the nearest image of neighboring particles. The minimum image convention is equivalent to truncating interactions between particles at a distance of $1/2L$, where L is the length of a cell side along the coordinate direction of interest. Cutting off all interactions for distances greater than $1/2L$ eliminates multiple interactions with the same particle, but may also limit the types of potential interactions that can be used in a given simulation. For example,

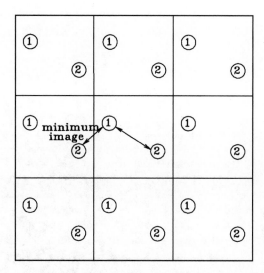

Figure 8.2   The minimum image convention ensures unique interactions for all pairs.

electrolyte interactions have a very long range due to the $1/r$ dependence shown in Equation (5.29). Very large cell sizes would therefore be required to adequately simulate systems in which particles interact with such a long-range potential function. Even the LJ potential extends over about four molecular diameters and thus requires a cubic cell of at least 8σ on a side. Later, we will discuss some time-saving techniques that are commonly used to help eliminate this problem.

Once forces have been determined from intermolecular separations, the accelerations are calculated from Equation (8.6). In the subroutines shown here, all variables are in dimensionless form, so the mass is unity and does not appear in SUBROUTINE *acc*. This procedure of updating the positions is used for each time step, and the algorithm is run both to equilibrate the system and to generate the thermophysical properties. Graphical display of the simulation is convenient for debugging purposes because glaring errors in the mechanics can often be readily spotted. For example, particles overlapping, collisions inconsistent with energy conservation, or incorrect periodic boundary conditions are quickly observed in a graphical output, whereas their presence may go undetected or be quite obscure in a list of numbers. The following driver program and subroutines for use with the preceding algorithmic subroutines graphically display the simulation in two dimensions as the system evolves in time.

```
REM ****************************************************
REM ** PROGRAM md.bas - programmed in QUICKBASIC    **
REM ** MOLECULAR DYNAMICS program with graphics     **
REM ****************************************************
```

```
DECLARE SUB initial ()
DECLARE SUB graphics ()
DECLARE SUB accel ()
DECLARE SUB periodic (k)
DECLARE SUB move ()
DECLARE SUB snapshot ()
DECLARE SUB final ()
DECLARE SUB LJ (r, force, potential)
DIM ball(500):            REM Array to hold graphical image
DIM x(3, 30), xo(3, 30), v(3, 30), a(3, 30), xnew(3)
CLS : KEY OFF
RANDOMIZE (TIMER)
INPUT "Number of dimensions"; nd
IF nd > 3 OR nd < 2 THEN
    PRINT "Error: only 2 or 3 dimensions allowed"
    STOP
END IF
INPUT "Number of particles per dimension"; nn
n = nn ^ nd
PRINT USING "   You have selected ### total particles"; n
INPUT "Number density"; rho
v = n / rho
L = v ^ (1 / nd)
rd = .5
dt = .016
dt2 = dt * dt
INPUT "Number of time steps per snapshot"; nsnap
INPUT "Maximum velocity"; vmax
CALL initial:                REM ** initialize positions and velocities
CALL graphics:               REM ** set up graphics screen
CALL accel:                  REM ** get initial accelerations
REM ** Main loop to move particles
virial = 0: pe = 0
WHILE k$ = ""
k$ = INKEY$
  FOR isnap = 1 TO nsnap:     REM ** integrate nsnap times before displaying
    CALL move
  NEXT
itime = itime + nsnap
CALL snapshot:               REM ** update graphics screen with positions
CALL final:                  REM ** output properties
WEND
CLOSE
SCREEN 2: SCREEN 0, 0, 0
END
```

```
SUB graphics
REM ***********************************************
REM ** set up graphics screen                **
REM ***********************************************
SHARED n, rd, L, x(), ball(), xo(), sx, sy, mx, my
SCREEN 1: CLS
m = L + rd
VIEW (0, 0)-(210, 199)
WINDOW (-rd - .01, -rd - .01)-(m + .01, m + .01)
CIRCLE (x(1, 1), x(2, 1)), rd, 1
PAINT (x(1, 1), x(2, 1)), 1
GET (x(1, 1) - rd, x(2, 1) - rd)-(x(1, 1) + rd, x(2, 1) + rd), ball
LINE (0, 0)-(L, L), 2, B
LINE (-rd, -rd)-(m, m), 2, B
PUT (x(1, 1) - rd, x(2, 1) - rd), ball
FOR i = 1 TO n
    xo(1, i) = x(1, i) - rd: xo(2, i) = x(2, i) - rd
    PUT (xo(1, i), xo(2, i)), ball
NEXT
END SUB


SUB snapshot
REM *************************************
REM ** put snapshot onto graphics screen **
REM *************************************
SHARED n, xo(), ball(), x(), rd
FOR i = 1 TO n
    PUT (xo(1, i), xo(2, i)), ball
    xo(1, i) = x(1, i) - rd
    xo(2, i) = x(2, i) - rd
    PUT (xo(1, i), xo(2, i)), ball
NEXT
END SUB
```

The above QUICKBASIC driver program serves two functions: it is the user interface and the logic controller. As a user interface it first asks for input concerning the run, including the number of dimensions (nd), the number of particles per dimension (nn), the number density (rho), and the maximum velocity. From this information the total number of particles (n) in the simulation and the volume (area for $nd = 2$) of a cubic (square for $nd = 2$) cell are calculated. The dimensionless time step is set at 0.016. It also asks for the number of time steps per snapshot. Each numerical integration is a time step, but we will want to display the results graphically less often to enhance the simulation speed. The graphical image of particle loci is updated only at each snapshot, which is some integer multiple of the actual integration time steps.

As a logic controller, the driver first calls SUBROUTINE *initial* to assign initial locations and velocities. It then calls SUBROUTINE *graphics* which sets up the graphics display screen by defining a viewport and setting up the coordinates of the window in accordance with the size of the cell. A border of just over one molecular radius is included on all sides of the window to prevent clipping of the molecule when its center approaches an edge of the cell. Graphical methods vary from computer to computer. SUBROUTINE *graphics,* written for IBM compatibles, draws a circle of radius one, fills it, picks up the graphic image in an array called box, and then erases the original by overlaying its image directly over the original. Once stored, the image of the molecule is placed at each of the lattice sites. The driver then calls SUBROUTINE *acc* to find the accelerations for the initial particle loci and then proceeds with the Verlet algorithm described previously. At snapshot intervals, the graphics screen is updated in SUBROUTINE *snapshot* by overlaying the particle image onto itself to erase it and then placing the image in the new particle location. A more realistic particle motion can be achieved via page flipping if the computer is equipped with an EGA or VGA card. The simulation on diskette associated with Example 8.1 illustrates such graphical representation of the simulation.

8.2 TIME-SAVING TRICKS

Molecular dynamics codes generally require little memory storage, but they are extremely CPU intensive. This is because the heart of the code is a double loop in which the interactions between each particle and its neighbors are calculated. The force calculations consume most of the time in MD simulations. Therefore, efforts to reduce CPU requirements must focus on reducing either the number of force calculations required or the time it takes to make the force calculation. You will see elements of both in the time-saving tricks discussed.

The most important and commonly used method to reduce computer time and cell sizes, even with longer range potentials, is to cut off the potential at a fixed distance, r_c, from the particle. In this procedure, potentials due to molecules within the cutoff distance are summed numerically as normal (see SUBROUTINES *accel* and *LJ,* for example). A correction is then used to account for the longer range effects, those due to the weaker interactions at distances greater than r_c. The relations given in Table 5.1 are used to calculate these corrections. To do so, one assumes that the rdf has become nearly unity for distances greater than r_c, and the corrections to each of the desired properties due to this truncated potential is computed from the corresponding equation in Table 5.1 with $g = 1$. For example, the correction to the potential energy due to this cutoff is

EXAMPLE

Example 8.1 Use the driver program and subroutines described in this chapter to put together a simple MD simulation code. Use the code to perform simulations on a 12-particle system in two dimensions. Start the simulation with a regularly spaced, square lattice and vary the starting density and allowed maximum velocity. Try to select conditions that would correspond to a solid, liquid, and gas to observe the initial crystal lattice "melt" into a liquid, "sublime" into a gas, or change lattice structures.

The simulations on the accompanying diskette have several "prerecorded" simulations available. That is, the simulation has been run in advance and the particle positions saved at periodic (snapshot) intervals. The snapshots are then played back when the program is run. This gives a smoother view of the molecular motion since the calculations are not being performed at the display time. The available simulations included are listed below.

1. *Gas simulation*—This simulation starts from a regular crystal which completely sublimes into the random motion of the gas particles.

2. *Liquid simulation*—This simulation also starts from a regular crystal lattice which then melts. The liquid then coalesces into a droplet with vapor space around it. When viewing the droplet, one should remember that periodic boundaries apply and so the droplet is still continuous when part of it is against one boundary and the other part is at the opposite boundary.

3. *Solid simulation*—Again the regular square lattice is the starting configuration, but the density is adequately high that it stays a solid. The crystal lattice structure does change, however, as the particles find a triangular lattice more energetically favorable.

4. *Self-diffusion*—This simulation emphasizes the fact that particles can be easily tagged and their mean-squared displacement used to determine the self-diffusion coefficient.

5. *Mixtures*—This simulation emphasizes that mixtures are just as easily simulated using appropriate molecular models for the two components.

6. *Diatomic molecule*—While the other simulations illustrate the application of MD simulations to the study of various properties and phases for simple spherical molecules, this simulation illustrates that site–site models can be used to more accurately represent structured molecules. The resultant simulations can include rotational and vibrational motion in addition to translational motion.

$$U_{corr} = 2\pi\rho N \int_{r_c}^{\infty} u(r)r^2 \, dr \, . \tag{8.13}$$

If the LJ potential is used in Equation (8.13) to perform the integration, the correction is found to be

$$U_{\text{corr}} = 8\pi N \rho \sigma^3 \epsilon \left[\frac{1}{9}\left(\frac{\sigma}{r_c}\right)^9 - \frac{1}{3}\left(\frac{\sigma}{r_c}\right)^3 \right].$$ (8.14)

Or, in terms of dimensionless variables,

$$U_{\text{corr}}^+ = 8\pi N \rho^+ \left[\frac{1}{9}(r_c^+)^{-9} - \frac{1}{3}(r_c^+)^{-3} \right].$$ (8.15)

Other long-range corrections can be calculated in a similar manner. For example, the long-range pressure correction would be

$$P_{\text{corr}} = -\frac{2\pi\rho^2}{3}\int_{r_c}^{\infty} \frac{du}{dr} r^3 \, dr = -\frac{16\pi\rho^2\sigma^3\epsilon}{9} \left[3\left(\frac{\sigma}{r_c}\right)^3 - 2\left(\frac{\sigma}{r_c}\right)^9 \right],$$ (8.16)

or

$$P_{\text{corr}}^+ = -\frac{16\pi\rho^{+2}}{9}[3(r_c^+)^{-3} - 2(r_c^+)^{-9}].$$ (8.17)

Using a cutoff potential with long-range analytical corrections is a considerable time saver in MD simulations. Truncation of the potential at r_c often eliminates a large number of force calculations especially for systems with lots of particles or for simulations at low densities. A standard value for the dimensionless cutoff of $r_c^+ = 2.5$ has evolved. For most properties, this cutoff provides a reasonably good trade-off between accuracy and efficiency. For example, a radius of $r^+ = 2.5$ around a particle defines a dimensionless spherical volume around the particle of 65.5, whereas an 1000-particle simulation performed at $\rho^+ = 0.5$ would include a dimensionless volume of 2000. One would therefore expect that on the average only about 3% of the particles would fall within the cutoff distance and be included in the force calculations.

Another time-saving technique is use of neighborhood lists. The neighborhood method evaluates the distance of all the other N-1 particles from each particle i periodically throughout the simulation. At that time, a list is constructed of all particles in the "neighborhood" of particle i. Generally the neighborhood is defined as a volume around molecule i of radius $r_c + r_b$ as shown in Figure 8.3. The radius of the neighborhood is slightly larger than the cutoff distance, say 0.3σ, so that particles do not move into the neighborhood between updates of the neighborhood list. Thus, the buffer distance, r_b, is chosen to be relatively small but must be large enough that particles do not move more than this distance between neighborhood list updates. The neighborhood list obviously increases the complexity of the code, but decreases considerably the CPU time because distances outside the neighborhood only need be computed every 10 to 20 time steps, at each neighborhood update. A simple way to implement the neighborhood list is to make one long array (on the order of $12N$ elements) that holds the ID numbers of the neighbors and then another array (of N) elements that

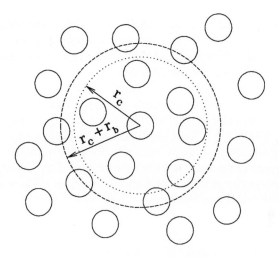

Figure 8.3   The neighborhood of particle *i*.

serves as a pointer to show where the neighbors for each molecule starts in the actual neighborhood list. For convenience, call the first array NABOR(i) and the second LIST(i). The code would then compute distances from particle 1 only for those particles with ID numbers stored as elements NABOR(LIST(1)) through NABOR(LIST(2)-1). Distances from particle 2 are only calculated for those particles with ID numbers stored as elements NABOR(LIST(2)) through NABOR(LIST(3)-1). Generalizing, forces are calculated for particle *i* for neighbor particles with ID's contained in the neighborhood list as elements NABOR (LIST(i)) through NABOR(LIST(i + 1)−1).

These, and other time-saving techniques, are important parts of a production code. Examples of their implementation have not been included in the simple code development of this chapter, but standard codes for implementation are available.[1,4] One such FORTRAN code is included on diskette as Appendix 8.

8.3 PROPERTY CALCULATIONS

Simulating molecular motion is only a means to an end, not the end itself. Properties must be related to molecular positions and velocities before the simulator can be used to calculate thermophysical properties.

Property values are calculated from time averages of mechanical variables in MD simulations. Mechanical variables can be evaluated at each time step from the positions and velocities of the particles. These values are summed as the simulation proceeds, and the time average is obtained from the accumulated value divided by the number of time steps over which it was obtained. If several averages are calculated for the same property during a run, a mean value of the averages and an estimate of the standard deviation can be determined. Generally, simulations between 1000 and 100,000 time steps are required, depending upon the property, to obtain accurate time averages for the properties. In PROGRAM *md*, used here as an example, averages are determined after every snapshot. The driver program calls SUBROUTINE *final* after the completion of *nsnap* time steps. SUBROUTINE *final* also divides the accumulated kinetic energy (*ke*) and potential energy (*pe*) by *nsnap* to form the time averages. Specific examples of property averages are discussed below. The procedures illustrated in the sample programs of this chapter are based on the NVE or microcanonical ensemble. Slightly different formulas are used for NVT and NPT simulations.[2,5]

```
SUB final
REM ** Calculate properties and write output **
SHARED nsnap, ke, pe, n, nd, L, virial, itime, dt
ke = ke / (nsnap * n):    REM ** time average kinetic energy **
pe = pe / (nsnap * n):    REM ** time average potential energy **
e = ke + pe:              REM ** find total energy **
temp = 2. * ke / nd:      REM ** calculate temperature **
REM ** calculate pressure **
pvirial = n * temp / L ^ nd + virial / (nd * L ^ nd * nsnap)
LOCATE 10, 32: PRINT itime
LOCATE 11, 30: PRINT USING "t=###.##"; itime * dt
LOCATE 13, 30: PRINT USING "KE=###.###"; ke
LOCATE 14, 30: PRINT USING "PE=###.###"; pe
LOCATE 15, 30: PRINT USING "E=###.###"; e
LOCATE 16, 30: PRINT USING "P=###.##"; pvirial
LOCATE 17, 30: PRINT USING "T=###.##"; temp
REM ** rezero accumulators **
ke = 0: pe = 0: virial = 0
END SUB
```

8.3.1 Potential Energy and Heat Capacity

The potential energy of the system is simply the sum of the pair potentials as shown in Equation (8.3). It is found by summing the total potential energy found from the pairwise interactions into an accumulating variable after each time step and dividing by the number of time steps. The potential energy represents the configurational internal energy U_c, or equivalently, the internal energy residual function at constant volume, $U - U^*$. This latter definition arises from the fact that the potential energy is calculated relative to the case of no interactions, that is, the ideal gas state at the same density conditions.

If the square of the potential energy is also collected at each step, the heat capacity can be obtained from a single simulation using the fluctuation Equation (2.72),

$$C_V = \frac{<U^2> - <U>^2}{kT^2}. \tag{8.18}$$

The heat capacity may alternatively be obtained from multiple simulations performed at slightly different temperatures using

$$C_V = \left(\frac{\partial U}{\partial T}\right)_V \approx \frac{\Delta U}{\Delta T}. \tag{8.19}$$

8.3.2 Kinetic Energy

The kinetic energy is found by summing the squared velocities

$$<ke> = \frac{1}{2}\sum_{i=1}^{N} \langle m_i v_i^2 \rangle. \tag{8.20}$$

8.3.3 Total Energy

The total energy of the system is the sum of the kinetic and potential energies

$$<E> = <pe> + <ke>. \tag{8.21}$$

For NVE simulations, the expectation value of the energy should be constant. In fact, the degree to which the energy is conserved is often used to monitor the efficacy of various parts of the simulation. For example, if the potential cutoff distance is too short and long-range effects not properly handled, significant variations of the energy with time might occur. Similarly, if the time step size is too long, larger fluctuations in the total energy result due to the abnormally high potential energies that result when molecules overlap repulsive potentials to a greater extent than they would for continuous motion. To compute values of the energy independent of the number of particles, the energy per particle is usually computed by dividing the total energy by N.

8.3.4 Temperature

Temperature is obtained from the kinetic energy in accordance with Equation (8.1), that is,

$$<T> = \frac{m}{dNk} \sum_{i=1}^{N} \langle v_i^2 \rangle . \qquad (8.22)$$

8.3.5 Pressure

The pressure is calculated from the virial theorem. We present the result here without proof:

$$PV = NkT + \frac{1}{d} \left\langle \sum_{i=1}^{N} \mathbf{r}_i \cdot \mathbf{F}_i \right\rangle , \qquad (8.23)$$

where $\mathbf{r}_i$ is the position vector of molecule i and $\mathbf{F}_i$ is the total vector force on that molecule. The second term in this equation, called the virial, is easily computed by summing the product of r_{ij} and F_{ij} right in the force subroutine itself, because

$$\sum_{i=1}^{N} \mathbf{r}_i \cdot \mathbf{F}_i = \sum_{i=1}^{N} \left(\sum_{k=1}^{3} r_k F_k \right)_i = \sum_i \sum_{j>i} \mathbf{r}_{ij} \cdot \mathbf{F}_{ij} = \sum_i \sum_{j>i} r_{ij} F_{ij} . \qquad (8.24)$$

This is the procedure used in SUBROUTINE *acc*.

The preceding properties can all be computed from the mechanical variables of the system. This is illustrated in Example 8.2.

Example 8.2   Starting from the simple MD program developed in Example 8.1, add a subroutine to calculate averages for the temperature, pressure, internal energy, and total energy.

The accompanying diskette allows a user to specify the maximum initial velocity to be assigned to the particles and the initial density. It then performs a simulation and shows the calculated values of the properties requested above. Since the code was written to show graphical movement of the particles, it is a two-dimensional code, and the corresponding properties are for two dimensions. The resultant PVT relation should not be taken as illustrative of a real or three-dimensional fluid. However, the student can put together a simple code from the subroutines in this chapter that can then be readily modified to three dimensions and can be used to study the equation of state of a LJ fluid.

The next property that we wish to examine is chemical potential. Because it is an entropic property, we do not know how to obtain it directly from molecular positions and momenta.

8.3.6 Chemical Potential

Imagine an MD simulation of N particles. Suppose at some point we insert an additional particle into the system. Let Z_+ be the configurational partition function with this new particle inserted and Z be the normal configurational partition function. Then Equation (2.70) requires that the ratio of these two quantities be

$$\frac{Z_+}{Z} = \frac{\int e^{-\beta U_+}\, d\mathbf{r}^N}{\int e^{-\beta U}\, d\mathbf{r}^N}. \tag{8.25}$$

This equation can be written more conveniently as an expectation value if we multiply and divide the numerator by $e^{-\beta U}$, that is,

$$\frac{Z_+}{Z} = \frac{\int e^{-\beta(U_+ - U)} e^{-\beta U} d\mathbf{r}^N}{\int e^{-\beta U} d\mathbf{r}^N} = \langle e^{-\beta \Delta U_+}\rangle, \tag{8.26}$$

where ΔU_+ represents the difference in potential energy between the $N + 1$ system with the new or test particle inserted and the simulated N-particle system. Note from this equation that the expectation value is based on the potential of the N-particle system; that is, it is the ordinary N-particle expectation value of the difference in energy due to inserting the test particle.

The chemical potential is related to the Helmholtz free energy by

$$\mu = \left(\frac{\partial A}{\partial N}\right)_{T,V}. \tag{8.27}$$

The derivative in this equation can in fact be found by the addition of a single particle to the simulation in analogy with that procedure described in the preceding paragraph. Using the relationship between A and Z [Equation (5.44)], we may then write for the residual chemical potential (relative to the ideal gas at the same T and ρ)

$$\mu^r = -kT\ln\left(\frac{Z_+}{Z}\right). \tag{8.28}$$

If we now substitute Equation (8.26) into Equation (8.28), we obtain

$$\mu^r = -kT\ln\langle e^{-\beta\Delta U_+}\rangle . \tag{8.29}$$

In practice, the expectation value shown above is calculated by inserting numerous "ghost" particles at one time. These ghost particles do not interact with the real particles of the simulation or the other ghost particles, but the real particles do interact with them. That is, we calculate the potential difference that would occur *if* the particles *were* inserted, but we don't actually insert the particles because the expectation value must be based on the N-particle ensemble average and we do not want to affect the dynamics of the N-particle simulation. This method for obtaining the chemical potential, developed by Widom,[6] is called either Widom's method or the *particle-insertion* method, for obvious reasons.

The most efficient way to apply Widom's method is to overlay temporarily a grid of ghost particles at predetermined times and calculate ΔU_+ for each of the ghost particles individually. This provides many values at each of the predetermined insertion steps and yields better statistics for the ensemble average indicated in Equation (8.29). Remember that the ghost particles are not literally inserted and therefore do not affect the mechanics of the simulation. Placing the ghost particles on a grid at periodic intervals in the simulation is equivalent to random insertions because the real particle positions are unknown and are random relative to the fixed grid of the ghost particles as depicted in Figure 8.4. Using a large grid of ghost particles and sampling at periodic times can

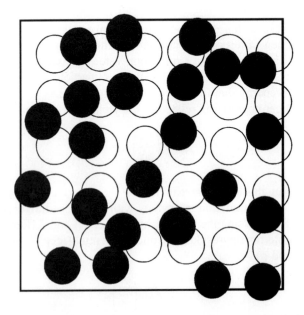

Figure 8.4   A regular grid of ghost particles overlaid at periodic intervals in the simulation can be used to obtain μ.

produce relatively accurate values of the chemical potential for low to moderate densities. At higher densities, most of the ghost particles overlap with real particles when inserted, and ΔU_+ becomes extremely large. Such insertions give virtually zero for $\exp(-\Delta U_+)$, the term averaged in Equation (8.29), and the statistics of the calculation deteriorate or it becomes impossible to determine an average.

As seen in Chapter 7, importance sampling can be used in such a situation to increase the sampling efficiency. Nevertheless, Widom's method is difficult to apply at relatively high densities of spherical molecules, and nearly impossible to implement for large, structured molecules. Other MC and MD techniques are currently being developed for these applications.

It should be noted that Equation (8.29) was really derived for the canonical ensemble. While the simple MD program introduced here is an NVE simulation, techniques currently exist to perform NVT and even NPT simulations. These latter simulations are becoming quite common in the literature. If one were to use the NVE ensemble to compute the chemical potential, Equation (8.29) should be modified to include temperature fluctuations that occur. While there is usually not a big difference that results, the more exact equation for the microcanonical ensemble is[2]

$$\mu^r = -k<T>\ln\left(\frac{\langle T^{3/2}e^{-\beta\Delta U_+}\rangle}{T^{3/2}}\right), \qquad (8.30)$$

where T is the instantaneous temperature computed from the particle velocities at the time of ghost particle insertion.

8.3.7 Transport Properties

A distinct advantage of MD over MC simulations is that particle velocities and time are an integral part of the simulation in MD simulations. This allows one to calculate rate information, including kinetic and transport coefficients, that cannot be obtained directly from MC simulations. As shown in Chapter 7, one can use MC random walk methods to obtain mean square displacements in simple systems, but an assumption about the time step must also be made in order to convert this information to diffusion coefficients. On the other hand, the self-diffusion coefficient can be readily obtained from MD simulations because the time steps are known quantities.

To obtain the self-diffusion coefficient D, we tag a particle and follow its trajectory from some arbitrarily chosen time, t_1, to some later time, t_2. Positions of this tagged particle can be obtained from the MD simulation relative to the original position at t_1 as a function of elapsed time t ($t = t_2 - t_1$) by

$$\boldsymbol{R}(t) = \boldsymbol{r}(t_2) - \boldsymbol{r}(t_1) \, . \tag{8.31}$$

In and of itself, $\boldsymbol{R}$ is not a very interesting quantity; the net time average of $\boldsymbol{R}$ is zero because displacements in positive and negative directions are equally probable. However, the average of the mean square displacement, R^2, is nonzero and should be related to the velocity at which the particle moves through the fluid. In fact, the well-known Einstein relation

$$D = \lim_{t \to \infty} \frac{\langle R(t)^2 \rangle}{2dt} \tag{8.32}$$

relates the self-diffusion coefficient to the mean square displacement (MSD). Here, as before, d is the dimensionality of the system. Note that Equation (8.32) requires that the slope of $R^2(t)$ versus t be taken at long time. Strictly speaking, D is related to the MSD by Equation (8.32) only in the thermodynamic limit. Application of Equation (8.31) also requires that the periodic boundary conditions not be included in the displacements. Problem 13 at the end of the chapter shows an easy way to do this.

A typical MSD plot is shown in Figure 8.5. Note that at very short times, the MSD has a quadratic region. This corresponds to the Knudsen region or times too short for multiple collisions. In practice, one generally averages the MSD over all particles. This greatly improves the statistics. Additionally, better statistics can usually be obtained by overlapping or nesting the displacement measurements. Thus, one might start t_1 at time step 100 and monitor positions for 100 subsequent time steps, then start a new displacement record at time step

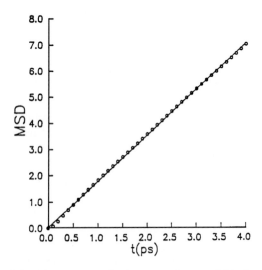

Figure 8.5   Mean square displacement from an MD simulation.

105 and keep track for this record to time step 205, and so on, as shown in Figure 8.6.

Similar *Einstein* or MSD relations can be derived for other transport properties. In general, a transport property γ can be related to a MSD function of the form

$$\gamma = \frac{<[A(t)-A(0)]^2>}{2dt} \tag{8.33}$$

where $A(t)$ is the value of the appropriate property at some time t and $A(0)$ is the value at the selected initial time. An equivalent approach to calculating transport properties is to use *time correlation* functions. The transport property can be written in terms of the time correlation function as

$$\gamma = \int_0^\infty <\dot{A}(t)\dot{A}(0)> \, dt \,, \tag{8.34}$$

where the dot indicates a time derivative. As we have seen, the appropriate variable to use for A in Equation (8.33) to obtain the diffusion coefficient is the particle position. The corresponding variable to calculate the diffusion coefficient from the time correlation function is therefore the time derivative of the particle position, the particle velocity. Equation (8.34) becomes an integral over the dot product of the velocity vector of a particle at two different times and is called the velocity time correlation function (VCF). The VCF tells us how strongly correlated the velocity of the particle is at some later time to the

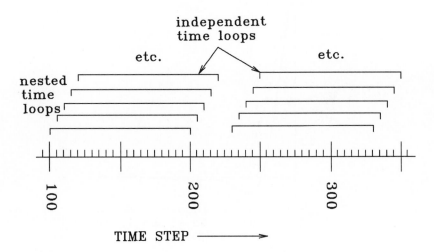

Figure 8.6 Overlap of time domains for parallel calculation of several mean square displacements.

initial value at time $t = 0$. For example, consider the normalized velocity correlation function

$$\text{VCF} = \frac{<v(t) \cdot v(0)>}{<v^2(0)>} \tag{8.35}$$

shown in Figure 8.7. At $t = 0$, the VCF is identically unity; that is, the velocity is perfectly correlated with itself since no time has elapsed. As time proceeds, the particle suffers collisions which change the particle's speed and direction. The instantaneous vector velocity becomes less and less correlated with its original value as more and more collisions reorient the direction of the particle's motion. Note that the curve in Figure 8.7 at the higher density actually shows a negative correlation between the current and original velocity. This corresponds to the approximate time when the molecule collides with the cage of molecules surrounding it; the collision changes the direction of the molecule and it often travels in the opposite direction. Thus the dot product of the vector velocities in Equation (8.35) will be negative. After many collisions, the molecule's velocity is uncorrelated with the original value and the *average* dot product between the current and original velocity will be zero.

We have used the self-diffusion coefficient as a convenient example to illustrate how the Einstein relation or the time correlation function can be used to obtain D. Other transport coefficients are also determined from similar formulas by using the appropriate mechanical variable for A in Equation (8.33)

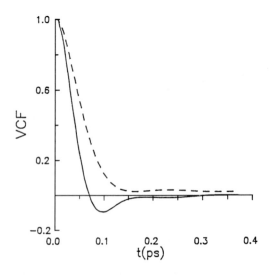

Figure 8.7 Typical velocity correlation functions at low (– – –) and high (——) densities.

or (8.34). Table 8.1 summarizes the two forms for various transport coefficients. The Einstein formulas contained in Table 8.1 are consistent with the derivation of Helfand[7] and are the forms currently used in simulations.[2] Note that the self-diffusion coefficient is a one-particle property while the other transport coefficients are fluid properties dependent upon all of the particles at each time step. What this means is that an MSD can be obtained for each particle, providing N values to be used as part of the averaging denoted by $<...>$. On the other hand, only one MSD is obtained for all N particles when calculating the other transport coefficients. To obtain the same level of statistical accuracy for these coefficients, one would need to include at least a factor of N more MSD's in

TABLE 8.1   Relations for Transport Coefficients in the Einstein and Time Correlation Forms

Property	Einstein Formula	Time Correlation Formula
Self-diffusion	$D = \dfrac{\langle [x_i(t) - x_i(0)]^2 \rangle}{2t}$	$D = \int_0^\infty \langle v_{x_i}(t) v_{x_i}(0) \rangle \, dt$
Shear viscosity	$\eta = \dfrac{m^2 \beta}{2Vt} \langle [x(t)\dot{y}(t) - x(0)\dot{y}(0)]^2 \rangle$	$\eta = \beta V \int_0^\infty \langle P_{xy}(t) P_{xy}(0) \rangle \, dt,$ where $P_{xy} = \dfrac{1}{V} \sum_i \left(p_{x_i} p_{y_i} + x_i f_{y_i} \right)$
Bulk viscosity	$\kappa = \dfrac{m^2 \beta}{2Vt} \langle [x(t)\dot{x}(t) - x(0)\dot{x}(0)]^2 \rangle$	$\kappa = \beta V \int_0^\infty \langle (P_{xx}(t) - P) \times (P_{xx}(0) - P) \rangle \, dt$
Thermal conductivity	$k' = \dfrac{k\beta^2}{2Vt} \langle [x(t)(E(t) - <E>) - x(0)(E(0) - <E>)]^2 \rangle$	$k' = \dfrac{k\beta^2}{V} \int_0^\infty \langle S_x(t) S_x(0) \rangle \, dt,$ where $S_x(t) = \dfrac{d}{dt} \sum_j x_j (E_j - <E>)$

Equations are written for a single dimension or pair of dimensions, although in practice, one would average over all of the possible dimensions or pairs of dimensions.

the averages than for the self-diffusion coefficient. However, McQuarrie[8] obtains the Einstein functions in a slightly different form than Helfand. The McQuarrie equations are of the form $<\Sigma[A(t)\ A(0)]^2>$, whereas the Helfand equations are of the form $<[\Sigma A(t)\ A(0)]^2>$. In the McQuarrie formalism, the other transport properties are thus single-particle properties like the self-diffusion coefficient. The two forms have recently been shown to differ by a single term.[9] This term was shown to be zero for long times in MD simulations,[9] and recently a theoretical verification has been advanced to show that this term is zero in the thermodynamic limit.[10] Sample simulations run with the McQuarrie and Helfand formalisms evidently agree numerically,[9] but there is greater statistical uncertainty with the Helfand formalism.

While the Einstein and time-correlation function approaches are equivalent mathematically, implementation of the methods is not equally easy. The Einstein equations are almost always easier to program, but the time correlations may be of some interest themselves in understanding relaxation of correlated motion. A difficulty with the time correlation functions has been observed at higher densities. There appears to be a long-time tail to the time correlation function; that is, it tends to oscillate around zero for considerable time. This persistence of the correlation function to long times can potentially cause difficulty in determining when all of the significant area under the curve has been included in the integrals shown in Table 8.1. There is yet considerable debate in the literature as to which procedure yields the most reliable results.

8.3.8 Mixture Properties

Simulation of mixture properties are handled in exactly the same manner as pure components. The only difference is that the identity of the particles (which component that particle is) must be kept track of so that the appropriate potential parameters (ϵ_{11}, ϵ_{12}, etc.) can be used to evaluate the pair forces.

We can also readily determine mixture excess properties by performing simulations on the pure components at the same temperature and pressure as the mixture simulations. Consider the case of the excess enthalpy, equivalently, the heat of mixing. The internal energy departure function is simply the sum of the pair potentials,

$$u - u^* = \sum_{i=1}^{N-1} \sum_{j=1}^{N} \mathbf{u}_{ij}. \tag{8.36}$$

Normally, one uses NPT simulations to obtain excesses properties. We can then get both the internal energy and the compressibility factor, z, at the same temperature and pressure from a single simulation and use these two values to obtain the enthalpy departure function,

$$h - h^* = (u - u^*) + (z - 1)RT \, . \tag{8.37}$$

By using this procedure for the pure components and the mixture at the same temperature and pressure, we can obtain the heat of mixing or excess enthalpy by subtracting the ideal mixture enthalpy from the actual mixture value; that is,

$$h^E \equiv \Delta h_{\mathrm{mix}} = (h - h^*)_{\mathrm{mix}} - \sum_i x_i(h - h^*)_i \, . \tag{8.38}$$

Similar procedures involving pure component and mixture simulations can be written for other excess properties. Because excess properties calculated in this manner involve the subtraction of two simulated values to obtain a value often relatively small compared to the total properties, large uncertainties may result if the simulations are not done particularly carefully.

8.4 SIMULATIONS WITH CONSTRAINTS

The basic MD code introduced in this chapter is for NVE simulations of spherical particles. In the discussion of property calculation that followed introduction of the basic code, we suggested the importance of simulations in other ensembles, such as NVT and NPT. Additionally, we need to be able to perform simulations using more realistic models of molecules, such as structured, multiatomic models of molecules containing vibrational, rotational, and internal bond-rotational modes. These complexities introduce constraints into the basic MD algorithm.

There are several ways to introduce constraints into the simulation. Bond-length constraints, for example, can be incorporated directly into the Lagrangian equations of motion using the methods discussed in Chapter 1. The equations of motion are solved with various algorithms, the most popular of which are *SHAKE* and *RATTLE*.[2] Instead of this approach, we will focus our discussion here on a particularly convenient MD simulation method that uses Gaussian, rather than Newtonian or Lagrangian, mechanics. The method is particularly convenient because exactly the same procedures can be used to impose bond constraints, to fix the temperature or pressure, or to perform nonequilibrium simulations representing shear, diffusion, or thermal conduction. This is only one of several approaches advanced in the literature, but it is a particularly elegant way to handle the problem of constraints with minimum change to the basic MD code.

8.4.1 Gauss's Principle

About 150 years ago, Gauss formulated a mechanics more general than Newton's based on what we now call Gauss's principle of least constraint.[12] It can easily handle both holonomic and nonholonomic constraints. Gauss referred to it as *the most fundamental dynamical principle*.[13] The discussion and development of Gaussian mechanics used here is essentially that presented by Evans and his co-workers.[12–15]

For a constraint that can be written in the form

$$g(\boldsymbol{r},\dot{\boldsymbol{r}},t) = 0 \,, \tag{8.39}$$

a differential constraint equation of the form

$$\boldsymbol{n}(\boldsymbol{r},\dot{\boldsymbol{r}},t) \cdot \ddot{\boldsymbol{r}} = s(\boldsymbol{r},\dot{\boldsymbol{r}},t) \tag{8.40}$$

can be generated. This is done by differentiating Equation (8.39) once for nonholonomic constraints or twice for holonomic. Recall from Chapter 1 that nonholonomic constraints depend on the velocity. Equation (8.40) defines a hyperplane in acceleration space where $\boldsymbol{n}$ is a vector normal to the hyperplane as shown in Figure 8.8. The dot product in the constraint equation projects the acceleration vector onto this hyperplane. Any acceleration that is to satisfy the constraint equation must therefore lie on this hyperplane. If the system were to evolve under Newtonian mechanics, the accelerations would be given by $m\ddot{\boldsymbol{r}} = \boldsymbol{F}$. These accelerations would not, in general, satisfy the constraint equation $g = 0$. To obtain the correct accelerations that do satisfy the constraint equation, we must somehow ensure that they lie within the constraint hyperplane, that is, that they must satisfy Equation (8.40). To make the discussion clearer, let's speak of forces rather than accelerations. For the moment, consider particles of unit mass. Gauss's principle of least constraint provides a prescription of how to project the Newtonian forces onto the constrained-force hyperplane. It states that the actual trajectories will deviate as little as possible, in a least squares sense, from the unconstrained Newtonian trajectory.[14] Equivalently, this requires that the magnitude of the *constraint force* is minimized along the correct trajectory. It is the normal projection which minimizes the magnitude of the constraint force. Therefore the minimum constraint force is some multiple of the normal

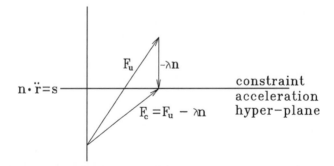

Figure 8.8   Projection of the unconstrained force $\boldsymbol{F}_u$ onto the constrained hyperplane (drawn for unit mass).

vector, n, say $-\lambda n$, where λ is a yet undetermined scaler multiplier. Gauss's prescription simply identifies the constraint force which must be added to the Newtonian force as $-\lambda n$, where n is defined by the differential constraint Equation (8.40). Thus we write Gauss's constrained equation of motion as

$$m\ddot{r} = \dot{p} = F_u - \lambda n .\qquad(8.41)$$

The first force term on the right represents the unconstrained or Newtonian force while the second term represents the constraint force. The relationship between these forces and the projection onto the constrained acceleration hyperplane is depicted in Figure 8.8.

To use Gaussian mechanics, we must first solve for the undetermined multiplier, λ. This is done by substitution of Equation (8.41) into Equation (8.40) to yield

$$n\cdot\ddot{r} = \frac{(n \cdot F_u) - \lambda n^2}{m} = s\qquad(8.42)$$

or

$$\lambda = \frac{(F_u \cdot n) - s}{mn^2} .\qquad(8.43)$$

Note that the multiplier λ is a function of particle positions, velocities, and Newtonian forces. In the MD code, we can compute the Newtonian forces based on interparticle distances and use these forces, positions, and velocities to find λ. Equation (8.41) is then used to obtain the constrained accelerations from which the new positions and velocities will be calculated.

The steps required to obtain the Gaussian equations of motion may be summarized as:

1. Differentiate the constraint function $g(r, \dot{r}, t) = 0$ with respect to time and identify the normal vector n by comparing the result to Equation (8.40). Any scaler factors can be absorbed into the definition of λ.

2. Include the constraint forces, $-\lambda n$, in the equations of motion.

3. Use the constrained equations of motion and the differential constraint equation to obtain a *linear* equation for λ.

Note that the constraint equation itself is never used, only the *differential* constraint equation. This means that the Gaussian equations will only act to maintain the constrained variables at their fixed values; they will not initially fix them at a desired value. Thus one must start the simulation with the appropriate values for bond lengths, temperature, and so forth; the differential constraint equation will keep the property at that value thereafter.* This is seldom a problem. An added advantage of the method, however, is that precise values of the constraint force are calculated right along with new particle positions. These constraint forces may, in and of themselves, be of value to the simulator. While the above general development may yet seem somewhat vague, two important applications of Gaussian mechanics will help solidify the concepts and implementation procedures.

8.4.2 Isothermal MD Simulations

The real advantage Gauss's formulation has over the Lagrangian method is the ability to treat nonholonomic constraints as easily as holonomic. An important nonholonomic constraint is the fixed temperature in NVT simulations. Because the system temperature is related to the square of the velocities, a constraint on temperature is equivalent to a constraint on velocities (i.e., nonholonomic). We shall use a Gaussian thermostat to keep the temperature constant as the system evolves. Note that one cannot use Newtonian mechanics to do this, because Newton's laws are conservative (i.e., constant total energy).

The constraint for the Gaussian thermostat is:

$$g(\mathbf{r}, \dot{\mathbf{r}}, t) = \sum_i \frac{1}{2} m\dot{\mathbf{r}}_i^2 - \frac{3}{2} NkT = 0 . \tag{8.44}$$

Using the prescription enumerated above, we differentiate g once to obtain:

$$\dot{g} = \sum_i m(\dot{\mathbf{r}}_i \cdot \ddot{\mathbf{r}}_i) = 0 , \tag{8.45}$$

or

$$\sum_i \dot{\mathbf{r}}_i \cdot \ddot{\mathbf{r}}_i = 0 . \tag{8.46}$$

Comparison with Equation (8.40) reveals that $s = 0$ and that $\mathbf{n}$ is $\dot{\mathbf{r}}$; that is, the constraint forces act along the individual velocity vectors of the particles to maintain a fixed temperature. This is certainly what we would expect from the relationship between temperature and particle velocity. We now use the known value of the projection vector $\mathbf{n}$ to write Equation (8.43) as

---

* Actually, there will be some drift over long times due to numerical round-off. In this case, one must either periodically put the system back into agreement with the constraints or use a feedback mechanism that adds a nonphysical force to compensate exactly for the nonphysical round-off errors.

$$\lambda = \frac{\displaystyle\sum_i (\boldsymbol{F}_{u,i} \cdot \dot{\boldsymbol{r}}_i)/m_i}{\displaystyle\sum_i \dot{\boldsymbol{r}}_i^2}.$$
(8.47)

Application of a Gaussian thermostat is therefore quite easy. We simply solve Equation (8.41) for each particle (where λ is given by Equation 8.47) instead of the normal Newtonian equation of motion. Implementation into a standard MD program is also quite easy. From known positions and velocities at time step t, we compute the Newtonian or unconstrained force on each particle $\boldsymbol{F}_{u,i}$ and the Gaussian constraint λ. This latter value is obtained from a dot product of the velocity and unconstrained force vectors, namely,

$$\lambda = \frac{\displaystyle\sum_i (F_x \dot{r}_x + F_y \dot{r}_y + F_z \dot{r}_z)_i}{m \displaystyle\sum_i (\dot{r}_x^2 + \dot{r}_y^2 + \dot{r}_z^2)_i}.$$
(8.48)

The constrained force, $\boldsymbol{F}_{u,i} - \lambda \boldsymbol{r}_i$, is then computed, and positions and velocities are advanced in the normal way using Equation (8.41) and an appropriate numerical integration technique. Implementation, therefore, only requires the addition of a couple of extra lines of code to compute λ and the constrained force.

8.4.3 Simulation of Structured Molecules

The assumption of spherical particles made to this point in our discussion was done to facilitate discussion and demonstration of the basic MD method. Simulations of models for real systems, however, often have fixed distance constraints between sites representing bonds between atoms within the molecule. Modeling of structured, nonspherical, or polyatomic molecules is done through the use of more sophisticated potentials as discussed in Chapter 5, site–site interaction methods being most commonly employed. The site–site treatment has two important effects upon the basic MD code. First, the CPU time requirements are increased. For spherical molecules, the number of force calculations is ostensibly N^2, although the various time-saving tricks mentioned in this chapter can reduce that number to approximately order N. Consider now a model with N_s LJ sites per molecule. The number of force calculations becomes of the order $(N \cdot N_s)^2$, $(N_s^2 \cdot N)$ employing the time-saving tricks. Considerable complication of the code will also occur due to the distance constraints which must be placed between bonded sites to represent bond lengths.

Consider now the application of Gaussian mechanics to the simulation of a structured, polyatomic molecule with fixed bond lengths. We will illustrate the procedure for a diatomic molecule. The method is the same, though the mathematics more complex, for polyatomic species. Additionally, the same method can be used to fix bond angles if one also constrains next-nearest-neighbor distances. The single constraint for a diatomic molecule is

$$g(r) = r_{12}^2 - d_{12}^2 = 0 , \tag{8.49}$$

where d_{12} is the fixed equilibrium bond distance and r_{12} is the vector between the two sites. Since this is an holonomic constraint, we differentiate g twice with respect to t to obtain the differential constraint equation:

$$\ddot{g} = 2\dot{r}_{12} \cdot \dot{r}_{12} + 2r_{12} \cdot \ddot{r}_{12} = 0 , \tag{8.50}$$

or, in the form of Equation (8.40),

$$r_{12} \cdot \ddot{r}_{12} = -(\dot{r}_{12} \cdot \dot{r}_{12}) . \tag{8.51}$$

We learn from this equation that the bond-vector acceleration, $\ddot{r}_{12}$, is constrained by a force that acts between the centers of the sites; that is, $n = r_{12}$. Again, this is not a surprise. Obviously the constraint to keep the two sites at a fixed distance must act between their centers. The equations of motion for the two particles can now be written as

$$\ddot{r}_1 = \frac{1}{m}(F_{u,1} - \lambda r_{12}) \tag{8.52}$$

$$\ddot{r}_2 = \frac{1}{m}(F_{u,2} + \lambda r_{12})$$

by realizing that the normal vector $r_{12} = r_2 - r_1$ that constrains the acceleration of site 1 has the opposite sign of the normal vector for the constraint on site 2.

We now find λ by substituting the equations of motion into the constraint equation. By subtracting the first of Equations (8.52) from the second,

$$\ddot{r}_{12} \equiv \ddot{r}_2 - \ddot{r}_1 = \frac{1}{m}(F_{u,12} + 2\lambda r_{12}) , \tag{8.53}$$

and then taking the dot product with r_{12}, we obtain

$$\frac{1}{m}[r_{12} \cdot F_{u,12} + 2\lambda(r_{12} \cdot r_{12})] = -\dot{r}_{12} \cdot \dot{r}_{12}$$

or

$$\lambda = -\frac{(r_{12} \cdot F_{u,12}) + m\dot{r}_{12}^2}{2r_{12}^2} . \tag{8.54}$$

Again this constraint is easily implemented into a standard MD code. The positions of the particles, their velocities, and the unconstrained or Newtonian force between pairs of particles, $F_{u,12}$, are already calculated in standard MD

[EXAMPLE]   **Example 8.3**   Run the program on the accompanying diskette to view the dynamics of a model for isobutane under Couette flow. The model consists of four equivalent LJ sites located at the four carbon centers. Bond lengths are fixed at the experimental values and a Gaussian thermostat is employed to remove the heat generated by the flow of viscous fluid.

codes, so one can use these quantities in Equation (8.54) to calculate λ immediately. The constrained forces are then calculated and Equations (8.52) are integrated using the standard methods. Again, only a few extra lines of code are required to implement the bond constraints.

We reiterate here that the above method will keep the bond lengths constant, but will not initially fix them at a specific value. The code must construct the molecules at the desired relative positions in the starting configuration. The system will then evolve in accordance with the constrained equations of motion, maintaining the relative positions fixed in the starting configuration.

Much more complex molecules can be handled in an analogous, although mathematically more cumbersome, manner. Using appropriate geometrical constraints, one can fix bond angles, conformations, and ring structures in the models. Other constraints may also be imposed such as a force to maintain a nonequilibrium flow. For example, one may constrain the fluid under constant shear to simulate Couette flow in order to determine the shear viscosity coefficient. Of course, multiple constraints may also be used. Imposition of bond constraints, a thermostat constraint, and a shear constraint may all be imposed at once to simulate the viscosity of a model, polyatomic fluid as in Example 8.3.[16]

REFERENCES

1. Gould, H., and Tobochnik, J., *An Introduction to Computer Simulation Methods. Applications to Physical Systems, Part 1,* Addison-Wesley, Reading, MA, 1988.

2. Allen, M.P., and Tildesley, D.J., *Computer Simulation of Liquids,* Clarendon Press, Oxford, 1987.

3. Verlet, L., "Computer 'experiments' on classical fluids. I. Thermodynamical properties of Lennard-Jones molecules," *Phys. Rev.* **1967**, *159,* 98–103.

4. Haile, J.M., *Molecular Dynamics Simulation. Elementary Methods,* Wiley, New York, 1992.

5. Cheung, P.S.Y., "On the calculation of specific heats, thermal pressure coefficients and compressibilities in molecular dynamics," *Mol. Phys.* **1977**, *33,* 519–526.

6. Widom, B., "Some topics in the theory of fluids," *J. Chem. Phys.* **1963**, *39,* 2808.

7. Helfand, E., "Transport coefficients from dissipation in a canonical ensemble," *Phys. Rev.* **1960**, *119,* 1–9.

8. McQuarrie, D.A., *Statistical Mechanics,* Harper & Row, New York, 1976.

9. Chialvo, A.A., and Debenedetti, P.G., "Use of the McQuarrie equation for the computation of shear viscosity via equilibrium molecular dynamics," *Phys Rev A* **1991**, *43*, 4289–4295.

10. Chialvo, A.A., Cummings, P.T., and Evans, D.J., "Relationship between McQuarrie and Helfand equations for the determination of shear viscosity from equilibrium molecular dynamics," *Phys. Rev. E,* **1993**, *47*, 1702.

11. Chialvo, A.A., and Cummings, P.T., "Unified expression for the calculation of thermal conductivity in the canonical ensemble," *Mol. Phys.* **1993**, *78*, 791.

12. Evans, D.J., Hoover, W.G., Failor, B.H., Moran, B., and Ladd, A.J.C., "Nonequilibrium molecular dynamics via Gauss's principle of least constraint," *Phys. Rev. A* **1983**, *28*, 1016–1021.

13. Evans, D.J., and Morriss, G.P., *Dynamics of Classical Liquids,* Academic Press, New York, 1989.

14. Hanley, H.J.M., and Evans, D.J., "Non-Newtonian molecular dynamics and thermophysical properties," *Int. J. Thermophys.* **1990**, *11*, 381–398.

15. Edberg, R., Evans, D.J., and Morriss, G.P., "Constrained molecular dynamics: Simulations of liquid alkanes with a new algorithm," *J. Chem. Phys.* **1986**, *84*, 6933–6939.

16. Rowley, R.L., and Ely, J.F., "Nonequilibrium molecular dynamics simulations of *n*-butane and isobutane viscosity," *Mol. Sim.* **1991**, *7*, 303–323.

17. Nicolas, J.J., Gubbins, K.E., Streett, W.B., and Tildesley, D.J., "Equation of state for the Lennard-Jones fluid," *Mol. Phys.* **1979**, *37*, 1429–1454.

18. Reynolds, W.C., *Thermodynamic Properties in SI,* Stanford University, Stanford, 1979.

19. Cheung, P.S.Y., and Powles, J.G., "The properties of liquid nitrogen. IV. A computer simulation," *Mol. Phys.* **1975**, *30*, 921–949.

PROBLEMS

Note: All of the following problems assume that the student has put together a working MD code from the subroutines presented in the chapter. Additionally, because the problems are simulations, considerable time and effort are required for each in addition to available computer hardware and a convenient programming language.

1. Modify the starting configuration of the basic MD code so that all particles are initially on lattice sites in the left half of a two-dimensional cell. Set up a counter that keeps track of the number of particles in the left half of the cell and run the simulation for 300 or 400 time steps of length 0.02.

   (a) What happens as a function of time if the initial maximum velocity is 1.0?

   (b) What happens as a function of time if the initial maximum velocity is 0.1?

2. Set up a three-dimensional MD simulation and run the program with time steps of 0.01. Compute and plot the dimensionless energy as a function of time. How can

one determine when the system has equilibrated, that is, that the system is sampling the appropriate phase space for the equilibrium fluid?

3. Set up a three-dimensional MD simulation and run the program with time steps of 0.01. Rescale the velocities as required to force all of the runs to be at a dimensionless temperature of $T^+ = 1.5$. Compute and plot the dimensionless energy and pressure of the system at dimensionless number densities of 0.02, 0.3, and 0.5. On the same graph, plot the ideal gas and van der Waals pressures corresponding to these number densities.

4. Set up a two-dimensional MD code that uses your computer's graphics to show the movement of the molecules. Start the simulation at a low temperature (small maximum velocity) and change the volume of the cell for 16 particles so that the resultant number density might reflect that of (a) a solid, (b) a liquid, and (c) a gas. Run the simulations and observe the behavior of these three phases.

5. Write a simple two-dimensional MD code to simulate a fluid contained in a tiny square cavity; that is, change the periodic boundary conditions to reflective so as to model elastic collisions with walls. Run the simulation and compare the pressure and energy of this fluid with that of a bulk fluid at the same density.

6. Use a two-dimensional simulation with graphics so that you can observe the motion of the particles. Select an initial density and maximum velocity. Set the code so that it will run for 50 time steps, reverse all of the velocities ($v_x = -v_x$, etc.), run for an additional 50 time steps, and stop. What do you observe about time reversal of the system? Repeat the simulation this time using 500 time steps. Do you observe anything different than before? Why or why not?

7. Use the velocities from an equilibrated three-dimensional simulation of at least 125 particles to make a histogram showing the number of particles versus their velocity. To do so, let v_{max} represent the largest absolute value of the velocity of any of the particles. Then divide the range between $-v_{max}$ and v_{max} into 25 equal divisions centered about zero. The bin size of your histogram will therefore be $\Delta v = 2v_{max}/25$. Distribute the particles among the 25 bins according to their velocities and plot the results. What can be said about the velocity distribution?

8. Add a neighbor list to a basic MD code. Set the cutoff distance at 2.5σ with a 0.3σ-thick buffer region. Set the neighbor list to be updated every 10 time steps. Run the code at $\rho^+ = 0.1$ and $T^+ \approx 1.0$ and compare the required CPU time per time step with and without the neighbor list. Also, print out the average number of neighbors per particle in the neighbor list.

9. Run an LJ simulation at $T^+ = 1.70$ and $\rho^+ = 0.35$ and compare values obtained for U^+ and P^+ to the literature[17] values of -2.27 and 0.39, respectively.

10. Run an LJ simulation at $T^+ = 0.81$ and $\rho^+ = 0.90$ and compare values obtained for U^+ and P^+ to the literature[17] values of -6.28 and 1.97, respectively.

11. Use an MD simulation to predict the pressure of Ar at 500 K and a specific volume of 0.1736 m³/kg. The literature value[18] is 0.6 MPa.

12. Use the fluctuation formula, Equation (8.18), to estimate the heat capacity of an LJ fluid at $T^+ = 2.5$ and $\rho^+ = 0.05$. Compare this to the ideal gas value for a monatomic fluid.

13. Use a three-dimensional simulation and plot the MSD to obtain the self-diffusion coefficient. The displacement *before* application of the periodic boundary conditions must be used. The easiest way to do this is to:

    (a) Find the new, uncorrected positions $r_{u,i}(t)$ from the previous step. Some of the particles will be outside the unit cell at this point because the periodic boundary conditions are yet to be applied.

    (b) Determine the displacement $\Delta R(\Delta t)$ for that time step from $r_{u,i}(t) - r_i(t-1)$ using the corrected (with boundary conditions) positions from the previous time step.

    (c) Find the new, corrected positions $r_i(t)$ by application of the periodic boundary conditions.

    (d) Find the total displacement by adding the displacement for the current time step into an accumulator; $\Delta R_{sum}(t) = \Delta R_{sum}(t-1) + \Delta R(\Delta t)$.

14. Write a simple two-dimensional (2-D) MD code to simulate a fluid in a 2-D pore. That is, use reflective boundary conditions for the vertical walls to model elastic collisions with a real wall and periodic boundary conditions for the horizontal boundaries. Run the simulation and compute the pore self-diffusion coefficient. Compare this with the bulk self-diffusion coefficient.

15. Run a two-dimensional graphical simulation of a bulk fluid at very low density. Start the simulation with molecules placed at regular lattice sites over the whole cell. Assign zero initial velocity to all of the particles. What happens in time and what does this physically represent?

16. Compute $g(r)$ from an MD simulation of Lennard-Jones molecules up to $r^+ = 1.5$ for the conditions given in Table A5.6 ($T^+ = 1.084$ and $\rho^+ = 0.805$) and compare your results to those shown in that table.

17. Add a Gaussian thermostat to a basic MD code. Run the code and plot the resultant temperatures and energies as a function of time.

18. Add the Gaussian bond constraint forces to a basic two-dimensional (2-D) MD code for the case of diatomic molecules. Also, modify the starting configuration so that pairs of atoms are placed on a regular 2-D lattice, but the separation distance between the two atoms in the pair is $d^+ = 0.329$. This is the approximate bond length for N_2 molecules using the atomic LJ parameters $\epsilon = 5.15 \times 10^{-22}$ J and $\sigma = 3.31$ Å. In the initial configuration, all bonds between the pairs may lie along the x axis. Choose initial velocities *for each pair* and apply the same value to each atom of the pair. Use the graphics capability of your computer to run the 2-D simulation and visually observe the fixed-bond distance algorithm. Note also the rotational motion of the particles induced from the torque experienced through the constraints.

19. Extend the code developed for nitrogen in Problem 17 to 3-D and perform a simulation at $\rho^+ = 0.35$ and $T^+ = 3.36$. Compute values of the pressure and internal energy to compare with literature[19] values of $P^+ = 0.16$ and $U^+ = -8.86$, respectively.

20. Consider a model of cyclopropane in which the three LJ sites form the vertices of an equilateral triangle. The sides of the triangle are of length d, the bond distance. For simplicity, define $R_1 = r_2 - r_1$, $R_2 = r_3 - r_1$, and $R_3 = r_3 - r_2$. Write down

the bond constraints in terms of the $\boldsymbol{R}_i$, differentiate them twice to find the differential constraint equations and the constraint forces. Then show that the equations of motion for the three sites can be written as

$$
\begin{bmatrix} \dot{p}_1 \\ \dot{p}_2 \\ \dot{p}_3 \end{bmatrix} = \begin{bmatrix} \boldsymbol{F}_1 \\ \boldsymbol{F}_2 \\ \boldsymbol{F}_3 \end{bmatrix} + \begin{bmatrix} -1 & -1 & 0 \\ 1 & 0 & -1 \\ 0 & 1 & 1 \end{bmatrix} \cdot \begin{bmatrix} \lambda_1 \boldsymbol{R}_1 \\ \lambda_2 \boldsymbol{R}_2 \\ \lambda_3 \boldsymbol{R}_3 \end{bmatrix}.
$$

9

LIQUID AND VAPOR PROPERTIES FROM THE VAN DER WAALS PARTITION FUNCTION

The methods of Chapter 6 are convenient and valuable for calculating properties of low-density gases. Using these methods, one can compute virial coefficients from a selected model for the intermolecular potential and use the virial equation of state to calculate the desired properties. At higher densities more virial coefficients are required in the expansion and the complexity of the calculations rapidly makes the method intractable. Worse yet, the virial expansion does not even converge for very dense gases or liquids. Chapters 7 and 8 illustrate numerical techniques that can be used to calculate properties at higher densities. Unfortunately, these methods are very CPU intensive and are therefore expensive to perform. The use of such methods to study the properties of a fluid is now becoming feasible for thermophysical property estimation, but implementation of the methods into larger design codes for engineering purposes such as separations and process design is yet beyond reasonable expectation. Applications of this kind, requiring repeated use of the thermophysical property generator, still require analytical equations which can be readily manipulated and used in thermodynamic identities. Alternative, approximate methods for obtaining the configurational partition function are a necessity for these kinds of applications with dense fluids.

At higher densities, particularly for liquids, an approach to obtaining properties from statistical mechanics is to model the liquid structure based on the similarities with crystalline solids. Although liquid molecules move in random motion, X-ray studies indicate that they spend most of their time trapped in cages created by the proximity of the other molecules. This suggests that models in which the molecules may move locally about a particular lattice site may be appropriate, albeit approximate, for calculating properties of dense gases and liquids.

9.1 VAN DER WAALS PARTITION FUNCTION

A general lattice partition function can be derived which will serve as the starting point for development of a number of different but useful theories. Consider a hypothetical lattice overlaid upon a model of the fluid. A two-dimensional representation of a face-centered lattice is shown in Figure 9.1. Let us associate one molecule with each of the N lattice sites in a volume V. Much like the Einstein model of Chapter 4, we assume that any one molecule is free to roam about its lattice site in the cage created by its nearest neighbors, while all other neighbors are considered fixed at their average positions on the other $N-1$ lattice sites. Let r_i be the vector position of this central molecule relative to its lattice site, a_1 be the distance to its nearest neighbors (the first coordination shell), and z_1 be the number of nearest neighbors in the first shell. Similarly, a_2 and z_2 are the distance and number of particles for the second coordination shell. Because the molecule is trapped or caged by the first coordination shell, its movement is limited to the range

$$0 \leq \mid r_i \mid \leq a_1 - d \tag{9.1}$$

where d is the molecular diameter, the distance excluded from the movement of the molecule due to the particle size. For hard spheres $d = \sigma$. But d is not

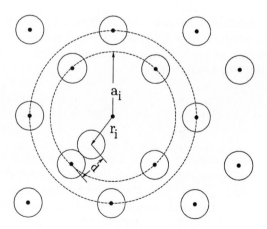

Figure 9.1 Lattice model for dense liquids.

clearly defined for soft potentials; its definition must be included as part of the model.

If we for the moment restrict all molecules to their lattice sites and assume pairwise additivity, the total potential energy of the system can be represented by

$$U = \sum_i \sum_{j > i} u_{ij} = \frac{Nu_0}{2} \quad \text{(all molecules at lattice sites)}, \tag{9.2}$$

where u_0 is the sum of all $N-1$ pair interactions with molecule i. There are $_NC_2 = N(N-1)/2$ pair interactions. The term u_0 contains the $N-1$ interactions with molecule i, and there are $N/2$ of these. Now we allow the central molecule to move within its cage, centered at its lattice site. The variable potential is now given by $u_0 + u_1(r_i)$, where the second term is a perturbation or deviation term from the lattice site value. Because each molecule can be considered as the central molecule, the total potential, including the variation due to molecules moving away from their lattice sites, is given by

$$U = \frac{Nu_0}{2} + \sum_{i=1}^{N} u_1(r_i) . \tag{9.3}$$

This perturbation approach to the cell potential allows u_0, a constant, to be removed from the integrals of the partition function. Thus,

$$Z = e^{-\frac{1}{2}\beta Nu_0} \int \exp[-\beta \sum_{i=1}^{N} u_1(r_i)] \, dr^N , \tag{9.4}$$

where again $\int dr^N$ indicates N integrals over the N vector positions of the particles (equivalently, $3N$ integrals over $3N$ coordinates). If we assume no correlation between adjacent cells or cages, then the N vector integrals can be factored into a product of N single integrals. Thus,

$$Z = e^{-\frac{1}{2}\beta Nu_0} \left(4\pi \int_0^{\infty} e^{-\beta u_1} r^2 \, dr \right)^N . \tag{9.5}$$

To evaluate the remaining integral a particular potential must be chosen. One possible method, generally for liquids, is to use a *mean-field* model. That is, the lattice potential u_0 is considered to be an average or smoothed potential over the whole cage area through which the molecule may wander, rather than a specific value applicable to the molecule at its lattice site. This means that u_1 is zero, but u_0 becomes an effective constant, no longer explicitly calculable from geometrical considerations. Thus,

$$u_1(r) = 0 \text{ for } 0 < r < a_1 - d$$
$$u_1(r) = \infty \text{ for } r > a_1 - d , \qquad \text{(mean-field approximation)}$$

which upon substitution into the configurational partition function yields,

$$Z = e^{-\frac{1}{2}\beta N u_0} \left(\frac{4\pi r^3}{3} \Big|_0^{a_1 - d} \right)^N = \left[\frac{4\pi(a_1 - d)^3}{3} \right]^N e^{-\frac{1}{2}\beta N u_0} . \qquad (9.6)$$

The term in brackets above is called the *free volume*. The name reflects the physical concept that the N molecules are free to roam in their cages, excluded from the entire cage volume only by the volume occupied by the particles themselves. To calculate the free volume, one would need geometrical informa- tion about the lattice structure itself (to get a_1) and a method for obtaining molecular diameters d for soft potentials. Alternatively, we may divest the theory from the explicit tie to a lattice while retaining the concept of free volume. This provides us with a generalized partition function loosely based on the lattice model, but without the requirement of explicit lattice information. The advantage of so doing is the increased flexibility obtained in the model, since a strict view of the liquid in terms of exact lattice locations for the particles is not expected to be particularly efficacious. The disadvantage is that one must now make semiempirical assumptions about the free volume, V_f, and the potential u_0 in order to develop equations of state and liquid mixture models. The resultant generalized partition function, is called the van der Waals partition function (VDW-PF). It is given by

$$Q = \frac{Q_{\text{int}} V_f^N}{N! \Lambda^{3N}} \exp\left(-\frac{N u_0}{2kT} \right) , \qquad (9.7)$$

where V_f, the free volume, replaces the term in brackets in Equation (9.6).

9.2 VAN DER WAALS EQUATION OF STATE

Suppose we choose to evaluate the VDW-PF using the Sutherland potential,

$$u = \left[\begin{array}{cc} \infty & r < \sigma \\ -\epsilon\left(\dfrac{\sigma}{r}\right)^6 & r \geq \sigma \end{array} \right] . \qquad (9.8)$$

The mean-field model discussed above averages or "smears out" the potential creating an effective potential over the range σ to ∞. Thus, to find the mean pair potential per unit volume for each lattice site, we must integrate the potential function with respect to the vector variable r from σ to ∞ and divide by the total volume. The volume factor arises from integration with respect to the vector $\boldsymbol{r}$. Recall from Chapter 5 that $\int d\boldsymbol{r} = \int 4\pi r^2 dr = V$. As previously mentioned, u_0 is the sum of the pair potentials between a central molecule and the surrounding $N-1$ other particles. The mean-field potential for a central molecule is therefore $N-1 \approx N$ times the smoothed pair potential. Thus,

$$u_0 = \frac{N}{V} \int_\sigma^\infty -\epsilon \left(\frac{\sigma}{r} \right)^6 d\boldsymbol{r} = -\frac{N\epsilon\sigma^6}{V} \int_\sigma^\infty 4\pi r^{-4} \, dr = -\frac{4\pi N\epsilon\sigma^3}{3V} = -\frac{2aN}{V}, \quad (9.9)$$

where a is defined as

$$a \equiv \frac{2\pi}{3}\epsilon\sigma^3 . \quad (9.10)$$

Excluded from the molecule's wandering domain is a volume of $4\pi\sigma^3/3$ corresponding to the overlap of molecular hard cores. Only one half of this can be attributed to the central molecule, the other half to the particles with which it collides. Thus we define an excluded volume per molecule, b, by

$$b \equiv \frac{2}{3}\pi\sigma^3 . \quad (9.11)$$

Substitution of this expression into Equation (9.10) yields

$$a = b\epsilon . \quad (9.12)$$

If we assume that the free volume in the van der Waals partition function may be taken as the total volume minus the excluded volume, $V_f = V - Nb$, then the total partition function may be written as

$$Q = \frac{Q_{\text{int}}(V - Nb)^N}{N!\Lambda^{3N}} \exp\left(\frac{N^2 a}{VkT} \right) . \quad (9.13)$$

Thermodynamic properties can now be obtained from the partition function in the usual way. For example, the free energy departure function is

$$\beta(A^* - A) = \ln \frac{Z}{V^N} = N\ln\left(\frac{V-Nb}{V} \right) + \frac{N^2 a}{VkT} . \quad (9.14)$$

The pressure, which depends only on the configurational partition function, is

$$P = kT\left(\frac{\partial \ln Z}{\partial V} \right)_{N,T} = NkT\left(\frac{\partial \ln(V-Nb)}{\partial V} \right)_{N,T} + kT\left(\frac{\partial(N^2 a/VkT)}{\partial V} \right)_{N,T} , \quad (9.15)$$

or

$$P = \frac{NkT}{V-Nb} - \frac{N^2a}{V^2}.$$ (9.16)

This is the famous van der Waals equation of state, usually rearranged in the form

$$\left(P + \frac{N^2a}{V^2}\right)(V - Nb) = NkT.$$ (9.17)

   While this is not the method used by van der Waals to arrive at this equation, we obtain some key insights into the physical assumptions and limitations of it through the statistical mechanical derivation. For example, knowing its relationship to the Sutherland potential permits evaluation of potential parameters from experimental data as shown in Example 9.1. One could also develop other, presumably improved, equations of state of the van der Waals type now that the limitations and assumptions inherent in the derivation of the van der Waals equation are understood. For example, we might use a different potential function in the development and remove the dependence on the Sutherland potential. Perhaps a more accurate method of obtaining the potential u_0 could be devised that would remove the limitations of the mean-field approximation. An improvement on the free volume assumption, since the particles are not hard spheres, might also increase the accuracy of the equation. These are only illustrative examples of how knowledge of the inherent assumptions upon which the equation rests can lead to continued improvement of it.

   Today, many of the most commonly used cubic equations of state are empirical modifications of Equation (9.17). A few of the most commonly used for engineering calculations are given in Table 9.1. As can be seen by these equations, the attractive term involving a has received the most attention. Primarily the modifications have focused on introducing a temperature dependence into a. This is reasonable in terms of the model. We should expect less volumetric exclusion for more energetic particles because they will penetrate more deeply into the repulsive core of their neighbors. Little has been done in modifying the repulsive term, b, in van der Waals's original equation. Once the equation of state has been derived from molecular theory, the parameters a and b that appear in cubic equations of state are generally obtained in terms of critical point properties, generally T_c and P_c, as is done in Example 9.1. There is an inflection point in the critical isotherm at the critical point as shown in Figure 7.10. Mathematically, this requires that

$$\left(\frac{\partial P}{\partial V}\right)_T = 0 = \left(\frac{\partial^2 P}{\partial V^2}\right)_T.$$

One can force the developed equation of state to agree at the critical point

Example 9.1   Using the van der Waals equation of state, determine Sutherland potential parameters appropriate for propane.

If one had considerable pressure-volume-temperature (PVT) data, the van der Waals equation of state could be used to regress values of a and b from which σ and ϵ could be computed in accordance with Equations (9.11) and (9.12). In this case we do not have the experimental data, but we can derive a relationship between the critical properties and a and b. Depicted in the figure at the right are three isotherms. At the critical point there is an inflection point in the critical isotherm. Mathematically, this condition requires that

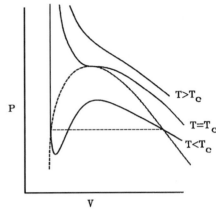

$$\left(\frac{\partial P}{\partial V}\right)_T = 0 = \left(\frac{\partial^2 P}{\partial V^2}\right)_T.$$

From Equation (9.16), the pressure may be obtained as

$$P = \frac{NkT}{V - Nb} - \frac{N^2 a}{V^2},$$

which when differentiated in accordance with the above equations provides two equations and two unknowns, namely,

$$\left(\frac{\partial P}{\partial V}\right)_T = -\frac{NkT_c}{(V_c - Nb)^2} + \frac{2N^2 a}{V_c^3} = 0 \quad \text{and} \quad \left(\frac{\partial^2 P}{\partial V^2}\right)_T = \frac{2NkT_c}{(V_c - Nb)^3} - \frac{6N^2 a}{V_c^4} = 0.$$

These two equations yield

$$a = b\epsilon = \frac{27}{64} \frac{k^2 T_c^2}{P_c} \quad \text{and} \quad b = \frac{2\pi}{3}\sigma^3 = \frac{kT_c}{8P_c}.$$

Solving the second equation for σ yields

$$\sigma = \left(\frac{3kT_c}{16\pi P_c}\right)^{1/3} = \left[\frac{(3)(1.381 \times 10^{-16} \text{ g·cm}^2/\text{s}^2\text{K})(369.8 \text{ K})}{(16\pi)(41.9 \text{ atm})(1.013 \times 10^6 \text{ g/cm·s}^2\text{atm})}\right]^{1/3} = 4.16 \text{ Å}.$$

Subsequently, the expression for a can be used to solve for ϵ/k:

$$\frac{\epsilon}{k} = \frac{a}{bk} = \frac{27}{8}T_c = \frac{(27)(369.8 \text{ K})}{8} = 1248 \text{ K}.$$

TABLE 9.1 Commonly Used Cubic Equations of State.

van der Waals

$$P = \frac{RT}{\overline{V} - b} - \frac{a}{\overline{V}^2} \qquad \overline{V} = \frac{V}{n}$$

$$a = 27RT_c^2/(64P_c) \qquad\qquad b = RT_c/(8P_c)$$

Redlich-
Kwong

$$P = \frac{RT}{\overline{V} - b} - \frac{a}{\overline{V}(\overline{V} + b)\sqrt{T}}$$

$$a = 0.42748R^2T_c^{2.5}/P_c \qquad\qquad b = 0.08664RT_c/P_c$$

Soave

$$P = \frac{RT}{\overline{V} - b} - \frac{a\alpha}{\overline{V}(\overline{V} + b)}$$

$$a = 0.42748R^2T_c^{\,2}/P_c \qquad\qquad b = 0.08664RT_c/P_c$$

$$\alpha = [1 + (0.48508 + 1.55171\omega - 0.15613\omega^2)(1 - T_r^{0.5})]^2$$

where ω is the acentric factor

Peng-
Robinson

$$P = \frac{RT}{\overline{V} - b} - \frac{a\alpha}{\overline{V}^2 + 2b\overline{V} - b^2}$$

$$a = 0.45724R^2T_c^{\,2}/P_c \qquad\qquad b = 0.07780RT_c/P_c$$

$$\alpha = [1 + (0.48508 + 1.55171\omega - 0.15613\omega^2)(1 - T_r^{0.5})]^2$$

by applying these two constraints and solving the resultant two simultaneous equations for a and b in terms of T_c and P_c.

The power of these equations of state lies in their relative simple analytical forms and their representation of both gas and liquid states. Appropriate equations of state essentially complete the thermodynamic description of fluids because exact thermodynamic identities can then be used to calculate virtually all of the desired thermodynamic properties.

Ways of doing so are covered in texts on classical thermodynamics and so are not further discussed here. An example of the use of an equation of state to calculate phase equilibria for a single-component fluid is provided as Example 9.2. This example suffices to illustrate the approach as well as to remind the reader of the relationship between the continuity of gas and liquid states spoken

---

Example 9.2   Determine the vapor pressure of isobutane at 25°C using the Soave equation of state.

The criteria for equilibrium between the vapor and liquid phases are $T_L = T_V$ and $P_L = P_V$. These criteria correspond to the horizontal lines drawn through the two-phase region of Figure 7.10 and represent equilibrium tie lines between the vapor and liquid phases. The continuous lines represent the isotherms from the equation of state. Notice that in the middle of the two-phase region the stability criterion of Equation (7.19) guarantees two equilibrium phases.

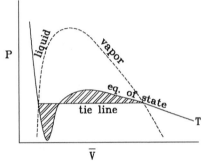

The problem of finding the vapor pressure is equivalent to finding where to place the horizontal tie line with respect to the curve from the equation of state. It can be readily shown that the placement of this tie line must be such that the actual area $P\Delta\bar{V}$ equals the area under the equation of state curve in the two-phase region. This is shown graphically in the figure at the right above. Mathematically, it requires that

$$\int_{\bar{V}_L}^{\bar{V}_V} P \, d\bar{V} = P_s(\bar{V}_V - \bar{V}_L),$$

where P is the pressure calculated from the equation of state and P_s is the saturation or vapor pressure which we seek.

To solve the above equation, we substitute the Soave equation of state in for P and integrate using partial fractions to obtain

$$RT\ln\left(\frac{\bar{V}_V - b}{\bar{V}_L - b}\right) + \frac{a\alpha}{b} \ln\left[\frac{(\bar{V}_V + b)\bar{V}_L}{(\bar{V}_L + b)\bar{V}_V}\right] = P_s(\bar{V}_V - \bar{V}_L).$$

This equation, in conjunction with the equation of state, can be used to solve for the vapor pressure. The solution can be found with math-solving packages, or one can use an iterative solution. In the latter case, one can guess a P and find the vapor and liquid roots $\bar{V}_L$ and $\bar{V}_V$ from the equation of state with the Newton–Raphson method. These values can then be plugged into the above equation to solve for a new $P_s = P$. This procedure is then repeated, iterating on the pressure until convergence is obtained. For the problem given above, we used the values of $T_c = 408.1$ K, $P_c = 3.6477$ MPa, and $\omega = 0.176$ to obtain $\bar{V}_L = 0.1132$ L/mol, $\bar{V}_V = 6.3298$ L/mol and the equilibrium vapor pressure $P_s = 0.3558$ MPa. This can be compared with a value of 0.345 MPa obtained by interpolation of the data given in *the Chemical Engineers' Handbook*.[2]

of by van der Waals and the actual fluid behavior that occurs at a phase transition. This relationship was previously illustrated in Figure 7.10.

9.3 LIQUID MIXTURE MODELS BASED ON THE VDW-PF

The VDW-PF, Equation (9.7), can also be written for mixtures. For a binary mixture

$$Q = \frac{(q_{1,\text{int}})^{N_1}(q_{2,\text{int}})^{N_2}}{(N_1!)(N_2!)\Lambda^{3N_1}\Lambda^{3N_2}} \cdot V_f^N \cdot e^{-\frac{1}{2}N\beta u_0} , \tag{9.18}$$

where the mixture free volume V_f and cell potential u_0 are now assumed to be compositional averages of the pure-component values. Obtaining reliable values for these terms is the crux of the problem in using the van der Waals partition function. Complications are certain to rise in trying to relate these parameters to other molecular constants because differences in size and steric effects will result in different free volumes for each type of molecule, and the interactions between unlike species will also differ from those between like molecules.

If we apply Equation (2.34) to the mixture as well as to each of the two pure components, we can write an expression for the free energy change upon mixing, ΔA_{mix}, in terms of pure-component partition functions, Q_i^0, and the mixture partition function, Q_m; namely,

$$\Delta A_{\text{mix}} = A_m - A_1^0 - A_2^0 = -kT\ln\left(\frac{Q_m}{Q_1^0 Q_2^0}\right) . \tag{9.19}$$

The merit in computing ΔA_{mix} directly, as in Equation (9.19), is the cancellation of terms that occurs in the mixture and pure-component partition functions when in the ratio shown in Equation (9.18). The same $N_i!$ and $\Lambda_i^{3N_i}$ terms are found in both the pure and mixture partition functions and will therefore cancel out when the partition functions are substituted into the ratio on the right side of Equation (9.19). Furthermore, it seems reasonable to assume that the internal modes are not greatly affected by the molecular environment because they are density independent. Thus, $q_{1,\text{int}}$ and $q_{2,\text{int}}$ may be assumed to be the same for both the mixture and the pure components. With these assumptions, Equation (9.18) can be written as

$$-\Delta A_{\text{mix}} = kT\ln\left(\frac{V_f^N}{V_{f,1}^{N_1} V_{f,2}^{N_2}}\right) - \frac{1}{2}\left(Nu_0 - N_1 u_{0,1} - N_2 u_{0,2}\right) . \tag{9.20}$$

From this equation, we see that ΔA_{mix} can be thought of as the sum of two terms,

$$\Delta A_{\text{mix}} = \Delta A_{\text{atherm}} + \Delta A_{\text{resid}} . \tag{9.21}$$

The first term on the right side of Equation (9.20), or ΔA_{atherm}, is an *athermal* contribution. It contributes to the free energy of mixing even when there is no difference between the interactions in the mixture and in the pure components, i.e., $Nu_0 = N_1 u_{0,1} + N_2 u_{0,2}$. The athermal contribution arises out of the entropic effects associated with the difference in free volume available to molecules in the mixture and in the pure components. The difference in free volumes is presumably attributable to size and steric effects. The second term on the right side of Equation (9.20), or ΔA_{resid}, is the residual free energy of mixing. It represents energetic effects due to differences between like and unlike interactions.

Equations (9.20) and (9.21) serve as a starting point for the development of many liquid mixture activity coefficient models. Many of the more successful mixture models used by chemical engineers today can be derived from these starting equations, although most of them were originally obtained using semiempirical approaches. However, just as derivation of the van der Waals equation of state from the van der Waals partition function provided a clearer picture of the inherent assumptions in the final equations and provided direction for improvement of the theory, so also does derivation of these mixture activity coefficient equations from the van der Waals partition function provide a clearer basis for improvement of the models than the semiempirical development. We examine in the following paragraphs several different assumptions that can be made to simplify either the free volume or the cell potential and the equations for ΔA_{atherm} and ΔA_{resid} that result from these assumptions. These models will be derived in terms of ΔA_{mix} for constant T and V mixing processes. This may seem an awkward approach because measurements of thermodynamic mixing properties are generally made at constant T and P conditions and therefore we really want the final mixture models to be expressed in terms of ΔG_{mix}. Doing it this way will allow us to use the canonical ensemble to derive an expression for ΔA_{mix}. We will then make the assumption that $\Delta A_{\text{mix}}(T, V) \approx \Delta G_{\text{mix}}(T, P)$ to arrive at the final form of the mixture model. Hildebrand and Scott[3] have shown that this approximation is quite good for liquid densities.

9.3.1 Free-Volume Models

Two of several possible relationships for ΔA_{atherm} can be obtained by making the following two assumptions about the free volume.

1. Assume the free volume is proportional to the number of molecules. If the mixture free volume is proportional to N and the pure-component free volumes are proportional to N_i then

$$\Delta A_{\text{atherm}} = -kT \ln\frac{V_f^N}{V_{f,1}^{N_1} V_{f,2}^{N_2}} = -kT \ln\frac{N^N}{N_1^{N_1}N_2^{N_2}}$$

$$= -kT \ln\frac{N^{(N_1+N_2)}}{(x_1 N)^{N_1}(x_2 N)^{N_2}} \tag{9.22}$$

$$= kT \ln(x_1^{N x_1} x_2^{N x_2}) = NkT \ln(x_1^{x_1} x_2^{x_2}) .$$

The assumption of proportionality between the free volume and the number of molecules therefore produces the ideal mixture model for the athermal portion of the free energy change upon mixing

$$\Delta A_{\text{atherm}} = NkT \sum_i x_i \ln x_i . \tag{9.23}$$

Usually, mixture properties are reported in terms of the excess properties. These are a more sensitive measure of mixture nonidealities because the ideal mixing term has been subtracted from the actual change in the property upon mixing. An athermal model based on this assumption would then be characterized by

$$A_{\text{atherm}}^E = 0 . \tag{9.24}$$

2. Assume the free volume is proportional to the pure-component molar volume, $V_{f,i} \propto V_i$. If the free volume of component i is assumed to be proportional to the total volume of pure component i in the mixture, then

$$\Delta A_{\text{atherm}} = -kT \ln\frac{V_f^{N_1+N_2}}{V_{f,1}^{N_1} V_{f,2}^{N_2}} = -kT \ln\frac{V_m^{N_1+N_2}}{V_1^{N_1}V_2^{N_2}} = kT \ln(\Phi_1^{N_1}\Phi_2^{N_2}) , \tag{9.25}$$

where Φ_i is the volume fraction of component i based on pure-component volumes; i.e., $\Phi_i = V_i/V_m$. This assumption leads to the famous Flory–Huggins equation for the athermal contribution to the free energy of mixing

$$\Delta A_{\text{atherm}} = NkT \sum_i x_i \ln \Phi_i . \tag{9.26}$$

For an athermal model based upon this assumption for the mixture free volume, the excess free energy would be

$$A_{\text{atherm}}^E = \Delta A_{\text{mix}} - \Delta A_{\text{mix}}^{id} = NkT \sum_i x_i \ln(\Phi_i/x_i) , \tag{9.27}$$

which is in fact the Flory–Huggins equation.[4]

9.3.2 Cell Potential Models

Mixture equations based on the residual portion of Equation (9.21) can be obtained by proposing a model for the difference between mixture and pure-component cell potentials. For convenience, let

$$\Delta(Nu) = Nu_0 - N_1 u_{0,1} - N_2 u_{0,2} , \qquad (9.28)$$

then

$$\Delta A_{\text{resid}} = \frac{1}{2}\Delta(Nu) . \qquad (9.29)$$

One could directly pose a model for $\Delta(Nu)$, but this is somewhat difficult because some sort of composition averaging would be necessary to calculate the mixture potential energy from the lattice model originally employed to introduce this term. An alternative procedure is to suggest a model for the residual portion of the internal energy, ΔU_{resid}, for the mixture itself and apply the thermodynamic identity

$$\frac{\Delta A_{\text{resid}}}{T} = \int_0^{1/T} \Delta U_{\text{resid}} \, d\left(\frac{1}{T}\right) . \qquad (9.30)$$

The disadvantage of this approach is that unlike true intermolecular potentials which are not a function of temperature, the value and even the form of ΔU_{resid} almost certainly is. Yet, the integration shown above is from essentially infinite temperature down to the system temperature. The fact that the model for ΔU_{resid} must be valid up to infinite temperature has often been overlooked in the development of these models and is often a weak point in their development. Nevertheless, it is not too difficult to suggest models for the residual internal energy that can be considered candidates for use in Equation (9.30) to develop a model for the residual free energy of mixing.

Three of the most commonly used equations for liquid mixture nonidealities can be derived from this type of thermodynamic integration over proposed models for the residual change in internal energy upon mixing. We shall show the derivation for one of the three and simply present the others in a table. As mentioned, these equations were not originally derived in the manner illustrated here, but derivation of them from the van der Waals partition function helps improve our understanding of their limitations and suggests logical methods for improvement. Many recent models, including the three listed here, are based on the concept of local compositions, which we now introduce before proceeding with the development of the models.

9.3.3 Local Composition Models

In Chapter 5, we found that thermodynamic properties could be calculated from knowledge of the radial distribution or pair correlation function. The rdf or pcf contains information about local structure, indicating deviations from the bulk density due to localized attractions and repulsions. It is therefore apparent that properties are primarily determined by the local structure of the fluid. Consider the lattice-based picture of a binary mixture crudely depicted in two dimensions in Figure 9.2. We focus on two different regions of the fluid, one with a molecule of type 1 at the center and one with a molecule of type 2 at the center. In this figure, the bulk compositions x_1 and x_2 are both 0.5 (equal numbers of each kind of molecule). But, the local compositions of the nearest neighbors differ from the bulk compositions owing to relative differences in the strength of the $i-j$ cross interactions from the $i-i$ and $j-j$ like interactions. Just counting molecules in Figure 9.2, the local mole fraction of molecule 2 around 1 is seen to be $x_{21} = 2/3$ ($x_{11} = 1/3$). Similarly, the local mole fraction of molecule 1 around a type 2 molecule differs from the bulk mole fraction, and $x_{12} = 2/3$ ($x_{22} = 1/3$).

From Equation (5.55), the number of nearest neighbors of component 1 surrounding another molecule of type 1 within a sphere of radius L is given by

$$N_{11} = 4\pi\rho_1 \int_0^L g_{11} r^2 \, dr .\qquad(9.31)$$

Similarly, the number of nearest neighbors of component 2 surrounding a central molecule of component 1 is

$$N_{21} = 4\pi\rho_2 \int_0^L g_{21} r^2 \, dr .\qquad(9.32)$$

Similar expressions can also be written for N_{12} and N_{22}, the number of nearest

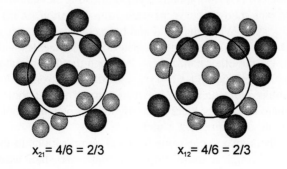

$$x_{21} = 4/6 = 2/3 \qquad x_{12} = 4/6 = 2/3$$

Figure 9.2   Local compositions x_{11} and x_{21} around a molecule of type 1 (*left*) and x_{12} and x_{22} around a molecule of type 2 (*right*).

neighbors of components 1 and 2, respectively, around a central molecule of component 2.

As mentioned, the local mole fractions depicted in Figure 9.2 are simply

$$x_{ji} = \frac{N_{ji}}{\sum_k N_{ki}}, \tag{9.33}$$

or in terms of rdf's

$$x_{ji} = \frac{4\pi\rho_j \int_0^L g_{ji}r^2 \, dr}{\sum_k 4\pi\rho_k \int_0^L g_{ki}r^2 \, dr}. \tag{9.34}$$

For example,

$$x_{11} = \frac{4\pi\rho_1 \int_0^L g_{11}r^2 \, dr}{4\pi\rho_1 \int_0^L g_{11}r^2 \, dr + 4\pi\rho_2 \int_0^L g_{21}r^2 \, dr} = \frac{x_1}{x_1 + x_2 G_{21}}, \tag{9.35}$$

where

$$G_{21} = \frac{4\pi \int_0^L g_{21}r^2 \, dr}{4\pi \int_0^L g_{11}r^2 \, dr}. \tag{9.36}$$

The factor G_{21} is a nonrandom factor indicating deviations from random mixing. If $G_{21} = 1$ then $x_{11} = x_1$, as seen from Equation (9.35). Similarly, if $G_{12} = 1$ then $x_{22} = x_2$. When the local and bulk compositions are equal, mixing is random and there is no preferential clustering of molecules—all interactions are equivalent. On the other hand, if $G_{21} > 1$ then the denominator in Equation (9.35) is greater than one and $x_{11} < x_1$, indicating a stronger local attraction between the unlike molecules than between pairs of type 1 molecules. And, if $G_{21} < 1$ then there is a higher local clustering of component 1 molecules around a central molecule of component 1 and $x_{11} > x_1$.

To relate the above expressions for local compositions to those that have been developed through a more empirical route, we shall assume that pair potentials can be replaced with potentials of mean force. These are effective pair potentials independent of r. In essence, they are averages of the true pair potential over all r. We will also choose the shell thickness L as the distance to the first coordination shell of the same type molecules as the central one. This distance is not clearly defined and becomes a weak point in the attempt to compare the more rigorously defined local compositions defined in the above equations to the less rigorous models originally used in the development of the mixture models. The student should understand that this is not a weakness in the use of local compositions in statistical mechanics, but only in trying to make a connection with the ad hoc definitions originally used to obtain the empirical form for the mixture models. Indeed, local compositions or local clustering is a real phenomenon due to the differences in like and unlike interactions between molecules in the mixture. One can perform either MC or MD simulations and calculate local compositions from Equations (9.31) to (9.33).[5] The deviation of the local compositions from the bulk values is a measure of those differences between the molecular interactions and ultimately the nonidealities of the mixture. Their values depend upon the choice of L. These points are further illustrated in Example 9.3. Thus, the weakness in the comparison of the more rigorous statistical mechanical local compositions to their empirical counterparts is primarily in identifying the coordination shell used in the empirical definitions.

Using the two assumptions mentioned above, the use of mean potentials and the assignment of L to the first coordination shell of the component in question, we may rewrite Equation (9.36) as

$$G_{21} = \frac{4\pi \displaystyle\int_0^{L_{21}} e^{-\beta <u>_{21}} r^2 \, dr}{4\pi \displaystyle\int_0^{L_{11}} e^{-\beta <u>_{11}} r^2 \, dr} = \frac{V_{21}}{V_{11}} e^{-\beta(<u>_{21} - <u>_{11})} . \qquad (9.37)$$

Note that the rdf's have now been replaced with exponentials of the mean potentials. This is the form proposed by Wilson[6] for the parameter G_{21} (though a different notation was used by Wilson). Other forms have been proposed for G_{21} some of which are shown in Table 9.2.

It is obvious from Equation (9.33) that local mole fractions satisfy the mole balance relation

---

EXAMPLE

Example 9.3   Use an MC program to generate two-dimensional configurations of a binary mixture containing equal numbers of the two components. Find the average local compositions x_{11}, x_{21}, x_{12}, and x_{22} for the configurations generated.

The program on the diskette allows the user to vary the relative strengths of the cross interactions and to change the size of L. The bulk compositions can also be varied. This allows the student to obtain a qualitative feel for the dependence of local compositions upon bulk composition, intermolecular potentials, and the definition of L.

TABLE 9.2 Popular Mixture Equations Based on Local Compositions

---

I. Wilson Equation[6]

Parameters:
$$\lambda_{21} = <u>_{21} - <u>_{11} \qquad \lambda_{12} = <u>_{12} - <u>_{22}$$

Relations:
$$G_{ji} = (V_j/V_i)\exp(-\lambda_{ij}/RT) \qquad G_{ii} = 1$$

G^E:
$$G^E = -RT[x_1\ln(x_1 + x_2G_{21}) + x_2\ln(x_2 + x_1G_{12})]$$

II. NRTL (Nonrandom Two-Liquid) Equation[7]

Parameters:
$$a_{12} \qquad a_{21} \qquad\qquad \alpha$$

Relations:
$$\tau_{ij} = a_{ij}/RT \quad G_{ij} = \exp(-\alpha\tau_{ij}) \quad G_{ii} = 1$$

G^E:
$$\frac{G^E}{RT} = x_1x_2\left(\frac{\tau_{21}G_{21}}{x_1 + x_2G_{21}} + \frac{\tau_{12}G_{12}}{x_2 + x_1G_{12}}\right)$$

III. UNIQUAC (Universal Quasi-Chemical) Equation[8]

Parameters:
$$a_{21} = <u>_{21} - <u>_{11} \qquad a_{12} = <u>_{12} - <u>_{22}$$

Constants:
$$q_i \qquad r_i \qquad\qquad z = 10$$

Relations:
$$l_i = \frac{z}{2}(r_i - q_i) - (r_i - 1) \qquad \tau_{ji} = \exp[-a_{ji}/RT]$$

$$\phi_i = \frac{q_ix_i}{\displaystyle\sum_j q_jx_j} \qquad\qquad \theta_i = \frac{r_ix_i}{\displaystyle\sum_j r_jx_j}$$

G^E:
$$\frac{G^E}{RT} = \sum_i x_i\left[\ln\frac{\phi_i}{x_i} + \frac{q_iz}{2}\ln\frac{\theta_i}{\phi_i} - q_i\ln(\theta_i + \theta_j\tau_{ji})\right], \quad j \neq i = 1,2$$

$$\sum_j x_{ji} = 1 . \tag{9.38}$$

Combination of this equation with Equation (9.35) permits us to write final expressions for the like and unlike local mole fractions. For molecule 1 at the center,

$$x_{11} = \frac{x_1}{x_1 + x_2 G_{21}} \quad \text{and} \quad x_{21} = \frac{x_2 G_{21}}{x_1 + x_2 G_{21}}. \tag{9.39}$$

The equations written for molecule 2 at the center are found by reversing the indices in the above expressions.

We will now return to the task at hand: using the concept of local compositions to develop a model for ΔU_{resid} that can be used in conjunction with Equation (9.30) to obtain a model for ΔA_{resid}.

9.3.4 Models for ΔA_{resid}

One approach to obtaining ΔU_{resid} to use in Equation (9.30) is to construct a model from the idea of local compositions. We will consider the fluid to be composed of two hypothetical pure fluids which mix ideally. On a molecular level, hypothetical fluid #1 consists of a type 1 molecule at the center with its corresponding first coordination shell of components 1 and 2 as depicted in Figure 9.2. Hypothetical fluid #2 consists of a type 2 molecule and its attendant first coordination shell. All of the actual mixture nonidealities are considered to be within the hypothetical pure fluids themselves. That is, the hypothetical fluids mix ideally, and nonidealities strictly arise from the interactions within each of the pure fluids. To formulate the model mathematically, let the internal energy of hypothetical pure fluid i be represented by $U^{(i)}$. In terms of these "pure-component" values for the hypothetical fluids, the mixture U is given by

$$U = x_1 U^{(1)} + x_2 U^{(2)}. \tag{9.40}$$

Using the notation of the previous section, we let $<u>_{ij}$ represent the average interaction energy between i-j pairs. The hypothetical pure-fluid internal energy is then

$$U^{(i)} = \sum_j x_{ji} <u>_{ji}. \tag{9.41}$$

Substituting Equation (9.41) into Equation (9.40) yields

$$\Delta U_{\text{resid}} = x_1(x_{11}<u>_{11} + x_{21}<u>_{21} - U_1) + x_2(x_{12}<u>_{12} + x_{22}<u>_{22} - U_2)$$

$$= x_1(<u>_{11} - U_1) + x_2(<u>_{22} - U_2)$$

$$+ x_1 x_{21}(<u>_{21} - <u>_{11}) + x_2 x_{12}(<u>_{12} - <u>_{22})$$

for the residual internal energy change upon mixing. Here, U_i is the pure-component internal energy, and we have made use of Equation (9.38). Substitution of the local compositions [cf. Equation (9.39)] into the above equation yields

$$\Delta U_{\text{resid}} = \sum_{i=1}^{2} x_i(<u>_{ii} - U_i)$$

$$+ x_1 x_2 \left[\frac{(<u>_{21} - <u>_{11})G_{21}}{x_1 + x_2 G_{21}} + \frac{(<u>_{12} - <u>_{22})G_{12}}{x_2 + x_1 G_{12}} \right]. \tag{9.42}$$

This equation can be simplified by examining the pure-component limits where ΔU_{resid} must be zero. The last term on the right side is a true excess term and vanishes at both pure-component limits due to the multiplicative factor $x_1 x_2$. Thus we find that

$$\lim_{x_i \to \infty} \Delta U_{\text{resid}} = <u>_{ii} - U_i = 0 \quad \text{or} \quad <u>_{ii} = U_i, \tag{9.43}$$

and

$$\Delta U_{\text{resid}} = x_1 x_2 \left[\frac{(<u>_{21} - <u>_{11})G_{21}}{x_1 + x_2 G_{21}} + \frac{(<u>_{12} - <u>_{22})G_{12}}{x_2 + x_1 G_{12}} \right]. \tag{9.44}$$

Substitution of this equation into Equation (9.30) and integration between 0 and an arbitrary $1/T$ yields, after considerable algebraic manipulation,

$$A_{\text{resid}}^{E} = -RT[x_1 \ln(x_1 + x_2 G_{21}) + x_2 \ln(x_2 + x_1 G_{12})]. \tag{9.45}$$

This is the Wilson equation (again our notation is slightly different than that ordinarily used in the Wilson equation). This expression has found wide use in correlating vapor–liquid equilibrium data because of its versatile composition dependence despite having such a simple form. The Wilson equation is just one of many forms that can be developed for the residual portion of the free energy change upon mixing. Many others exist in the literature. The G^E form for the three most popular local composition models is given in Table 9.2.

Example 9.4 illustrates the relationship of the parameters in the model to thermodynamic properties and to the local compositions. It is interesting that the local compositions obtained from the models do not agree even though they may fit the experimental data equally well. While local compositions are an actual part of liquid mixtures, values of the local compositions predicted from regression of experimental data using the models in Table 9.2 are not accurate. This is obvious by the discrepancy shown in Example 9.4 between the Wilson and NRTL local compositions. This nonphysical relation has also been demonstrated rigorously by comparison of values obtained from the semiempirical equations applied to model fluids to those obtained from MD simulations. Usually, the semiempirical equations of Table 9.2 considerably overpredict the clustering effect and the local compositions deviate more from the bulk compositions than predicted by MD simulations.[5,10] Thus one should view the local compositions of these models only as effective values that in some way compensate for the

Example 9.4   The equilibrium vapor mole fraction above a liquid mixture of acetone(1) + hexane(2) in which $x_1 = 0.6609$ is $y_1 = 0.6362$ at 20°C according to the DECHEMA data handbook.[9] The measured pressure at this condition is 237.70 mm Hg while the pure-component vapor pressures at this temperature are 185.5 mm Hg and 120.3 mm Hg, respectively. Determine the parameters in the Wilson and NRTL equations and compare the local compositions which each model predicts.

At this low of pressure, we may neglect fugacity coefficients and the Poynting correction factor and write the equilibrium constraints as

$$x_i \gamma_i P_i^* = y_i P.$$

We can solve for the activity coefficients at the requested condition to obtain

$$\gamma_1 = \frac{y_1 P}{x_1 P_1^*} = \frac{(0.6363)(237.7)}{(0.6609)(185.5)} = 1.234 \quad \text{and} \quad \gamma_2 = \frac{(0.3637)(237.7)}{(0.3391)(120.3)} = 2.120.$$

Appendix 9 contains the activity coefficient forms of the local composition models discussed in this chapter. The expressions for $\ln(\gamma_1)$ and $\ln(\gamma_2)$ can be used to provide two equations from which the two unknowns G_{12} and G_{21} can be solved. We did this using TKSolver© software to obtain:

Wilson		
Calculated	$G_{12} = 0.318$	$G_{21} = 0.261$
DECHEMA[9]	$G_{12} = 0.295$	$G_{21} = 0.279$
NRTL		
Calculated	$G_{12} = 0.729$	$G_{21} = 0.756$
DECHEMA[9]	$G_{12} = 0.729$	$G_{21} = 0.747$

For the NRTL model, we used $\alpha = 0.2913$, the value given in the DECHEMA tables. The values obtained from DECHEMA were regressed from vapor–liquid equilibrium data over the entire composition range rather than at a single composition. These values can be used in conjunction with Equation (9.39) to obtain the local compositions predicted by the equations:

Wilson	$x_{11} = 0.882$	$x_{21} = 0.118$	$x_{22} = 0.617$	$x_{12} = 0.383$
NRTL	$x_{11} = 0.723$	$x_{21} = 0.277$	$x_{22} = 0.413$	$x_{12} = 0.587$

assumptions and inadequacies inherent in the models rather than as actual representations of the local compositions present in the mixture.

9.3.5 Combined Models

The above illustrations showed how different assumptions about V_f and Δu_0 led to different forms for ΔA_{atherm} and ΔA_{resid}. Many of the empirical mixture models for the excess free energy are in fact based solely on one or the other term. One could formulate additional expressions for the mixture starting from the van der Waals partition function and making other reasonable assumptions about V_f or Δu_0. There are undoubtedly many other mixture models that could be obtained by clever and insightful development of a free volume and a cell potential. Combination of these two contributions into a single model would be more consistent with the complete van der Waals partition function. To date, only a relatively few mixture models have been developed which attempt to include both contributions. The Wang–Chao model[11] is one that does include both contributions, although the correlation of experimental data is not significantly improved by the added complexity. UNIQUAC[8] also includes both terms and has become quite popular.

9.3.6 Group Contribution Models

It is often convenient to consider interactions between distinct functional groups that comprise the molecules, rather than between the molecules themselves. This is very similar to the site–site interactions discussed in Chapter 5, but differs in the way the molecule is divided into interacting groups. In the case of group contributions, the division is made on the basis of distinct chemical functional groups. This has several advantages, the two most important of which are:

1. Potential models located at several sites within the molecule can better approximate the real molecular potential than a single potential model located at the center of mass. This is the site–site idea previously introduced in Chapter 5.
2. Fewer potential parameters need be tabulated because of the much smaller number of possible functional groups than molecules comprised of the groups.

For illustrative convenience, consider a simple two-dimensional lattice, a portion of which is depicted in Figure 9.3. Rather than molecules, functional groups are located at lattice sites. In the case depicted here, isopropanol is represented by two CH_3 groups, one CH group, and one OH group. Butane is represented by two CH_3 groups and two CH_2 groups. This is certainly only an approximation because all CH_2 groups, for example, are not equivalent. Induction effects due to electron-withdrawing or electron-donating groups at other locations in the molecule are not accounted for, nor are steric effects between closely located groups.

Lee and Haile[12] have shown that relationships for the configurational properties similar to those given in Table 5.1 can be written for site–site potentials based on pairwise additivity. In the following equations, subscripted indices i and j refer to molecular species, superscripted indices a and b refer to functional groups, lowercase n is the number of groups, and uppercase N is the number of molecules. Using Table 5.2, the configurational internal energy can be written as

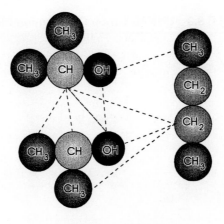

4 Unique Groups
8 Interaction Types

Figure 9.3 Two-dimensional lattice representation of the functional-group approach.

$$U_c = \frac{2\pi}{V} \sum_i \sum_j N_i N_j \sum_a^{n_i} \sum_b^{n_j} \int u^{ab} g_{ij}^{ab} \, d\mathbf{r} \,. \tag{9.46}$$

In this notation, n_i is the total number of groups on molecule i and $n_i = \sum_a n_i^a$. In general, a generic configurational thermodynamic property J_c can be written in the form

$$J_c = \frac{1}{2V} \sum_i \sum_j N_i N_j \sum_a^{n_i} \sum_b^{n_j} \int J_{ij}^{ab} d\mathbf{r} \tag{9.47}$$

where J_{ij}^{ab} is a function of the site–site potential and the site–site radial distribution function.

Several group contribution methods have been developed. The most popular is UNIFAC (a group contribution method based on the UNIQUAC local composition model shown in Table 9.2). Basically, the derivation of UNIFAC assumes that different groups have different volume and surface area contributions to the molecule.[13] The surface fractions and volume fractions of the different groups will affect the properties as does the strength of the interactions between

TABLE 9.3   UNIFAC Group Contribution Model

$$\ln\gamma_i = \ln\frac{\phi_i}{x_i} + \frac{z}{2}q_i\ln\frac{\theta_i}{\phi_i} + l_i + \frac{\phi_i}{x_i}\sum_{j=1}^{n} l_j x_j + \sum_{\text{groups } k} v_k^{(i)}[\ln\Gamma_k - \ln\Gamma_k^{(i)}]$$

$$\ln\Gamma_k = Q_k\left[1 + \ln\frac{\Theta_{kk}}{\Theta_k} - Q_k \sum_{\text{[all groups } m]} \Theta_{mm}\Psi_{km} \right]$$

$$\phi_i \equiv \frac{x_i r_i}{\displaystyle\sum_{j=1}^{n} x_j r_j} \qquad \theta_i \equiv \frac{x_i q_i}{\displaystyle\sum_{j=1}^{n} x_j q_j} \qquad r_i \equiv \sum_k v_k^{(i)} R_k \qquad q_i \equiv \sum_k v_k^{(i)} Q_k$$

$$\Theta_m \equiv \frac{X_m Q_m}{\displaystyle\sum_{\text{all groups } k} X_k Q_k} \qquad \Theta_{mn} \equiv \frac{\Theta_n \Psi_{mn}}{\displaystyle\sum_{\text{all groups } k} \Theta_k \Psi_{kn}} \qquad \Psi_{mn} \equiv \exp\left(-\frac{A_{mn}}{T}\right)$$

where $v_k^{(i)}$ represents the number of group k in molecule i, group values R_k and Q_k and group–group interactions, A_{ji}, are tabulated. X_m is the mole fraction of group m in the mixture. Other variables are defined as in UNIQUAC (see Table 9.2).

---

the different kinds of groups. Table 9.3 contains the UNIFAC equation for activity coeffients and the defining equations for the terms used in the equation.

Group contribution methods do not only apply to free energy models. They can also be used directly in developing the partition function and using it to obtain an equation of state. Such is the case with the model developed by Chao and co-workers[14] which we will use here as a prototype. Starting with the van der Waals partition function, one can write

$$Z = w\left(\Pi_i \Psi_i^{n_i}\right) e^{-\beta U_0},\qquad(9.48)$$

where w is a combinatorial factor representing the degeneracy for the number of different ways these chained groups may be placed on a regularly spaced lattice, and Ψ_i is the molecular cell free-volume term for molecule i. Instead of postulating a form for the entire molecular free volume, a form in terms of the individual group free volumes is assumed:

$$\Psi_i = \Pi_a \Psi_a^{n_i^q}.\qquad(9.49)$$

Chao represented the dependence of the molecular free volume on density with a form derivable from the Carnahan–Starling[15] equation for hard spheres (cf. Chapter 10),

$$\Psi_1 = v \exp\left[-\frac{4(v - 3)}{(v - 1)^2} \right],\tag{9.50}$$

where $v = V/V^{\odot}$, V is the actual volume at the desired T and P, and $V^{\odot}$ is the hard core volume for the molecule, found by adding up tabulated values of $V^{\odot}$ for each group within the molecule.

Similarly, U_0 can be written in terms of mean-field (averaged over r) local *group* interactions, $<u>^{ab}$, and the local group compositions, n^{ab},

$$U_0 = \sum_{a > b}\sum n^{ab}<u>^{ab}.\tag{9.51}$$

The group local compositions are themselves written as a function of the mean interaction potential $<u>$ as was done in the preceding section. Finally, thermodynamic properties can be calculated from the configurational partition function

$$\ln Z = \ln w + N\left[\ln v - \frac{4v - 3}{(v - 1)^2} \right] - \sum_{a > b}\sum \beta n^{ab}<u>^{ab}\tag{9.52}$$

if values for $V^{\odot}$ and $<u>$ are known for each of the constituent groups.

In practice, values for the group parameters in this and other group contribution methods such as UNIFAC are obtained by reversing the procedure described above. Namely, experimental data are used to regress the group parameters in conjunction with Equation (9.52) and the appropriate relationship between the desired property and the partition function Z. This is a very time-consuming and tedious procedure because a large quantity of experimental data is required to regress each group constant. For example, values for group interactions between CH_x groups are established by regressing all of the available data on various hydrocarbon mixtures. Once the interactions between different CH_x groups have been established, data for mixtures of CH_3–NH_2 + butane, pentane, hexane, and so on; CH_3–CH_2–NH_2 + butane, pentane, hexane, and so on; and other primary amines with these same aliphatic hydrocarbons can be used to regress the data to find average interaction parameters between NH_2 and CH_2 groups. In this manner, large tables of group interaction coefficients can be built up over time.

This section has been but a brief, simplified introduction to group contribution methods. The methods are powerful examples of the types of predictive methods that can be developed for fluids from the van der Waals partition function and lattice concepts. There yet remains much to be done in the development of group contribution methods, and it is currently an area of considerable active research. Group contribution techniques are very attractive to industrial users because only a relatively small database of group interaction constants is required to work in conjunction with a design simulator. Once the database is in place, no experimental information is required by the user to make predictions on a variety of compounds and their mixtures. Both of the relations highlighted here, modified UNIFAC[16] and Chao,[14] are computer methods that require considerable programming. We have not therefore felt it important to give the forms of these equations and values of the parameters thus far regressed. If one truly desires to work with these equations on a more fundamental basis, the original works should be studied. A synposis of the methods with examples for heats of mixing is also available.[17] Additionally, standard thermodynamic textbooks usually do a good job teaching the use of UNIFAC. Rather, we have supplied working versions of UNIFAC on the accompanying diskette. Example 9.5 illustrates the use of such computer programs to calculate properties. Similar kinds of code for the original UNIFAC are quite often available as supplements to standard thermodynamic textbooks.

9.4 OTHER PROPERTIES FROM LOCAL COMPOSITIONS

Group contribution models are often formulated in terms of either G^E or the equation of state. Other thermodynamic properties can then be obtained using appropriate thermodynamic identities. For example, if we have a local composition model for G^E which accurately includes the composition, temperature, and pressure dependencies, then we can obtain H^E, V^E, C_p^E, S^E by rigorous thermodynamic differentiation with respect to T and P, and we can find all of the partial molar properties and activity coefficients by differentiation with respect to composition. Obtaining accurate predictions of the other thermodynamic properties depends upon (1) the consistency of the model and (2) the values of the parameters.

With respect to model consistency, we implied earlier that the empirical local compositions do not agree with those computed from MD. We must conclude that they are effective values that compensate for other deficiencies in the model. Worse yet, current models for G^E do not contain the appropriate temperature dependence when constant parameters are used.[17] While G^E and H^E are exactly related through the Gibbs–Helmholtz relationship, the same set of

---

Example 9.5 Use the modified UNIFAC method[16] to compute the excess enthalpy of a 50 mol% mixture of 1-butanol (1) and benzene (2) at 25°C and 1 atm. This is primarily a computer method because of the complexity involved, and the accompanying disk will be used to obtain the solution. Readers who wish to understand better how the method works should consult the original papers or the examples given in reference 17. The modified UNIFAC method gives 1.112 kJ/mol which can be compared to the experimental value of 1.035 kJ/mol.[18]

parameters generally cannot be used for both G^E and H^E predictions. It is often chancy to fit H^E data and then use the resultant parameters to obtain G^E-related data. Some models can be used with care in this mode, but caution should be exercised in doing so. A discussion in reference 17 about this point can guide the interested reader. An early remedy to this problem was to use the forms of the equation, as derived from the master equation for G^E using the exact thermodynamic relations, but to then use different interaction parameters for each different property. Parameters for each property were regressed from data for that property. This required separate interaction tables for vapor–liquid equilibria (VLE), liquid–liquid equilibria (LLE), and H^E calculations.

More recent efforts to resolve the inconsistencies have focused on adding additional empirical temperature dependence into the model by making the original parameters temperature dependent. The basic form of the model is thus retained, but additional temperature flexibility is added by releasing the constraint on the parameters being independent of temperature. For example, in one modification of UNIFAC[16] each A_{ij} is replaced with $A_{ij,1} + A_{ij,2}(T - T_0) + A_{ij,3}[T\ln(T_0/T) + (T - T_0)]$. This adds an empirical temperature dependence to the model, but also increases the number of fitted parameters, in this case from two to six for each pair of groups. The important point is that these parameters are then regressed using a variety of properties such as VLE, LLE, H^E, C_P^E, and so forth. This permits good multiproperty predictions for the above properties because the group interactions were all regressed using data from the same properties.

The concepts of local compositions and group contributions can also be applied to the calculation of transport properties, though the application is not as direct as for thermodynamic properties. The idea behind the extension to transport properties is that the fluid structure must determine all of the properties of the fluid. Therefore, if local compositions have physical significance in establishing the value of excess properties of a mixture, they should also have a determining role in transport property values. Finding the connection between the structure and the transport property is the difficulty. Unlike thermodynamic properties for which exact relations between the properties exist, the relationship between fluid structure and transport coefficients must be developed through additional theories and models.

One of the first attempts to apply the idea of local compositions to transport coefficients produced a model for prediction of mixture thermal conductivities from NRTL parameters regressed from VLE data.[19] The implicit assumption made was that the local compositions obtained from the NRTL equation are the physical local compositions actually existing in the liquid. We have seen that recent simulations indicate that this is probably not true, but it turns out that the effectiveness of the thermal conductivity correlation produced is not compromised by this problem. The development of the thermal conductivity model then follows closely the development shown on pages 337 and 338 for the free energy. The fluid is viewed as consisting of two pure hypothetical fluids which interact ideally; all fluid nonidealities are ascribed to interactions with the pure hypothetical fluids. Thus, we may write analogous to Equation (9.40),

$$k = \sum_{i=1}^{n} w_i k^{(i)} .$$

(9.53)

A mass fraction average is used here because k appears to be much more linear for ideal binary mixtures when plotted as a function of mass fraction than mole fraction. Analogous to Equation (9.41), the thermal conductivity of the hypothetical fluid is given in terms of the local mass fractions:

$$k^{(i)} = \sum_{j=1}^{n} w_{ji} k_{ji} .$$

(9.54)

It is relatively easy to show that the same relationships expressed in Equation (9.39) also hold for the interconversion of local and bulk mass fractions; namely,

$$w_{11} = \frac{w_1}{w_1 + w_2 G_{21}} \quad \text{and} \quad w_{21} = \frac{w_2 G_{21}}{w_1 + w_2 G_{21}} .$$

(9.55)

We can then substitute Equations (9.55) in Equation (9.54), identify k_{ii} terms as pure-component values k_i^0, and obtain the working expression for the mixture thermal conductivity analogous to Equation (9.44),

$$k = \sum_{i=1}^{n} w_i k_i^0 + \sum_{i=1}^{n} w_i \left[\frac{\sum_{j=1}^{n} w_j G_{ji}(k_{ji} - k_i^0)}{\sum_{m=1}^{n} w_m G_{mi}} \right] .$$

(9.56)

Only specification of the cross, binary thermal conductivity interaction k_{ji} remains to complete the definition of the model. To do this, we choose an intuitive rule that the binary mixture k of components 1 and 2 equals k_{12} (and also k_{21}) when the mole fractions x_{12} and x_{21} are equal. There is nothing rigorous in this rule, but it is the choice of this rule that compensates for the nonphysical nature of the local compositions used in the original development and frees it from the strict requirement of the original hypothesis. Mathematically, one can show that this rule requires that k_{ij} is calculated from

$$k_{ij} = \frac{w_i^* w_{ii}^* k_i^0 + w_j^* w_{jj}^* k_j^0}{w_i^* w_{ii}^* + w_j^* w_{jj}^*}$$

(9.57)

where

$$w_1^* = \frac{M_1\sqrt{G_{21}}}{M_1\sqrt{G_{21}} + M_2\sqrt{G_{12}}}. \tag{9.58}$$

This completely fixes all terms in the working Equation (9.56) in terms of the local composition variables G_{ji}. There are no adjustable parameters and the equation is entirely dependent upon the pure-component values and the NRTL local composition parameters. Note that the binary mass-fraction constants w_i^* are constants fixed by the NRTL parameters in Equation (9.58). However, the same relationships between the w_i^* and w_{ii}^* exist as between the variable bulk and local compositions, namely, Equation (9.55).

To use this method to obtain mixture thermal conductivity, one would either regress NRTL parameters from VLE data or obtain the values directly from one of several tabulations. These values are then used to compute the mass-fraction constants w_i^* for each of the constituent binaries. Equations (9.55)

Example 9.6   Use the local composition thermal conductivity model to predict the thermal conductivity of mixtures of water and acetone at 20°C.

The DECHEMA handbook[20] indicates NRTL parameters for this system of A_{21}/R = 225.7 K, A_{12}/R = 413.8 K, and α = 0.3. Using the relationships in Table 9.2, we obtain G_{21} = 0.794 and G_{12} = 0.655. We now use Equation (9.58) to obtain

$$w_1^* = \frac{(18.02)(\sqrt{0.794})}{(18.02)(\sqrt{0.794}) + (58.08)(\sqrt{0.655})} = 0.2546; \qquad w_2^* = 0.7454.$$

From Equations (9.55) we obtain,

$$w_{11}^* = \frac{0.2546}{0.2546 + (0.7454)(0.794)} = 0.3008;$$

$$w_{22}^* = \frac{0.7454}{0.7454 + (0.2546)(0.655)} = 0.8172.$$

We use here k_1^0 = 599 mW/(m·K) and k_2^0 = 161.7 mW/(m·K), respectively. The cross term for this binary pair is therefore [from Equation (9.57)],

$$k_{12} = \frac{(0.2546)(0.3008)(599) + (0.7454)(0.8172)(161.7)}{(0.2546)(0.3008) + (0.7454)(0.8172)} = 210.5 \ \frac{\text{mW}}{\text{m·K}}.$$

This value, together with the k_i^0 and G_{ji} values already obtained, can be used in conjunction with Equation (9.56) to obtain the thermal conductivity at any desired composition. The simplified equation for the case of a binary mixture is

$$k = w_1 k_1^0 + w_2 k_2^0 + w_1 w_2 \left[\frac{G_{21}(k_{21} - k_1^0)}{w_1 + w_2 G_{21}} + \frac{G_{12}(k_{12} - k_2^0)}{w_2 + w_1 G_{12}} \right].$$

Note the similarity in form between the NRTL equations for free energy and thermal conductivity. The final results (———) are compared in the figure with experimental

Example 9.6   Continued

data (·) and the ideal portion of the equation (——), the mass fraction average of the pure-component values.

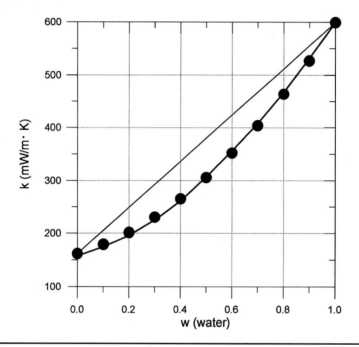

are used to obtain values of w_{ii}^* which can be used in conjunction with Equation (9.57) to obtain the cross thermal conductivity terms for each binary pair. Finally, the thermal conductivity of the mixture can be determined at any composition using Equation (9.56). This procedure is illustrated in Example 9.6. A similar local composition method has also been developed for liquid mixture shear viscosity.[21]

In Chapter 5, two fundamental approaches to thermodynamic properties are emphasized. The first is direct evaluation of the configurational partition function while the second approach restructures the difficulties associated with interactions into the pair correlation function. While the two methods are equivalent, different simplifying approximations lend themselves more readily to one approach or the other. In this chapter we focus on simplifying assumptions that might be used in the partition function approach. One basic set of assumptions, based on a lattice-like view of the liquid state, leads us to the van der Waals partition function. Additional assumptions allow us to develop equations of state and mixture free energy models directly from the configurational partition function itself. A parallel approach in which we try to make assumptions on the pair correlation function is the focus of the next chapter. In it, we try to make reasonable assumptions for the pcf that will render solvable the integral equations involving the pcf. This provides a direct route to thermodynamic properties through the equation of state derived as the pressure equation in Table 5.1.

REFERENCES

1. Rowlinson, J.S., *J.D. van der Waals: On the Continuity of the Gaseous and Liquid States,* North Holland, Amsterdam, 1988.

2. Perry, R.H., and Green, D.W., *Chemical Engineers' Handbook,* 6th ed., McGraw-Hill, New York, 1984.

3. Hildebrand, J.H., and Scott, R.L., *The Solubility of Nonelectrolytes,* 3rd ed., Reinhold, New York, 1950.

4. Prausnitz, J.M., Lichtenthaler, R.N., and de Azevedo, E.G., *Molecular Thermodynamics of Fluid-Phase Equilibria,* Prentice-Hall, Englewood Cliffs, NJ, 1986.

5. Gierycz, P., Tanaka, H., and Nakanishi, K., "Molecular-dynamics studies of binary mixtures of Lennard-Jones fluids with differing component sizes," *Fluid Phase Equilib. 16,* 241–253 (1984).

6. Wilson, G.M., "Vapor-liquid equilibrium. XI: A new expression for the excess free energy of mixing," *J. Am. Chem. Soc.* **1964**, *86,* 127–130.

7. Renon, H., and Prausnitz, J.M., "Local compositions in thermodynamic excess functions for liquid mixtures," *AIChE J.* **1968**, *14,* 135–144.

8. Abrams, D.S., and Prausnitz, J.M., "Statistical thermodynamics of liquid mixtures: A new expression for the excess Gibbs energy of partly or completely miscible systems," *AIChE J.* **1975**, *21,* 116–128.

9. Doring, R., Knapp, H., Oellrich, L.R., Plöcker, U.J., and Prausnitz, J.M., *Vapor-Liquid Equilibria for Mixtures of Low-Boiling Substances,* DECHEMA, Frankfurt, 1982.

10. Lee, K.-H., Sandler, S.I., and Monson, P.A., "Local compositions and the square-well fluid," *Int. J. Thermophys.* **1986**, *7,* 367–379.

11. Wang, W., and Chao, C.K., "The complete local concentration model activity coefficients," *Chem. Eng. Sci.* **1983**, *38,* 1483–1492.

12. Lee, L.L., and Haile, J.M., "Group contribution methods for molecular mixtures. I. Interaction site models," *Fluid Phase Equilib.* **1988**, *43,* 231–261.

13. Fredenslund, A., Jones, R.L., and Prausnitz, J.M., "Group contribution estimation of activity coefficients in nonideal liquid mixtures," *AIChE J.* **1975**, *21,* 1086–1098.

14. Mitta, T., Turek, E.A., Greenkorn, R.A., and Chao, K.C., "A group contribution molecular model of liquids and solutions," *AIChE J.* **1977**, *23,* 144–160.

15. Carnahan, N.F., and Starling, K.E., "Equation of state for nonattracting spheres," *J. Chem. Phys.* **1969**, *51,* 635–636.

16. Larsen, B.L., Rasmussen, P., and Fredenslund, A., "A modified UNIFAC group-contribution model for prediction of phase equilibria and heats of mixing," *Ind. Eng. Chem. Res.* **1987**, *26,* 2274–2286.

17. Christensen, J.J., Rowley, R.L., and Izatt, R.M., *Handbook of Heats of Mixing* Suppl. Vol., John Wiley, New York, 1988.

18. Brown, I., Fock, W., and Smith, F., "Heats of mixing. V. Systems of *n*-alcohols with *n*-hexane," *Aust. J. Chem.* **1964**, *17*, 1106–1118.

19. Rowley, R.L., "A local composition model for multicomponent liquid mixture thermal conductivities," *Chem. Eng. Sci.* **1982**, *37*, 897–904.

20. Gmehling, J., and Onken, U., *Vapor-Liquid-Equilibrium Data Collection; Dechema Data Series*, Vol. 1, DECHEMA, Frankfurt, 1977.

21. Wei, I.C., and Rowley, R.L., "A local composition model for multicomponent liquid mixture shear viscosity," *Chem. Eng. Sci.* **1985**, *40*, 401–408.

22. Villamañán, M.A., and van Ness, H.C., "Excess thermodynamic properties for acetonitrile/ water," *J. Chem. Eng. Data* **1985**, *30*, 445–446.

PROBLEMS

VAN DER WAALS PARTITION FUNCTION

1. Using the generalized van der Waals partition function, derive the van der Waals equation of state for the Lennard-Jones cutoff potential model (same as Lennard-Jones for $r > \sigma$, but same as hard sphere for $r < \sigma$). Use the conditions at the critical point to determine σ and ϵ in terms of critical constants for your new equation of state. Then calculate values for the Lennard-Jones cutoff potential parameters for CO_2 ($T_c = 304.2$ K and $P_c = 7.3$ MPa) and compare these to Sutherland potential parameters consistent with the critical point. Explain any differences.

2. The van der Waals equation of state can also be obtained using a square-well potential model in the van der Waals partition function, just as was done for the Sutherland potential.

   (a) Obtain an expression for the van der Waals constants a and b in terms of the square-well potential parameters σ, ϵ, and g.

   (b) Use the square-well parameters from Appendix 5 to calculate a (L^2atm/mol^2) and b (L/mol) for CO_2. Note: experimental values are 3.611 L^2atm/mol^2 and 0.0429 L/mol, respectively.

3. Estimate Sutherland parameters for isobutane using its critical properties of $T_c = 408.2$ K and $P_c = 3.65$ MPa.

4. The vapor pressure of acetone is 100 mm Hg at 7.7°C and its normal boiling point is 56.5°C. Find the van der Waals constants a and b that best describe these data and then find the corresponding Sutherland parameters.

5. Find the vapor pressure of *n*-hexane at 30°C using the Peng–Robinson equation of state.

6. Suggested mixing rules for the Redlich–Kwong equation of state are

$$a = \sum_i \sum_j x_i x_j a_{ij} \;\; ; \;\; a_{ij} = \sqrt{a_i a_j} \;\; ; \;\; b = \sum_i x_i b_i \, .$$

Determine the compressibility factor for a mixture containing 30 mol% acetone and 70 mol% hexane at 50°C.

7. The enthalpy departure function $(H^* - H)/RT_c$ for propane is 0.648 at 600 K and 7.0 MPa. Determine the van der Waals constants and the corresponding Sutherland parameters for propane from these data.

8. Calculate the enthalpy and entropy departure functions, $(H^* - H)/RT_c$ and $(S^* - S)/R$, for ammonia at 405.6 K and 5.565 atm from the Redlich–Kwong equation of state.

MIXTURE MODELS

9. NRTL parameters have been found to be $\alpha = 0.2$, $a_{12}/R = 438$ K, and $a_{21}/R = 341$ K for mixtures of methanol (1) + n-hexane (2) at 25°C.

   (a) Compute the local mole fractions x_{ij} at 50 mol% and 25°C.

   (b) Compute ΔG_{mix} at 0.1 mole fraction intervals over the entire composition range at 25°C and plot the data.

   (c) Explain why the ΔG_{mix} plot looks as it does and indicate how local compositions play a role in what occurs.

10. Wilson parameters for mixtures of hexane (1) and heptane (2) at moderate temperatures and pressures are $\lambda_{12}/R = -259.1$ K and $\lambda_{21}/R = 626.2$ K. Values for mixtures of acetonitrile (1) and water (2) under similar conditions are $\lambda_{12}/R = 71.92$ K and $\lambda_{21}/R = 987.3$ K. Compute the local compositions for equimolar mixtures of each of these two systems at 30°C. Are the differences in magnitude between the local and bulk compositions what you might expect given the nature of the components in the two different systems? Explain.

11. Repeat Problem 10 using the NRTL model. Model parameters for these two systems are $a_{12}/R = 616.3$ K, $a_{21}/R = -364.0$ K, $\alpha = 0.316$ for hexane + heptane and $a_{12}/R = 654.9$ K, $a_{21}/R = 503.3$ K, $\alpha = 0.5352$ for acetonitrile + water.

12. Use the data given in Problems 10 and 11 and compare the local compositions predicted by the Wilson and NRTL equations for $x_1 = 0.2, 0.5,$ and 0.8 for mixtures of acetonitrile + water and hexane + heptane at 30°C.

13. The NRTL parameters for ethanol (1) + benzene (2) mixtures are $a_{12}/R = 588.7$ K, $a_{21}/R = 263.1$ K, and $\alpha = 0.518$. Assuming these values are independent of temperature, calculate and plot the local mole fractions as a function of temperature from 0°C to 100°C for an equimolar mixture of the two components.

OTHER PROPERTIES FROM LOCAL COMPOSITIONS

14. Using the modified UNIFAC method, determine the heat of mixing for 1-butanol (1) + n-pentane (2) at 25°C and 1 atm at the compositions shown below.

Compare the predicted values to the experimental values[23] given below.

x_1	h^E(J/mol)	x_1	h^E(J/mol)
0.8946	98.44	0.3825	503.93
0.8000	188.03	0.2839	516.57
0.6917	289.77	0.1453	453.76
0.5075	437.05	0.0482	319.79

15. Compute and plot the x-y equilibrium values for mixtures of acetone and toluene at 1 atm pressure using UNIFAC for the liquid phase activity coefficients.

16. Use the UNIQUAC parameters given below to determine if mixtures of n-hexane (1) and nitroethane (2) are completely miscible at $-40°C$.

comp. i	r	q	a_{1i}(K)	a_{2i}(K)
1	4.5	3.86	0	-5.86
2	2.68	2.41	231	0

17. Use the modified UNIFAC method on the diskette to obtain activity coefficients for a 30 mol% mixture of chloroform in acetone at 20°C and at 80°C. Use these values to obtain G^E at these two temperatures. Also obtain H^E for the mixtures at these two temperatures. Comment on the agreement or lack of agreement between the resultant values and the Gibbs–Helmholtz relation.

18. Use the H^E data given below for the acetonitrile (1) + water (2) system, measured by Villamañán and van Ness,[22] to regress NRTL parameters. Then, use these parameters to construct an equilibrium phase diagram at 150.00 mm Hg; i.e., plot y vs. x equilibrium mole fractions.

x_1	H^E(J/mol)	x_1	H^E(J/mol)	x_1	H^E(J/mol)
0.0501	113.0	0.4457	1137.2	0.9007	661.8
0.1066	319.3	0.5989	1255.1	0.9579	318.1
0.1999	626.6	0.6988	1218.8	0.9858	115.3
0.2475	755.4	0.7511	1147.6		
0.3432	969.8	0.8494	891.9		

19. Compute the thermal conductivity of a mixture of (70 wt%) methanol (1) and (30 wt%) carbon tetrachloride (2) at 20°C. The pure-component thermal conductivities at this temperature are 209.6 and 108.2 mW/m·K, respectively. NRTL parameters obtained from VLE data are $a_{12}/R = 473.7$ K, $a_{21}/R = 880.5$ K, and $\alpha = 0.496$. Compare your result with the experimental value of 174.3 mW/m·K.

20. Compute the thermal conductivity of a mixture of (45.9 wt%) carbon tetrachloride (1) and (54.1 wt%) 1-propanol (2) at 37°C. The pure component thermal conductivities at this temperature are 102.6 and 153.9 mW/m·K, respectively. NRTL parameters obtained from VLE data are $a_{12}/R = 739.1$ K, $a_{21}/R = -70.9$ K, and $\alpha = 0.186$. Compare your result with the experimental value of 121.5 mW/m·K.

10

THERMOPHYSICAL PROPERTIES FROM INTEGRAL EQUATIONS OVER THE PCF

Chapters 5 through 9 all contain approaches to the prime problem of calculating configurational properties for interacting systems. While simple in concept, we have seen that this problem is actually very difficult to solve. In theory, properties can be obtained by either solving for the configurational partition function

$$Z = \int \ldots \int e^{-\beta U} \, d\mathbf{r}_1 \ldots d\mathbf{r}_N \tag{10.1}$$

and using the formulas from Chapter 2, or, equivalently, by computing the pair correlation function (pcf)

$$g = \frac{N!}{\rho^2 (N-2)! Z} \int \ldots \int e^{-\beta U} \, d\mathbf{r}_3 \ldots d\mathbf{r}_N \tag{10.2}$$

and using the formulas in Table 5.1.

In practice, the above integrals cannot be solved explicitly, and so the approximate methods of Chapters 6 and 9 and the numerical or simulation methods of Chapters 7 and 8 are often used. The simulation methods are particularly valuable for testing the approximations inherent in analytical methods because both can be based on the same potential model. Both approximate and simulation methods also provide important methods for obtaining thermophysical properties of real fluids if appropriate potential models are used and the calculations are done in regions where the simplifying assumptions are valid. In this chapter, direct approaches toward solving the above integral equations, particularly Equation (10.2), are discussed.

10.1 RECURSION FORMULAS

As a general starting point for the pcf equations, we expand the total potential U in Equation (10.2) and develop a recursive formula between pair and higher order correlation functions. Differentiation of Equation (10.2) with respect to r_1, assuming pairwise additivity of potentials leads to

$$kT\frac{\partial g_{12}}{\partial r_1} + \frac{\partial u_{12}}{\partial r_1}g_{12} + \rho\int\frac{\partial u_{13}}{\partial r_1}\,g^{(3)}\,dr_3 = 0\,, \tag{10.3}$$

after considerable algebraic manipulation. The double subscript notation introduced in Equation (10.3) is used to identify interacting particles. Thus u_{12} stands for the pair potential between molecules 1 and 2, and g_{12} represents the pcf based on u_{12}. Equation (10.3) is a recursive or hierarchal formula because it relates the *pair* correlation function to the *triplet* correlation function $g^{(3)}$. A similar relation holds between triplet correlation functions and $g^{(4)}$, between $g^{(4)}$ and $g^{(5)}$, and so on. These higher order correlation functions are defined in the same manner as the pcf [cf. Equation (5.51)]; that is,

$$g^{(3)} = \frac{\rho^{(3)}}{\rho^3}\,, \tag{10.4}$$

where $\rho^{(3)}$ is the triplet joint probability density function. In its general form, the recursion formula

$$kT\frac{\partial g^{(h)}}{\partial r_1} + \sum_{j=2}^{h}\frac{\partial u_{1j}}{\partial r_1}\,g^{(h)} + \rho\int\frac{\partial u_{1,h+1}}{\partial r_1}\,g^{(h+1)}\,dr_{h+1} = 0 \tag{10.5}$$

shows that lower order correlation functions are given in terms of an integral over the next higher order correlation function. Carried to the limit, there would be N-1 coupled equations in an N-component system, one each for the distribution functions $g^{(2)}$ through $g^{(N)}$. These recursive relations are exact for pairwise additive potentials, but they are of little value because of our inability to calculate the higher order terms. Remember, the only reason we introduced these higher terms was an attempt to calculate $g^{(2)}$. Only when some additional assumption is made about a relationship between $g^{(h)}$ and $g^{(h+1)}$ can there be a closure of the formulas. Closure would then provide unique additional equations, permitting solution of all of the $g^{(h)}$ below the closure level.

By applying different types of closure assumptions to the above recursion formulas, different implicit equations for the pcf are obtained. These equations are all difficult to solve, requiring numerical solutions, and all of them rely upon pairwise additivity in addition to the closure assumption. Unfortunately, it appears that results calculated at high densities are quite sensitive to the selected closure assumption, and integral equations derived from the recursion formulas are generally not as accurate as integral equations based on the direct correlation function discussed in the next section.

The simplest closure approximation was proposed by Kirkwood in the 1930s. If the probability of observing some particular configuration of three molecules occupying positions 1, 2, and 3 is pairwise independent, then the joint probability can be written as a product of the independent probabilities and

$$g^{(3)} = g_{12} \cdot g_{23} \cdot g_{13} \,. \tag{10.6}$$

This assumption, generally called the superposition approximation, when substituted into Equation (10.5) yields the Born, Green, and Yvon (BGY) equation[1]

$$\text{BGY:} \quad kT\frac{\partial g_{12}}{\partial r_1} + \frac{\partial u_{12}}{\partial r_1}g_{12} + \rho\int\frac{\partial u_{13}}{\partial r_1}\, g_{12}g_{23}g_{13}\, d r_3 = 0\,. \tag{10.7}$$

This equation is now closed because it involves only *pair* correlation functions and the pair potentials. If a model for u_{ij} is chosen, the pair correlation functions can be obtained numerically from this equation and similar equations written for g_{13} and g_{23}.

10.2 DIRECT CORRELATION FUNCTION

Since the late 1950s, integral equations have been derived not by closure of the recursion equation but through a direct correlation function. Ornstein and Zernike proposed a division of the total correlation function h_{12} into a direct and an indirect part. Recall [Equation (5.52)] that the total correlation function, h, is defined as $g-1$ and that it represents the *absolute* correlation or influence between two particles. This is in contrast to the *relative* correlation represented by g. As shown in Figure 10.1, the total influence of particle 2 on 1 can be thought of as a direct 1-2 influence plus a combination of indirect influences. It is convenient to view these latter effects as indirect interaction routes such as 1-3-2 (1 influenc-

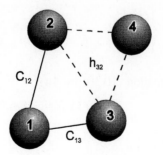

Figure 10.1   The total correlation function includes contributions from the direct, (———) and indirect, (---), correlations between molecules 1 and 2.

ing 3 which in turn influences 2), 1-3-4-2, 1-3-. . . .-2, and so forth. The quite famous Ornstein–Zernike (OZ) equation

$$\text{OZ:} \quad h_{12} = c_{12} + \rho \int c_{13} h_{32} \, d\mathbf{r}_3 \tag{10.8}$$

serves as a defining equation for the direct correlation, c_{12}, in terms of the total correlation function.

Physically this equation implies that the total pair correlation between molecules 1 and 2, h_{12}, is the sum of the direct correlation between the two particles, c_{12}, and the indirect contribution resulting from the direct influence of 1 upon a third particle and then its total influence (through any path) upon particle 2. Because c and h are probability functions, the indirect contribution is a product of probabilities weighted by the density and averaged over all positions of molecules designated as 3 as shown in Equation (10.8). The indirect effects in Equation (10.8) could also be expanded in terms of direct correlations by recursive use of the OZ equation, as is also implied in the simplified schematic of Figure 10.1.

It is interesting to note the effective lengths of these correlation functions. If the OZ equation is multiplied by $d\mathbf{r}_2$ and integrated from 0 to ∞ with respect to $\mathbf{r}_2$, one obtains

$$\int h_{12} \, d\mathbf{r}_2 = \int c_{12} \, d\mathbf{r}_2 + \rho \int \int h_{23} c_{13} \, d\mathbf{r}_3 d\mathbf{r}_2 \,, \tag{10.9}$$

or in terms of integrals over scalar r variables,

$$4\pi \int hr^2 \, dr = 4\pi \int cr^2 \, dr + 16\pi^2 \rho \left(\int hr^2 \, dr \right) \left(\int cr^2 \, dr \right). \tag{10.10}$$

Division of Equation (10.10) by $4\pi \int hr^2 \, dr$ yields

$$\frac{\int cr^2 \, dr}{\int hr^2 \, dr} = 1 - 4\pi\rho \int cr^2 \, dr \,. \tag{10.11}$$

Similarly, division of Equation (10.10) by $4\pi \int cr^2 \, dr$ yields

$$\frac{\int cr^2 \, dr}{\int hr^2 \, dr} = \left(1 + 4\pi\rho \int hr^2 \, dr \right)^{-1} . \tag{10.12}$$

Equating Equations (10.11) and (10.12) implies that

$$1 - 4\pi\rho\int cr^2\, dr = \left(1 + 4\pi\rho\int hr^2\, dr\right)^{-1}. \tag{10.13}$$

The right side of Equation (10.13) also appears in the compressibility Equation (5.72), which we reproduce here as:

$$\beta\left(\frac{\partial P}{\partial\rho}\right)_{T,N} = \left(1 + 4\pi\rho\int hr^2\, dr\right)^{-1}. \tag{10.14}$$

We may therefore write immediately

$$\beta\left(\frac{\partial P}{\partial\rho}\right)_{T,N} = 1 - 4\pi\rho\int_0^\infty cr^2\, dr. \tag{10.15}$$

From the discussion on critical phenomena in Chapter 7, one recognizes the partial derivative in Equation (10.14) as the inverse of the susceptibility. The left side of this equation therefore goes to zero at the liquid–vapor critical point. This requires that the right side of Equation (10.14) diverges, or that $h(r)$ must approach ∞ faster than r^{-3}. Thus h has a very long range indeed in the near critical region. As mentioned in Chapter 7, the divergence of the correlation length leads to the observed critical opalescence characteristic of near-critical systems. The scattering is due to absorption and reemission of the light when the correlation length is approximately equal in magnitude to the wavelength of the incident light. On the other hand, Equation (10.15) indicates that the integral over c must approach a finite value at the critical point. We see, therefore, that $c(r)$ is short-ranged compared to $h(r)$ in the critical region.

Integral equations are generally put in terms of several varieties of correlation functions, some of which have been introduced previously and some of which are defined here. Let us define the function $\phi(r)$ by

$$\phi(r_{ij}) \equiv e^{-\beta u_{ij}}. \tag{10.16}$$

Note that $\phi(r)$ is related in a very simple way to a convenience function defined in Chapter 6, the Mayer f-function. In fact, the relationship between $\phi(r)$ and $f(r)$ is identical to that between $g(r)$ and $h(r)$, namely

$$f = \phi - 1 \qquad \text{and} \qquad h = g - 1. \tag{10.17}$$

Another correlation function, defined strictly for notational convenience in developing the final integral equations, is $y(r)$:

$$y(r_{ij}) \equiv \frac{g(r_{ij})}{\phi(r_{ij})} = g(r_{ij})e^{\beta u_{ij}}. \tag{10.18}$$

To avoid confusion, Table 10.1 can be used as a quick reference to the definitions of these convenience functions.

TABLE 10.1 Definitions of Several Convenience Functions Used in Integral Equations

Function	Name	Definition
c	Direct correlation function	$h - \rho \int ch\, dr$
ϕ	——	$e^{-\beta u}$
f	Mayer f-function	$\phi - 1$
g	Pair correlation function	$\rho^{(2)}/\rho^2$
h	Total correlation function	$g - 1$
y	——	g/ϕ

Solution of the OZ equation to obtain the pcf, from which other thermodynamic properties are obtained, requires an additional equation relating c and g, just as Equation (10.3) required a closure assumption. Two ad hoc formulations of the relationship between the various correlation functions have produced quite good property prediction techniques. These two assumptions produce the most commonly used pcf or integral equation methods. We develop these two methods in the next section.

10.3 PY AND HNC EQUATIONS

The density expansion techniques developed in Chapter 6 can be used to obtain an expansion for the joint density distribution $\rho^{(2)}$, hence $g(r)$. The expansion methods are algebraically messy, and because we will have no need for the expansion itself, we only write the low-density limit,

$$\lim_{\rho \to 0} g(r_{ij}) = e^{-\beta u_{ij}} = \phi(r_{ij}) . \tag{10.19}$$

The proof of this relation can be found elsewhere.[1] In the low-density limit, the relationship between these convenience correlation functions is quite simple:

$$\lim_{\rho \to 0}: \quad g = \phi = f + 1 = h + 1 = c + 1 = e^{-\beta u} . \tag{10.20}$$

Equation (10.18) therefore requires that

$$\lim_{\rho \to 0} y = 1 . \tag{10.21}$$

The Percus–Yevick (PY) equation and hypernetted chain (HNC) equations are obtained by assuming the following relationships between c, g, and h *at all densities:*

$$\text{PY:} \quad c = \frac{fg}{\phi} = fy = g(1 - e^{\beta u}) \tag{10.22}$$

$$\text{HNC:} \quad c = h - \ln(g\phi) = g - 1 - \ln g - \beta u. \tag{10.23}$$

These are approximate relationships derived by neglecting certain terms in the density expansion of c. Note, however, that the PY assumption can also be thought of as retaining the low-density relationship between the ratios c/f and g/ϕ at *all densities*. When the above approximations are substituted into the OZ equation, the so-called PY and HNC equations

$$\text{PY:} \quad y_{12} = 1 + \rho \int f_{13} y_{13} h_{23} \, d\mathbf{r}_3 \tag{10.24}$$

$$\text{HNC:} \quad \ln y_{12} = \rho \int (h_{13} - \ln g_{13} - \beta u_{13})(g_{23} - 1) \, d\mathbf{r}_3 \tag{10.25}$$

are obtained.[2]

Equations (10.24) and (10.25) are nonlinear, integro-differential equations. They are solvable, though they are complex and must be solved numerically for most potentials. Only for the hard-sphere potential can analytical solutions be obtained for these equations. Solution of the OZ equation with either the PY or HNC assumption yields values for all three correlation functions (c, h, and g) as a function of r. We are primarily interested in the pcf since knowledge of it permits calculation of all of the thermodynamic properties from the relationships given in Tables 5.1 and 5.2. A comparison of the results for the HNC and PY solutions of a LJ fluid is shown in Figure 10.2. Also shown in this figure are neutron diffraction results which can be considered direct experimental measurement of the rdf.

In the next section, we show how the analytical solutions of the PY and HNC equations can be used to obtain hard-sphere properties. Later in this chapter, we will illustrate the use of numerical techniques to solve the PY equation for the Lennard-Jones fluid. Once the numerical solution of $y(r)$ or $g(r)$ has been obtained from the PY or HNC equation, the integrals developed in Chapter 5 can be solved numerically to obtain thermodynamic properties.

10.4 HARD-SPHERE EQUATIONS

Although real fluids are not composed of hard spheres, there are several important reasons for studying hard-sphere fluids.

1. Analytical solutions can be obtained to provide clear information about the

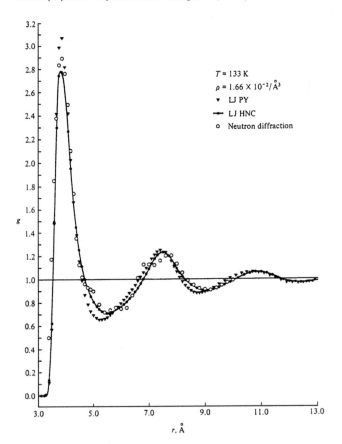

Figure 10.2   The rdf calculated from PY and HNC theories for a LJ fluid compared to neutron diffraction experimental results. (Reproduced by permission from Khan, A.A. *Phys. Rev.* **1964**, 136(5A), 1260.)

relationship between molecular parameters and configurational properties.

2. Thermodynamic and transport properties depend only on the value of g at the hard-sphere contact distance, g_σ, not on g as a function of r.

3. Liquid properties are predominated by the repulsive forces and therefore the hard-sphere model serves as a convenient reference for perturbation theories.

4. Real fluids do behave like hard-sphere fluids in the high-temperature limit, providing a comparison at one extreme against which more realistic models may be judged.

5. The assumption of pairwise additivity is exact for hard-sphere fluids.

The hard-sphere potential,

$$u_{ij} = \begin{pmatrix} \infty & r \leq \sigma_{ij} \\ 0 & r > \sigma_{ij} \end{pmatrix},$$ (10.26)

is particularly convenient for calculating configurational properties because except at molecular contact, intermolecular separation does not affect fluid properties. This greatly simplifies the integrals involved in property calculation. For example, the hard-sphere configurational internal energy is obtained quite easily from Equation (5.60),

$$U_c = 2\pi\rho N \int_0^\infty u_{ij} g_{ij} r^2 \, dr .$$ (10.27)

As is seen in Chapter 6, the nice feature of a segmented potential like that of the hard sphere is that integrals involving the potential can be conveniently split into regions over which the potential is constant, linear, or otherwise easily handled. For the hard-sphere potential, the integral is split into two easily handled integrals: one from 0 to σ and the other from σ to ∞. Because hard spheres cannot overlap, $g_{ij} = 0$ in the range $0 \leq r \leq \sigma$, and the integrand vanishes in this domain. Likewise, the integrand is zero over the domain $\sigma < r < \infty$ because $u_{ij} = 0$ in this region. Thus, the integrand is everywhere zero for a hard-sphere fluid, and $U_c^{hs} = 0$. We will use the superscript hs to indicate values obtained explicitly for a hard-sphere fluid.

The equation of state for hard spheres can also be analytically determined. To do so, we make use of the Dirac delta function, $\delta(x-a)$, which has the unique and useful properties:

$$\begin{bmatrix} \delta(x-a) = \infty & x = a \\ \delta(x-a) = 0 & x \neq a \end{bmatrix},$$

$$\left| \int \delta(x-a) \, dx \right| = 1 \quad \text{and} \quad \int f(x)\delta(x-a) \, dx = f(a).$$ (10.28)

The derivative of the hard-sphere pair potential which appears in the pressure equation for a pure fluid, Equation (5.64),

$$P = \rho kT - \frac{2\pi\rho^2}{3} \int_0^\infty \frac{du}{dr} g r^3 \, dr$$ (10.29)

is related to the Dirac delta function. This can be seen from the derivative

$$\frac{de^{-\beta u}}{dr} = -\beta e^{-\beta u} \frac{du}{dr} = \begin{cases} \infty & r=\sigma \\ 0 & r\neq\sigma \end{cases}$$ (10.30)

and its integral

$$\left| \int_0^\infty \frac{de^{-\beta u}}{dr} \, dr \right| = \left| e^{-\beta u} \Big|_0^\infty \right| = |e^0 - e^{-\infty}| = 1. \tag{10.31}$$

Because the function $de^{-\beta u}/dr$ is everywhere zero [cf. Equation (10.30)] except at $r = \sigma$, where it is an infinite spike, and because its integral satisfies the criterion of Equation (10.28), this function must itself be the Dirac delta function; that is,

$$\frac{de^{-\beta u}}{dr} = \delta(r-\sigma). \tag{10.32}$$

The desired expression for du/dr for use in Equation (10.29) can therefore be obtained by combining Equations (10.30) and (10.32) to yield

$$\frac{du}{dr} = - kTe^{\beta u} \, \delta(r-\sigma). \tag{10.33}$$

Once identification of the relationship between du/dr and $\delta(r-\sigma)$ has been made, the integration posed in Equation (10.29) can be immediately performed using the convenient properties of the Dirac delta function given in Equation (10.28). Thus,

$$P^{hs} = \rho kT + \frac{2}{3}\pi kT\rho^2\sigma^3 g_\sigma^{hs} = \rho kT\left[1 + \frac{2}{3}\pi\rho\sigma^3 g_\sigma^{hs}\right], \tag{10.34}$$

where g_σ^{hs} is the rdf evaluated at the contact distance $r = \sigma$.

An analytical solution for the PY Equation (10.24) for hard spheres has been obtained for g_σ^{hs}. The solution is generally written in terms of the closest-packed volume, ζ_3, defined as

$$\zeta_3 = \frac{\pi}{6}\rho\sigma^3. \tag{10.35}$$

In fact, combinations of ρ and σ raised to various powers occur so often in these equations that it is advantageous to generalize the form of this variable to

$$\zeta_k = \frac{\pi}{6}\rho\sigma^k \text{ (pure)} \quad \text{and} \quad \zeta_k = \frac{\pi}{6}\sum_i \rho_i\sigma_i^k \text{ (mixture)}, \tag{10.36}$$

realizing that the closest-packed volume is given by $k = 3$. The PY analytical solution for the hard-sphere rdf at contact is compactly written in terms of ζ_3 as

$$\text{PY: } g_\sigma^{hs} = \frac{1}{1 - \zeta_3} + \frac{3\zeta_3}{2(1 - \zeta_3)^2} = \frac{1 + \frac{1}{2}\zeta_3}{(1 - \zeta_3)^2}. \tag{10.37}$$

An empirical expression for g_σ^{hs}, developed by Carnahan and Starling (CS),[3] has also found widespread use because of its agreement with MD simulation results. Either the CS equation,

$$
\text{CS: } g_\sigma^{hs} = \frac{1}{1 - \zeta_3} + \frac{3\zeta_3}{2(1 - \zeta_3)^2} + \frac{\zeta_3^2}{2(1 - \zeta_3)^3} = \frac{1 - \frac{1}{2}\zeta_3}{(1 - \zeta_3)^3}, \tag{10.38}
$$

TABLE 10.2 Analytical Equations for Pure Hard-Sphere Fluids Using the Pressure (p) and Compressibility (c) Forms of the PY Approximation

$$
U_c^{hs} = 0
$$

$$
P^{hs} = \rho kT + \frac{2}{3}\pi kT \sigma^3 \rho^2 g_\sigma^{hs}
$$

$$
\mu^{hs,r} = \frac{2}{3}\pi kT \left\{ \left[\frac{\partial}{\partial N} \left(N^2 \sigma^3 \int_\infty^V \frac{1}{V^2} g_\sigma^{hs} \, dV \right) \right]_{T,V} \right\}
$$

$$
\text{PY: } g_\sigma^{hs} = \frac{1 + \frac{1}{2}\zeta_3}{(1 - \zeta_3)^2}
$$

$$
\text{PY}_p: \frac{P^{hs}}{\rho kT} = \left[\frac{1 + 2\zeta_3 + 3\zeta_3^2}{(1 - \zeta_3)^2} \right]
$$

$$
\text{PY}_c: \frac{P^{hs}}{\rho kT} = \left[\frac{1 + \zeta_3 + \zeta_3^2}{(1 - \zeta_3)^3} \right]
$$

$$
\text{PY}_p: \frac{A^{hs,r}}{NkT} = \frac{6\zeta_3}{1 - \zeta_3} + 2\ln(1 - \zeta_3)
$$

$$
\text{PY}_c: \frac{A^{hs,r}}{NkT} = \frac{3\zeta_3 - \frac{3}{2}\zeta_3^2}{(1 - \zeta_3)^2} - \ln(1 - \zeta_3)
$$

$$
\text{PY}_c: \frac{\mu^{hs,r}}{kT} = -\ln(1 - \zeta_3) + \frac{\pi P_{\text{PY}_c}^{hs}\sigma^3}{6kT} + \frac{3\zeta_2\sigma}{1 - \zeta_3} + \frac{3\zeta_1\sigma^2}{1 - \zeta_3} + \frac{9\zeta_2^2\sigma^2}{2(1 - \zeta_3)^2}
$$

or the PY equation may be used in Equation (10.34) to obtain an equation of state for hard-sphere fluids. Alternatively, the PY or CS equations can be used in conjunction with the compressibility Equation (5.72) to obtain a slightly different equation of state. It should be recalled that unlike the pressure equation, the compressibility equation does not depend upon pairwise additivity.

Methods similar to those used above to obtain U_c and P can be used to obtain other properties for hard spheres and their mixtures in conjunction with Tables 5.1 and 5.2. Several properties using the CS and PY assumptions have been summarized in Tables 10.2 (see p. 363) and 10.3 (see p. 371) for pure components and in Table 10.4 for mixtures. You may notice that many of the pure-fluid equations in Tables 10.2 and 10.3 could be simplified further and written entirely in terms of ζ_3. We have left them in this slightly more cumbersome form on purpose, so that the form is the same as those used for the mixture equations in Table 10.4 (see p. 372). In practice, one would use the simplified equations directly.

There is no clear preference for one equation over the other. While neither theory can be tested by comparison to experimental data—there are no real hard-sphere fluids—the accuracy of the assumptions used in their derivations can be checked by comparison to MD results. In such a comparison, the computer simulations may be viewed as exact "experimental" data for hard spheres because the simulations contain none of the assumptions inherent in the theories. Figure 10.3 (see p. 367) compares values for g calculated from PY and CS theories to those obtained from MD simulations. It is interesting that the empirical CS does a better job of predicting g_σ than PY. However, predictions from the PY or CS methods derived from the compressibility equation (identified with the subscript c as compared to the equations derived from the pressure equation marked with a p subscript) are comparable as shown in Figure 10.4 (see p. 368). It is evident from this figure that PY_p is less accurate at higher densities. Finally, in Figure 10.5 (see p. 370) a comparison of compressibility factors derived from the HNC_p, HNC_c, PY_p, PY_c, BGY, and Kirkwood theories is made to MD-generated "experimental" data for hard spheres. It is apparent that the superposition approximation upon which both the BGY and Kirkwood equations are based is only adequate up to dimensionless densities of about 0.4, after which it fails significantly. Equations based on the OZ equation are considerably better than those based on the superposition principle.

Properties of hard-sphere fluids are reasonably easy to calculate because of the closed form of the equations and the fact that the rdf need only be evaluated at contact. Examples 10.1 and 10.2 illustrate the use of these hard-sphere equations.

It is wise to remember that the hard-sphere fluid theory is not appropriate for estimation of most real-fluid properties, because the attraction between the molecules is entirely neglected. For example, one could not use real liquid densities, unless they were quite compressed, to extract information about the

Example 10.1   Compute the residual chemical potential of a hard-sphere fluid at $\zeta_3 = 0.5$.

We will use the CS equation here and simplify it before substituting in values. The σ's in the CS equation of Table 10.3 can be combined immediately with the ζ_i's to provide an equation entirely in terms of ζ_3. Thus,

$$\frac{\mu^{hs,r}}{kT} = -\ln(1 - \zeta_3) + \frac{P_{CS}^{hs}\zeta_3}{\rho kT} + \frac{6\zeta_3}{1 - \zeta_3} + \frac{9\zeta_3^2}{2(1 - \zeta_3)^2} + 3\ln(1 - \zeta_3) + \frac{3\zeta_3}{(1 - \zeta_3)}$$

$$- \frac{3\zeta_3^2}{2(1 - \zeta_3)^2} - 2\ln(1 - \zeta_3) + \frac{\zeta_3(2 - \zeta_3)}{1 - \zeta_3}.$$

We may now collect like terms to obtain

$$\frac{\mu^{hs,r}}{kT} = \frac{P_{CS}^{hs}\zeta_3}{\rho kT} + \frac{7\zeta_3}{1 - \zeta_3} + \frac{3\zeta_3^2}{(1 - \zeta_3)^2} + \frac{\zeta_3^2}{1 - \zeta_3}.$$

If we now substitute the CS equation for the pressure, we obtain,

$$\frac{\mu^{hs,r}}{kT} = \frac{\zeta_3 + \zeta_3^2 + \zeta_3^3 - \zeta_3^4}{(1 - \zeta_3)^3} + \frac{7\zeta_3}{1 - \zeta_3} + \frac{3\zeta_3^2}{(1 - \zeta_3)^2} + \frac{\zeta_3^2}{1 - \zeta_3}$$

$$= \frac{8\zeta_3 - 9\zeta_3^2 + 3\zeta_3^3}{(1 - \zeta_3)^3}.$$

Finally, we may evaluate the residual chemical potential by substituting in the value of 0.5 for ζ_3 to obtain

$$\frac{\mu^{hs,r}}{kT} = 17.0.$$

hard-sphere parameters because of the strong influence of the attractions in the real fluid. Rather the main use of the hard-sphere equations is as a starting point for additional theory development.

10.5 HARD CONVEX BODIES

The integral equations have also been solved for geometries other than hard spheres. Analytical equations have been developed for hard bodies of nonspherical shapes, such as ellipsoids, spherocylinders, and tetrahedra. Equations are particularly available for hard convex bodies, solid shapes for which any line intersecting two points on the surface of the object must lie entirely within the volume of the body. The most common example is that of a spherocylinder or

Example 10.2   If a 150 cm³ box contains 30 marbles of 1 cm diameter and 20 marbles of 2 cm diameter, compute the expected radial distribution functions at contact.

We first compute the various packing fractions ζ_i from the given density information:

$$\zeta_1 = (\rho_A\sigma_A + \rho_B\sigma_B)\cdot\pi/6 = [(30)(1)/150 + (20)(2)/150]\cdot\pi/6 = 0.244$$

$$\zeta_2 = (\rho_A\sigma_A^2 + \rho_B\sigma_B^2)\cdot\pi/6 = 0.384$$

$$\zeta_3 = (\rho_A\sigma_A^3 + \rho_B\sigma_B^3)\cdot\pi/6 = 0.663.$$

We can now calculate the three unique radial distribution functions from the formula in Table 10.4:

$$g_{\sigma11}^{hs} = \frac{1}{1 - 0.663} + \frac{(3)(1)(0.384)}{(2)(1 - 0.663)^2} + \left(\frac{1}{2}\right)^2 \frac{(2)(0.384)^2}{(1 - 0.663)^3} = 9.97$$

$$g_{\sigma12}^{hs} = \frac{1}{1 - 0.663} + \frac{(3)(1)(2)(0.384)}{(3)(1 - 0.663)^2} + \left(\frac{2}{3}\right)^2 \frac{(2)(0.384)^2}{(1 - 0.663)^3} = 13.15$$

$$g_{\sigma22}^{hs} = \frac{1}{1 - 0.663} + \frac{(3)(4)(0.384)}{(4)(1 - 0.663)^2} + \frac{(2)(0.384)^2}{(1 - 0.663)^3} = 20.82$$

The general trends illustrated by these values make physical sense. It seems much more probable that the large marbles are contacting each other and that the smaller marbles can move in the interstitial sites created by these contacts. Finally, the probability is lowest for contact between two smaller marbles because of the smaller relative surface area for contact when the big marbles are mixed in.

hard rod. The geometry of these particles may better approximate the shape of some real particles, but the resultant equations should still not be used for real fluids because of the absence of attractions. The equations are, however, also useful for perturbation theories. We tabulate some of the properties of these hard convex bodies in Table 10.5 in terms of some common geometrical parameters: $\bar{r}$ is the mean radius of curvature of the convex core, s is the total surface area of a particle, b is the volume of the convex core, and $c = \bar{r}^2$. For mixtures, the values of b, $\bar{r}$, s, and c are just taken as the mole fraction average of the pure component values of the corresponding terms. Thus, for a sphere, $b = 4\pi r^3/3$, $s = 4\pi r^2$, and $\bar{r} = r$. For a spherocylinder of radius r and side length x, $b = 4\pi r^3/3 + \pi r^2 x$, $s = 4\pi r^2 + 2\pi rx$, and $\bar{r} = r + x/4$. One can make similar geometrical definitions for cylinders, tetrahedrons, and other objects. The thermodynamic properties for such fluids can then be obtained from the formulas in Table 10.5 (see p. 373).[4]

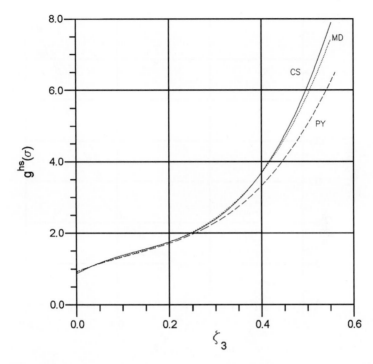

Figure 10.3 Comparison of PY and CS radial distribution functions with MD values.

10.6 NUMERICAL SOLUTIONS FOR CONTINUOUS POTENTIALS

The PY and HNC equations can be solved for continuous potentials, but numerical methods must be used due to the increased complexity of the resultant equations. A discussion of the methodology behind these often elaborate numerical solutions is outside the scope of this text. Some of these methods are easy enough to use that one can generate from them values for $g(r)$ at regular, closely spaced intervals in r without an understanding of the mathematical methods involved. These $g(r)$ values can then be used in tabular form to numerically integrate the equations of Tables 5.1 and 5.2 and obtain thermodynamic properties.

A particularly robust integral equation-solving routine that can be used for either the HNC or PY equations was developed by Gillan.[5] A QUICKBASIC code is included (on diskette) in Appendix 10. This code is essentially a translation of the FORTRAN code available in Lee's book.[4] The equation numbers referenced in the remarks of the code refer to the equation numbers in Gillan's

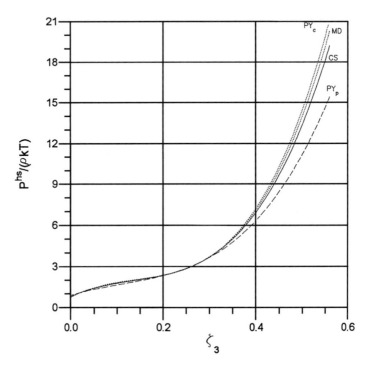

Figure 10.4 Comparison of integral equation compressibility factors to MD results.

paper. Figure 10.6 (see p. 374) shows an example of the rdf generated by the code. As previously mentioned, solution of Equation (10.24) or (10.25) yields $h(r)$ and $c(r)$ in addition to $g(r)$. Again from Figure 10.6 one can see the short-range nature of $c(r)$ relative to the propagated correlations contained within $g(r)$ and $h(r)$. In Example 10.3, tabulated values of $g(r)$ generated with the code given in Appendix 10 at the conditions shown in Figure 10.6 are used to numerically integrate (using Simpson's rule) the pressure equation. This example is sufficiently illustrative of the technique that the reader should be able to apply similar procedures for the computation of other properties.

While analytical relations for the LJ fluid cannot be obtained directly from the integral equations, a large number of MD and MC simulations have been performed on this fluid, so much so, that correlations for the LJ equation of state over a wide range of temperatures and pressures have been developed. These computer "experimental data" have provided an adequate data base for quite accurate representation of the LJ fluid in an analytical form. Two equations of state have been published to date[6,7]; we show the most recent[7] in Table 10.6. Whether an equation of state is obtained directly from the integral equations or from correlation of simulation data is really immaterial. Once one has a viable

Example 10.3   Compute P^+ for a LJ fluid using the PY pressure equation at $T^+ = 1.0$ and $\rho^+ = 0.7$.

From Table 5.1,

$$P = \rho kT - \frac{2}{3}\pi\rho^2 \int_0^\infty \frac{du}{dr} g(r) r^3 \, dr \,.$$

This equation can be put in dimensionless form by multiplying by σ^3/ϵ and recalling that $P^+ = P\sigma^3/\epsilon$, $\rho^+ = \rho\sigma^3$, and $T^+ = kT/\epsilon$. Thus,

$$P^+ = \rho^+ T^+ - \frac{2}{3}\pi\rho^{+2} \int_0^\infty \frac{du^+}{dr^+} g(r) r^{+3} \, dr^+.$$

The derivative of the pair potential for a LJ fluid is

$$\frac{du^+}{dr^+} = -24[2(r^+)^{-13} - (r^+)^{-7}].$$

Substitution of this equation into the pressure equation yields

$$P^+ = \rho^+ T^+ + 16\pi\rho^{+2}\left[\int_0^5 [2(r^+)^{-10} - (r^+)^{-4}]g(r) \, dr^+ + \int_5^\infty [2(r^+)^{-10} - (r^+)^{-4}] \, dr^+\right].$$

The above integral has been split into two contributions. The first contribution ($0 \le r^+ \le 5$) is numerically calculated using Gillan's solution method for the PY equation as contained in Appendix 10. For this problem we generated values of $g(r)$ over the domain and saved them in a file for later access by a program that performs the numerical integration. For brevity, the values are not listed here, but they are plotted in Figure 10.6. The second integral is a long-range correction term (for $r^+ > 5$). It can be analytically integrated by assuming that $g(r) = 1$ over this domain just as we did for the long-range corrections for MD simulations [cf. Equation (8.16)].

The above integration was carried out with Simpson's rule using values of the integrand at every 0.05 r^+ for 100 integration steps. The integrand was set to zero when $g(r) = 0$ to avoid the divergence problem of the derivative of the pair potential at small values of r^+. Finally,

$$P^+ = 0.7 + 16\pi(0.7)^2(-0.00111 - 0.00267) = 0.607 \,.$$

This value is in poor agreement with the value of 0.023 obtained from the MC simulations performed by Adams.[8] Accurate pressures are particularly difficult to calculate because of the integrand's sensitivity to r near the first coordination shell.

equation of state for the model fluid, many thermophysical properties can be obtained using the standard thermodynamic relationships. For example one can obtain the residual Helmholtz free energy and entropy from:

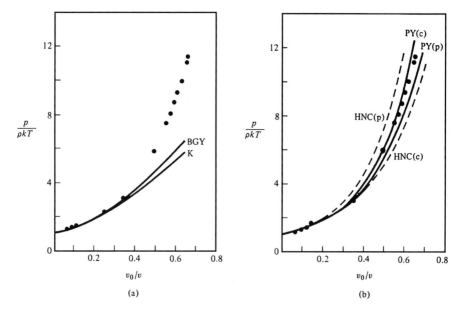

Figure 10.5 Comparison of hard-sphere compressibility factors obtained from MD simulations to those calculated from (*a*) theories based on the superposition principle and (*b*) theories based on the OZ equation ($v_o/v = 6\zeta_3/\pi\sqrt{2} = \rho^+/\sqrt{2}$). Reproduced, with permission, from Henderson, D., *Annual Review of Physical Chemistry* Vol. 15, p. 31, © 1964 by Annual Reviews Inc.

$$A^{+,r} = \int_0^{\rho^+} (P^+ - \rho^+ T^+) \frac{d\rho^+}{\rho^{+2}} \quad \text{and} \quad S^{+,r} = \int_0^{\rho^+} \left[\rho^+ - \left(\frac{\partial P^+}{\partial T^+}\right)_{\rho^+} \right] \frac{d\rho^+}{\rho^{+2}} . \quad (10.39)$$

The power of this method is illustrated in Example 10.4 (see p. 376) where we calculate the residual Helmholtz free energy from the LJ equation of state.

10.7 PERTURBATION TECHNIQUES

Some of the most powerful and accurate methods for calculating thermophysical properties are perturbation techniques. Perturbation theories are based on finding a strong similarity between the new system of interest and a reference fluid for which properties can be accurately calculated. One would want to choose the reference fluid based on its adequacy with respect to two considerations: (1) the contribution of the reference fluid to the total property should predominate, and (2) values for the reference fluid properties should be easily calculable at the desired conditions. The hard-sphere equations developed in Section 10.4

TABLE 10.3 Analytical Equations for Pure Hard-Sphere Fluids Using the Pressure (p) and Compressibility (c) Forms of the CS Approximation

$$U_c^{hs} = 0$$

$$P^{hs} = \rho kT + \frac{2}{3}\pi kT\sigma^3\rho^2 g_\sigma^{hs}$$

$$\frac{A^{hs,r}}{NkT} = \frac{4\zeta_3 - 3\zeta_3^2}{(1 - \zeta_3)^2}$$

$$\text{CS: } g_\sigma^{hs} = \frac{1 - \frac{1}{2}\zeta_3}{(1 - \zeta_3)^3}$$

$$\text{CS}_p: \frac{P^{hs}}{\rho kT} = \left[\frac{1 + \zeta_3 + \zeta_3^2 - \zeta_3^3}{(1 - \zeta_3)^3}\right]$$

$\text{CS}_c:$ P^{hs} not available in analytical form

$$\text{CS}_p: \frac{\mu^{hs,r}}{kT} = -\ln(1 - \zeta_3) + \frac{\pi P_{cs_p}^{hs}\sigma^3}{6kT} + \frac{3\zeta_2\sigma}{1 - \zeta_3} + \frac{3\zeta_1\sigma^2}{1 - \zeta_3} + \frac{9\zeta_2^2\sigma^2}{2(1 - \zeta_3)^2}$$

$$+ 3\left(\frac{\zeta_2\sigma}{\zeta_3}\right)\left[\ln(1 - \zeta_3) + \frac{\zeta_3}{1 - \zeta_3} - \frac{\zeta_3^2}{2(1 - \zeta_3)^2}\right]$$

$$- \left(\frac{\zeta_2\sigma}{\zeta_3}\right)^3\left[2\ln(1 - \zeta_3) + \frac{\zeta_3(2 - \zeta_3)}{1 - \zeta_3}\right]$$

$\text{CS}_c:$ μ^{hs} not available in analytical form

constitute a suitable reference system for liquids and liquid mixtures in terms of these criteria. We have already seen that analytical expressions (Tables 10.2–10.4) can be written for the hard-sphere fluid, and MD simulations indicate that repulsive forces predominate in determining the properties of liquids.

Perturbation techniques, like other methods based on direct solution of the integral equations, are generally quite complex and require computer solutions. Several different approaches are currently being developed. Rather than discuss any one particular method in detail, a generalized methodology of the perturbation approach will be illustrated with a simpler, but less accurate, paradigm. The basis of the method is division of the intermolecular pair potential into a reference potential, u_0, and a perturbation term, u_1:

$$u = u_0 + u_1. \tag{10.40}$$

The configurational partition function, assuming pairwise additivity, is then given by

TABLE 10.4 Analytical Equations for Hard-Sphere Fluid Mixtures Using the Pressure and Compressibility Forms of the PY and CS Approximations

$$U_c^{hs} = 0$$

$$P^{hs} = kT\sum_i \rho_i + \frac{2}{3}\pi kT\sum_i\sum_j \rho_i\rho_j\sigma_{ij}^3 g_{\sigma_{ij}}^{hs}$$

$$\mu_i^{hs,r} = \frac{2}{3}\pi kT\left\{\left[\frac{\partial}{\partial N_i}\left(\sum_j\sum_k N_j N_k \sigma_{jk}^3 \int_\infty^V \frac{1}{V^2} g_{\sigma_{jk}}^{hs}\, dV\right)\right]_{T,V}\right\}$$

$$PY{:}\ g_{\sigma_{ij}}^{hs} = \frac{1}{1-\zeta_3} + \frac{3\sigma_i\sigma_j\zeta_2}{(\sigma_i+\sigma_j)(1-\zeta_3)^2}$$

$$CS{:}\ g_{\sigma_{ij}}^{hs} = \frac{1}{1-\zeta_3} + \frac{3\sigma_i\sigma_j\zeta_2}{(\sigma_i+\sigma_j)(1-\zeta_3)^2} + \left(\frac{\sigma_i\sigma_j}{\sigma_i+\sigma_j}\right)^2\frac{2\zeta_2^2}{(1-\zeta_3)^3}$$

$$PY_p{:}\ P^{hs} = \frac{6kT}{\pi}\left[\frac{\zeta_0}{1-\zeta_3} + \frac{3\zeta_1\zeta_2}{(1-\zeta_3)^2} + \frac{3\zeta_2^3}{(1-\zeta_3)^3} - \frac{3\zeta_3\zeta_2^3}{(1-\zeta_3)^3}\right]$$

$$PY_c{:}\ P^{hs} = \frac{6kT}{\pi}\left[\frac{\zeta_0}{1-\zeta_3} + \frac{3\zeta_1\zeta_2}{(1-\zeta_3)^2} + \frac{3\zeta_2^3}{(1-\zeta_3)^3}\right]$$

$$CS_p{:}\ P^{hs} = \frac{6kT}{\pi}\left[\frac{\zeta_0}{1-\zeta_3} + \frac{3\zeta_1\zeta_2}{(1-\zeta_3)^2} + \frac{3\zeta_2^3}{(1-\zeta_3^3)} - \frac{\zeta_3\zeta_2^3}{(1-\zeta_3)^3}\right]$$

$CS_c{:}$ P^{hs} not available in analytical form

$\dfrac{\mu_i^{hs,r}}{kT}$ = same formulas as in Tables 10.2 and 10.3, but replace σ with σ_i

$$Z = \int\!\ldots\!\int e^{-\beta\Sigma\Sigma(u_0+u_1)}\, d\mathbf{r}_1\ldots d\mathbf{r}_N\,. \tag{10.41}$$

If Equation (10.41) is both multiplied and divided by Z_0, the configurational partition function based solely on the reference potential u_0, then

$$Z = Z_0\frac{\int\!\ldots\!\int e^{-\beta\Sigma\Sigma u_0}\, e^{-\beta\Sigma\Sigma u_1}\, d\mathbf{r}_1\ldots d\mathbf{r}_N}{Z_0} = Z_0\langle e^{-\beta U_1}\rangle_0\,, \tag{10.42}$$

where the $<\ >_0$ notation represents an ensemble average *over the reference system* and U represents the pairwise sum of potentials. The configurational Helmholtz free energy is found from the usual relationship,

$$\frac{A_c}{kT} = -\ln Z = -\ln Z_0 - \ln\langle e^{-\beta U_1}\rangle_0\,. \tag{10.43}$$

The first term on the right side of Equation (10.43) is simply the configurational

TABLE 10.5 Properties of Hard Convex Bodies

$$\frac{A - A^*}{NkT} = -\ln(1 - \rho b) + \frac{\bar{r}s}{b}\frac{1}{1 - \rho b}$$

$$+ \frac{cs^2}{3b^3}\left[\frac{1}{2(1 - \rho b)^2} - \frac{1}{1 - \rho b}\right] - \frac{\bar{r}s}{b} + \frac{cs^2}{6b^2}$$

$$\frac{P}{\rho kT} = \frac{1}{1 - \rho b} + \frac{\bar{r}s\rho}{(1 - \rho b)^2} + \frac{1}{3}\frac{cs^2\rho^2}{(1 - \rho b)^3}$$

$$U_c = 0; \qquad \frac{H_c}{NkT} = \frac{1}{1 - \rho b} + \frac{\bar{r}s\rho}{(1 - \rho b)^2} + \frac{1}{3}\frac{cs^2\rho^2}{(1 - \rho b)^3}$$

$$\frac{S_c}{Nk} = \ln(1 - \rho b) - \frac{\bar{r}s}{b}\frac{1}{1 - \rho b} - \frac{cs^2}{3b^2}\left[\frac{1}{2(1 - \rho b)^2} - \frac{1}{1 - \rho b}\right] + \frac{\bar{r}s}{b} - \frac{cs^2}{6b^2}$$

$$\frac{\mu_i}{kT} = \ln(\rho_i b_i) - \ln(1 - \rho b) + \frac{\rho}{1 - \rho b}(\bar{r}_i s + s_i \bar{r} + b_i) + \frac{\rho^2(\bar{r}_i^2 s^2 + 2b_i \bar{r}s)}{2(1 - \rho b)^2}$$

$$+ \frac{\rho^3 b_i cs^2}{3(1 - \rho b)^3}$$

Helmholtz free energy (divided by kT) of the reference fluid, and the second term is the free energy due to the perturbation of the potential; that is,

$$A_c = A_c^0 + A_c^1. \tag{10.44}$$

If the reference potential is carefully chosen to keep U_1 small relative to the total potential, then the exponential shown in Equation (10.43) can be expanded as a series, and the perturbed Helmholtz free energy can be written as

$$\frac{A_c^1}{kT} = -\ln\left[1 - \beta\left\langle U_1 \right\rangle_0 + \frac{1}{2}\beta^2\left\langle U_1^2 \right\rangle_0 + \ldots\right]. \tag{10.45}$$

The closer the similarity between the test- and reference-fluid potentials, the more effective the perturbation method becomes. We will assume in this development that only the linear term in $<U_1>$ contributes significantly to the free energy. In this case, the expansion of the natural logarithm

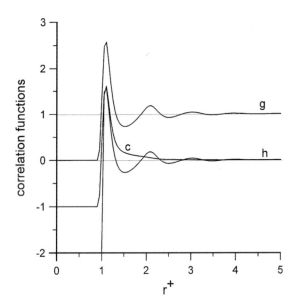

Figure 10.6   Correlation functions generated from the code in Appendix 10 at $T^* = 1.0$ and $\rho^* = 0.7$.

$$\ln(1 + x) = x - \frac{1}{2}x^2 + \frac{1}{3}x^3 - \ldots \tag{10.46}$$

allows Equation (10.45) to be simplified considerably to yield

$$A_c^1 = \langle U_1 \rangle_0 - \frac{\beta}{2}\left(\langle U_1^2 \rangle_0 - \langle U_1 \rangle_0^2\right) + \ldots \simeq \langle U_1 \rangle_0 . \tag{10.47}$$

Finally, the expectation value of the perturbed part of the potential can, like any other expectation value, be written in terms of either the configurational partition function or the radial distribution function. In terms of the reference rdf, the resulting equations for pure fluids and mixtures are:

$$A_c = A_c^0 + 2\pi\rho N \int_0^\infty u_1 g_0 r^2 \, dr \tag{10.48}$$

$$A_c = A_c^{0,\text{mix}} + 2\pi V \sum_i \sum_j \rho_i \rho_j \int_0^\infty u_1 g_0 r^2 \, dr .$$

The computational advantage of the perturbation technique is readily seen in Equation (10.48). Note that g_0 and A_c^0 depend only upon the reference system

TABLE 10.6 Lennard-Jones Equation of State[7]

$$P^+ = \rho^+ T^+ + \sum_{n=2}^{9} C_n \rho^{+n} + \exp(-3\rho^{+2}) \sum_{n=1}^{6} D_n \rho^{+(2n+1)}$$

$$C_2 = a_1 T^+ + a_2 T^{+1/2} + a_3 + a_4 T^{+-1} + a_5 T^{+-2}$$

$$C_3 = a_6 T^+ + a_7 + a_8 T^{+-1} + a_9 T^{+-2}$$

$$C_4 = a_{10} T^+ + a_{11} + a_{12} T^{+-1}$$

$$C_5 = a_{13} \qquad C_6 = a_{14} T^{+-1} + a_{15} T^{+-2} \qquad C_7 = a_{16} T^{+-1}$$

$$C_8 = a_{17} T^{+-1} + a_{18} T^{+-2} \qquad C_9 = a_{19} T^{+-2}$$

$$D_1 = a_{20} T^{+-2} + a_{21} T^{+-3} \qquad D_2 = a_{22} T^{+-2} + a_{23} T^{+-4}$$

$$D_3 = a_{24} T^{+-2} + a_{25} T^{+-3} \qquad D_4 = a_{26} T^{+-2} + a_{27} T^{+-4}$$

$$D_5 = a_{28} T^{+-2} + a_{29} T^{+-3} \qquad D_6 = a_{30} T^{+-2} + a_{31} T^{+-3} + a_{32} T^{+-4}$$

n	a_n	n	a_n	n	a_n	n	a_n
1	0.84531598E0	9	−0.45234862E4	17	0.10640889E2	25	−0.12688462E2
2	0.30571078E1	10	−0.12993269E0	18	0.49784815E3	26	0.19387014E5
3	−0.85104041E1	11	0.99774642E1	19	−0.35300307E3	27	0.37694886E2
4	0.16967935E0	12	−0.61403440E2	20	0.45063864E4	28	0.33787599E4
5	−0.87630366E0	13	0.14075363E2	21	0.52839362E1	29	−0.18540186E3
6	0.18958969E1	14	0.43189008E2	22	0.13570873E5	30	0.84869787E4
7	−0.48670878E1	15	0.11077769E4	23	−0.77976650E1	31	0.97138367E2
8	0.24220330E2	16	−0.35789072E2	24	0.16647996E5	32	−0.15136581E2

and can be calculated directly from the reference equations. There has been a decoupling between the potential and the rdf in the integrand because they are different orders in the perturbation scheme. The remaining integral can now be calculated because the r dependence of both u_1 and g_0 are known. Additional properties can be calculated either from Equation (10.48) using standard thermodynamic identities or from their relationships to the configurational partition function given by

$$\ln Z = \ln Z_0 - 2\pi\beta\rho N \int_0^\infty u_1 g_0 r^2 \, dr + \dots \quad \text{(pure)}$$

(10.49)

$$\ln Z = \ln Z_0 - 2\pi\beta \sum_i \sum_j \rho_i \rho_j V \int_0^\infty u_{1,ij} g_{0,ij} r^2 \, dr + \dots \quad \text{(mixture)}.$$

As already mentioned, the hard-sphere fluid serves as a convenient reference. Although Tables 10.2 to 10.4 contain closed, analytical forms of the

Example 10.4   Calculate the residual Helmholtz free energy for an LJ fluid at $\rho^+ = 0.2$ and $T^+ = 1.179$.

The dimensionless configurational Helmholtz free energy is obtained from Equation (10.39),

$$A^{+,r} = \int_0^{\rho^+} (P^+ - \rho^+ T^+) \frac{d\rho^+}{\rho^{+2}}.$$

But the integrand in this equation can be written as,

$$\frac{P^+ - \rho^+ T^+}{\rho^{+2}} = \sum_{n=2}^{9} C_n \rho^{+(n-2)} + \exp(-3\rho^{+2}) \sum_{n=1}^{6} D_n \rho^{+(2n-1)}.$$

Integration of this function with respect to ρ^+ is difficult due to the nonlinear exponential term. We will therefore integrate the first summation term analytically and use Simpson's rule to integrate the second group of terms numerically. The Helmholtz free energy can then be written as

$$A^{+,r} = \sum_{n=2}^{9} \frac{C_n}{(n-1)} \rho^{+(n-1)} + \int_0^{\rho^+} \exp(-3\rho^{+2}) \sum_{n=1}^{6} D_n \rho^{+(2n-1)} \, d\rho^+$$

Performing the indicated integration for the conditions given, we find a pressure of $P^+ = 0.086$ and $A^{+,r} = 3.24$. The MD simulation for this point yields a pressure of $P^+ = 0.095$.

required equations for the reference fluid, there is a subtle complication in applying the hard-sphere expansion (HSE) method. It is not apparent what value should be used for the hard-sphere diameter σ that appears in the reference fluid equations because the total potential of the real fluid is not that of a hard sphere. For example, to treat a Lennard-Jones fluid with the HSE theory, one would first divide the pair potential into a hard-sphere portion and a residual or perturbation contribution in accordance with Equation (10.40). This division may itself be difficult for complex potentials, but the subtle problem of identifying an effective σ from the Lennard-Jones potential to use in the hard-sphere reference equations is of special concern. Unfortunately, it appears that thermodynamic properties are very sensitive to the chosen effective hard-sphere diameter, d. Moreover, because most potentials are soft, the most efficacious value of d probably varies with density and/or temperature.

Several techniques have been proposed in the literature for calculating effective hard-sphere diameters with varying degrees of success. In some expansion techniques, such as that by Barker and Henderson,[9] the effective hard-sphere diameter can be chosen to make second-order terms in the expansion vanish. In their method, Barker and Henderson compute d from

$$d = \int_0^\sigma (1 - e^{-\beta u})\, dr .$$ (10.50)

A variational technique has also been proposed wherein d is adjusted until the Helmholtz free energy of the system is minimized. Another alternative is to choose the hard-sphere diameter as the distance of closest approach for head-on collisions of particles each moving at the average velocity for the specified temperature. This allows d to be computed in terms of σ for the real potential and the dimensionless temperature. For the Lennard-Jones potential this can be approximated by

$$d \simeq \sigma^{LJ} (1 - 0.05 T^+) .$$ (10.51)

This simple perturbation method developed here serves primarily as an introduction to the more elaborate and accurate methods in the literature. However, it can be readily applied to obtain approximate values of properties by using a very simple potential. We define a hard-core Lennard-Jones potential as a combination of the Lennard-Jones potential for $r > \sigma$ with the infinite repulsion of the hard-sphere model at $r = \sigma$. The r dependence of this potential is depicted in Figure 10.7. The use of this hard-core potential is for pedagogical convenience here and avoids the above issue of the effective hard-sphere diameter, which has become a topic of considerable discussion and research effort. The properties predicted by this method could be improved upon by using a more sophisticated potential model. The separation of the potential into the reference and perturbation parts is particularly easy for this potential because the reference potential is an integral part of the overall model. Thus, we have

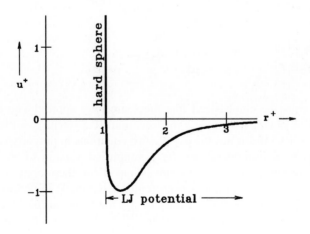

Figure 10.7   Schematic of LJ "hard-core" potential as a function of r^+.

$$u_0 = \begin{bmatrix} \infty & r \le r \\ 0 & r > \sigma \end{bmatrix} \text{ and} \tag{10.52}$$

$$u_1 = \begin{bmatrix} 0 & r \le \sigma \\ 4\epsilon[(r^+)^{-12} - (r^+)^{-6}] & r > \sigma \end{bmatrix}. \tag{10.53}$$

When we use this perturbation potential in Equation (10.49), we obtain

$$\ln Z = \ln Z^{hs} - 2\pi\beta V \sum_i \sum_j \rho_i \rho_j \int_{\sigma_{ij}}^{\infty} u_{1,ij} g_{ij}^{hs} r^2 \, dr . \tag{10.54}$$

Even for this simplistic model, rather complex equations are obtained when $g_{ij}^{hs}(r)$ obtained from the PY or HNC equation is used to calculate properties. Again, strictly for the purpose of pedagogical simplicity we set $g^{hs} = 1$ for all r to enable direct integration of the perturbation term. One is forced to endure the mathematical complexities and perform the integration numerically if more accurate values of the properties are desired. By simplifying the integrand in the examples shown here, we calculate the perturbation term much as we have treated the long-range correction in MD simulations. Computed with $g = 1$, the perturbation term is not expected to be very accurate since even for hard spheres $g(r)$ has the behavior depicted in Figure 7.9.

Nevertheless, using this approximation for g and performing the indicated integrations, we obtain

$$\ln Z = \ln Z^{hs} + \frac{16\pi V}{9kT} \sum_i \sum_j \rho_i \rho_j \epsilon_{ij} \sigma_{ij}^3 , \tag{10.55}$$

$$P = P^{hs} - \frac{16\pi}{9} \sum_i \sum_j \rho_i \rho_j \epsilon_{ij} \sigma_{ij}^3 , \tag{10.56}$$

and

$$\mu_k = \mu_k^{hs} - \frac{32\pi}{9} \sum_i \rho_i \epsilon_{ik} \sigma_{ik}^3 . \tag{10.57}$$

Again it is must be emphasized that these are only approximate expressions since they were obtained by integrating Equation (10.54) with $g = 1$ for all values of r. Example 10.5 illustrates the use of such equations in property calculations.

The method introduced here is a simplified version of the expansion methods currently being used and investigated for thermophysical property calculations. Significant progress is currently being made in perturbation techniques, and the accuracy and viability of the methods can be illustrated with that developed by Leland and co-workers.[10,11] They expand the potential as

$$u = u^{hs} + u^{sym} + u^{asym}, \tag{10.58}$$

Example 10.5   Compute the solubility of nitrogen in benzene at 25 °C using the hard-core Lennard-Jones potential if the partial pressure of N_2 is 50 atm. Assume that the density of the liquid phase is the same as that of pure benzene at these conditions; namely, 0.8786 g/cm^3 or $\rho = 0.00678$ molecules/Å^3.

At equilibrium,

$$\mu_{N_2}^G = \mu_{N_2}^L.$$

For the gas phase,

$$\mu_{N_2}^G = \mu_{N_2}^{o,id} + kT\ln f_{N_2} = kT\ln \frac{P^o \Lambda_{N_2}^3}{kT q_{N_2,int}} + kT\ln P_{N_2},$$

where it is assumed that the partial fugacity coefficient of N_2 is unity and the standard state pressure for μ^o and P^o is 1 atm. The chemical potential in the liquid phase is found using the hard-core Lennard-Jones potential for the perturbation term,

$$\mu_{N_2}^L = \mu_{N_2}^{hs} - \frac{32\pi}{9}\sum_{i=1}^{2} \rho_i \epsilon_{i,N_2} \sigma_{i,N_2}^3 .$$

Note that the attractive term in the above equation involves only molecular interactions with N_2. For example, with benzene named as component 1 and nitrogen as component 2, only ϵ_{12}, ϵ_{22}, σ_{12}, and σ_{22} are involved in μ_2. It should also be remembered that $\rho_i = x_i \rho$.

The hard-sphere chemical potential is given by the PY solution shown in Tables 10.2 to 10.4. Thus,

$$\beta\mu_{N_2}^{L,hs} = \ln\frac{\rho_{N_2}\Lambda_{N_2}^3}{q_{N_2,int}} - \ln(1 - \zeta_3) + \frac{1}{6}\frac{\pi P_{PY}^{hs}\sigma_{N_2}^3}{kT} + \left[\frac{3\zeta_2\sigma_{N_2}}{1 - \zeta_3} + \frac{3\zeta_1\sigma_{N_2}^2}{1 - \zeta_3} + \frac{9\zeta_2^2\sigma_{N_2}^2}{2(1 - \zeta_3)^2}\right].$$

Equating the two chemical potentials and rearranging the resultant equation, leads to

$$\ln x_{N_2} = \ln\left(\frac{P_{N_2}}{\rho kT}\right) + \ln(1 - \zeta_3) - \frac{\pi P_{PY}^{hs}\sigma_{N_2}^3}{6kT} - \frac{3\zeta_2\sigma_{N_2}}{1 - \zeta_3} - \frac{3\zeta_1\sigma_{N_2}^2}{1 - \zeta_3} \tag{10.59}$$

$$- \frac{9\zeta_2^2\sigma_{N_2}^2}{2(1 - \zeta_3)^2} + \frac{32\pi}{9kT}\sum_{i=1}^{2} \rho_i \epsilon_{i,N_2}\sigma_{i,N_2}^3,$$

where P_{PY}^{hs} is obtained from the compressibility equation,

$$P_{PY_c}^{hs} = \frac{6kT}{\pi}\left[\frac{\zeta_0}{1 - \zeta_3} + \frac{3\zeta_1\zeta_2}{(1 - \zeta_3)^2} + \frac{3\zeta_2^3}{(1 - \zeta_3)^3}\right].$$

Equation (10.59) is an implicit equation for the solubility of N_2 which can be solved in any of a number of ways. Because this equation should converge rather rapidly, a simple method of successive substitution is suggested. The computer code to do the calculations is shown below to illustrate the calculation of each of the terms in the above equation.

Example 10.5   Continued

For the benzene (1) + nitrogen (2) problem, we use the following molecular parameters:[2]

$$\sigma_1 = 4.91 \text{ Å} \qquad \sigma_2 = 3.694 \text{ Å}$$

$$\epsilon_1/k = 440 \text{ K} \qquad \epsilon_2/k = 95 \text{ K}$$

and the cross terms are defined by the Lorentz–Berthelot combining rule:

$$\sigma_{12} = (\sigma_1 + \sigma_2)/2 \qquad \epsilon_{12} = (\epsilon_1\epsilon_2)^{1/2}.$$

Using these values, the program first calculates ζ_k values from the initial estimate of x_2 and the density of the liquid solution. These values are used to calculate P_{PY}^{hs} and each of the terms shown in Equation (10.59). Finally, the next estimate of x_2 is found by taking the exponent of the now known value of the right side of Equation (10.59). The program is written so that it prints out the new value of x_2 and stops to allow the user to decide if adequate convergence has been achieved. Intermediate values are shown below. The final value is $x_2 = 0.0246$, which compares quite favorably to the literature value of 0.0220.

Iteration	x_2
0	0.01
1	0.0234
3	0.0245
4	0.0246
5	0.0246

```
REM*****************************************************
REM Example 10.5 - Calculation of nitrogen solubility
REM*****************************************************
DECLARE SUB eos ()
DECLARE SUB zetasub ()
DIM sig (2, 2), eps (2, 2), x(2), zeta (0 TO 3)
pi = 3.14159: k = 1.3806E-16
sig(1, 1) = 4.91 : sig(2, 2) = 3.694
sig(1, 2) = (sig(1, 1) + sig(2, 2))/2
sig(2, 1) = sig(1, 2)
eps(1, 1) = 440 * k : eps (2, 2) = 95 * k
eps(1, 2) = SQR(eps(1, 1) * eps(2, 2))
eps(2, 1) = eps(1, 2)
t = 298.15                :REM set up run conditions
pn2 = 50
convertp = 1.01325E-18    :REM converts dynes/cm^2 to ergs/A^3
pn2 = pn2 * convertp
x(2) = .01                :REM initial guess of x
again: x(1) = 1 - x(2)
  rho = .00678
  CALL zetasub            :REM compute ζ values
```

Example 10.5   Continued

```
REM calculate each term in equation (10.60)
term1 = LOG (pn2 / (rho * k * t))
term2 = LOG (1 - zeta(3))
CALL eos
term3 = pi * phs * sig(2, 2) ^ 3 / (6 * k * t)
term4 = 3 * zeta(2) * sig(2, 2) / (1 − zeta(3))
term5 = 3 * zeta(1) * sig(2, 2) ^ 2 / (1 − zeta(3))
term6 = 9 * zeta(2) ^ 2 * sig(2, 2) ^ 2 / (2 * (1 − zeta (3)) ^ 2)
coef = 32 * pi * rho / (9 * k * t)
sum = x(1)*eps(1, 2)*sig(1, 2) ^ 3 + x(2)*eps(2, 2)*sig(2, 2)^3
term7 = coef * sum
rhs = term1 + term2 − term3 − term4 − term5 − term6 + term7
x(2) = EXP (rhs)    :REM exponentiate right hand side
PRINT x(2)
PRINT "To continue press <space bar>; to quit press <Q>"
pause: k$ = INKEY$: IF k$ = "" THEN GOTO pause
 IF k$ = " " THEN
   GOTO again
 ELSEIF k$ <> "q" AND k$ <> "Q" THEN
   GOTO pause
 END IF
END


SUB eos    :REM compute hs pressure from PY(c) equation
SHARED zeta(), pi, k, t, phs
z = 1 − zeta(3)
arg = zeta(0) / z + 3 * zeta(1) * zeta(2) / z ^ 2 + 3 zeta(2) ^ 3 / z ^ 3
phs = 6 * k * t * arg / pi
END SUB


SUB zetasub  :REM calculate zeta values
SHARED zeta(), pi, x(), sig(), rho
FOR k = 0 TO 3
 zeta(k) = rho * pi / 6 * (x(1) * sig(1, 1) ^ k + x(2) * sig(2, 2) ^ k)
NEXT
END SUB
```

where u^{sym} contains the dispersion forces and u^{asym} accounts for dipole–dipole, dipole–quadrupole, quadrupole–quadrupole, and so forth, interactions. Although the hard-sphere model is used for the reference fluid, the additional terms are evaluated from other real reference fluid properties. Shown in Table 10.7 are the type of results possible with such methods. Certainly, extension of these perturbation methods to more complex molecules for which a molecular potential cannot be readily represented causes additional problems and added complexity.

TABLE 10.7   Results from the HSE Theory[11]

Components	x_1	$T(°F)$	P(psia)	Z(exp)	Z(HSE)
CH_4-C_3H_8	0.5	400	200	0.9799	0.9802
CH_4-C_3H_8	0.5	400	2000	0.8799	0.8725
CH_4-C_3H_8	0.5	400	6000	1.0955	1.0952
CH_4-C_3H_8	0.5	400	10000	1.4589	1.4589
C_3H_8-CO_2	0.3	40	1000	0.1832	0.1826
C_3H_8-CO_2	0.3	40	8000	1.2494	1.2665
C_3H_8-CO_2	0.5	40	1000	0.2040	0.2032
C_3H_8-CO_2	0.5	40	8000	1.4217	1.4295
C_3H_8-CO_2	0.7	40	1000	0.2221	0.2214
C_3H_8-CO_2	0.7	40	8000	1.5753	1.5885

We have introduced perturbation methods with a very simple pedagogical example. In so doing, we have only provided the briefest of introductions, to the many sophisticated perturbation techniques that are now becoming usable and more accurate. Interested readers can find a more extensive introduction to perturbation techniques in the book by Lee.[4]

10.8 ENSKOG THEORY FOR TRANSPORT COEFFICIENTS

Somewhat related to the integral equation approach for thermodynamic properties is an approach for obtaining transport properties derived from kinetic theory. While the original methods developed from concepts of hard-sphere molecular collisions in the gas phase, the resultant formulas have also been extended to other potentials and to dense gases and liquids. In this formulation, a master equation, the Boltzmann equation, is derived from fundamental statistical mechanics. The Boltzmann equation cannot be solved exactly, but a series solution, known as the Chapman–Enskog solution, is commonly used to solve the Boltzmann equation for various orders in the series. In some ways this is akin to the solution of Equation (10.3) by a recursive relation. The Boltzmann equation itself is simply a conservation equation much like those commonly used by engineers for mass (continuity equation), momentum, and energy. But, this conservation equation is for the distribution function itself.

Development of the Boltzmann equation is beyond the scope of an introductory text such as this, but let's look at some of its underpinnings. Because the number of systems in an ensemble approaches infinity, the set of phase-space points that can represent the system becomes quite dense, effectively continuous. We can therefore talk about a density of phase points in terms of the *distribution function* $f(p, q, t)$. In this notation, $f(p, q, t)$ is the normalized distribution of the fraction of phase space points contained in the volume element $dq_1 dq_2 ...dp_{3N}$.

Because each phase point evolves in time according to the equations of motion that describe the system, so also f must obey some complex, composite equation of motion. But phase points are conserved, they are neither created nor destroyed, and so a general conservation equation can be written down for the distribution function. This equation is the *Liouville equation,* probably the most fundamental equation of statistical mechanics,

$$\frac{\partial f}{\partial t} + \sum_{j=1}^{3N}\left(\frac{\partial H}{\partial p_j}\frac{\partial f}{\partial q_j} - \frac{\partial H}{\partial q_j}\frac{\partial f}{\partial p_j}\right) = 0\,, \tag{10.60}$$

where H is the Hamiltonian. If we could but solve this equation for f, we could immediately compute the ensemble average of any dynamical variable in the usual way:

$$<A(t)> = \int A(p, q, t)f(p, q, t)\; dp^{3N}dq^{3N}. \tag{10.61}$$

From the Liouville equation, the conservation of the distribution function for each type of particle, f_j, can be obtained as

$$\frac{\partial f_j}{\partial t} + v_j\cdot\nabla_r f_j + \frac{X_j}{m_j}\cdot\nabla_{v_j} f_j = 2\pi\sum_i \int\int (f_i'f_j' - f_i f_j)v_{ij}\; db\; dv_i\,, \tag{10.62}$$

where v_j is the linear velocity vector of a molecule of species j and X_j is any external force acting on particles j. Equation (10.62) is Boltzmann's equation. The terms on the left represent the normal conservation terms of accumulation, molecular convection, and forced convection, respectively. The term on the right represents scattering from the volume element due to interparticle collisions. In this view, f_i' represents the distribution before collision and f_i represents it after collision. The remaining terms have to do with integrating over the whole collisional cross-sectional area. Thus, $v_{ij} = |v_i - v_j|$ is the magnitude of the relative approach velocity of the particles as they advance toward collision, and db is a relative distance that the colliding species are apart in a direction normal to the relative velocity vector between them. That is, the integral over db represents a collisional cross-sectional area inside of which the molecules will collide and change direction.

Not surprisingly, the Boltzmann equation can not be solved exactly. Rather, a series solution of the form

$$f = \frac{1}{\epsilon}f^{[0]} + f^{[1]} + \epsilon f^{[2]} + \dots , \tag{10.63}$$

called the Chapman–Enskog method, is used to obtain successive terms. Here, ϵ is an ordering parameter, not a smallness factor, which allows terms of like order to be collected and the equation to be partitioned into separate equations for each order. Then ϵ is set to unity.

If Equation (10.63) is substituted in Equation (10.62), we obtain a set of equations for the $f^{[j]}$. As you might expect, accuracy improves with increasing orders, but the complexity of the solution also becomes increasingly menacing very rapidly. The solution for $f^{[0]}$,

$$f^{[0]} = \rho \left(\frac{m}{2\pi kT} \right)^{\frac{3}{2}} \exp \left[\frac{-m(v - v_\mathrm{o})^2}{2kT} \right], \tag{10.64}$$

is rather easy to obtain. This is the familiar equilibrium or Maxwell–Boltzmann distribution of particles. The equation for $f^{[1]}$ is quite complex, but can be solved to yield information about the dispersion in time of the particles. From these fluxes, the transport coefficients can be obtained. $f^{[2]}$ is extremely difficult to solve.

The transport coefficients obtained from the solution of $f^{[1]}$ are given in Table 10.8 for intermolecular potential models of the form $u(r) = \epsilon f(r/\sigma)$, like those we have used throughout the book. The term $\Omega^{+(i,i)}$ is a dimensionless form of the collision integral obtained from the scattering portion of the Boltzmann equation. These collision integrals must be obtained for each different potential. All $\Omega^{+(i,i)}$ are identically unity for the hard-sphere potential. Indeed the hard-sphere value of these integrals are the terms used to make the Ω dimensionless.

TABLE 10.8 First Approximation $f^{[1]}$ Values
for Low-Density Transport Coefficients
from the Boltzmann Equation[1]

$$\eta = \frac{5(\pi mkT)^{\frac{1}{2}}}{16\pi\sigma^2\Omega^{+(2,2)}}$$

$$k = \frac{25C_v}{32N\pi\sigma^2\Omega^{+(2,2)}} \left(\frac{\pi kT}{m} \right)^{\frac{1}{2}}$$

$$D = \frac{3}{8\pi\rho\sigma^2\Omega^{+(1,1)}} \left(\frac{\pi kT}{m} \right)^{\frac{1}{2}}$$

Values of $\Omega^{+(i,i)}$ are: (1) all unity for hard spheres and (2) tabulated in Appendix 10 for LJ fluids.

We tabulate values[12] for the collision integrals obtained for the LJ potential in Appendix 10. Values for other potential models can be obtained from reference 12.

The Chapman–Enskog equations in Table 10.8 are valid only for low-density gases. The primary assumptions in the solution are that only binary collisions are important and that molecules have sizes small relative to their mean free path. Obviously, these assumptions are very restrictive as the density increases. Enskog modified the Boltzmann equation to free it of these two assumptions so that it could be applied to dense gases and liquids. He was able to solve the equations for hard spheres and the results form part of the Enskog theory. Others have extended the Enskog theory to a few other selected simple potentials, but the results are often quite complex. The Enskog equations for hard spheres, however, can be written simply as perturbations of the low-density gas results of Table 10.8. We do so in Table 10.9 in terms of the variable

$$Y = 4\,\zeta_3 g_\sigma^{hs}\,. \tag{10.65}$$

Using the symbols k_o, η_o, and D_o to represent the low-density limit given by the equations in Table 10.8, we can express the Enskog equations in relatively simple form as can be observed in Table 10.9. Table 10.10 shows that the values from the Enskog theory agree quite well with those obtained from MD simulations. This is also true of the results obtained in Examples 10.6 and 10.7 which illustrate use of the Chapman–Enskog and Enskog equations. While these equations are strictly applicable only to hard-sphere fluids, Enskog suggested that they could also be applied to real fluids if Y is calculated by

$$Y = \frac{1}{\rho kT}\left[T\left(\frac{\partial P}{\partial T}\right)_V\right] - 1 \tag{10.66}$$

rather than by Equation (10.65). In so doing, one would use the actual fluid

---

TABLE 10.9 Enskog Equations for Transport Coefficients as a Function of Density

$$\frac{\eta}{4\eta_o\zeta_3} = \frac{1}{Y} + 0.800 + 0.761Y$$

$$\frac{k}{4k_o\zeta_3} = \frac{1}{Y} + 1.20 + 0.755Y$$

$$\frac{D}{4D_o\zeta_3} = \frac{1}{Y}$$

The subscript o indicates the low-density values from Table 10.8.

TABLE 10.10   Comparison of the
Enskog Theory with MD Results[1]

ρ^+	D^{MD}/D^E	η^{MD}/η^E	k^{MD}/k^E
0.014	1.02	1.01	0.98
0.071	1.03	1.00	0.99
0.141	1.03	0.99	
0.283	1.09	0.99	0.97
0.471	1.22	1.02	1.00
0.707	1.14	1.10	1.07
0.786	0.95	1.18	1.03
0.884	0.76	1.44	1.05
0.943	0.55	2.24	1.07

properties or equation of state to obtain the various quantities in Equation (10.66). In spite of the approximate nature of the theory, the results from such calculations are often quite good.

Although the equations in Table 10.8 were developed for spherical molecules, they can also be applied to polyatomic species with reasonably good results as long as an appropriate "effective" or spherically averaged potential is used to model the polyatomic species. This is not, however, the case for thermal conductivity where the transfer of energy between translational and internal energy modes becomes quite important. Generally, the Eucken factor is introduced to account for this energy exchange and to provide a viable method for calculating the thermal conductivity using[12]

$$\frac{kM}{\eta C_v} = 1 + \frac{9R}{4C_V}. \tag{10.67}$$

One should be aware, however, that regression of potential parameters for polyatomic fluids from experimental transport data provides only "effective" parameters and caution should be exercised when using these values to predict other properties or even when predicting the same property at conditions considerably removed from those used in the regression.

The equations in Tables 10.8 and 10.9 are also only given for pure components. Hirschfelder, et al.[12] provide analytical equations for mixtures that are quite long, albeit relatively straightforward to use. It is perhaps easier, however, to use the pure-component values obtained from the Enskog theory and find the mixture value using available empirical equations for mixtures that involve the pure components.[13] These correlations and empirical prediction equations are summarized and analyzed in reference 13. The mutual diffusion coefficient, on the other hand, is not defined in pure fluids, so we give its form from the

Example 10.6   Compare the viscosities predicted by the low-density Chapman–Enskog equations for Ar between 200 K and 500 K, to the experimental data in reference 12. Use both the hard-sphere and the LJ predictions for comparison.

We will use the LJ parameters from Appendix 5 for Ar; namely, $\sigma = 3.418$ Å and $\epsilon/k = 124$ K. We will also take σ_{LJ} to represent the hard-sphere diameter. In order to do a comparison with experimental data, we will perform the calculations at the conditions shown in the table below, where experimental data are available.[12] The collision integrals for the LJ potential are found by converting each temperature to T^+ $= kT/\epsilon$ and then interpolating within the collision integral table in Appendix 10. For hard spheres, $\Omega^{+(2,2)} = 1.0$ at all temperatures. Both T^+ and $\Omega^{+(2,2)}$ for the LJ fluid are shown in the table below for the selected temperatures.

Using the equation from Table 10.8 and setting $\Omega^{+(2,2)} = 1.0$, we can simplify the hard-sphere equation to:

$$\eta^{hs} = \frac{5[\pi(39.93 \text{ g}/6.022 \times 10^{23})(1.3806 \times 10^{-16} \text{ g} \cdot \text{cm}^2/\text{s}^2\text{K})]^{0.5}}{16\pi(3.418 \times 10^{-8} \text{ cm})^2}\sqrt{T}$$

$$= \frac{1.444 \times 10^{-5} \text{ g}}{\text{cm}\cdot\text{s}\cdot\text{K}^{\frac{1}{2}}}\sqrt{T}.$$

Values for the hard spheres can now be calculated at each of the desired temperatures and entered into the table below. Values for the LJ potential are also now readily obtained by dividing the hard-sphere values by $\Omega^{+(2,2)}$. These values are entered into the table below. Note the very good agreement between LJ and experimental values.

			10^{-4}g/(cm·s)		
T/K	T^+	$\Omega^{+(2,2)}$	η^{exp}	η^{hs}	η^{LJ}
100	0.806	1.774	0.0839	1.44	0.081
140	1.13	1.499	1.146	1.71	1.14
180	1.45	1.279	1.447	1.94	1.52
220	1.77	1.230	1.739	2.14	1.74
260	2.10	1.157	2.014	2.33	2.01
300	2.42	1.104	2.270	2.50	2.26

Enskog theory here:

$$D_{12} = 0.0026280\frac{\sqrt{T^3(M_1 + M_2)/2M_1M_2}}{P\sigma_{12}^2\Omega_{12}^{+(1,1)}T_{12}^+}, \tag{10.68}$$

where $T_{12}^+ = kT/\epsilon_{12}$ and M_i is the molecular weight of component i.

In the next chapter, we will investigate methods which are also important in further development of perturbation techniques, but which also stand on their own. The corresponding states methods are interesting because they do not

Example 10.7   Compute the density dependence of the viscosity of N_2 at 50°C over the mass density range 0.1 to 0.5 g/cm³ and compare to experimental values in reference 12.

For N_2, we use the LJ parameters $\sigma = 3.681$ Å and $\epsilon/k = 91.5$ from Appendix 5. At 50°C, or 323 K, we therefore have a dimensionless temperature of $T^+ = 323/91.5 = 3.53$. Interpolating in the collision integral table in Appendix 10, we obtain $\Omega^{+(2,2)} = 0.998$ for this temperature. As in Example 10.6, we calculate the low-density solution first to obtain $\eta_o = 1.877 \times 10^{-4}$ g/(cm · s).

Because the experimental data given in the table below are at particular mass densities, we first find a relationship between mass density and the variables ζ_3 and Y that appear in the Enskog equation. We then plug in the desired mass density to obtain ζ_3, Y and ultimately η to directly compare with the experimental value. For N_2 we may write

$$\zeta_3 = \frac{\pi}{6}\rho\sigma^3 = \frac{\pi \sigma^3}{6m}\rho_m = \frac{\pi(3.681 \times 10^{-8})^3(6.022 \times 10^{23})}{(6)(28)}\rho_m = 0.5617 \, \rho_m \, .$$

Combining this equation with (10.65) and the CS equation for g_σ^{hs} we may also write

$$Y = \frac{\zeta_3(4 - 2\zeta_3)}{(1 - \zeta_3)^3} \, .$$

Using these equations we compute ζ_3 and Y. These are in turn substituted into the Enskog equation.

$$\eta = (4\eta_o\zeta_3)\left(\frac{1}{Y} + 0.800 + 0.761Y\right)$$

to yield the results summarized in the table below. The last column represents the values obtained[12] if Equation (10.66) is used in place of (10.65).

g/cm³			10^{-4} g/(cm·s)			
ρ_m	ζ_3	Y	η_o	$\eta^{(10.65)}$	$\eta^{(10.66)}$	η^{exp}
0.1083	0.061	0.285	1.877	2.07	2.05	2.088
0.2067	0.116	0.633	1.877	2.49	2.24	2.373
0.2875	0.161	1.007	1.877	3.10	2.66	2.737
0.3528	0.198	1.385	1.877	3.83	3.08	3.129
0.4053	0.228	1.752	1.877	4.62	3.48	3.509
0.4786	0.269	2.381	1.877	6.12	4.18	4.163

require explicit evaluation of the configurational partition function. Rather, these methods use known configurational properties for a reference fluid in place of an analytical expression. Properties of other fluids are then computed directly from the reference fluid at the appropriate conditions where the fluids behave the same. This requires the assumption that the potentials are *conformal*, mathematically equivalent, so that equivalent conditions between the reference and test fluids can be found. At these equivalent or corresponding conditions the two fluids will have equivalent reduced properties.

REFERENCES

1. McQuarrie, D.A., *Statistical Mechanics,* Harper & Row, New York, 1976.

2. Reed, T.M., and Gubbins, K.E., *Applied Statistical Mechanics,* McGraw-Hill, New York, 1973.

3. Carnahan, N.F., and Starling, K.E., "Equation of state for nonattracting rigid spheres," *J. Chem. Phys.* **1969**, *51,* 635–636.

4. Lee, L.L., *Molecular Thermodynamics of Nonideal Fluids,* Butterworths, Boston, 1988.

5. Gillan, M.J., "A new method of solving the liquid structure integral equations," *Mol. Phys.* **1979**, *38,* 1781–1794.

6. Nicolas, J.J., Gubbins, K.E., Streett, W.B., and Tildesley, D.J., "Equation of state for the Lennard-Jones fluid," *Mol. Phys.* **1979**, *37,* 1429–1454.

7. Adachi, Y., Fijihara, I., Takamiya, M., and Nakanishi, K., "Generalized equation of state for Lennard-Jones fluids—I. Pure fluids and simple mixtures," *Fluid Phase Equilib.* **1988**, *39,* 1–38.

8. Adams, D.J., "Grand canonical ensemble Monte Carlo for a Lennard-Jones fluid," *Mol. Phys.* **1975**, *29,* 307–311.

9. Barker, J.A., and Henderson, D., "Perturbation theory and equation of state for fluids: The square-well potential," *J. Chem. Phys.* **1967**, *47,* 2856–2861; "Perturbation theory and equation of state for fluids. II. A successful theory of liquids," *J. Chem. Phys.* **1967**, *47,* 4714–4721.

10. Mansoori, G.A., and Leland, T.W., "Statistical thermodynamics of mixtures: A new version for the theory of conformal solution," *J. Chem. Soc. Faraday Trans. II* **1972**, *68,* 320–344.

11. Chen, Y.P., Angelo, P., Naumann, K.-H., and Leland, T.W., "Effective molecular dimensions for compounds in dense fluid mixtures and their use in thermodynamic computations," *Proceedings of the Eighth Symposium on Thermophysical Properties,* Vol. 1, Sengers, J.V., ed., ASME, New York, 1982, pp. 24–37.

12. Hirschfelder, J.O., Curtis, C.F., and Bird, R.B., *Molecular Theory of Gases and Liquids,* John Wiley, New York, 1965.

13. Reid, R.C., Prausnitz, J.M., and Poling, B.C., *The Properties of Gases and Liquids,* 4th ed., McGraw-Hill, New York, 1987.

PROBLEMS

HARD-SPHERE FLUIDS

1. Derive equations for the Helmholtz free energy departure function and for the entropy departure function of a hard-sphere fluid in terms of g_σ, then evaluate these two functions for n-butane at 300 K and 50 atm. You should use $\sigma = 4.812$ Å, the PY_c equation of state to obtain ρ, and the CS equation for g_σ.

2. Show that the Carnahan–Starling hard-sphere equation of state can be written in the form

$$Z_{CS} = \frac{1}{3}\left(2Z_{PY_c} + Z_{PY_p}\right)$$

where Z is the compressibility factor PV/kT.

3. Plot isotherms of P^+ versus ρ^+ (over the range $0 < \rho^+ < 0.5$) for propane at $T^+ = 0.2$ and 1.0 using the CS equation. Compare these plots with those for an ideal gas and for the van der Waals equation of state. Use $\sigma = 4.30$ Å for the hard sphere diameter. *Hint:* Use Equations (9.11) and (9.12) to eliminate a and b from the vdw equation of state; then convert it to dimensionless form.

4. Starting from the CS pressure equation, derive an expression for the dimensionless residual entropy, S^{+r} and Helmholtz free energy, A^{+r} for hard-sphere fluids. Explain the simple relationship between the two quantities. Sketch a plot of S^{+r} versus ζ_3 and discuss why it appears the way it does.

5. Derive an expression for the thermal expansivity coefficient, α_P, and the isothermal compressibility coefficient, β_T, from the PY_c equation. Compute α_P and β_T for O_2 at 63.1 K using $\sigma = 3.30$ Å and compare with the experimental values of 3.66×10^{-3} K^{-1} and 11.0×10^{-11} cm²/dyn, respectively. Recall that these quantities are defined by

$$\alpha_P = \frac{1}{V}\left(\frac{\partial V}{\partial T}\right)_P \qquad \beta_T = -\frac{1}{V}\left(\frac{\partial V}{\partial P}\right)_T$$

6. Compute the configurational enthalpy for a hard-sphere fluid at 300 K and a packing fraction of $\zeta_3 = 0.3$.

7. Compute excess internal energy and the excess enthalpy of mixing for a 50 mol% hard-sphere mixture at 200 K and 5 MPa. Use the PY_c equation and assume that $\sigma_1 = 5$ Å and $\sigma_2 = 10$ Å. Note that the definition of excess mixing properties requires the pure fluids and mixture to be at the same temperature and pressure. Thus you will need to find the corresponding density of the mixture and pure components to complete this problem.

8. Compute the chemical potentials (using the PY_c equations) of each component in a hard-sphere mixture at 200 K and $\rho = 3 \times 10^{-4}$ Å^{-3}, assuming that the mixture contains 30 mol% of the smaller component ($\sigma_1 = 5$ Å) and 70 mol% of the larger component ($\sigma_2 = 10$ Å).

9. Use the CS equation to calculate how the mixture density is affected by the size distribution of the components in a mixture at constant dimensionless pressure and temperature. In particular, select $\sigma_1 = 4$ Å, let $P^+/T^+ = 1$, assume 50 mol% of each component, and determine the mixture density for each of the three values $\sigma_2 = 4$, 8, and 16 Å.

10. Derive the expressions for $A^{hs,r}$ given in Table 10.2 from the corresponding pressure equations.

HARD CONVEX BODIES

11. Express the equations for the compressibility factor and the Helmholtz free energy departure function in terms of the packing fraction ζ_3 if the convex bodies are taken to be spheres. How does the equation of state compare to the PY equations?

12. Suppose the molecules in a fluid are spherocylinders of diameter σ and side length 2σ. Compare on the same plot, the compressibility factors of the spherocylinder fluid and the hard-sphere fluid.

NUMERICAL SOLUTION OF PY EQUATION

13. Saturated liquid CO_2 at 250 K has a mass density of 1.046 g/cm³. Use Gillan's method to obtain $g(r)$ and then use Simpson's rule to numerically obtain the vapor pressure of CO_2 at this temperature. The LJ parameters for CO_2 can be taken as $\sigma = 3.8322$ Å and $\epsilon/k = 230.56$ K.

LENNARD-JONES EQUATION OF STATE

14. Calculate from the LJ equation of state given in Table 10.6 the second virial coefficient for methane at 180 K. Compare this with the experimental value in Appendix 6.

15. Repeat Problem 3 using the LJ equation of state and corresponding LJ parameters for propane instead of the CS equation and hard-sphere diameter.

16. In this problem, we will compare a couple of points on the coexistence curves of the LJ fluid and of Ar. The critical properties of the LJ fluid are approximately[7] $T_c^+ = 1.273$, $P_c^+ = 0.118$, and $\rho_c^+ = 0.284$. How do these compare with the values for Ar? The saturated vapor volume of Ar at 120 K (which also corresponds to 1.215 MPa) is 16.66 cm³/g. Convert these conditions to T^+, P^+, and ρ^+. Then compare this ρ^+ to that predicted by the LJ eos at the same T^+ and P^+.

17. The specific volume of Ar at 400 K and 30 MPa is 2.95 cm³/g. How does this compare to the value predicted for the specific volume of a LJ fluid at the same conditions?

18. Calculate the isothermal compressibility factor in atm⁻¹ for Ar at $T^+ = 1.661$ and $\rho^+ = 0.6$ using the LJ eos.

HARD-SPHERE EXPANSION THEORY

19. Using the HSE theory, derive an expression for the Helmholtz free energy of a square-well fluid. Evaluate the perturbation contribution to the configurational Helmholtz free energy for n-butane at 300 K and 50 atm (the same conditions as in Problem 1). You may use the density calculated in Problem 1 and the parameters $\sigma = 4.812$ Å, $\epsilon/k = 387$ K, and $g_\sigma = 1.476$. Then use the hard-sphere value computed in Problem 1 to obtain the total configurational Helmholtz free energy.

20. Using the hard-core Lennard-Jones potential, the perturbation method developed in the text and a constant value of unity for g:

    (a) derive an expression for U_c^+/N in terms of T^+ and ρ^+, and

    (b) compute H_c^+/N at $T^+ = 1.0$ and $\rho^+ = 0.7$ using the PY_c equation.

21. Derive equations for the thermal expansivity and the isothermal compressibility coefficients of a pure fluid for the hard-core Lennard-Jones potential starting from the pressure equation derived in the text, using PY_c for the hard-sphere term.[2] Then calculate the thermal expansivity and compressibility coefficients for pure liquid nitrogen at 75 K. At this temperature the density of the saturated liquid is 0.817 g/cm^3.

22. Derive an expression for the chemical potential of a mixture using the hard-core Lennard-Jones potential and assuming that the molecules have dipole–dipole and dipole–polarization interactions in addition to the repulsive and dispersive forces.

23. For a sparingly soluble gas dissolved in a liquid, the partial molal heat of solution is related to Henry's constant, K_a, by

$$\Delta H_a = H_a^{soln} - H_a^G = -RT^2 \left(\frac{\partial \ln \gamma_a K_a}{\partial T} \right)_P$$

Use the procedure illustrated in Example 10.5 to obtain an equation for the partial molal heat of solution using the hard-sphere expansion technique and the hard-core Lennard-Jones potential. Then calculate the solubility and the partial molal heat of solution for Ar in benzene at 25°C if the partial pressure of Ar is 1 atm and the gas phase is considered ideal. Use the Lennard-Jones parameters in Appendix 5 for the potential parameters. *Note:* the experimental value for the partial molal heat of solution for Ar in benzene at 25°C is 420 cal/mol.

24. Compute and plot the excess Gibbs free energy of a mixture of CO_2 and n-C_5H_{12} at 300 K and 1 atm, based on the HSE theory and the hard-core Lennard-Jones potential.

25. Compute and plot the excess internal energy and the excess enthalpy for a mixture of CO_2 and n-C_5H_{12} at 300 K and 1 atm, based on the HSE theory and the hard-core Lennard-Jones potential.

26. Plot isotherms of P versus ρ for propane at 300 K and 100 K using HSE and the hard-core Lennard-Jones potential model. Compare these plots with those for an ideal gas and for the van der Waals equation of state.

ENSKOG THEORY

27. Plot the density dependence of D for a hard sphere fluid at 300 K from $\zeta_3 = 0$ to $\zeta_3 = 0.6$ using the Enskog theory and the CS theory. Take the hard-sphere diameter to be 3.29 Å.

28. Calculate the diffusion coefficient of acetone vapor at 500 K and 0.5 atm using potential parameters from Appendix Table A5.5.[2] Use these values to first obtain an effective LJ potential as in Equation (5.37) and then use the effective parameters to compute the self-diffusion coefficient.

29. Use the viscosity data in the table below to obtain best estimates of ϵ/k and σ for the LJ representation of neon.[2]

T (K)	η (μP)
1000	701.9
1200	789.6
1400	872.7
1600	952.1

30. Calculate the thermal conductivity of Kr at 194.7 , 373.2, and 579.1 K at low densities and compare with the experimental values[12] of 152, 272, and 388 [10^{-7} cal/(cm·s·K)], respectively.

31. Compute the viscosity of CO_2 at 40.3°C at mass densities of 0.1, 0.38, 0.45, and 0.59 g/cm^3. Compare these values with the experimental data[12] of 1.8, 2.75, 3.16, and 4.26 [10^{-4}g/(cm · s)], respectively.

32. Calculate the diffusion coefficient for the gas pair nitrogen–oxygen at 0°C and 1 atm. Compare your result to the experimental value of 0.181 cm^2/s.[1] For the mixed interaction parameters use the Lorentz–Berthelot combining rules.

33. Use the Eucken correction factor to calculate the thermal conductivity of CO_2 at 200 K and 300 K. Compare these values with the experimental values of 227 and 398 [10^{-7} cal/(cm·s ·K)], respectively.

34. The data below are reported values for the product PD_{12} in equal molar mixtures of krypton and argon.[2] From the given information, estimate the cross LJ interactions σ_{12} and $(\epsilon/k)_{12}$. Are these consistent with the LB combining rules?

T (K)	$100 \times PD_{12}$ (cm^2 atm/s)
169.3	4.72
231.1	8.60
295.0	13.58
400.0	23.66

11

THERMOPHYSICAL PROPERTIES FROM CORRESPONDING STATES

11.1 CONFORMAL FLUID THEORY

While the emphasis of the last two chapters is on the analytical formulation of properties from the configurational partition function, in this chapter we focus on obtaining fluid properties without ever calculating the partition function. Instead, measured properties of a reference fluid are used to represent the solution of the partition function if some connection can be made between the molecular interactions that characterize the properties of the reference fluid and those in the fluid whose properties we desire (called the test fluid in this chapter). Macroscopic properties of the fluid are determined by the relative positions and velocities of the molecules. These are in turn governed by the intermolecular forces between the molecules. If the form of the intermolecular forces is identical for two fluids, then the two fluids are said to be *conformal*. For example, all Lennard-Jones fluids are conformal to each other, but not to hard-sphere fluids. Similarly, the forces between molecules in real fluids are often conformal to one another, although the exact form for those forces may not be known. On the other hand, one would not expect strongly polar fluids to be conformal to nonpolar fluids, so one must carefully match the test and reference fluids if accurate predictions of properties are to be made.

Note that conformality requires only that the form of the intermolecular potential be the same for the two fluids, not that the potential parameters be equivalent numerically. This is because the potentials then become identical when expressed in terms of dimensionless variables. Thus, at T^+, P^+, and ρ^+, conditions made dimensionless with the potential parameters, conformal potentials are equivalent and will produce equivalent reduced properties in the two fluids.

Only configurational properties need be considered here; we have previously seen how to handle the properties associated with translational and internal modes. Consider two fluids whose total intermolecular potential can be written in the form

$$U = \epsilon\Phi\,(q_1^+, q_2^+ \ldots q_{3N}^+) \quad \text{or} \quad U^+ = \Phi\,(q_1^+, q_2^+ \ldots q_{3N}^+)\,, \qquad (11.1)$$

where Φ represents some function, perhaps an unknown function, of the dimensionless coordinates $(q_i^+ = q_i/\sigma)$ of all the particles in the system. While the functionality of Φ is arbitrary, the fluids are conformal if Φ is the *same* functionality for both fluids. This equation does not require or imply pairwise additivity, only that the parameterized form of the total potential be equivalent in the two fluids. However, it is often convenient to think in terms of pair interactions, and we can then compare the parameterized shapes of the pair potential wells to determine conformality. Note that all of the potential models discussed so far are factorable into the form of Equation (11.1); that is, the dimensionless potential U^+ is a function only of dimensionless position. This is further illustrated in Figure 11.1 where it is seen that conformality implies the ability to *scale* one potential to obtain the other, whereas a lack of conformality is due to a difference in shape between the potentials.

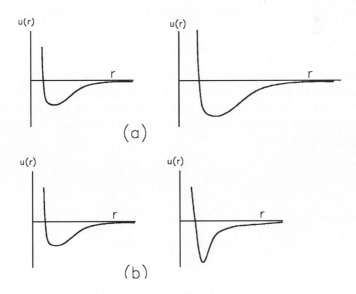

Figure 11.1   (*a*) Conformal potentials are distinguished strictly by a scaling factor, whereas (*b*) nonconformal potentials have different shapes.

11.2 CORRESPONDING STATES

We expect that conformal fluids will have similar properties when they are in similar states, that is, states that correspond to one another with respect to energy and density such that the molecular interactions are equivalent in terms of the dimensionless or parameterized intermolecular potential well. We have often used the following dimensionless state variables in this text

$$T^+ = \frac{kT}{\epsilon}, \quad V^+ = \frac{V}{\sigma^3}, \quad \text{and} \quad P^+ = P\frac{\sigma^3}{\epsilon} \tag{11.2}$$

in anticipation of the very facts that we now seek to establish: that appropriate dimensionless properties of conformal solutions are equal when expressed in terms of independent properties made dimensionless in terms of potential parameters.

Note that the configurational partition function for a conformal fluid [Equation (11.1)] can be written in terms of scaled positions and state variables as,

$$Z = \sigma^{3N} \int_0^{V^{+1/3}} \dots \int_0^{V^{+1/3}} \exp\left(-\frac{\Phi}{T^+}\right) dq_1^+ \dots dq_{3N}^+ . \tag{11.3}$$

If we use the known properties of a reference fluid to identify the configurational partition function in various states, no explicit function for the total potential energy need be postulated and Equation (11.3) need not be formally integrated. However, *if we were* to integrate Equation (11.3), Z would only be a function of σ, T^+, V^+, and N, that is,

$$Z = \sigma^{3N} f''(T^+, V^+, N). \tag{11.4}$$

The function f'' must be an *universal* function for all conformal fluids because we started with an universal function Φ. It is convenient to fix N at Avogadro's number so that all of the properties will be per mole. We may formally write the configurational pressure, which is also the total pressure, using the usual relationship with Z. Thus,

$$P = kT \left(\frac{\partial \ln f'' (T^+, V^+)}{\partial V}\right)_T , \tag{11.5}$$

or in terms of the dimensionless pressure,

$$P^+ = \frac{kT\sigma^3}{\epsilon}\left(\frac{\partial \ln f''}{\partial V}\right)_T = T^+\left(\frac{\partial \ln f''}{\partial V^+}\right)_T . \tag{11.6}$$

Again, we need not explicitly differentiate Equation (11.6), only realize that *if we did,* we would obtain yet another universal function for all conformal fluids of the form

$$P^+ = f'(T^+, V^+).$$ (11.7)

Because f' is a universal function, identical values of T^+ and V^+ must yield identical values of P^+ for all conformal fluids. Simply put, Equation (11.7) states that P^+ is the same as that of all other *conformal fluids* at the same dimensionless T^+ and V^+.

Currently there are more extensive data bases for the critical properties (T_c, P_c, and V_c) than there are for ϵ and σ, so it is convenient to express Equation (11.7) in terms of critical constants. We follow a procedure used by Reed and Gubbins.[1] First, we use the mathematical criteria for the critical point,

$$\left(\frac{\partial P}{\partial V}\right)_T = 0 = \left(\frac{\partial^2 P}{\partial V^2}\right)_T. \quad \text{(at the critical point)}$$ (11.8)

A transformation to dimensionless variables and introduction of Equation (11.7) into Equation (11.6) yields

$$\left(\frac{\partial^2 \ln f''}{\partial V^{+2}}\right)_{T^+} = 0 = \left(\frac{\partial^3 \ln f''}{\partial V^{+3}}\right)_{T^+}. \quad \text{(at the critical point)}$$ (11.9)

These two simultaneous equations could in principle be solved to obtain values of T^+ and V^+ at the critical point. Here, we simply represent the values obtained from such a procedure as constants, C_i, since the actual values are unimportant. Thus,

$$T_c^+ = C_1 \quad \text{and} \quad V_c^+ = NC_2.$$ (11.10)

Likewise a value of P^+ can be obtained at the critical point from Equation (11.6), that is,

$$P_c^+ = T_c^+ \left(\frac{\partial \ln f''}{\partial V^+}\right)_{T^+,C} = C_3.$$ (11.11)

Equations (11.10) and (11.11) provide the necessary relations between the molecular potential parameters ϵ and σ and the commonly tabulated constants T_c, P_c, and V_c. We now use these relations to eliminate the potential parameters in favor of the critical constants. Thus,

$$T_c^+ = \frac{kT_c}{\epsilon} = C_1 \quad \text{or} \quad \frac{\epsilon}{k} = \frac{T_c}{C_1},$$

$$V_c^+ = \frac{V_c}{\sigma^3} = NC_2 \quad \text{or} \quad \sigma^3 = \frac{V_c}{NC_2},$$ (11.12)

$$P_c^+ = P_c\frac{\sigma^3}{\epsilon} = C_3 \quad \text{or} \quad \frac{\epsilon}{\sigma^3} = \frac{P_c}{C_3},$$

from which

$$T^+ = \frac{kT}{\epsilon} = \frac{TC_1}{T_c} = C_1 T_r \,,$$

$$V^+ = \frac{V}{\sigma^3} = \frac{VNC_2}{V_c} = NC_2 V_r \,, \tag{11.13}$$

$$P^+ = P\frac{\sigma^3}{\epsilon} = \frac{PC_3}{P_c} = C_3 P_r \,.$$

Substitution of these values into Equation (11.7) yields an equation in terms of reduced variables, scaled relative to the critical point:

$$P_r = f(T_r, V_r) \,, \tag{11.14}$$

where again f is a universal function valid for all conformal fluids.

Generally, corresponding states equations are expressed in terms of the compressibility factor, z. Thus,

$$z_r = \frac{z}{z_c} = \frac{P_r V_r}{T_r} = g'(T_r, V_r) \,, \tag{11.15}$$

where Equation (11.14) has been used to obtain the last equality. The value of z at the critical point, z_c, is a constant which could be absorbed into the arbitrary function g', so

$$z = z(T_r, V_r) \,. \tag{11.16}$$

Because experimental values for V_c are not as accurately known as P_c and because most experimental work is performed at a specified pressure rather than volume, it is convenient to invert Equation (11.14) and write it in the form

$$V_r = g(T_r, P_r) \,, \tag{11.17}$$

which when used with Equation (11.16) yields

$$z = z(T_r, P_r) \,. \tag{11.18}$$

This is the usual form for corresponding states equations of state. It is valid only to the extent that the fluids are conformal.

The conformality of various fluids is easily checked by plotting values of z over a range of corresponding state conditions. To the extent that z is a universal function of T_r and P_r as shown in Equation (11.18), the fluids are conformal. Examples of this kind of comparison are shown in Figure 11.2 for a variety of fluids and in Figure 11.3 for a few alkanes. Note that the corresponding states theory is capable of approximating z for most of these fluids, but that deviations become substantial for nonspherical fluids and fluids that interact through asymmetric or specific interactions, such as polar association and hydrogen bonding.

A second way to check for conformality is to compare z_c values for various fluids. The value of z at the critical point is given by

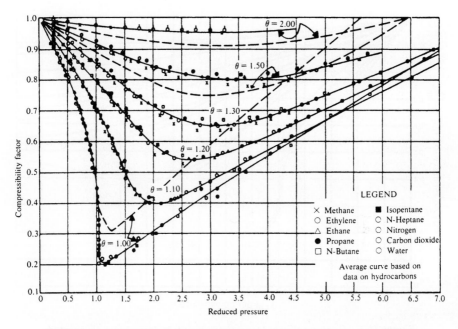

Figure 11.2 Compressibility factor of common gases in corresponding states ($\theta = T/T_c$ after Su and Chang[2]). (Reprinted from Su, G.-J., and Chang, C.-H.[2] *Ind. Eng. Chem.* **1946,** *38,* 802–806. Published 1946 by the American Chemical Society.)

$$z_c = \frac{P_c V_c}{R T_c},\tag{11.19}$$

which in conjunction with Equations (11.12) and (11.13) can also be written as

$$z_c = \frac{C_2 C_3}{C_1}.\tag{11.20}$$

Thus, the value of z_c is universal to the degree that the fluids are conformal. Table 11.1 shows that simple, spherical molecules are reasonably conformal and are therefore expected to obey corresponding states. Deviations from corresponding states are expected to be more severe as the molecular geometry and potential field deviate from spherical symmetry, as is evidenced in the table.

Corresponding states theory, in terms of the variables used in Equation (11.7), is a simple scaling of properties relative to the potential energy function. Thus when molecules are in equivalent states relative to the potential energy and forces between the molecules, the macroscopic properties should be the same. In terms of the variables of Equation (11.18), corresponding states is a simple scaling of the properties relative to the critical point of the fluid as

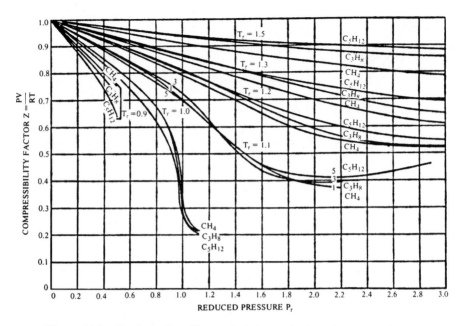

Figure 11.3 Conformality of lower chain-length hydrocarbons. (Reprinted, from Brown, G.G., et al.[3] *Ind. Eng. Chem.* **1931**, *24*, 513–515. Published 1931 by the American Chemical Society.)

TABLE 11.1 Comparison of z_c for Various Fluids

Molecule	z_c	Molecule	z_c
He	0.302	CHF_3	0.259
Ne	0.311	CCl_4	0.272
Ar	0.291	$CHCl_3$	0.259
Kr	0.288	CH_3Cl	0.269
Xe	0.287	CH_3F	0.240
N_2	0.290	CH_3NO_2	0.208
O_2	0.288	C_2H_6	0.285
Cl_2	0.285	C_3H_8	0.281
F_2	0.288	C_4H_{10}	0.274
HCl	0.249	C_5H_{12}	0.263
HF	0.117	$C(CH_3)_4$	0.269
CH_4	0.288	C_6H_6	0.271
CF_4	0.276	C_6H_{14}	0.264

z_c values were obtained from reference 4.

illustrated in Figure 11.4. That is, scaling properties relative to the critical points of the two fluids is equivalent to scaling the PVT domain of the two fluids and requiring them to match at the critical point.

In practice, general correlations have been developed to obtain z as a function of T_r and P_r. Figure 11.5 is one example of a generalized chart that has been prepared based on smoothing of several different reference fluids. Example 11.1 is a simple example of the use of such general correlations. Tabular data are also available. For example, Table 11.3 represents tabular data using methane as the reference fluid.

Use of the corresponding states concept is certainly not restricted to the compressibility factor. In fact, other thermodynamic properties can be readily derived from the T_r and P_r dependence of z through rigorous thermodynamic identities. Thus if one has a general correlation for $z(T_r, P_r)$, then the correlation can be integrated and differentiated in accordance with these thermodynamic identities in order to obtain correlations for the other properties. Numerical tables of such correlations for other properties may be found in Appendix 11. These techniques and results are discussed in textbooks on classical thermodynamics, and interested readers are referred to those sources. However, the use of the corresponding states principle does not depend on having such correlations. One must only select an appropriate (conformal) reference fluid of known properties and find the corresponding state in the test fluid. An illustration of the use of corresponding states to calculate vapor pressures from a particular reference fluid is provided as Example 11.2.

Transport properties can also be calculated with simple corresponding states methods, though the results are generally not as good. Example 11.3 illustrates the general procedure. First the transport property is made dimensionless with some proper combination of the molecular parameters ϵ, σ, and m. This is most conveniently done using dimensional analysis with these three

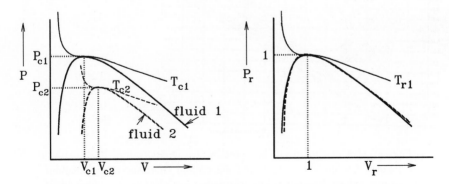

Figure 11.4 Scaling of the *PVT* domain with corresponding states. Vapor–liquid domes and critical isotherms of two fluids may appear different until scaled relative to the critical point.

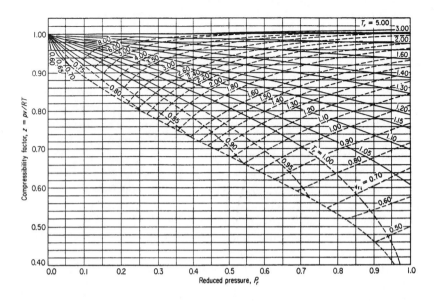

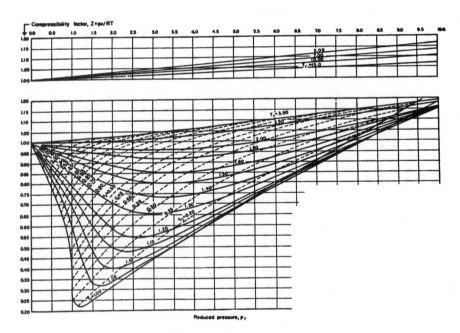

Figure 11.5 Generalized compressibility charts.[5] Top chart shows expanded low-pressure region and the bottom chart shows the medium-pressure region. (Reproduced by permission from Nelson, L.C., and Obert, E.F. *Chem. Eng.* **1954**, *61*(7), 205–206.)

Example 11.1   Compute the molar volume of isobutane at 428.6 K and 27.38 bar.

To find the reduced properties for this condition, we divide the given T and P values by the corresponding critical properties. For isobutane, T_c = 408.2 K and P_c = 36.5 bar. Thus,

$$T_r = \frac{T}{T_c} = \frac{428.6 \text{ K}}{408.2 \text{ K}} = 1.05; \qquad P_r = \frac{P}{P_c} = \frac{27.38 \text{ bar}}{36.5 \text{ bar}} = 0.75.$$

From the top chart of Figure 11.5, the compressibility factor is seen to be 0.74. The molar volume is therefore

$$V = \frac{zRT}{P} = \frac{(0.74)(83.14 \text{ cm}^3\text{bar/mol·K})(428.6 \text{ K})}{27.38 \text{ bar}} = 963.1 \text{ cm}^3/\text{mol}.$$

Example 11.2   Estimate the vapor pressure of CCl_4 at 23°C from the vapor pressure data of benzene given below.

Benzene data: CCl_4 data:

T_c = 562.1 K P_c = 48.3 atm T_c = 556.4 K P_c = 45.0 atm

$T(°C)$	7.6	15.4	26.1	42.2
P(mm Hg)	40	60	100	200

We plot $\ln P_r$ versus $1/T_r$ on the plot at the right because the Clausius–Clapeyron equation indicates that this will nearly linearize the data. The values plotted are:

$10^3/T$	3.56	3.47	3.34	3.17
$\ln P_r$	−6.82	−6.42	−5.91	−5.21

At 23°C, CCl_4 has a reduced temperature of 0.532, or $10^3/T_r$ = 3.377. This point is located on the plot of benzene data shown at the right, from which we estimate that $\ln P_r$ = −6.057 for CCl_4. This corresponds to a vapor pressure of 80 mm Hg compared to the experimental value of 100 mm Hg.

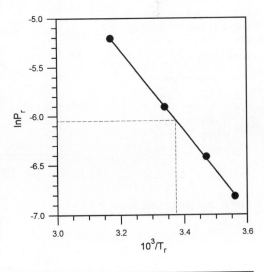

Example 11.3   Using the saturated liquid viscosity data and molecular constants given below for Ar, calculate the viscosity of CCl_4 at 300 K. Assume that liquid viscosity is independent of pressure.

Argon data:

$T(K)$	$\eta(mP)$
100	1.65
110	1.33
120	1.11
130	0.90

$\sigma = 3.498$ Å $= 3.498 \times 10^{-8}$ cm

$\epsilon/k = 119$ K $\Rightarrow \epsilon = 1.66 \times 10^{-14}$ g·cm²/s²

$M = 39.95$ g/mol $\Rightarrow m = 6.33 \times 10^{-23}$ g

To make viscosity dimensionless using molecular parameters, we do a dimensionless analysis on η:

$$\eta \ [=] \ P \ [=] \ \text{g/cm·s} \ [=] \ \sigma^x m^y \epsilon^z \ [=] \ \text{cm}^x \text{g}^y(\text{g·cm}^2/\text{s}^2)^z \ [=] \ \text{g}^{y+z}\text{cm}^{x+2z}\text{s}^{-2z}$$

$$\Rightarrow y + z = 1, \quad x + 2z = -1, \quad \text{and} \quad -2z = -1$$

$$\Rightarrow z = 1/2, \quad x = -2, \quad \text{and} \quad y = 1/2.$$

Thus,

$$\eta^+ = \frac{\eta\sigma^2}{\sqrt{m\epsilon}} \ .$$

Dimensionless values corresponding to the experimental T and η data can now be obtained from the molecular parameters:

T^+	η^+
0.840	1.93
0.924	1.55
1.01	1.30
1.09	1.05

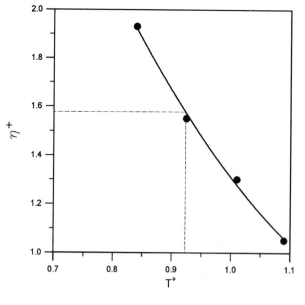

These data are plotted at the right.

The reduced state for the test fluid is

$$T^+ = \frac{300 \text{ K}}{327 \text{ K}} = 0.917,$$

which, from the figure, corresponds to $\eta^+ = 1.6$. Finally, the actual viscosity is found using the parameters for CCl_4 ($\sigma = 5.88$ Å, $\epsilon/k = 327$ K, $M = 153.84$ g/mol):

Example 11.3   Continued

$$\eta = \eta^+ \frac{\sqrt{m\epsilon}}{\sigma^2} = 1.57 \text{ mP}.$$

This does not agree very well with the experimental value of 8.8 mP.

---

parameters. Then for any given state T^+ and P^+, the dimensionless transport property of the test fluid is obtained from the reference fluid value. Finally, the actual test fluid property is calculated from the dimensionless value.

11.3 VAN DER WAALS n-FLUID THEORIES

Mixture properties can also be computed using corresponding states. Empirical equations of state for pure fluids are often extended to mixtures by treating the mixture as though it were a hypothetical pure fluid. The mixture therefore obeys the same form of the equation of state, but the parameters must be composition dependent. In practice then, one must have an ad hoc mixing rule between the pure-component and mixture parameters for the equation of state. In essence, we treat the mixture with a one-fluid theory.

Statistical mechanics helps elucidate part of the problem. The exact pressure equation for a mixture, as shown in Table 5.2, is

$$\frac{P}{\rho kT} = 1 - \frac{2\pi\rho}{3kT}\sum_i\sum_j x_i x_j \int_0^\infty \frac{du_{ij}}{dr} g_{ij} r^3 \, dr. \tag{11.21}$$

Note that this equation contains a known explicit function of composition, as well as an unknown implicit composition dependence in $g_{ij}(r;\rho, T, x)$. Once we know something about the composition dependence of g_{ij}, the entire composition dependence of P is known, and the problem is essentially resolved. The approximations made in the n-fluid theories are on the relations between the mixture and pure rdf's. First, we rewrite the integral in Equation (11.21) in dimensionless variables and compare the mixture and the pure-fluid equations

$$\frac{P}{\rho kT} = 1 - \frac{2\pi\rho}{3kT}\sum_i\sum_j x_i x_j \sigma_{ij}^3 \epsilon_{ij} \int_0^\infty \frac{\partial u^+}{\partial r^+} g_{ij} \, (r^+)^3 \, dr^+ \tag{11.22}$$

$$\frac{P}{\rho kT} = 1 - \frac{2\pi}{3kT}\rho\sigma_0^3\epsilon_0 \int_0^\infty \frac{\partial u^+}{\partial r^+} g_0(r^+)^3 \, dr^+ \tag{11.23}$$

where the subscript 0 is used to indicate a pure reference fluid. One assumes in the one-fluid theory that all the rdf's can be approximated with the reference fluid rdf at conditions reduced with respect to an average mixture σ and ϵ. Thus,

$$g_{ij}\left(\frac{r}{\sigma_{ij}}; \rho, T, x\right) \simeq g_0\left(\frac{r}{\sigma_0}; \rho\sigma_0^3, \frac{kT}{\epsilon_0}\right). \tag{11.24}$$

What this does is remove the composition dependence in g_{ij} by equating it to the pure fluid g_0 whose state variables are reduced by the size and energy parameters of the "hypothetical" single fluid. Because the conformal mixture theory assumes that the values of the thermodynamic properties of the reference fluid are equal to those of the mixture, we may now equate Equations (11.22) and (11.23) to obtain[6]

$$\epsilon_0\sigma_0^3 = \sum_i \sum_j x_i x_j \epsilon_{ij} \sigma_{ij}^3 \tag{11.25}$$

and

$$\sigma_0^3 = \sum_i \sum_j x_i x_j \sigma_{ij}^3. \tag{11.26}$$

Thus in the one-fluid theory, the mixture is assumed to be a pure hypothetical fluid conformal with a reference fluid. We then calculate the equivalent σ_0 and ϵ_0 values with which to compare to the reference fluid by summing the interactions with respect to composition, as in Equations (11.25) and (11.26). The Lorentz–Berthelot combining rules are usually used for the cross-interaction parameters, though one should recognize that this is an additional ad hoc assumption.

These mixing rules for ϵ and σ can also be expressed in terms of critical constants by use of Equations (11.12). These equations provide the basic relationships between molecular properties and critical properties, and therefore provide a bridge between corresponding states methods in terms of dimensionless variables using molecular reducing parameters and those using reduced variables in terms of critical properties. The pseudocritical constants for the one-fluid mixing rule correspond to

$$T_{cm} = \frac{\sum_i \sum_j x_i x_j T_{cij} V_{cij}}{V_{cm}} \tag{11.27}$$

$$V_{cm} = \sum_i \sum_j x_i x_j V_{cij}. \tag{11.28}$$

If the Lorentz–Berthelot rules are used for the molecular parameters, then

$$T_{cij} = \sqrt{T_{cii}T_{cij}}$$

$$P_{cij} = \frac{\sqrt{P_{cii}P_{cjj}V_{cii}V_{cjj}}}{V_{cij}} \tag{11.29}$$

$$V_{cij} = \frac{1}{8}(V_{cii}^{1/3} + V_{cjj}^{1/3})^3$$

$$z_{ij} = \frac{1}{2}(z_{cii} + z_{cjj}) \, .$$

The general procedure in using these pseudocritical constants for corresponding states calculations is to obtain T_{cij}, V_{cij}, and P_{cij}, in that order, from Equations (11.29). Then one can obtain V_{cm} from Equation (11.28) and T_{cm} from Equation (11.27). Often the pseudocritical pressure is desired. It is frequently found from

$$P_{cm} = \frac{z_{cm}RT_{cm}}{V_{cm}}, \tag{11.30}$$

where z_{cm} is found using the double sum average over z_{cij} as in Equation (11.28).

One can develop additional mixing rules based on higher order values of n in the van der Waals n-fluid theory. For example, if one assumes that

$$g_{AA}\left(\frac{r}{\sigma_{AA}}; \rho, T, x\right) \simeq g_0\left(\frac{r}{\sigma_{0A}}; \rho\sigma_{0A}^3, \frac{kT}{\epsilon_{0A}}\right)$$

$$g_{BB}\left(\frac{r}{\sigma_{BB}}; \rho, T, x\right) \simeq g_0\left(\frac{r}{\sigma_{0B}}; \rho\sigma_{0B}^3, \frac{kT}{\epsilon_{0B}}\right) \tag{11.31}$$

$$g_{AB} = \frac{1}{2}(g_{AA} + g_{BB})$$

so that two reference fluids are involved, denoted by the subscripts $0A$ and $0B$, then the van der Waals two-fluid mixing rules for the reference parameters to be used in the corresponding states calculations are obtained:[6]

$$\sigma_{0A}^3 = \sum_j x_j\sigma_{jA}^3 \qquad \sigma_{0B}^3 = \sum_j x_j\sigma_{jB}^3$$

$$\tag{11.32}$$

$$\epsilon_{0A}\sigma_{0A}^3 \sum_j x_j\epsilon_{jA}\sigma_{jA}^3 \qquad \epsilon_{0B}\sigma_{0B}^3 \sum_j x_j\epsilon_{jB}\sigma_{jB}^3 \, .$$

Similarly, the three-fluid theory assumes that[6]

$$
\begin{aligned}
g_{AA}\left(\frac{r}{\sigma_{AA}}; \rho, T, x\right) &\simeq g_0\left(\frac{r}{\sigma_{AA}}; \rho\sigma_{AA}^3, \frac{kT}{\epsilon_{AA}}\right) \\[2mm]
g_{BB}\left(\frac{r}{\sigma_{BB}}; \rho, T, x\right) &\simeq g_0\left(\frac{r}{\sigma_{BB}}; \rho\sigma_{BB}^3, \frac{kT}{\epsilon_{BB}}\right) \\[2mm]
g_{AB}\left(\frac{r}{\sigma_{AB}}; \rho, T, x\right) &\simeq g_0\left(\frac{r}{\sigma_{AB}}; \rho\sigma_{AB}^3, \frac{kT}{\epsilon_{AB}}\right).
\end{aligned}
\tag{11.33}
$$

The various n-fluid theories provide ways in which equations of state developed for pure fluids can be applied to mixtures. This can be done either in terms of the potential parameters themselves, or in terms of the mixing rules they provide for pseudocritical mixture properties when used in conjunction with Equations (11.12), as in Equations (11.27) to (11.29). Thus far, testing of these theories indicates that the two-fluid theory is not as accurate as the one-fluid theory. It appears that the three-fluid theory may be better than both the one- and two-fluid theories, but this has not yet been fully verified. We illustrate the use of the one-fluid theory to calculate the viscosity of a mixture in Example 11.4. As we see in this example, the viscosity is quite sensitive to the reference fluid chosen. This indeed is the same problem that caused a large deviation in the predicted value in Example 11.3. To do accurate corresponding states work, one must correct for size/shape and polar effects on the property. We will show two ways to do this in the next two sections. With size/shape and polar corrections added, corresponding states becomes a powerful way to predict transport properties as well as thermodynamic properties.

11.4 POLAR FLUIDS

Figure 11.1 and Table 11.1 indicate that polar and nonpolar fluids are not conformal to each other when treated in terms of two-parameter corresponding states. As we saw in Chapter 5, molecules exhibiting both dispersion and polar interactions can be made conformal if angle-averaged dipole moments are used. One would expect this to be valid only for slightly polar species that do not have directionally specific interactions, such as hydrogen bonding. Equations (5.36) through (5.39) illustrate the conformality of the nonpolar and polar Lennard-Jones-type potential when using F as a scaling or shape factor to include the angle-averaged polar contributions. Equation (5.39) lists the scaling factor, F, for the Lennard-Jones parameters as

Example 11.4   Using the one-fluid mixing rules, estimate the viscosity of a liquid mixture containing 22.5 mol% carbon tetrachloride and 77.5 mol% cyclohexane at 298.15 K and 1 atm.

While there are easier correlations and methods with which to do this problem, it serves adequately to illustrate the procedures of the one-fluid theory and points out the shortcoming of two-parameter corresponding states. From Appendix 11, we obtain the critical properties of the two pure fluids and tabulate them below. Note that we have calculated the values of V_c from the values of T_c and P_c using Equation (11.19).

	CCl_4	$c\text{-}C_6H_{14}$
T_c (K)	556.4	553.5
P_c (atm)	45.0	40.17
M (g/mol)	153.84	84.16
z_c	0.272	0.273
V_c (cm³/mol)	276.0	308.7

Next, we calculate the cross-interactions using Equations (11.29):

$$T_{cij} = \sqrt{(556.4)(553.5)} = 555.0 \text{ K}$$

$$V_{cij} = \frac{1}{8}[(276.0)^{1/3} + (308.7)^{1/3}]^3 = 292.0 \text{ cm}^3/\text{mol}.$$

We can then use Equations (11.28) and (11.27), in that order, to obtain pseudocritical constants for the mixture:

$$V_{cm} = x_1^2 V_{c11} + 2x_1 x_2 V_{c12} + x_2^2 V_{c22}$$

$$= (0.225)^2(276) + (2)(0.225)(0.775)(292) + (0.775)(308.7) = 301.2 \text{ cm}^3/\text{mol}$$

$$T_{cm} = \frac{x_1^2 T_{c11} V_{c11} + 2x_1 x_2 T_{c12} V_{c12} + x_2^2 T_{c22} V_{c22}}{V_{cm}} = 554.2 \text{ K}.$$

From these values, one can easily obtain $z_{cm} = 0.272$ and $P_{cm} = 41.15$ atm, this latter quantity being calculated from Equation (11.30). This yields a reduced temperature and pressure for the mixture of $T_r = 298.2/554.2 = 0.538$ and $P_r = 1/41.15 = 0.024$, respectively.

We must now turn to a reference fluid at the same reduced conditions. Viscosity can be made dimensionless using critical properties much as in Equation (11.3). Normally one writes the dimensionless viscosity as $\eta\xi$ where $\xi = V_c^{2/3}(T_c M)^{-1/2}$. There are various correlations available for pure fluids.[4,7] If we use methane as a reference fluid, we find $\eta\xi = 0.0555$. If we use pentane, we obtain $\eta\xi = 0.0817$. The discrepancy between these two values indicates a failure of the two-parameter corresponding states method for the fluids involved. This is primarily because of the difference in size and shape of the molecules in the mixture and the reference molecules.

We shall see how to correct for this shortly, but for now we may take the dimensionless viscosity and convert to the desired viscosity of the mixture. Using

Example 11.4   Continued

$$\xi = \frac{V_c^{2/3}}{\sqrt{T_{cm}M}} = \frac{301.2^{2/3}}{\sqrt{(554.2)(99.84)}} = 0.191 ,$$

where M is the mean molecular weight of the mixture, we obtain $\eta_{mix} = 0.29$ cP with methane as the reference and 0.43 cP with pentane as the reference. These values still do not compare favorably with the experimental value of 0.84 cP.

$$F = 1 + \frac{\frac{1}{3}\beta\mu_a^2\mu_b^2 + \mu_a^2\alpha_b + \mu_b^2\alpha_a}{4\epsilon^o\sigma^{o6}} ,\qquad(11.34)$$

which is then used to obtain effective LJ parameters via

$$\epsilon = \epsilon^o F^2 \text{ and } \sigma = \frac{\sigma^o}{F^{1/6}} .\qquad(11.35)$$

We now follow the same procedure used in Section 11.2 to develop the corresponding states relation in terms of critical properties. Thus,

$$P^+ = f'(T^+, V^+),\qquad(11.36)$$

and the critical point constraints of Equations (11.8) are again used to determine the relationship of the molecular parameters to the critical properties. Thus,

$$P_c^+ = \frac{P_c\sigma^3}{\epsilon} = \frac{P_c\sigma^{o3}}{\epsilon^o F_c^{5/2}} = C_3$$

$$T_c^+ = \frac{kT_c}{\epsilon} = \frac{kT_c}{\epsilon^o F_c^2} = C_1 \qquad(11.37)$$

$$V_c^+ = \frac{V_c}{\sigma^3} = \frac{V_c\sqrt{F_c}}{\sigma^{o3}} = C_2 .$$

Finally, the transformation to reduced properties can be made. We illustrate it here for P:

$$P^+ = \frac{P\sigma^3}{\epsilon} = \frac{P\sigma^{o3}}{\epsilon^o F^{5/2}} = \frac{PC_3 F_c^{5/2}}{P_c F^{5/2}} = P_r C_3\left(\frac{F_c}{F}\right)^{5/2}.\qquad(11.38)$$

Similar manipulations with T^+ and V^+ yield

$$P^+ = C_3 P_r' \text{ where } P_r' = \left(\frac{P}{P_c}\right)\left(\frac{F_c}{F}\right)^{5/2}$$

$$T^+ = C_1 T_r' \text{ where } T_r' = \left(\frac{T}{T_c}\right)\left(\frac{F_c}{F}\right)^2 \qquad(11.39)$$

$$V^+ = C_2 V_r' \quad \text{where} \quad V_r' = \left(\frac{V}{V_c}\right)\left(\frac{F_c}{F}\right)^{-1/2}.$$

Because the same form of the potential has been used here as was used with nonpolar fluids, exactly the same functionality holds for the polar equation of state as for the nonpolar, at least to the extent that the angle-averaged potentials adequately describe the thermophysical properties. Substitution of the above expressions into Equation (11.27) results in

$$P_r' = f(T_r', V_r'), \tag{11.40}$$

where f is exactly the same functionality that appears in Equation (11.14). Thus to the extent that an angle-averaged potential can be used for slightly polar fluids, their potential can be made conformal to the nonpolar potential with the appropriate adjustment of the reduced conditions. This method of making fluid potentials conformal to a reference fluid potential is the concept behind the introduction of so-called *shape factors*. In Equation (11.39), the factors of $(F_c/F)^x$, called shape factors, are used to further scale the critical constants. The physical approximation inherent in the mathematics is that the simple corresponding states theory is still valid if appropriate shape factors are used to modify or adjust the critical constants. This is equivalent to scaling the potential parameters with appropriate shape factors so that the pair potential is conformal to that of the reference fluid.

We reiterate that the above procedure is based on a spherically averaged potential. Use of these results for strongly polar fluids or molecules which contain angle-specific polar interactions is not advised.

11.5 CORRECTIONS TO TWO-PARAMETER CORRESPONDING STATES

As we have seen, two-parameter (ϵ and σ, or T_c and P_c) corresponding states theory is valid only for conformal fluids. It loses its effectiveness as molecular potentials deviate from spherical symmetry due to either molecular structure/geometry or polar/orientational effects. The method of shape factors is only one way to adjust the two constants to obtain conformality. Another method often used by engineers is a perturbation technique. The dimensionless property is expanded about a simple spherical reference fluid for which two-parameter corresponding states applies, and perturbational terms are added to correct for geometrical and polar effects. For example, consider a dimensionless property, J, expanded about a simple reference fluid at the same reduced temperature and pressure,

$$J(T_r, P_r) = J_0(T_r, P_r) + \left(\frac{\partial J}{\partial \alpha}\right)_{T, P, \beta}\bigg|_0 (\alpha - \alpha_0)$$

$$+ \left(\frac{\partial J}{\partial \beta}\right)_{T, P, \alpha}\bigg|_0 (\beta - \beta_0) + \dots ,$$

(11.41)

where the third and fourth parameters α and β represent the geometrical and polar contributions, respectively.[7] The derivatives indicate how much the property J changes due to these effects and can be approximated using two additional reference fluids. Let J_1 represent the property J of a nonspherical, nonpolar reference fluid at the same T_r and P_r under consideration. Similarly, let J_2 represent the property J of a nonspherical and polar reference fluid, again at the same T_r and P_r. Numerical approximations for the derivatives in terms of these two additional reference fluids are

$$\left(\frac{\partial J}{\partial \alpha}\right)_0 = \frac{J_1 - J_0}{\alpha_1 - \alpha_0}$$

(11.42)

and

$$\left(\frac{\partial J}{\partial \beta}\right)_0 = \frac{J_2 - J_2'}{\beta_1 - \beta_0},$$

(11.43)

where J_2' represents the property of a molecule geometrically identical to reference fluid 2 but without the polar interactions.[7] J_2' is calculated from the first two terms of Equation (11.41), replacing the derivative with Equation (11.42). Thus,

$$J_2' = J_0 + \left(\frac{J_1 - J_0}{\alpha_1 - \alpha_0}\right)(\alpha_2 - \alpha_0) .$$

(11.44)

Because the simple reference fluid is spherical and nonpolar, $\alpha_0 = 0$ and $\beta_0 = 0$. Similarly, because β_2' is also for a nonpolar (hypothetical) fluid, $\beta_2' = 0$. Without loss of generality, one can define $\beta_2 = 1$. This references all other β values to the reference fluid because only the ratio β/β_2 appears in Equation (11.41). Substitution of Equations (11.42) through (11.44) into Equation (11.41) yields,

$$J = J_0 + \frac{\alpha}{\alpha_1}(J_1 - J_0) + \beta\left[(J_2 - J_0) - \frac{\alpha_2}{\alpha_1}(J_1 - J_0)\right],$$

(11.45)

or more simply written as[7]

$$J(T_r, P_r) = J_0(T_r, P_r) + \alpha J^{(1)}(T_r, P_r) + \beta J^{(2)}(T_r, P_r), \qquad (11.46)$$

where

$$J^{(1)} = \frac{(J_1 - J_0)}{\alpha_1} \quad \text{and} \quad J^{(2)} = \left[(J_2 - J_0) - \frac{\alpha_2}{\alpha_1} (J_1 - J_0) \right]. \qquad (11.47)$$

Lee and Kesler[8] developed this method (LK) for nonpolar fluids using the acentric factor ω in place of the geometric parameter α. Thus their three-parameter corresponding state equation ($\beta = 0$) is written as

$$J = J_0 + \omega J^{(1)}. \qquad (11.48)$$

The LK method uses a Benedict–Webb–Rubin–Starling equation of state for the two reference fluids, methane and n-octane. In practice, one would calculate J_0 and J_1 at the desired T_r and P_r from the reference equations of state. The deviation function $J^{(1)}$ could then be obtained using Equation (11.47). Finally, J would be obtained from Equation (11.46) using ω as the proportionality constant that adds the deviation due to acentric interactions. Because the acentric factor ω is not a purely geometrical parameter (it is obtained from vapor pressure data which includes polar effects as well as size/shape interactions), Equation (11.48) works quite well even for substances that have some polar nature to them. It, however, does not predict the properties of strongly polar substances very well.

The use of Equation (11.48) is not restricted to thermodynamic properties, but also provides considerable improvement to the prediction of transport properties.[9-11] It is not the only way of correcting two-parameter corresponding states methods to make them more accurate for transport properties. For example, TRAPP[9] is a commonly used computer prediction code for transport properties that uses shape factors to modify the reduction parameters used to make the fluids conformal. We will not go into the details of TRAPP here, but continue our discussion of the perturbation method. There is still some question as to which approach works best for transport properties. In Examples 11.5 and 11.6 we illustrate the LK method as it is applied to both thermodynamic and transport properties. Table 11.3 contains values of z_0 and Table 11.4 contains values of the size/shape deviation term $z^{(1)}$. Similar tables for other thermodynamic properties can be found in Appendix 11.

Wilding and Rowley[7] have extended the LK method to include polar fluids. They retain α as a purely geometrical parameter in Equation (11.46) to completely separate size/shape effects from polar effects. α is calculated directly from the radius of gyration of the molecule, and β is regressed from a single liquid density value at a known condition. This extended Lee–Kesler (ELK), four-parameter, corresponding states method reduces to the LK method for

---

Example 11.5   Compare the molar volume of CO_2 at 282.8 K and 43.7 atm as predicted by two- and three-parameter (LK) corresponding states.

The critical properties for CO_2 from Appendix 11 are 304.1 K and 72.84 atm, respectively. These correspond to reduced conditions of $T_r = 0.93$ and $P_r = 0.60$. From Tables 11.3 and 11.4, we find $z_0 = 0.6635$ and $z^{(1)} = -0.1662$. The compressibility factor for two-parameter corresponding states is simply the z_0 value itself. For three-parameter corresponding states, we must also use the acentric factor, which for CO_2 is 0.239. Thus the predicted compressibility factor is

$$z = z_0 + \omega z^{(1)} = 0.6635 + (0.239)(-0.1662) = 0.6238.$$

The molar volume is then found from $V = zRT/P$, or

$$V = (z)(82.064)(282.8)/(43.7) = (z) \, 531.07 \text{ cm}^3/\text{mol}.$$

Finally, the values obtained are V (two-parameter) $= 352.4$ cm^3/mol and V (three-parameter) $= 331.3$ cm^3/mol.

---

nonpolar fluids because α was correlated against the radius of gyration in such a way that α and ω are very nearly identical for nonpolar fluids. Values of α and β for ELK are given in Table 11.2 for a number of polar fluids. The polar deviation term $J^{(2)}$ is determined from Equation (11.47) using an equation of state for water[12] to calculate properties for the polar reference fluid J_2.

ELK is primarily a computer method. The reference equations of state are coded so that all the thermodynamic properties can be generated for any given condition. For rapid hand calculations of properties, tables of the deviation functions $J^{(i)}$ have been prepared at regular T_r and P_r intervals using the procedure described above. The tables for z are reproduced here as Tables 11.3 to 11.5. The solid stair-step line in these tables is the usual location for the liquid-vapor transition. Shown as Table 11.6 are values of z_0 and deviation terms $z^{(i)}$ in the vicinity of this line for the opposite phase of that given in the primary tables. Access to these values permits convenient interpolation near a phase boundary as illustrated in Example 11.7. Agreement with experiment is generally quite good as shown in Example 11.7.

Other properties can also be determined analogously. In particular, other thermodynamic properties can be obtained from exact thermodynamic relations with the compressibility factor. However, when using ELK to calculate enthalpies, entropies, or fugacity coefficients, the β_H values listed in Table 11.2 should be used instead of the volumetric parameter β. Transport property tables can also be developed. Tables similar to Tables 11.3 to 11.5 are also available for enthalpy, fugacity, entropy,[13] and viscosity[10] in Appendix 11. Finally, we mention that other parameters have also been developed for four-parameter corresponding states methods which also represent fluid properties quite well. For example, ELK is very similar to a method developed by Wu and Stiel[14] which also uses

Example 11.6 Calculate the viscosity of toluene at 395.2 K and 30.0 MPa using both two- and three-parameter corresponding states. Compare these values with the experimental value of 0.295 cP.

We use essentially an LK method for the three-parameter corresponding states calculation. It uses methane and octane as the two reference fluids.[10] The conditions given in the problem statement correspond to reduced conditions of $T_r = 0.668$ and $P_r = 7.32$. From the charts in Appendix 11, we find the simple-fluid and deviation values at these conditions to be $(\eta\xi)_0 = 10.119 \times 10^6$ and $(\eta\xi)^{(1)} = 6.075 \times 10^6$, respectively. (Actually these values were taken from the computer program that generated the values in Appendix 11). While only the first value is required for the two-parameter calculation, the two values must be combined to obtain the three-parameter corresponding states dimensionless viscosity:

$$(\eta\xi) = (\eta\xi)_0 + \omega\,(\eta\xi)^{(1)} = 10.119 \times 10^6 + (0.263)(6.057 \times 10^6) = 1.17 \times 10^7.$$

For use with this method, the parameter ξ is defined as

$$\xi = \left(\frac{RT_cN_0^2}{P_c^4M^3}\right)^{\frac{1}{6}}.$$

Care must be taken with the units here, but if MKS units are used throughout, no problem arises. For toluene, we find

$$\xi = \left(\frac{(8.314)(591.8)(6.022 \times 10^{23})^2}{(4.1 \times 10^6)^4(0.9214)^3}\right)^{\frac{1}{6}} = 4479\ \frac{\text{m·s}}{\text{kg}}\ .$$

Finally, we determine η by multiplying the appropriate dimensionless value $(\eta\xi)$ by ξ. For two-parameter corresponding states this gives $\eta = 0.226$ cP; for three-parameter corresponding states, $\eta = 0.259$ cP which is about 12% below the experimental value. Incidently, if the value of α from ELK is used instead of ω, the final result is 0.316 cP, or about 7% higher than the experimental value.

methane, octane, and water as the three reference fluids, but uses the acentric factor and the Stiel polarity factor as the third and fourth parameters. Both methods work about equally well.

The corresponding states method has been one of the most important advances in thermodynamics in the recent past. It allows replacement of analytical or formal solutions of the configurational partition function with experimental data for a reference fluid. Care must be used to ensure that the reference and test fluids are conformal, but the procedure for finding the test fluid property from a corresponding state of the reference fluid is quite straightforward in most cases. Corresponding states is a powerful technique with a sound basis in statistical mechanics and many as of yet untapped potentials.

TABLE 11.2 Values of α, β and β_H for Polar Compounds

No.	Formula	Compound	α	β	β_h
1	NO_2	Nitrogen dioxide	0.0742	0.711	2.433
2	HBr	Hydrogen bromide	0.0048	0.078	0.232
3	HCl	Hydrogen chloride	0.0104	0.483	0.355
4	HI	Hydrogen iodide	0.0042	0.009	0.122
5	H_2O	Water	0.0250	1.000	1.000
6	H_3N	Ammonia	0.0378	0.794	0.680
7	H_4N_2	Hydrazine	0.0801	0.407	0.774
8	CCl_4	Carbon tetrachloride	0.2522	−0.048	−0.204
9	$CHCl_3$	Chloroform	0.2242	−0.067	−0.026
10	CHN	Hydrogen cyanide	0.0268	1.706	1.154
11	CHF_3	Trifluoromethane	0.1444	0.467	0.352
12	CH_2Cl_2	Dichloromethane	0.1464	0.333	0.167
13	CH_2O	Formaldehyde	0.0596	1.169	0.666
14	CH_3Cl	Methyl chloride	0.0757	0.313	0.233
15	CH_4O	Methyl alcohol	0.0819	0.909	1.536
16	CH_4S	Methyl mercaptan	0.0874	0.189	0.201
17	CH_5N	Methylamine	0.0911	0.467	0.645
18	C_2H_3N	Acetonitrile	0.1033	1.556	0.661
19	$C_2H_4Cl_2$	1,1-Dichloroethane	0.2063	0.008	0.101
20	$C_2H_4Cl_2$	1,2-Dichloroethane	0.1926	0.160	0.271
21	C_2H_4O	Acetaldehyde	0.1192	0.778	0.565
22	$C_2H_4O_2$	Acetic acid	0.1689	1.041	0.858
23	C_2H_6O	Ethyl alcohol	0.1383	0.494	1.603
24	C_2H_6O	Dimethyl ether	0.1280	0.188	0.225
25	C_2H_6S	Dimethyl sulfide	0.2270	0.063	−0.122
26	C_2H_6S	Ethyl mercaptan	0.1462	0.164	0.137
27	C_3H_6O	Acetone	0.1822	0.603	0.396
28	$C_3H_6O_2$	Ethyl formate	0.1944	0.317	0.287
29	$C_3H_6O_2$	Methyl acetate	0.1936	0.380	0.415
30	C_3H_8O	Propyl alcohol	0.1818	0.396	1.425
31	C_3H_8O	Isopropyl alcohol	0.1809	0.465	1.553
32	C_3H_9N	n-Propylamine	0.1868	0.214	0.376
33	$C_4H_6O_3$	Acetic anhydride	0.2638	−0.020	2.006
34	$C_4H_8O_2$	Ethyl acetate	0.2411	0.343	0.390
35	C_4H_8O	Methyl ethyl ketone	0.2204	0.437	0.336
36	$C_4H_{10}O$	n-Butyl alcohol	0.2288	0.279	1.175
37	$C_4H_8O_2$	Isobutyric acid	0.2404	0.696	1.229
38	$C_4H_8O_2$	Methyl propionate	0.2366	0.294	0.371
39	$C_4H_{10}O$	Ethyl ether	0.2204	0.165	0.199
40	$C_4H_{11}N$	Diethyl amine	0.2225	0.213	0.257
41	$C_5H_{10}O$	Methyl isopropyl ketone	0.2479	0.149	0.263
42	$C_5H_{10}O$	2-Pentanone	0.2693	0.131	0.244
43	C_6H_5Br	Bromobenzene	0.2535	0.118	−0.020

Table 11.2 Continued

No.	Formula	Compound	α	β	β_h
44	C_6H_5Cl	Chlorobenzene	0.2634	0.065	−0.050
45	C_6H_6O	Phenol	0.2615	−0.244	0.576
46	C_6H_7N	Aniline	0.2455	0.178	0.448
47	$C_6H_{12}O$	Cyclohexanol	0.2497	0.539	0.896
48	$C_6H_{12}O$	Methyl isobutyl ketone	0.2638	0.215	0.388
49	$C_6H_{14}O$	Diisopropyl ether	0.2749	−0.027	0.203
50	C_7H_8O	m-Cresol	0.2909	0.179	0.529
51	C_7H_8O	o-Cresol	0.2786	−0.132	0.503
52	C_7H_8O	p-Cresol	0.2806	−0.251	0.726

Reproduced by permission from Wilding, W.V., et al. *Int. J. Themophys.* **1987,** *8,* 717–735.

Example 11.7   Calculate the vapor and liquid compressibility factors of saturated ammonia at 300 K. The vapor pressure of ammonia at this temperature is 10.42 atm.

The critical temperature and pressure for ammonia are T_c = 405.6 K and P_c = 111.3 atm. Saturation therefore corresponds to the reduced conditions:

$$T_r = \frac{T}{T_c} = \frac{300 \text{ K}}{405.6 \text{ K}} = 0.7398 \qquad P_r = \frac{P}{P_c} = \frac{10.42 \text{ atm}}{111.3 \text{ atm}} = 0.0936.$$

At the conditions of this example the entries in Tables 11.3 to 11.5 are for the vapor phase, and double interpolation within the table can be used to estimate values for z_0, $z^{(1)}$, and $z^{(2)}$, namely,

$$z_0 = 0.9181 \qquad z^{(1)} = -0.0771 \qquad z^{(2)} = -0.0405.$$

The values of α and β are obtained from Table 11.2. They are α = 0.0378 and β = 0.794. Finally, these values are substituted into Equation (7.39) to obtain the saturated vapor compressibility factor:

$$z = 0.9181 + (0.0378)(-0.0771) + (0.794)(-0.0405) = 0.8830.$$

This is in excellent agreement with the experimental value of 0.8836.

Calculation of the liquid compressibility factor requires use of the auxiliary table, Table 11.6, which contains values for the phase opposite that of the primary table in the phase transition region. Again we use a double interpolation within the table to obtain:

$$z_0 = 0.00159 \qquad z^{(1)} = -0.0068 \qquad z^{(2)} = -0.0048.$$

When substituted into Equation (11.39), these values yield:

$$z = 0.00159 + (0.0378)(-0.0068) + (0.794)(-0.0048) = 0.0118.$$

This is also in excellent agreement with the experimental value of 0.0118 for saturated liquid ammonia.

TABLE 11.3 Compressibility Factor for the Simple Reference Fluid, Z_0

Z_0								P_r						
T_r	0.01	0.05	0.10	0.20	0.40	0.60	0.80	1.00	1.20	1.50	2.00	4.00	7.00	10.00
0.45	0.0022	0.0110	0.0221	0.0442	0.0882	0.1322	0.1762	0.2200	0.2638	0.3294	0.4384	0.8704	1.5077	2.1338
0.50	0.0021	0.0103	0.0207	0.0413	0.0825	0.1326	0.1647	0.2056	0.2465	0.3077	0.4092	0.8110	1.4017	1.9801
0.55	0.9804	0.0098	0.0195	0.0390	0.0778	0.1166	0.1553	0.1939	0.2323	0.2899	0.3853	0.7620	1.3137	1.8520
0.60	0.9849	0.0093	0.0186	0.0371	0.0741	0.1109	0.1476	0.1842	0.2207	0.2753	0.3657	0.7213	1.2398	1.7440
0.65	0.9881	0.9377	0.0178	0.0356	0.0710	0.1063	0.1415	0.1765	0.2113	0.2634	0.3495	0.6872	0.1773	1.6519
0.70	0.9904	0.9504	0.8958	0.0344	0.0687	0.1027	0.1366	0.1703	0.2038	0.2538	0.3364	0.6588	1.1241	1.5729
0.75	0.9922	0.9598	0.9165	0.0336	0.0670	0.1001	0.1330	0.1656	0.1981	0.2464	0.3260	0.6352	1.0787	1.5047
0.80	0.9935	0.9669	0.9319	0.8539	0.0661	0.0985	0.1307	0.1626	0.1942	0.2411	0.3182	0.6160	1.0400	1.4456
0.85	0.9946	0.9725	0.9436	0.8810	0.0061	0.0983	0.1300	0.1614	0.1924	0.2382	0.3132	0.6007	1.0071	1.3943
0.90	0.9954	0.9768	0.9528	0.9015	0.7800	0.1006	0.1321	0.1630	0.1935	0.2383	0.3114	0.5882	0.9793	1.3496
0.93	0.9959	0.9790	0.9573	0.9115	0.8059	0.6635	0.1359	0.1664	0.1963	0.2405	0.3122	0.5841	0.9648	1.3257
0.95	0.9961	0.9803	0.9600	0.9174	0.8206	0.6967	0.1410	0.1705	0.1998	0.2432	0.3138	0.5815	0.9561	1.3108
0.97	0.9963	0.9815	0.9652	0.9227	0.8338	0.7240	0.5580	0.1779	0.2055	0.2474	0.3164	0.5796	0.9480	1.2968
0.98	0.9965	0.9821	0.9637	0.9253	0.8398	0.7360	0.5887	0.1844	0.2097	0.2503	0.3182	0.5719	0.9442	1.2901
0.99	0.9966	0.9826	0.9648	0.9277	0.8455	0.7471	0.6138	0.1954	0.2154	0.2538	0.3204	0.5784	0.9406	1.2835
1.00	0.9967	0.9832	0.9659	0.9300	0.8509	0.7574	0.6353	0.2889	0.2237	0.2583	0.3229	0.5780	0.9372	1.2772
1.01	0.9968	0.9837	0.9669	0.9322	0.8561	0.7671	0.6542	0.4648	0.2370	0.2640	0.3260	0.5778	0.9339	1.2710
1.02	0.9969	0.9842	0.9679	0.9343	0.8610	0.7761	0.6710	0.5146	0.2629	0.2715	0.3297	0.5778	0.9307	1.2650
1.05	0.9971	0.9855	0.9707	0.9401	0.8743	0.8002	0.7130	0.6026	0.4437	0.3131	0.3452	0.5790	0.9222	1.2481
1.10	0.9975	0.9874	0.9747	0.9485	0.8930	0.8323	0.7649	0.6880	0.5984	0.4580	0.3953	0.5851	0.9110	1.2232
1.20	0.9981	0.9904	0.9808	0.9611	0.9205	0.8779	0.8330	0.7858	0.7363	0.6605	0.5605	0.6155	0.8990	1.1844
1.30	0.9985	0.9926	0.9852	0.9702	0.9396	0.9083	0.8764	0.8438	0.8111	0.7624	0.6908	0.6681	0.8998	1.1580
1.50	0.9991	0.9954	0.9909	0.9818	0.9636	0.9456	0.9278	0.9103	0.8933	0.8689	0.8328	0.7884	0.9297	1.1339
2.00	0.9997	0.9986	0.9972	0.9944	0.9892	0.9842	0.9796	0.9754	0.9715	0.9664	0.9599	0.9611	1.0328	1.1516
2.50	0.9999	0.9997	0.9944	0.9989	0.9981	0.9975	0.9971	0.9969	0.9970	0.9976	0.9996	1.0215	1.0866	1.1763
3.00	1.0000	1.0002	1.0004	1.0008	1.0018	1.0030	1.0043	1.0057	1.0074	1.0101	1.0153	1.0446	1.1075	1.1848
4.00	1.0001	1.0005	1.0010	1.0021	1.0043	1.0066	1.0090	1.0115	1.0140	1.0179	1.0249	1.0567	1.1136	1.1773

TABLE 11.4 Size/Shape Deviation in Compressibility Factor, $z^{(1)}$

T_r \ P_r	0.01	0.05	0.10	0.20	0.40	0.60	0.80	1.00	1.20	1.50	2.00	4.00	7.00	10.00
0.45	−0.0009	−0.0047	−0.0094	−0.0187	−0.0374	−0.0560	−0.0745	−0.0929	−0.1113	−0.1387	−0.1480	−0.3612	−0.6162	−0.8606
0.50	−0.0009	−0.0045	−0.0090	−0.0181	−0.0360	−0.0539	−0.0716	−0.0893	−0.1069	−0.1330	−0.1762	−0.3440	−0.5831	−0.8099
0.55	−0.0296	−0.0043	−0.0086	−0.0172	−0.0343	−0.0513	−0.0682	−0.0849	−0.1015	−0.1263	−0.1669	−0.3238	−0.5446	−0.7521
0.60	−0.0203	−0.0041	−0.0082	−0.0164	−0.0326	−0.0487	−0.0646	−0.0803	−0.0960	−0.1192	−0.1572	−0.3026	−0.5047	−0.6929
0.65	−0.0137	−0.0680	−0.0078	−0.0156	−0.0309	−0.0461	−0.0611	−0.0759	−0.0906	−0.1123	−0.1476	−0.2816	−0.4653	−0.6346
0.70	−0.0093	−0.0502	−0.0948	−0.0148	−0.0294	−0.0438	−0.0579	−0.0718	−0.0855	−0.1057	−0.1385	−0.2611	−0.4270	−0.5785
0.75	−0.0064	−0.0339	−0.0739	−0.0143	−0.0282	−0.0417	−0.0550	−0.0681	−0.0808	−0.0996	−0.1298	−0.2414	−0.3901	−0.5250
0.80	−0.0044	−0.0228	−0.0487	−0.1097	−0.0272	−0.0401	−0.0526	−0.0648	−0.0767	−0.0940	−0.1217	−0.2222	−0.3545	−0.4740
0.85	−0.0029	−0.0152	−0.0319	−0.0718	−0.0268	−0.0391	−0.0509	−0.0622	−0.0731	−0.0888	−0.1138	−0.2032	−0.3201	−0.4254
0.90	−0.0019	−0.0099	−0.0205	−0.0442	−0.1118	−0.0396	−0.0503	−0.0604	−0.0701	−0.0840	−0.1059	−0.1837	−0.2862	−0.3788
0.93	−0.0015	−0.0075	−0.0154	−0.0326	−0.0763	−0.1592	−0.0514	−0.0602	−0.0687	−0.0810	−0.1007	−0.1718	−0.2661	−0.3516
0.95	−0.0012	−0.0062	−0.0126	−0.0262	−0.0589	−0.1110	−0.0540	−0.0607	−0.0678	−0.0788	−0.0967	−0.1634	−0.2526	−0.3339
0.97	−0.0010	−0.0050	−0.0101	−0.0208	−0.0450	−0.0770	−0.1623	−0.0623	−0.0669	−0.0759	−0.0921	−0.1545	−0.2391	−0.3163
0.98	−0.0009	−0.0044	−0.0090	−0.0184	−0.0390	−0.0641	−0.1100	−0.0641	−0.0661	−0.0740	−0.0893	−0.1499	−0.2322	−0.3075
0.99	−0.0008	−0.0039	−0.0079	−0.0161	−0.0335	−0.0531	−0.0796	−0.0680	−0.0646	−0.0715	−0.0861	−0.1451	−0.2254	−0.2989
1.00	−0.0007	−0.0034	−0.0069	−0.0140	−0.0285	−0.0435	−0.0588	−0.0718	−0.0609	−0.0678	−0.0824	−0.1401	−0.2185	−0.2902
1.01	−0.0006	−0.0030	−0.0060	−0.0120	−0.0240	−0.0351	−0.0429	−0.0223	−0.0473	−0.0621	−0.0778	−0.1349	−0.2116	−0.2816
1.02	−0.0005	−0.0026	−0.0051	−0.0102	−0.0198	−0.0277	−0.0303	−0.0062	−0.0227	−0.0524	−0.0722	−0.1295	−0.2047	−0.2731
1.05	−0.0003	−0.0015	−0.0029	−0.0054	−0.0092	−0.0097	−0.0032	0.0220	0.1059	0.0451	−0.0432	−0.1523	−0.1835	−0.3641
1.10	0.0000	0.0000	0.0001	0.0007	0.0038	0.0106	0.0236	0.0476	0.0897	0.1630	0.0698	−0.0751	−0.1469	−0.2056
1.20	0.0004	0.0019	0.0040	0.0084	0.0190	0.0326	0.0499	0.0719	0.0991	0.1477	0.1990	0.0304	−0.0678	−0.1231
1.30	0.0006	0.0030	0.0061	0.0125	0.0267	0.0429	0.0612	0.0819	0.1048	0.1420	0.1991	0.1435	0.0176	−0.0423
1.50	0.0008	0.0039	0.0078	0.0158	0.0323	0.0497	0.0677	0.0864	0.1055	0.1345	0.1806	0.2525	0.1717	0.1058
2.00	0.0008	0.0039	0.0078	0.0155	0.0310	0.0464	0.0617	0.0767	0.0916	0.1133	0.1476	0.2517	0.3097	0.3096
2.50	0.0007	0.0034	0.0068	0.0135	0.0268	0.0399	0.0528	0.0654	0.0778	0.0958	0.1245	0.2189	0.3052	0.3475
3.00	0.0006	0.0029	0.0059	0.0117	0.0232	0.0345	0.0456	0.0565	0.0672	0.0828	0.1076	0.1925	0.2817	0.3385
4.00	0.0005	0.0023	0.0046	0.0091	0.0182	0.0270	0.0357	0.0443	0.0527	0.0651	0.0849	0.1554	0.2378	0.2994

TABLE 11.5 Polar Deviation in Compressibility Factor, $Z^{(2)}$

T_r \ P_r	0.01	0.05	0.10	0.20	0.40	0.60	0.80	1.00	1.20	1.50	2.00	4.00	7.00	10.0
0.45	−0.0005	−0.0027	−0.0054	−0.0109	−0.0218	−0.0328	−0.0439	−0.0550	−0.0662	−0.0830	−0.1114	−0.2275	−0.4084	−0.5941
0.50	−0.0005	−0.0027	−0.0055	−0.0110	−0.0220	−0.0331	−0.0442	−0.0553	−0.0664	−0.0832	−0.1113	−0.2249	−0.3986	−0.5750
0.55	−0.0222	−0.0027	−0.0055	−0.0109	−0.0218	−0.0328	−0.0433	−0.0547	−0.0657	−0.0821	−0.1096	−0.2200	−0.3866	−0.5540
0.60	−0.0130	−0.0027	−0.0054	−0.0107	−0.0215	−0.0322	−0.0430	−0.0537	−0.0644	−0.0805	−0.1073	−0.2141	−0.3736	−0.5326
0.65	−0.0073	−0.0434	−0.0053	−0.0106	−0.0211	−0.0316	−0.0421	−0.0525	−0.0630	−0.0786	−0.1046	−0.2077	−0.3604	−0.5115
0.70	−0.0043	−0.0278	−0.0605	−0.0103	−0.0207	−0.0309	−0.0412	−0.0514	−0.0615	−0.0767	−0.1019	−0.2012	−0.3473	−0.4911
0.75	−0.0025	−0.0154	−0.0400	−0.0102	−0.0203	−0.0303	−0.0403	−0.0502	−0.0601	−0.0748	−0.0992	−0.1948	−0.3345	−0.4714
0.80	−0.0015	−0.0087	−0.0212	−0.0626	−0.0199	−0.0298	−0.0395	−0.0492	−0.0588	−0.0730	−0.0966	−0.1884	−0.3220	−0.4525
0.85	−0.0008	−0.0048	−0.0113	−0.0314	−0.0198	−0.0294	−0.0389	−0.0483	−0.0576	−0.0713	−0.0940	−0.1821	−0.3096	−0.4342
0.90	−0.0004	−0.0024	−0.0057	−0.0151	−0.0546	−0.0294	−0.0386	−0.0476	−0.0566	−0.0698	−0.0915	−0.1756	−0.2974	−0.4163
0.93	−0.0003	−0.0015	−0.0035	−0.0093	−0.0311	−0.0910	−0.0388	−0.0475	−0.0561	−0.0689	−0.0899	−0.1715	−0.2900	−0.4057
0.95	−0.0002	−0.0010	−0.0024	−0.0064	−0.0212	−0.0537	−0.0395	−0.0476	−0.0559	−0.0683	−0.0887	−0.1687	−0.2850	−0.3988
0.97	−0.0001	−0.0006	−0.0014	−0.0041	−0.0140	−0.0326	−0.0895	−0.0482	−0.0558	−0.0676	−0.0875	−0.1658	−0.2800	−0.3918
0.98	−0.0001	−0.0004	−0.0010	−0.0032	−0.0111	−0.0253	−0.0555	−0.0490	−0.0558	−0.0672	−0.0868	−0.1643	−0.2775	−0.3883
0.99	0.0001	−0.0002	−0.0007	−0.0023	−0.0086	−0.0194	−0.0378	−0.0506	−0.0558	−0.0668	−0.0860	−0.1628	−0.2750	−0.3849
1.00	0.0000	−0.0001	−0.0003	−0.0015	−0.0064	−0.0145	−0.0263	−0.0581	−0.0556	−0.0662	−0.0852	−0.1612	−0.2724	−0.3814
1.01	0.0000	0.0001	0.0000	−0.0008	−0.0044	−0.0104	−0.0179	−0.0172	−0.0546	−0.0654	−0.0842	−0.1595	−0.2699	−0.3780
1.02	0.0000	0.0002	0.0002	−0.0002	−0.0027	−0.0050	−0.0114	−0.0079	−0.0441	−0.0640	−0.0830	−0.1578	−0.2673	−0.3745
1.05	0.0001	0.0005	0.0009	0.0014	0.0013	0.0007	0.0012	0.0072	0.0296	−0.0439	−0.0774	−0.1523	−0.2594	−0.3641
1.10	0.0002	0.0009	0.0017	0.0031	0.0055	0.0080	0.0116	0.0180	0.0292	0.0380	−0.0460	−0.1412	−0.2456	−0.3468
1.20	0.0002	0.0012	0.0024	0.0050	0.0092	0.0137	0.0183	0.0245	0.0311	0.0411	0.0363	−0.1072	−0.2156	−0.3120
1.30	0.0002	0.0013	0.0026	0.0051	0.0101	0.0150	0.0199	0.0249	0.0300	0.0371	0.0424	−0.0595	−0.1820	−0.2770
1.50	0.0002	0.0012	0.0023	0.0047	0.0092	0.0136	0.0178	0.0213	0.0253	0.0299	0.0345	−0.0023	−0.1155	−0.2106
2.00	0.0001	0.0005	0.0014	0.0027	0.0059	0.0079	0.0103	0.0124	0.0143	0.0165	0.0187	0.0076	−0.0464	−0.1130
2.50	0.0001	0.0004	0.0007	0.0015	0.0029	0.0042	0.0054	0.0065	0.0074	0.0084	0.0092	0.0006	−0.0363	−0.0844
3.00	0.0000	0.0002	0.0009	0.0007	0.0014	0.0020	0.0026	0.0030	0.0034	0.0036	0.0035	−0.0048	−0.0344	−0.0735
4.00	0.0000	0.0000	0.0000	0.0000	0.0000	0.0001	−0.0003	−0.0003	−0.0005	−0.0009	−0.0020	−0.0104	−0.0329	−0.0624

TABLE 11.6   Auxiliary (Opposite Phase) Compressibility Factors

Z_0–aux	P_r						
T_r	0.01	0.05	0.10	0.20	0.40	0.60	0.80
0.45	0.9645	0.8222					
0.50	0.9740	0.8695					
0.55	0.0020	0.8999	0.7993				
0.60	0.0019	0.9211	0.8405				
0.65	0.0018	0.0089	0.8707	0.7367			
0.70	0.0017	0.0086	0.0172	0.7805	0.5498		
0.75	0.0018	0.0085	0.0169	0.8181	0.6122		
0.80	0.0020	0.0086	0.0168	0.0332	0.6659	0.4746	
0.85		0.0092	0.0174	0.0336	0.7222	0.5346	
0.90			0.0203	0.0364	0.0685	0.6040	0.4034
0.93				0.0422	0.0735	0.1047	0.4439
0.95				0.0528	0.0822	0.1116	0.4853
0.97					0.1092	0.1312	0.1532
0.98					0.1527	0.1615	0.1703
0.99					0.3276	0.2800	0.2324

$z^{(1)}$–aux	P_r						
T_r	0.01	0.05	0.10	0.20	0.40	0.60	0.80
0.45	−0.0582	−0.2899					
0.50	−0.0445	−0.2210					
0.55	−0.0009	−0.1429	−0.2844				
0.60	−0.0008	−0.0949	−0.1856				
0.65	−0.0008	−0.0039	−0.1261	−0.2422			
0.70	−0.0008	−0.0038	−0.0075	−0.1684	−0.3158		
0.75	−0.0009	−0.0037	−0.0072	−0.1297	−0.2200		
0.80	−0.0013	−0.0040	−0.0073	−0.0139	−0.1683	−0.2187	
0.85		−0.0052	−0.0083	−0.0144	−0.1504	−0.1693	
0.90			−0.0125	−0.0179	−0.0286	−0.1580	−0.1465
0.93				−0.0256	−0.0340	−0.0424	−0.1418
0.95				−0.0397	−0.0444	−0.0490	−0.1532
0.97					−0.0785	−0.0714	−0.0643
0.98					−0.1361	−0.1095	−0.0828
0.99					−0.3809	−0.2715	−0.1621

$z^{(2)}$–aux	P_r						
T_r	0.01	0.05	0.10	0.20	0.40	0.60	0.80
0.45	−0.0708	−0.3531					
0.50	−0.0399	−0.1990					
0.55	−0.0005	−0.1101	−0.2200				
0.60	−0.0005	−0.0665	−0.1326				
0.65	−0.0005	−0.0026	−0.0860	−0.1710			

Table 11.6   Continued

$z^{(2)}$—aux	P_r						
T_r	0.01	0.05	0.10	0.20	0.40	0.60	0.80
0.70	−0.0005	−0.0026	−0.0052	−0.1199	−0.2388		
0.75	−0.0006	−0.0026	−0.0051	−0.0885	−0.1770		
0.80	−0.0009	−0.0028	−0.0052	−0.0100	−0.1334	−0.2012	
0.85		−0.0028	−0.0052	−0.0101	−0.1019	−0.1567	
0.90			−0.0064	−0.0110	−0.0202	−0.1196	−0.1655
0.93				−0.0141	−0.0220	−0.0301	−0.1393
0.95				−0.0163	−0.0240	−0.0317	−0.1213
0.97					−0.0297	−0.0360	−0.0423
0.98					−0.0458	−0.0465	−0.0472
0.99					−0.0945	−0.0797	−0.0649

REFERENCES

1. Reed, T.M., and Gubbins, K.E., *Applied Statistical Mechanics,* McGraw-Hill, New York, 1973.

2. Su, G.-J., and Chang, C.-H., "Generalized equation of state for real gases," *Ind. Eng. Chem.* **1946**, *38,* 802–806.

3. Brown, G.G., Souders, M., Jr., and Smith, R.L., "Pressure-volume-temperature relations of paraffin hydrocarbons," *Ind. Eng. Chem.* **1931**, *24,* 513–515.

4. Reid, R.C., Prausnitz, J.M., and Poling, B.C., *The Properties of Gases and Liquids,* 4th ed., McGraw-Hill, New York, 1987.

5. Nelson, L.C., and Obert, E.F., "Generalized compressibility charts," *Chem. Eng.* **1954**, *61*(7), 205–206.

6. Lee, L.L., *Molecular Thermodynamics of Nonideal Fluids,* Butterworths, Boston, 1988.

7. Wilding, W.V., and Rowley, R.L., "A four-parameter corresponding-states method for the prediction of thermodynamic properties of polar and nonpolar fluids," *Int. J. Thermophys.* **1986**, *7,* 525–539.

8. Lee, B.I., and Kesler, M.G., "A generalized thermodynamic correlation based on three-parameter corresponding states," *AIChE J.* **1975**, *21,* 510–527.

9. Ely, J.F., and Hanley, H.J.M., "Prediction of transport properties. 1. Viscosity of fluids and mixtures," *Ind. Eng. Chem. Fund.* **1981**, *20,* 323–332.

10. Okeson, K.J., and Rowley, R.L., "A four-parameter corresponding-states method for prediction of Newtonian, pure-component viscosity," *Int. J. Thermophys.* **1991**, *12,* 119–136.

11. Teja, A.S., and Rice, P., "Generalized corresponding states method for the viscosities of liquid mixtures," *Ind. Eng. Chem. Fund.* **1981**, *20,* 77–81.

12. Haar, L., Gallagher, J.S., and Kell, G.S., *NBS/NRC Steam Tables,* Hemisphere, Washington, DC, 1984.

13. Wilding, W.V., Johnson, J K., and Rowley, R.L., "Thermodynamic properties and vapor pressures of polar fluids from a four-parameter corresponding-states method," *Int. J. Thermophys.* **1987**, *8,* 717–735.

14. Wu, G.Z.A., and Stiel, L.I., "A generalized equation of state for the thermodynamic properties of polar fluids," *AIChE J.* **1985**, *31,* 1632–1644.

15. Perry, R.H., and Green, D.W., *Chemical Engineers' Handbook,* 6th ed., McGraw-Hill, New York, 1984.

PROBLEMS

CORRESPONDING STATES

1. The surface tension of saturated liquid argon at 84.1 K is 12 dynes/cm.[1] Calculate the surface tension of saturated liquid nitrogen at the same reduced temperature using simple corresponding states. At what temperature is the nitrogen in a corresponding state?

2. The following viscosities have been reported for krypton:

$T(K)$	$\eta(\mu P)$
134.4	117.8
152.5	133.0
176.0	153.4
200.9	174.8
225.7	196.1

   Using the above information, determine the viscosity of methane at 100 K.

3. The melting temperature of pure solid xenon varies with pressure as given in Table 11.A.[1] Using the corresponding states principle, determine the melting temperatures of the pure solids shown in Table 11.B at the pressures listed in that table. Measured melting temperatures are also given in Table 11.B. Discuss discrepancies between calculated and measured values.

TABLE 11.A

P (atm)	T_{mp} (K)
271	171.4
1275	207.4
2050	232.8
2692	252.8

TABLE 11.B

Molecule	P (atm)	T_{mp} (K)
Argon	967.8	106.3
Nitrogen	967.8	82.3
Krypton	2692	185.5
Methane	2692	146.4

4. The dimensionless product $(PD)^+$ for Ar has the values given below as a function of dimensionless temperature. Here, D is the self-diffusion coefficient in units of cm²/s. From these data, determine D for Kr at 1 atm and 360.7 K and compare your

results to the experimental value of 0.130 cm²/s. Explain why your calculated value agrees or disagrees with the experimental value.

T^+	$(PD)^+$
0.23	0.02
1.23	0.21
2.46	0.80
3.04	1.18

5. Estimate the density of CO at 159.5 K and 120.8 atm.

6. Use the mathematical requirements for the critical point, Equations (11.8), to show that for the van der Waals equation of state, $b = V_c/3$ and $a = 9RT_cV_c/8$. Using these values and the value of P_c that these imply, show that the van der Waals equation can be written as

$$\left(P_r + \frac{3}{V_r^2}\right)(3\overline{V}_r - 1) = 8T_r.$$

What is the value of z_c for all van der Waals fluids? Which of the fluids in Table 11.1 are most conformal with the van der Waals fluid?

7. The Antoine equation

$$\log P^* = A - \frac{B}{T + C}$$

is often used to correlate vapor pressure data. The Antoine constants for cyclohexane are $A = 6.84498$, $B = 1203.526$, and $C = 222.863$ where T is given in °C and P^* is in mm Hg. Convert this equation to a corresponding states correlation of the form

$$\log P_r^* = A' - \frac{B'}{T_r + C'}$$

and determine A', B', and C' from the values of A, B, and C given for cyclohexane. Then use the new equation to calculate the vapor pressure of benzene at 300 K and 400 K. The experimental values are 103.63 and 2649.2 mm Hg, respectively.

8. An approximation for the heat of vaporization ΔH_{vap} can be made from the Clausius–Clapeyron equation

$$\frac{d\ln P^*}{dT} = \frac{\Delta \overline{H}_{vap}}{RT^2}.$$

Use the general correlation developed in Problem 7 to obtain a generalized correlation for the heat of vaporization as a function of reduced properties. Again using cyclohexane as the reference fluid, estimate the heat of vaporization of benzene at the normal boiling point, that is, 455.0 K. The experimental value is 30.7 kJ/mol.

9. *n*-Hexane is compressed isothermally at 609 K from 38.62 atm to 148.6 atm. Compute the compressibility factor at the initial and final states. Why are these two values so similar?

ONE-FLUID THEORY

10. Use the one-fluid mixing rules to predict the molar volume of a 80 mol% methane + 20 mol% butane mixture at 25°C and 39.1 atm.

11. Using the information given in Problem 4 and the one-fluid mixing rules, estimate the self-diffusion coefficient in cm²/s for the hypothetical pure fluid which represents a 50–50 mol% mixture of Kr and Xe at 360.7 K. Note that in a binary mixture we have self diffusion coefficients of each component as well as the mutual diffusion coefficient. The coefficient calculated in this problem is none of these, but rather an average self-diffusion coefficient for the mixture itself.

12. Estimate as best you can, the expected viscosity of a 25 mol% mixture of hexane in CCl₄ at 300 K. Use Kr as the reference fluid and the data given in Problem 2.

POLAR FLUIDS

13. Estimate the vapor pressure of acetone at 140°C using experimental data for krypton available from *the Chemical Engineers' Handbook*.[15]

14. Determine the compressibility factor of a 20 mol% mixture of component A in B at 400 K and 10^8 dynes/cm² pressure if pure A has a compressibility factor of 0.8 when in a corresponding state. Then determine the T^+ and P^+ of this state. The molecular parameters are:

component A: $\epsilon°/k = 200$ K $\sigma = 4.0$ Å $\mu = 2.0 \times 10^{-6}$ ergs$^{1/2}$Å$^{2/3}$
component B: $\epsilon°/k = 300$ K $\sigma = 6.0$ Å $\mu = 0$

15. Calculate the self diffusion coefficient of water at 300 K using the data in Problem 4 for Ar as a reference.

16. Compute the shape factors for ethanol at 200 K and 1.2 atm. Then use corresponding states to obtain the molar volume of ethanol at this temperature.

EXTENDED CORRESPONDING STATES

17. Compute the density of liquid methanol at 0°C and 20 atm.

18. The viscosity of *n*-octane at a reduced pressure P_r of 0.044 and a reduced temperature T_r of 0.5 is 4.86×10^{-3} g/(cm·s); that for methane at the same reduced conditions

is 1.45×10^{-3} g/(cm·s). Formulate a corresponding states method that accounts for size/shape differences and use your method to determine as best you can the viscosity of *n*-decane at these same reduced conditions.

Property	Methane	Octane	Decane
T_c (K)	190.6	568.8	617.6
V_c (cm³/mol)	99.0	492.0	603.0
M (g/mol)	16	114	142
ω (acentric factor)	0.0	0.394	0.490

19. Use ELK and the tables in Appendix 11 to calculate the enthalpy departure function and fugacity coefficient of ammonia at 405.6 K and 5.565 atm.

20. Use ELK and the tables in Appendix 11 to calculate the viscosity of liquid *n*-hexane at a reduced temperature of 0.7 and a reduced pressure of 0.8. (Ans: 0.186 cP)

21. Use ELK and the tables in Appendix 11 to calculate the viscosity of ammonia vapor at $T = 385.23$ K and $P = 44.52$ atm. (Ans: 142.5 μP)

22. Use ELK to calculate the molar volume and the entropy departure function for HCl at 194.8 K and 246 atm. (Ans: 30.19 cm³/mol and -41.66 J/mol·K)

APPENDIX 1

PHYSICAL CONSTANTS AND CONVERSION FACTORS

A1.1 PHYSICAL CONSTANTS

Quantity	Symbol	Value
Avogadro's number	N_0	6.022×10^{23}
Planck's constant	h	6.626×10^{-27} erg·s
Boltzmann's constant	k	1.3806×10^{-16} erg/(molec·K)
Gas constant	R	8.3143 J/mol·K = 1.987 cal/(mol·K)
		8.3143×10^7 ergs/(mol·K)
Speed of light	c	2.998×10^{10} cm/s
Proton charge	e	4.8032×10^{-10} esu
Electron mass	m_e	9.1096×10^{-28} g
Atomic mass unit	amu	1.6605×10^{-24} g
Universal gravitation constant	G	6.67×10^{-11} Nm^2/kg^2

A1.2 CONVERSION FACTORS

A1.2.1 Energy

	erg	eV	cm⁻¹	K	J	cal
erg	1	6.2420×10^{11}	5.0348×10^{15}	7.2441×10^{15}	10^{-7}	2.3901×10^{-8}
eV	1.6021×10^{-12}	1	8065.7	1.1605×10^{4}	1.6021×10^{-19}	3.8390×10^{-20}
cm⁻¹	1.9862×10^{-16}	1.2398×10^{-4}	1	1.4388	1.9862×10^{-23}	4.7471×10^{-24}
K	1.3804×10^{-16}	8.6167×10^{-5}	0.69502	1	1.3804×10^{-23}	3.2993×10^{-24}
J	10^{7}	6.42420×10^{18}	5.0348×10^{22}	7.2441×10^{22}	1	0.23901
cal	4.184×10^{7}	2.612×10^{19}	2.107×10^{23}	3.031×10^{23}	4.184	1

A1.2.2 Pressure

	N·m⁻² (Pa)	bar	dyn·cm⁻²	atm	torr
N·m⁻² (Pa)	1	10^{-5}	10	9.869×10^{-6}	7.501×10^{-3}
bar	10^{5}	1	10^{6}	0.9869	750.1
dyn·cm⁻²	0.1	10^{-6}	1	9.869×10^{-7}	7.501×10^{-4}
atm	1.01325×10^{5}	1.01325	1.01325×10^{6}	1	760
torr	133.3	1.333×10^{-3}	1.333×10^{3}	1.316×10^{-3}	1

A1.2.3 Miscellaneous

1 N = 1 kg·m/s² = 10^5 dynes = 10^5 g·cm/s²
1 m = 100 cm = 1×10^{10} Å
1 esu of charge = 1 (erg·cm)$^{0.5}$
1 esu of dipole moment = 1 (erg·cm³)$^{0.5}$
1 esu of quadrupole moment = 1 (erg·cm⁵)$^{0.5}$
1 esu of polarizability = 1 cm³
1 D (Debye) = 10^{-18} dipole esu
1 B (Buckingham) = 10^{-26} quad. esu

APPENDIX 2

GAUSS INTEGRALS

Integrals of the form

$$I_m = \int x^m e^{-x^2} \, dx \quad (m > -1)$$

occur frequently in statistical mechanics and are sometimes called Gauss Integrals. The simplest case is when $m = 0$. This integral is

$$I_0 = \int_{-\infty}^{\infty} e^{-x^2} \, dx = 2\int_0^{\infty} e^{-x^2} \, dx = \sqrt{\pi}.$$

The more general case where m is nonzero, and not necessarily even an integer, may be reduced to the widely tabulated gamma function $\Gamma(z)$ using the substitutions $x^2 = y$, $2dx = y^{-1/2}dy$. This yields

$$I_m = 2\int_0^{\infty} x^m e^{-x^2} \, dx = \int_0^{\infty} y^n e^{-y} \, dy = \Gamma(n + 1), \quad \left[n = \frac{1}{2}(m - 1) \right].$$

The gamma function satisfies the recursion relation

$$\Gamma(n + 1) = n\Gamma(n).$$

Values of the gamma function for $n \geq 2$ can be obtained from the recursion relation and tabulated values for $n < 2$. The latter are given in Table A2.1

TABLE A2.1   Gamma Function

n	$\Gamma(n)$	n	$\Gamma(n)$	n	$\Gamma(n)$	n	$\Gamma(n)$
1.00	1.00000	1.26	0.90440	1.52	0.88708	1.78	0.92623
1.02	0.98884	1.28	0.90072	1.54	0.88818	1.80	0.93138
1.04	0.97844	1.30	0.89747	1.56	0.88964	1.82	0.93685
1.06	0.96874	1.32	0.89464	1.58	0.89142	1.84	0.94261
1.08	0.95973	1.34	0.89222	1.60	0.89352	1.86	0.94869
1.10	0.95135	1.36	0.89115	1.62	0.89592	1.88	0.95507
1.12	0.94359	1.38	0.88931	1.64	0.89864	1.90	0.96177
1.14	0.93642	1.40	0.88785	1.66	0.90167	1.92	0.96877
1.16	0.92980	1.42	0.88676	1.68	0.90500	1.94	0.97610
1.18	0.92373	1.44	0.88604	1.70	0.90864	1.96	0.98374
1.20	0.91817	1.46	0.88566	1.72	0.91258	1.98	0.99171
1.22	0.91311	1.48	0.88563	1.74	0.91683	2.00	1.00000
1.24	0.90852	1.50	0.88623	1.76	0.92137		

APPENDIX 3

MOLECULAR SPECTROSCOPIC CONSTANTS

Appendix 3 data are accessed from the companion diskette programs. APPEND3.EXE will be copied to your hard drive when you install the programs from the diskette. Run APPEND3.EXE to access data for selected compounds for (1) rotational and vibrational constants and (2) energies associated with internal rotation about a bond.

APPENDIX 4

QUADRATIC FORM

A homogeneous second-degree expression in n variables of the form

$$Q(x) = a_{11}x_1^2 + 2a_{12}x_1x_2 + \ldots + 2a_{1n}x_1x_n$$
$$+ a_{22}x_2^2 + \ldots \qquad + 2a_{22}x_2x_n \qquad \text{(A4.1)}$$
$$+ \ldots$$
$$+ \ldots \qquad + a_{nn}x_n^2$$

is an equation in *quadratic form*. In many applications it is desirable to transform this expression into a sum of squares, removing the cross-product terms. One way to do this is by Lagrange's method. We will illustrate the procedure with a concrete example rather than with a general proof.

Consider the equation

$$Q = x_1^2 + 5x_2^2 + 2x_3^2 + 4x_1x_2 + 2x_1x_3 + 6x_2x_3, \qquad \text{(A4.2)}$$

which is of quadratic form. First, we group together all terms containing x_1:

$$Q = (x_1^2 + 4x_1x_2 + 2x_1x_3) + (5x_2^2 + 2x_3^2 + 6x_2x_3). \qquad \text{(A4.3)}$$

Next, we add and subtract appropriate terms to complete the square for the first term,

$$Q = (x_1^2 + 4x_1x_2 + 2x_1x_3 + 4x_2x_3 + 4x_2^2 + x_3^2) - (4x_2x_3 + 4x_2^2 + x_3^2)$$
$$+ (5x_2^2 + 2x_3^2 + 6x_2x_3) \qquad \text{(A4.4)}$$
$$= (x_1 + 2x_2 + x_3)^2 + (x_2^2 + 2x_2x_3 + x_3^2).$$

Note that none of the terms added and subtracted contain x_1.

We can now apply the transform

$$y_1 = x_1 + 2x_2 + x_3 \tag{A4.5}$$

to obtain

$$Q = y_1^2 + (x_2^2 + 2x_2x_3 + x_3^2). \tag{A4.6}$$

Successive steps of the preceding procedure can then be used on any remaining terms. In our example, the remaining term is already a perfect square so that

$$Q = y_1^2 + (x_2 + x_3)^2. \tag{A4.7}$$

Finally, the transform

$$y_2 = x_2 + x_3 \tag{A4.8}$$

can be identified to complete the procedure and yield

$$Q = y_1^2 + y_2^2. \tag{A4.9}$$

Thus the transforms

$$y_1 = x_1 + 2x_2 + x_3 \quad \text{and} \quad y_2 = x_2 + x_3 \tag{A4.10}$$

are seen to convert the quadratic form Equation (A4.2) to the sum of squares form of Equation (4.9).

APPENDIX 5

INTERMOLECULAR POTENTIAL PARAMETERS

A5.1 EMPIRICAL PARAMETERS FOR POTENTIAL MODELS

Parameters for the various intermolecular potential models are usually obtained by adjusting the parameters to provide the best fit (usually in a least-squares sense) between theory based on the model and experimental data. Lines of constant potential around the center of these simple models are spherically symmetric, which is certainly not true of real molecules with the possible exception of the noble gases. Nevertheless, these models are generally applied to much more complex molecules. This means that the parameters regressed by comparison to measured properties are effective parameters. The deficiency of the model in representing the true potential is absorbed in the parameters themselves. The problem with this is that those inadequacies of the model may affect different properties to a greater or lesser extent. The net result is that the parameters may often give considerably poorer results when applied to other properties or conditions. Thus in the following tables, the property from which the parameters were obtained is specified. You should be aware that because of the *effective* nature of the parameters obtained in this manner, the use of a parameter obtained from one property to predict another may be a good approximation on occasion but is not always reliable. Attempts have been made to use multiple properties in the regression of the parameters. Generally this will provide better results for all properties, at the expense of higher accuracy for any one property.

Uniqueness is another problem in regressing empirical potential model parameters from experimental data. That is, many of the models have two or three adjustable parameters. Unfortunately, these parameters are coupled to some extent and therefore multiple *sets* of values can be found which yield comparable results. Often one will find two sets of parameters in the literature which are quite different but which represent the data about equally well. This is not only due to the difficulties associated with the inverse problem (determining potentials from properties), but also to the effective nature of the model representations. While either set may be appropriately used to predict properties, do not mix values, take averages of the values, or make interpolations based on sequences of values. Very poor results will usually be obtained by using values of the parameters that were not simultaneously regressed together as a set.

TABLE A5.1   Empirical Square-Well
Potential Parameters from
Virial Coefficients[1,2]

Substance	σ (Å)	g	ϵ/k (K)
Ne	2.382	1.87	19.5
Ar	3.162	1.85	69.4
Kr	3.362	1.85	98.3
Xe	3.76	1.85	127.7
N_2	3.299	1.87	53.7
CO_2	3.917	1.83	119
CH_4	3.40	1.85	88.8
C_2H_4	3.347	1.677	222
C_2H_6	3.535	1.652	244
C_3H_6	4.511	1.373	382
C_3H_8	4.316	1.460	339
C_3H_{10}	4.418	1.464	347
1-Butene	5.592	1.249	492
2-Methylpropene	5.570	1.254	490
Trans-2-butene	5.276	1.324	465
Cis-2-butene	5.747	1.215	537
n-C_4H_{10}	4.812	1.476	387
$C(CH_3)_4$	5.422	1.45	382.6
n-C_7H_{16}	6.397	1.314	629
CF_4	4.103	1.48	191.1
CCl_3F	4.534	1.545	399
$CHCl_2F$	2.797	2.321	306
CCl_2F_2	4.812	1.394	345
CCl_2F-$CClF_2$	3.697	2.075	335
CH_3Cl	4.294	1.337	469
NH_3	2.902	1.268	692
H_2O	2.606	1.199	1260

TABLE A5.2   Empirical Sutherland
Potential Parameters from
Virial Coefficients[1]

Substance	$\sigma(\text{Å})$	ϵ/k (K)
Ar	2.972	305.3
Kr	3.128	4.221
Xe	3.337	682.8
N_2	3.194	277.3
CH_4	3.294	434.8
$C(CH_3)_4$	5.421	832.2
$n\text{-}C_5H_{12}$	4.755	1096.8
Benzene	5.220	1070.0
CF_4	4.124	442.7
CO_2	3.629	594.3

TABLE A5.3   Empirical Kihara Potential
Parameters from Viscosity and
Second Virial Data[1,2]

Substance	$d(\text{Å})$	$\sigma(\text{Å})$	ϵ/k (K)
Ar	0.334	3.344	143.26
Kr	0.416	3.587	206.68
Xe	0.472	3.913	283.12
CO_2	1.361	3.501	469.73
CH_4	0.767	3.505	232.20
C_2H_4	0.815	3.912	328.21
C_2H_6	1.130	3.977	425.32
C_3H_8	1.300	4.519	493.71
$n\text{-}C_4H_{10}$	1.876	4.830	672.32
$C(CH_3)_4$	2.025	5.395	625.88
$n\text{-}C_5H_{12}$	2.473	5.396	777.37
C_6H_6	2.411	4.938	975.37
$n\text{-}C_7H_{16}$	3.197	5.996	1023.30

TABLE A5.4   Empirical Lennard-Jones Potential Parameters[1,2,3]

Substance	Gas viscosity data		Virial coefficients		Combined	
	σ(Å)	ϵ/k (K)	σ(Å)	ϵ/k (K)	σ(Å)	ϵ/k (K)
H_2	2.915	38.0	2.87	29.2		
D_2	2.948	39.3	2.87	31.1		
He	2.576	10.2	2.63	6.03		
Ne	2.789	35.7	2.749	35.60		
Ar	3.418	124	3.499	118.13	3.429	121.85
Kr	3.498	225	3.846	162.74	3.684	174.68
Xe	4.055	229	4.100	222.32	4.067	224.83
N_2	3.681	91.5	3.694	96.26	3.663	96.92
O_2	3.433	113	3.58	117.5		
CO	3.590	110	3.763	100.2		
CO_2	3.996	190	4.416	192.25	3.832	230.56
NO	3.470	119	3.17	131		
N_2O	3.879	220	4.59	189		
SO	4.290	252				
SO_2	4.290	252				
SF_6			5.51	200.9		
F_2	3.653	112				
Cl_2	4.115	357				
Br_2	4.268	520				
I_2	4.982	550				
CH_4	3.822	137	4.010	142.87	3.678	166.78
C_2H_2	4.221	185				
C_2H_4	4.232	205	4.433	202.52	4.200	219.01
C_2H_6	4.418	230	5.220	194.14	4.221	274.48
C_3H_8	5.061	254	5.637	242		
n-C_4H_{10}	5.339	309.74	7.152	223.74	5.003	398.92
i-C_4H_{10}	5.341	313				
n-C_5H_{12}	5.769	345	8.540	217.69	5.282	474.15
$C(CH_3)_4$	6.520	183.02	7.420	233.66	5.638	357.13
n-C_6H_{14}	5.909	413				
n-C_7H_{16}	7.144	256.76	10.220	239.47	5.715	621.23
n-C_8H_{18}	7.451	320				
n-C_9H_2O	8.448	240				
cyc-C_6H_{12}	6.093	324				
C_6H_6	5.270	440	8.443	247.50	4.776	638.31
CH_3Cl	3.375	855				
CH_2Cl_2	4.759	406				
$CHCl_3$	5.430	327				
CCl_4	5.881	327				
C_2N_2	4.38	339				
CS_2	4.438	488				

TABLE A5.4 Continued

Substance	Gas viscosity data		Virial coefficients		Combined	
	σ(Å)	ϵ/k (K)	σ(Å)	ϵ/k (K)	σ(Å)	ϵ/k (K)
COS	4.13	335				
HCl	3.305	360				
HI	4.123	324				
Hg	2.898	851				
$SnCl_4$	4.540	1550				
$SnBr_4$	6.666	465				
CH_3OH	3.666	452				
C_2H_5OH	4.370	415				
$(CH_3)_2O$	4.264	412				
$(C_2H_5)_2O$	5.539	351				
$(CH_3)_2CO$	4.669	519				

TABLE A5.5   Empirical Lennard-Jones Parameters and Polar Constants for Polar Molecules[2,3]

Substance	$\sigma°$ (Å)	$\epsilon°/k$ (K)	μ (D)	α (Å^3)	Q (B)
HCl	3.458	274.6	1.08	2.63	3.8
CO			0.112	1.93	−2.5
CO_2			0	2.59	−4.3
CS_2			0	8.21	3.0
HCN			2.98	2.6	3.1
SO_2	3.895	369.3	1.63	3.72	1.7
NH_3	2.932	376.9	1.47	2.26	−1
H_2O	3.329	209.1	1.85	1.49	
$CHCl_3$	5.355	344.3	1.13	8.23	
CH_2Cl_2	4.921	362.3	1.57	6.48	
CH_3Cl	4.449	228.2	1.87	4.56	
$(C_2H_5)_2O$	5.660	320.4	1.15	8.73	
$(CH_3)_2CO$	5.085	310.4	2.88	6.33	
C_2H_5OH	4.575	327.8	1.69	5.62	
CH_3COOCH_3	5.026	422.1	1.72	6.6	
$CH_3COOC_2H_5$	5.314	463.7	1.78	9.44	

A5.2 THREE-BODY DISPERSION INTERACTIONS

The three-body interaction terms can be derived from quantum theory for the simultaneous interaction of three isolated molecules and is usually put in a form known as the Axilrod–Teller equation. For the geometry shown in Figure A5.1, the Axilrod–Teller equation can be written as[6]

$$u(r_i\, r_j\, r_k) = \frac{v(1 + 3\cos\theta_i\, \cos\theta_j\, \cos\theta_k)}{r_{ij}^3\, r_{jk}^3\, r_{ik}^3} \tag{A5.1}$$

where v is a constant. The equation can also be expressed entirely in terms of the vector positions of the molecules as

$$u(r_j\, r_j\, r_k) = \frac{v(r_{ij}^2 r_{jk}^2 r_{ik} - 3(\boldsymbol{rik} \cdot \boldsymbol{rjk})(\boldsymbol{rik} \cdot \boldsymbol{rij})(\boldsymbol{rij} \cdot \boldsymbol{rjk})}{r_{ij}^5 r_{jk}^5 r_{ik}^5}. \tag{A5.2}$$

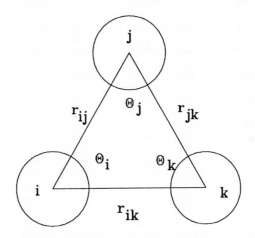

Figure A5.1   Geometry and symbols used in Equations (A5.1) and (A5.2).

A5.3 CORRELATION FUNCTIONS FOR A LENNARD-JONES FLUID

Appendix 10 contains a numerical method[7] for calculating the pair-correlation or radial distribution function $g(r)$, the direct correlation function $c(r)$, and the total correlation function $h(r)$. This method produces the results given in Table A5.6 for these functions for a Lennard-Jones fluid at the dimensionless conditions $T^+ = kT/\epsilon = 1.0843$ and $\rho^+ = \rho\sigma^3 = 0.8054$.

TABLE A5.6 Correlation Functions for a Lennard-Jones
Fluid at $T^+ = 1.0843$ and $\rho^+ = 0.8054$

r^+	$c(r)$	$h(r)$	$g(r)$	r^+	$c(r)$	$h(r)$	$g(r)$
0.00	−21.0842	−1.0000	0.0000	2.55	0.0121	−0.0907	0.9093
0.05	−20.6482	−1.0000	0.0000	2.60	0.0110	−0.0677	0.9323
0.10	−19.5088	−1.0000	0.0000	2.65	0.0101	−0.0421	0.9579
0.15	−18.0080	−1.0000	0.0000	2.70	0.0093	−0.0162	0.9838
0.20	−16.4211	−1.0000	0.0000	2.75	0.0085	0.0081	1.0081
0.25	−14.8908	−1.0000	0.0000	2.80	0.0078	0.0291	1.0291
0.30	−13.4676	−1.0000	0.0000	2.85	0.0072	0.0457	1.0457
0.35	−12.1580	−1.0000	0.0000	2.90	0.0065	0.0568	1.0568
0.40	−10.9524	−1.0000	0.0000	2.95	0.0059	0.0616	1.0616
0.45	−9.8379	−1.0000	0.0000	3.00	0.0053	0.0597	1.0597
0.50	−8.8027	−1.0000	0.0000	3.05	0.0048	0.0511	1.0511
0.55	−7.8374	−1.0000	0.0000	3.10	0.0043	0.0369	1.0369
0.60	−6.9353	−1.0000	0.0000	3.15	0.0038	0.0191	1.0191
0.65	−6.0917	−1.0000	0.0000	3.20	0.0034	0.0004	1.0004
0.70	−5.3038	−1.0000	0.0000	3.25	0.0031	−0.0164	0.9836
0.75	−4.5701	−1.0000	0.0000	3.30	0.0028	−0.0292	0.9708
0.80	−3.8907	−1.0000	0.0000	3.35	0.0025	−0.0367	0.9633
0.85	−3.2668	−1.0000	0.0000	3.40	0.0023	−0.0388	0.9612
0.90	−2.6951	−0.9941	0.0059	3.45	0.0021	−0.0361	0.9639
0.95	−1.8371	−0.6401	0.3599	3.50	0.0019	−0.0297	0.9703
1.00	0.0000	0.7588	1.7588	3.55	0.0018	−0.0208	0.9792
1.05	1.4055	1.7952	2.7952	3.60	0.0017	−0.0109	0.9891
1.10	1.6111	1.7017	2.7017	3.65	0.0016	−0.0011	0.9989
1.15	1.2652	1.1239	2.1239	3.70	0.0014	0.0076	1.0076
1.20	0.8772	0.5652	1.5652	3.75	0.0013	0.0144	1.0144
1.25	0.5943	0.1649	1.1649	3.80	0.0012	0.0191	1.0191
1.30	0.4145	−0.0880	0.9120	3.85	0.0012	0.0213	1.0213
1.35	0.3052	−0.2347	0.7653	3.90	0.0011	0.0210	1.0210
1.40	0.2388	−0.3101	0.6899	3.95	0.0010	0.0186	1.0186
1.45	0.1972	−0.3389	0.6611	4.00	0.0009	0.0144	1.0144
1.50	0.1696	−0.3369	0.6631	4.05	0.0008	0.0091	1.0091
1.55	0.1500	−0.3142	0.6858	4.10	0.0008	0.0032	1.0032
1.60	0.1350	−0.2773	0.7227	4.15	0.0007	−0.0026	0.9974
1.65	0.1228	−0.2305	0.7695	4.20	0.0007	−0.0075	0.9925
1.70	0.1123	−0.1764	0.8236	4.25	0.0006	−0.0111	0.9889
1.75	0.1030	−0.1169	0.8831	4.30	0.0006	−0.0131	0.9869
1.80	0.0946	−0.0530	0.9470	4.35	0.0005	−0.0133	0.9867
1.85	0.0871	0.0145	1.0144	4.40	0.0005	−0.0121	0.9879
1.90	0.0802	0.0848	1.0848	4.45	0.0005	−0.0095	0.9905
1.95	0.0736	0.1548	1.1548	4.50	0.0004	−0.0062	0.9938
2.00	0.0669	0.2122	1.2122	4.55	0.0004	−0.0025	0.9975
2.05	0.0592	0.2373	1.2373	4.60	0.0004	0.0010	1.0010
2.10	0.0507	0.2181	1.2181	4.65	0.0004	0.0040	1.0040
2.15	0.0422	0.1613	1.1613	4.70	0.0003	0.0063	1.0063
2.20	0.0345	0.0859	1.0859	4.75	0.0003	0.0076	1.0076
2.25	0.0281	0.0116	1.0116	4.80	0.0003	0.0080	1.0080
2.30	0.0233	−0.0489	0.9511	4.85	0.0003	0.0074	1.0074
2.35	0.0196	−0.0899	0.9101	4.90	0.0003	0.0061	1.0061
2.40	0.0169	−0.1115	0.8885	4.95	0.0003	0.0043	1.0043
2.45	0.0149	−0.1163	0.8837	5.00	0.0002	0.0022	1.0022
2.50	0.0133	−0.1080	0.8920				

A5.4 SITE-SITE POTENTIAL PARAMETERS

The following tables are a summary of site–site LJ potential parameters and structure parameters developed by Jorgensen and co-workers.[4,5]

TABLE A5.7 Standard Geometrical Parameters for Organic Compounds

Hydrocarbons		Alcohols		Ethers	
$r(C-C)$	1.535	$r(OH)$	0.945	$r(CO)$	1.410
$r(C=C)$	1.34	$r(CO)$	1.430	$r(C-C_0)$	1.516
$r(CC)_{aromatic}$	1.40	$r(C-C_0)$	1.512	$\angle COC$	112.0
$\angle CCC$	109.47	$\angle COH$	108.5		
$\angle C-C=C$	124.0	$\angle CCO$	107.8		

Bond lengths are denoted by r and are given in Angstroms; bond angles are denoted by the symbol $\angle$ and are given in degrees.

TABLE A5.8 Optimized Lennard-Jones Parameters for Hydrocarbons

Group	Example	σ (Å)	ϵ/k (K)
CH_2/CH_3	Generic methylene	3.923	72.0
CH_4	Methane	3.730	147.96
CH_3 (C_1)	Ethane	3.775	104.17
CH_3 (C_2)	n-Butane	3.905	88.07
CH_3 (C_3)	Isobutane	3.910	80.52
CH_3 (C_4)	Neopentane	3.960	72.97
CH_2 (sp^3)	n-Butane	3.905	59.39
CH_2 (sp^2)	1-Butene	3.850	70.46
CH (sp^3)	Isobutane	3.850	40.26
CH (sp^2)	2-Butenes	3.800	57.87
CH (aromatic)	Benzene	3.750	55.36
C (sp^3)	Neopentane	3.800	25.16
C (sp^2)	Isobutene	3.750	52.84

REFERENCES

1. Hirschfelder, J.O., Curtiss, C.F., and Bird, R.B. *Molecular Theory of Gases and Liquids,* John Wiley, New York, 1954.

2. Reed, T.M., and Gubbins, K.E. *Applied Statistical Mechanics,* McGraw-Hill, New York, 1973.

3. Bird, R.B., Stewart, W.E., and Lightfoot, E.N. *Transport Phenomena,* John Wiley, New York, 1960.

4. Jorgensen, W.L., Madura, J.D., and Swenson, C.J. "Optimized intermolecular potential functions for liquid hydrocarbons," *J. Am. Chem. Soc.* **1984,** *106,* 6638.

5. Jorgensen, W.L. "Transferable intermolecular potential functions for water, alcohols, and ethers. Application to liquid water," *J. Am. Chem. Soc.* **1981,** *103,* 335.

6. Allen, M.P., and Tildesley, D.J. *Computer Simulation of Liquids,* Oxford, New York, 1987.

7. Lee, L.L. *Molecular Thermodynamics of Nonideal Fluids,* Butterworths, Boston, 1988.

APPENDIX 6

VIRIAL COEFFICIENTS

Appendix 6 data are accessed from the companion diskette programs. APPEN-D6.EXE will be copied to your hard drive when you install the programs from the diskette. Run APPEND6.EXE to access second and third virial coefficients for selected compounds.

APPENDIX 7

GIBBS ENSEMBLE

Appendix 7 contains QUICKBASIC subcodes that illustrate the three moves involved in simulation of the Gibbs ensemble. APPEND7.TXT is an ASCII file that is loaded onto your hard disk when you install the programs from the diskette. It can be read with any text editor.

APPENDIX 8

NVT CODE FOR LJ FLUIDS

Appendix 8 contains a generic FORTRAN code that performs NVT MD simulations of fluids. The code is a modified version of a standard NVT code whose origin is unknown. However, significant modifications to the base code have been made by Professor James F. Ely, Department of Chemical Engineering, Colorado School of Mines. APPEND8.TXT is an ASCII file that is loaded onto your hard disk when you install the programs from the diskette. It can be read with any text editor.

APPENDIX 9

LOCAL COMPOSITION MODELS

A9.1 ACTIVITY COEFFICIENT FORMS FOR LC MODELS

A9.1.1 Wilson Equation

$$\ln \gamma_1 = -\ln(x_1 + x_2 G_{21}) + x_2 \left[\frac{G_{21}}{x_1 + G_{21}x_2} - \frac{G_{12}}{x_2 + x_1 G_{12}} \right]$$

$$\ln \gamma_2 = -\ln(x_2 + x_1 G_{12}) + x_1 \left[\frac{G_{12}}{x_2 + G_{12}x_1} - \frac{G_{21}}{x_1 + x_2 G_{21}} \right]$$

A9.1.2 NRTL Equation

$$\ln \gamma_1 = x_2^2 \left[\tau_{21} \left(\frac{G_{21}}{x_1 + x_2 G_{21}} \right)^2 + \frac{\tau_{12} G_{12}}{(x_2 + x_1 G_{12})^2} \right]$$

$$\ln \gamma_2 = x_1^2 \left[\tau_{12} \left(\frac{G_{12}}{x_2 + x_1 G_{12}} \right)^2 + \frac{\tau_{21} G_{21}}{(x_1 + x_2 G_{21})^2} \right]$$

A9.1.3 UNIQUAC Equation

$$\ln \gamma_i = \ln \gamma_i \text{ (combinatorial)} + \ln \gamma_i \text{ (residual)}$$

$$\ln \gamma_i \text{ (combinatorial)} = \ln\frac{\phi_i}{x_i} + \frac{z}{2}q_i \ln\frac{\theta_i}{\phi_i} + l_i - \frac{\phi_i}{x_i} \sum_j x_j l_j$$

$$\ln \gamma_i \text{ (residual)} = -q_i\left[1 - \ln\left(\sum_j \theta_j\tau_{ji}\right) - \sum_j \frac{\theta_j\tau_{ij}}{\sum_k \theta_k\tau_{kj}} \right]$$

A9.2 EXCESS ENTHALPY FORMS FOR LC MODELS

A9.2.1 Wilson Equation

$$H^E = \sum_i x_i \frac{\sum_j x_j G_{ji} a_{ji}}{\sum_k G_{ki} x_k}$$

A9.2.2 NRTL Equation

$$H^E = G^E - \sum_i x_i^2 \frac{\sum_j x_j a_{ji}^2 G_{ji}\alpha}{RT\left(\sum_k G_{ki} x_k\right)^2}$$

A9.2.3 UNIQUAC Equation

$$H^E = \sum_i q_i' x_i \frac{\sum_j \theta_j' a_{ji} G_{ji}}{\left(\sum_k \theta_k' G_{ki}\right)}$$

A9.3 UNIFAC PARAMETERS

TABLE A9.1   Group Constants for UNIFAC

Class	Group	Q	R	Example of use
CH_2	CH_3	0.848	0.9011	Ethane: $2CH_3$
	CH_2	0.540	0.6744	Propane: $2CH_3$, $1CH_2$
	CH	0.228	0.4469	Isobutane: $3CH_3$, $1CH$
	C	0.000	0.2195	2,2-Dimethylpropane: $4CH_3$, $1C$
$C=C$	$CH_2=CH$	1.176	1.3454	Propene: $1CH_2=C$, $2CH_3$
	$CH_2=C$	0.988	1.1173	2-Methylpropene: $1CH_2=C$, $2CH_3$
	$CH=CH$	0.867	1.1167	2-Butene: $1CH=CH$, $2CH_3$
	$CH=C$	0.676	0.8886	2-Methyl-2-butene: $1CH=C$, $3CH_3$
	$C=C$	0.485	0.6605	2,3-Dimethyl-2-butene: $1C=C$, $4CH_3$
$C\equiv C$	$CH\equiv C$	1.088	1.2920	Propyne: $1CH\equiv C$, $1CH_3$
	$C\equiv C$	0.784	1.0613	2-Butyne: $1C\equiv C$, $2CH_3$
ACH	ACH	0.400	0.5313	Benzene: $6ACH$
OH	OH	1.200	1.0000	Propanol: $1CH_3$, $2CH_2$, $1OH$
CH_2CO	CH_3CO	1.488	1.6724	Acetone: $1CH_3CO$, $1CH_3$
	CH_2CO	1.180	1.4457	3-Penatanone: $1CH_2CO$, $2CH_3$, $1CH_2$
CHO	CHO	0.948	0.9980	Acetaldehyde: $1CHO$, $1CH_3$
COOC	CH_3COO	1.728	1.9031	Methyl acetate: $1CH_3COO$, $1CH_3$
	CH_2COO	1.420	1.6764	Methyl propanoate: $1CH_2COO$, $2CH_3$
CH_2O	CH_3O	1.088	1.1450	Dimethyl ether: $1CH_3O$, $1CH_3$
	CH_2O	0.780	0.9183	Diethyl ether: $1CH_2CO$, $2CH_3$, $1CH_2$
	CHO	0.468	0.6908	Diisopropyl ether: $1CHO$, $4CH_3$, $1CH$
COOH	COOH	1.224	1.3013	Acetic acid: $1COOH$, $1CH_3$
	HCOOH	1.532	1.5280	Formic acid: $1HCOOH$
CH_2NH_2	CH_3NH_2	1.544	1.5959	Methylamine: $1CH_3NH_2$
	CH_2NH_2	1.236	1.3692	Ethylamine: $1CH_2NH_2$, $1CH_3$
	$CHNH_2$	0.924	1.1417	Isopropylamine: $1CHNH_2$, $2CH_3$
C_2NH	CH_3NH	1.244	1.4337	Dimethylamine: $1CH_3NH$, $1CH_3$
	CH_2NH	0.936	1.2070	Diethylamine: $1CH_2NH$, $2CH_3$, $1CH_2$
	CH_2NH	0.936	1.2070	Diethylamine: $1CH_2NH$, $2CH_3$, $1CH_2$
	CHNH	0.624	0.9795	Diisopropylamine: $1CHNH$, $4CH_3$, $1CH$
C_3N	CH_3N	0.940	1.1865	Trimethylamine: $1CH_3N$, $2CH_3$
	CH_2N	0.632	0.9597	Triethylamine: $1CH_2N$, $3CH_3$, $2CH_2$
CH_2CH	CH_3CN	1.724	1.8701	Acetonitrile: $1CH_3CN$
	CH_2CN	1.416	1.6434	Propionitrile: $1CH_2CN$, $1CH_3$

TABLE A9.1   Continued

Class	Group	Q	R	Example of use
CH_2NO_2	CH_3NO_2	1.868	2.0086	Nitromethane: $1CH_2NO_2$
	CH_2NO_2	1.560	1.7818	Nitroethane: $1CH_2NO_2$, $1CH_3$
	CHNO	1.248	1.5544	2-Nitropropane: $1CHNO_2$, $2CH_3$
Cl	Cl-1	0.720	1.4654	1-Chloropropane: 1Cl-1, $1CH_3$, $2CH_2$
	Cl-2	0.728	1.2380	2-Chloropropane: 1Cl-2, $2CH_3$, 1CH
CH_2Cl_2	CH_2Cl_2	1.988	2.2564	Dichloromethane: $1CH_2Cl_2$
$CHCl_3$	$CHCl_3$	2.410	2.8700	Chloroform: $1CHCl_3$
CCl_4	CCl_4	2.910	3.3900	Carbon tetrachloride: $1CCl_4$
Br	Br	0.832	0.9492	Bromoethane: 1Br, $1CH_3$, $1CH_2$
Me_2SO	Me_2SO	2.472	2.8266	Dimethyl sulfoxide: $1Me_2SO$
PYRID	PYRID	2.113	2.9993	Pyridine: 1pyrid
ACF	ACF	0.524	0.6948	Hexafluorobenzene: 6ACF
ACH_2	$ACCH_3$	0.968	1.2663	Toluene: $1ACCH_3$, 5ACH
	$ACCH_2$	0.660	1.0396	Ethylbenzene: $1ACCH_2$, $1CH_3$, 5ACH
	ACCH	0.348	0.8121	Isopropylbenzene: 1ACCH, $2CH_3$, 5ACH
$ACNO_2$	$ACNO_2$	1.104	1.4199	Nitrobenzene: $1ACNO_2$, 5ACH
ACCl	ACCl	0.844	1.1562	Chlorobenene: 1ACCl, 5ACH
$ACNH_2$	$ACNH_2$	0.816	1.0600	Aniline: $1ACNH_2$, 5ACH
ACBr	ACBr	0.952	0.8000	Bromobenzene: 1ACBr, 5ACH

Data taken from reference 1.

A9.3.2 Interaction Constants for UNIFAC

The tables on the following pages contain the interaction parameters between *main* groups as listed in the preceding table. Interactions between all subgroups are the same as between their corresponding main groups. All parameters are given in units of Kelvins and represent the A_{mn} parameter shown in Table 9.3 in the body of the text. The data are taken from reference 2.

TABLE A9.2 UNIFAC Group Interactions

	CH$_2$	C=C	ACH	ACCH$_2$	OH	CH$_3$OH	H$_2$O	ACOH	CH$_2$CO	CHO
CH$_2$	0.000	86.020	61.130	76.500	986.500	697.000	1318.000	1333.000	476.800	677.000
C=C	−35.360	0.000	38.810	74.150	524.100	787.600	270.600	526.100	182.600	448.800
ACH	−11.120	3.446	0.000	167.000	636.100	637.400	903.800	1329.000	25.770	347.300
ACCH$_2$	−69.700	−113.600	−146.800	0.000	803.200	603.300	5695.000	884.900	−52.100	586.600
OH	156.400	457.000	89.600	25.820	0.000	−137.100	353.500	−259.700	84.000	−203.600
CH$_3$OH	16.510	−12.520	−50.000	−44.500	249.100	0.000	−181.000	−101.700	23.390	306.400
H$_2$O	300.000	496.100	362.300	377.600	−299.100	289.600	0.000	324.500	−195.400	−116.000
ACOH	275.80	217.500	25.340	244.200	−451.600	−265.200	−601.800	0.000	−356.100	−271.100
CH$_2$CO	26.760	42.920	140.100	365.800	164.500	108.700	472.500	−133.100	0.000	−37.360
CHO	505.700	56.300	23.390	106.000	529.000	−340.200	480.800	−155.600	128.000	0.000
CCOO	114.800	132.100	85.840	−170.000	245.400	249.600	200.800	−36.720	372.200	185.100
HCOO	329.300	110.400	18.120	428.000	139.400	227.800	n.a.	n.a.	385.400	−236.500
CH$_2$O	83.360	26.510	52.130	65.690	237.700	238.400	−314.700	−178.500	191.100	−7.838
CH$_2$NH$_2$	−30.480	1.163	−44.850	296.400	−242.800	−481.700	−330.400	n.a.	n.a.	n.a.
C$_2$NH	65.330	−28.700	−22.310	223.000	−150.000	−370.300	−448.200	n.a.	394.600	n.a.
C$_3$N	−83.890	−25.380	−223.900	109.900	28.600	−406.800	−598.800	n.a.	225.300	n.a.
ACNH$_2$	1139.000	2000.000	247.500	762.800	−17.400	−118.100	−341.600	−253.100	−450.300	n.a.
PYRIDINE	−101.600	−47.630	31.870	49.800	−132.300	−378.200	−332.900	−341.600	29.100	n.a.
CH$_2$CN		24.820	−40.620	−22.970	−138.400	185.400	162.600	242.800	n.a.	−2875.00

COOH	315.300	1264.000	62.320	89.860	-151.000	339.800	-66.170	-11.000	-297.800	-165.500
Cl	91.460	40.250	4.680	122.900	562.200	529.000	698.200	n.a.	286.300	-47.510
CH$_2$Cl$_2$	34.010	-23.500	121.300	140.800	527.600	669.900	708.700	n.a.	82.860	190.600
CHCl$_3$	36.700	51.060	288.500	69.900	742.100	649.100	826.800	n.a.	552.100	242.800
CCl$_4$	-78.450	160.900	-4.700	134.700	856.300	709.600	1201.000	10000.0	372.000	n.a.
ACCl	106.800	70.320	-97.270	402.500	325.700	612.800	-274.500	622.300	518.400	n.a.
CH$_2$NO$_2$	-32.690	-1.996	10.380	-97.050	261.600	252.600	417.900	n.a.	-142.600	n.a.
ACNO$_2$	5541.000	n.a.	1824.000	-127.800	561.600	n.a.	360.700	n.a.	-101.500	n.a.
CS$_2$	-52.650	16.620	21.500	40.680	609.800	914.200	1081.000	1421.000	303.700	n.a.
CH$_3$SH	-7.481	n.a.	28.410	19.560	461.600	448.600	n.a.	n.a.	160.600	n.a.
Furfural	-25.310	82.640	157.300	128.800	521.600	n.a.	23.480	n.a.	317.500	n.a.
DOH	139.900	n.a.	221.400	150.600	267.600	240.800	-137.400	838.400	135.400	n.a.
I	128.000	n.a.	58.680	26.410	501.300	431.300	n.a.	n.a.	138.000	245.900
Br	-31.520	174.600	-154.200	1112.000	524.900	494.700	n.a.	n.a.	-142.600	n.a.
C≡C	-72.880	41.380	n.a.	68.950	-25.870	n.a.	n.a.	n.a.	443.600	n.a.
Me$_2$SO	50.490	64.070	-2.504	-143.200	389.300	695.000	-240.000	n.a.	110.400	354.000
ACRY	-165.900	573.000	-123.600	397.400	218.800	218.800	386.600	n.a.	n.a.	183.800
ClCC	47.410	124.200	395.800	419.100	738.900	528.000	n.a.	n.a.	-40.900	n.a.
ACF	-5.132	-131.700	-237.200	-157.300	649.700	645.900	n.a.	n.a.	n.a.	13.890
DMF	-31.950	249.000	-133.900	-240.200	64.160	172.200	-287.100	n.a.	97.040	n.a.
CF$_2$	147.300	62.400	140.600	n.a.	n.a.	n.a.	n.a.	n.a.	n.a.	n.a.

	CCOO	HCOO	CH$_2$O	CH$_2$N$_2$	C$_2$NH	C$_3$N	ACNH$_2$	Pyridine	CH$_2$CN	COOH
CH$_2$	232.100	507.000	251.500	391.500	255.700	206.600	920.700	287.800	597.000	663.500
C=C	37.850	333.500	214.500	240.900	163.900	61.110	749.300	280.500	336.900	318.900
ACH	5.994	287.100	32.140	161.700	122.800	90.490	648.200	-4.449	212.500	537.400
ACH$_2$	5688.00	197.800	213.100	19.020	-49.290	23.500	664.200	52.800	6096.000	872.300
OH	101.100	267.800	28.060	8.642	42.700	-323.000	-52.390	170.000	6.712	199.000
CH$_3$OH	-10.720	179.700	-128.600	359.300	-20.980	53.900	489.700	580.500	53.280	-202.000
H$_2$O	72.870	n.a.	540.500	48.890	168.000	304.000	243.200	459.000	112.600	-14.090
ACOH	-449.400	n.a.	-162.900	n.a.	n.a.	n.a.	119.900	-305.500	n.a.	408.900
CH$_2$CO	-213.700	-190.400	-103.600	n.a.	-174.200	-169.000	6201.000	7.341	481.700	669.400
CHO	-110.300	766.000	304.100	n.a.	n.a.	n.a.	475.500	n.a.	n.a.	497.500
CCOO	0.000	-241.800	-234.500	n.a.	-73.500	-196.700	n.a.	n.a.	494.600	660.200
HCOO	1167.000	0.000	-234.000	-78.360	n.a.	n.a.	n.a.	-233.400	-47.250	-268.100
CH$_2$O	461.300	457.300	0.000	0.000	251.500	5422.000	-200.700	213.200	-18.510	664.600
CH$_2$NH$_2$	n.a.	n.a.	222.100	127.400	-107.200	-41.110	n.a.	n.a.	358.900	n.a.
C$_2$NH	136.000	n.a.	-56.080	38.890	0.000	-189.200	n.a.	n.a.	147.100	n.a.
C$_3$N	2889.000	n.a.	-194.100	-15.070	865.900	0.000	n.a.	n.a.	n.a.	n.a.
ACNH$_2$	-294.800	n.a.	n.a.	n.a.	n.a.	n.a.	0.000	89.700	-281.600	n.a.
PYRIDINE	n.a.	554.400	-156.100	n.a.	n.a.	n.a.	117.400	0.000	-169.700	-396.000
CH$_2$CN	-266.600	99.370	38.810	-157.300	-108.500	n.a.	777.400	134.300	0.000	-153.700
COOH	-256.300	193.900	-338.500	n.a.	n.a.	n.a.	493.800	-313.500	n.a.	0.000

Cl	35.380	n.a.	225.400	131.200	n.a.	n.a.	429.700	n.a.	54.320	519.100
CH₂Cl₂	-133.000	n.a.	-197.700	n.a.	n.a.	-141.400	140.800	587.300	258.600	543.300
CHCl₃	176.500	235.600	-20.930	n.a.	n.a.	-293.700	n.a.	18.980	74.040	504.200
CCl₄	129.500	351.900	113.900	261.100	91.130	316.900	898.200	368.500	492.000	631.000
ACCl	-171.100	383.300	-25.150	108.500	102.200	2951.000	334.900	n.a.	363.500	993.400
CH₂NO₂	129.300	n.a.	-94.490	n.a.	n.a.	n.a.	n.a.	n.a.	0.283	n.a.
ACNO₂	n.a.	n.a.	n.a.	n.a.	n.a.	n.a.	134.900	2475.000	n.a.	n.a.
CS₂	243.800	201.500	112.400	106.700	n.a.	n.a.	n.a.	n.a.	335.700	n.a.
CH₂SH	n.a.	n.a.	63.710	n.a.	n.a.	n.a.	n.a.	n.a.	161.000	n.a.
Furfural	-146.300	n.a.	-87.310	n.a.	n.a.	n.a.	n.a.	n.a.	n.a.	570.600
DOH	152.000	n.a.	9.207	n.a.	n.a.	n.a.	192.300	n.a.	169.600	n.a.
I	21.920	n.a.	476.600	n.a.	n.a.	n.a.	n.a.	n.a.	n.a.	616.600
Br	24.370	n.a.	736.400	n.a.	n.a.	n.a.	n.a.	-42.710	136.900	5256.000
C≡C	n.a.	n.a.	n.a.	n.a.	n.a.	n.a.	n.a.	n.a.	329.100	n.a.
Me₂SO	41.570	n.a.	-93.510	n.a.	n.a.	-257.200	n.a.	n.a.	n.a.	-180.200
ACRY	175.500	n.a.	n.a.	n.a.	n.a.	n.a.	n.a.	n.a.	-42.310	n.a.
ClCC	611.300	134.500	-217.900	n.a.	n.a.	n.a.	n.a.	281.600	335.200	898.200
ACF	n.a.	n.a.	167.300	n.a.	-198.800	116.500	n.a.	159.800	n.a.	n.a.
DMF	-82.120	-116.700	-158.200	49.700	n.a.	-185.200	343.700	n.a.	150.600	-97.770
CF₂	n.a.	n.a.	n.a.	n.a.	n.a.	n.a.	n.a.	n.a.	n.a.	n.a.

	Cl	CH_2Cl_2	$CHCl_3$	CCl_4	ACCl	CH_2NO_2	$ACNO_2$	CS_2	CH_3SH	Furfural
CH_2	35.930	53.760	24.900	104.300	11.440	661.500	543.000	153.600	184.400	354.600
C=C	-36.870	58.550	-13.990	-109.700	100.100	357.500	n.a.	76.300	n.a.	262.900
ACH	-18.810	-144.400	-231.900	3.000	187.000	168.000	194.900	52.070	-10.430	-64.690
ACH_2	-114.100	-111.000	-80.250	-141.300	-211.000	3629.000	4448.000	-9.451	393.600	48.490
OH	75.620	65.280	-98.120	143.100	123.500	256.500	157.100	488.900	147.500	-120.500
CH_3OH	-38.320	-102.500	-139.400	-44.760	-28.250	75.140	n.a.	-31.090	17.500	n.a.
H_2O	325.400	370.400	353.700	497.500	133.900	220.600	399.500	887.100	n.a.	188.000
ACOH	n.a.	n.a.	n.a.	1827.000	6915.000	n.a.	n.a.	8484.000	n.a.	n.a.
CH_2CO	-191.700	-130.300	-354.600	-39.200	-119.800	137.500	548.500	216.100	-46.280	-163.700
CHO	751.900	67.520	-483.700	n.a.	n.a.	n.a.	n.a.	n.a.	n.a.	n.a.
CCOO	-34.740	108.900	-209.700	54.570	442.400	-81.130	n.a.	183.000	n.a.	202.300
HCOO	n.a.	n.a.	-126.200	179.700	24.280	n.a.	n.a.	n.a.	103.900	n.a.
CH_2O	301.100	137.800	-154.300	47.670	134.800	95.180	n.a.	140.900	-8.538	170.100
CH_2NH_2	-82.920	n.a.	n.a.	-99.810	30.050	n.a.	n.a.	n.a.	-70.140	n.a.
C_2NH	n.a.	n.a.	n.a.	71.230	-18.930	n.a.	n.a.	n.a.	n.a.	n.a.
C_3N	n.a.	n.a.	-352.900	-262.000	-181.900	n.a.	n.a.	n.a.	n.a.	n.a.
$ACNH_2$	287.000	-111.000	n.a.	882.000	617.500	n.a.	-139.300	n.a.	n.a.	n.a.
PYRIDINE	n.a.	-351.600	-114.700	-205.300	n.a.	n.a.	2845.000	n.a.	n.a.	n.a.
CH_2CN	4.933	-152.700	-15.620	-54.860	-4.624	-0.515	n.a.	230.900	0.460	n.a.
COOH	13.410	-44.700	39.630	183.400	-79.080	n.a.	n.a.	n.a.	n.a.	-208.900

	Cl	CH_2Cl_2	$CHCl_3$	CCl_4	ACCl	CH_2NO_2	$ACNO_2$	CS_2	CH_2SH	Furfural
Cl	0.000	108.300	249.600	62.420	153.000	32.730	86.200	450.100	59.020	n.a.
CH_2Cl_2	-84.530	0.000	n.a.	56.330	223.100	108.900	n.a.	116.600	n.a.	n.a.
$CHCl_3$	-157.100	17.970	0.000	-30.100	192.100	n.a.	534.700	132.200	n.a.	-64.380
CCl_4	11.800	-8.309	51.900	0.000	-75.970	490.900	2213.000	320.200	n.a.	546.700
ACCl	-129.700	-9.639	-0.227	248.400	0.000	132.700	533.200	n.a.	n.a.	n.a.
CH_2NO_2	113.000	n.a.	n.a.	-34.680	132.900	0.000	0.000	n.a.	n.a.	n.a.
$ACNO_2$	1971.000	n.a.	-26.060	514.600	-123.100	-85.120	0.000	0.000	n.a.	n.a.
CS_2	-73.090	n.a.	n.a.	-60.710	n.a.	277.800	n.a.	0.000	n.a.	n.a.
CH_2SH	-27.940	n.a.	n.a.	n.a.	n.a.	n.a.	n.a.	n.a.	0.000	0.000
Furfural	n.a.	n.a.	48.480	-133.200	n.a.	481.300	n.a.	n.a.	n.a.	0.000
DOH	n.a.	-40.820	21.760	n.a.	n.a.	64.280	2448.000	-27.450	n.a.	n.a.
I	-262.300	-174.500	n.a.	48.490	-185.300	125.300	4288.000	n.a.	n.a.	n.a.
Br	n.a.	n.a.	n.a.	77.500	n.a.	174.400	n.a.	n.a.	n.a.	n.a.
$C{\equiv}C$	n.a.	n.a.	n.a.	n.a.	n.a.	n.a.	n.a.	n.a.	85.700	n.a.
Me_2SO	383.200	-215.000	-343.600	-58.430	n.a.	n.a.	n.a.	n.a.	n.a.	n.a.
ACRY	n.a.	n.a.	n.a.	-85.150	n.a.	379.400	n.a.	167.900	n.a.	n.a.
ClCC	n.a.	301.900	-149.800	-134.200	n.a.	n.a.	n.a.	n.a.	n.a.	n.a.
ACF	n.a.	n.a.	n.a.	-124.600	n.a.	n.a.	n.a.	n.a.	-71.000	n.a.
DMF	n.a.	n.a.	n.a.	-186.700	n.a.	223.600	n.a.	n.a.	n.a.	n.a.
CF_2	n.a.	n.a.	n.a.	n.a.	n.a.	n.a.	n.a.	n.a.	n.a.	n.a.

	DOH	I	Br	C≡C	Me$_2$SO	ACRY	ClCC	ACF	DMF	CF$_2$
CH$_2$	3025.000	335.800	479.500	298.900	526.500	689.000	-4.189	125.800	485.300	-2.859
C=C	n.a.	n.a.	183.800	31.140	179.000	-52.870	-66.460	359.300	-70.450	449.400
ACH	210.400	113.300	261.300	n.a.	169.900	383.900	-259.100	389.300	245.600	22.670
ACH$_2$	4975.000	259.000	210.000	n.a.	4284.000	-119.200	-282.500	101.400	5629.000	n.a.
OH	-318.900	313.500	202.100	727.800	-202.100	74.270	225.800	44.780	-143.900	n.a.
CH$_3$OH	-119.200	212.100	106.300	n.a.	-399.300	-5.224	33.470	-48.250	-172.400	n.a.
H$_2$O	12.720	952.000	n.a.	n.a.	-139.000	160.800	n.a.	n.a.	319.000	n.a.
ACOH	-687.100	n.a.	n.a.	n.a.	n.a.	n.a.	n.a.	n.a.	n.a.	n.a.
CH$_2$CO	71.460	53.590	245.200	-246.600	-44.580	n.a.	-34.570	n.a.	-61.700	n.a.
CHO	n.a.	117.00	n.a.	n.a.	n.a.	-339.200	172.400	n.a.	-268.800	n.a.
CCOO	-101.700	148.300	18.880	n.a.	52.080	-28.610	-275.200	n.a.	85.330	n.a.
HCOO	n.a.	n.a.	n.a.	n.a.	n.a.	n.a.	-11.400	n.a.	308.900	n.a.
CH$_2$O	-20.110	-149.500	-202.300	n.a.	128.800	n.a.	240.200	-274.000	254.800	n.a.
CH$_2$NH$_2$	n.a.	n.a.	n.a.	n.a.	n.a.	n.a.	n.a.	n.a.	-164.000	n.a.
C$_2$NH	n.a.	n.a.	n.a.	n.a.	n.a.	n.a.	n.a.	570.900	n.a.	n.a.
C$_3$N	n.a.	n.a.	n.a.	n.a.	243.100	n.a.	n.a.	-196.300	22.050	n.a.
ACNH$_2$	0.100	n.a.	n.a.	n.a.	n.a.	n.a.	n.a.	n.a.	-334.400	n.a.
PYRIDINE	n.a.	n.a.	-60.780	n.a.	n.a.	n.a.	160.700	-158.800	n.a.	n.a.
CH$_2$CN	177.500	n.a.	-62.170	-203.000	n.a.	81.570	-55.770	n.a.	-151.500	n.a.
COOH	n.a.	228.400	-95.000	n.a.	-463.600	n.a.	-11.160	n.a.	-228.000	n.a.

Cl	n.a.	−344.400	n.a.	n.a.	n.a.	−168.200	n.a.	n.a.	n.a.
CH$_2$Cl$_2$	177.600	315.900	n.a.	215.000	n.a.	−91.800	n.a.	n.a.	n.a.
CHCl$_3$	86.400	n.a.	n.a.	363.700	n.a.	111.200	n.a.	n.a.	n.a.
CCl$_4$	247.800	146.600	n.a.	337.700	369.500	187.100	215.200	498.600	n.a.
ACCl	n.a.	593.400	−27.700	n.a.	n.a.	n.a.	n.a.	n.a.	n.a.
CH$_2$NO$_2$	304.300	10.170	n.a.	n.a.	n.a.	10.760	n.a.	−223.100	n.a.
ACNO$_2$	2990.000	−124.000	n.a.	n.a.	n.a.	n.a.	n.a.	n.a.	n.a.
CS$_2$	292.700	n.a.	n.a.	31.660	n.a.	−43.370	n.a.	n.a.	n.a.
CH$_2$SH	n.a.	n.a.	n.a.	n.a.	n.a.	n.a.	n.a.	78.920	n.a.
Furfural	n.a.	n.a.	n.a.	−417.200	n.a.	n.a.	n.a.	n.a.	n.a.
DOH	0.000	n.a.	n.a.	n.a.	n.a.	n.a.	n.a.	302.200	n.a.
I	n.a.	n.a.	n.a.	n.a.	n.a.	n.a.	n.a.	n.a.	n.a.
Br	n.a.	0.000	0.000	32.900	n.a.	n.a.	n.a.	n.a.	n.a.
C≡C	n.a.	n.a.	n.a.	n.a.	n.a.	2073.000	n.a.	−119.800	n.a.
Me$_2$SO	535.800	−111.200	n.a.	0.000	n.a.	n.a.	n.a.	−97.710	n.a.
ACRY	n.a.	n.a.	631.500	n.a.	0.000	−208.800	n.a.	−8.804	n.a.
ClCC	n.a.	n.a.	n.a.	n.a.	837.200	0.000	0.000	255.000	n.a.
ACF	n.a.	n.a.	n.a.	n.a.	n.a.	n.a.	n.a.	n.a.	−117.200
DMF	−191.700	n.a.	6.699	136.600	5.150	−137.700	n.a.	0.000	−5.579
CF$_2$	n.a.	n.a.	n.a.	n.a.	n.a.	n.a.	185.600	55.800	0.000

REFERENCES

1. Christensen, J.J., Rowley, R.L., and Izatt, R.M. *Handbook of Heats of Mixing* (suppl. vol.), John Wiley, New York, 1988.

2. Walas, S.M. *Phase Equilibria in Chemical Engineering,* Butterworth Publishers, Stoneham, 1985.

APPENDIX 10

NUMERICAL SOLUTION OF INTEGRAL EQUATIONS AND COLLISION INTEGRALS

A10.1 GILLAN'S METHOD

On the accompanying diskette is a QUICKBASIC program that uses the method developed by Gillan M.J., (*Mol. Phys.* **1979,** *38,* 1781–1794), to obtain numerical solutions for the PY or HNC equations. This code is essentially a translation of the FORTRAN code given in L.L. Lee (*Molecular Thermodynamics of Nonideal Fluids,* Butterworths, Boston, 1988). APPEND10.TXT is loaded to your hard drive when the install program is run. Any ASCII or text editor can read the file.

A10.2 COLLISION INTEGRALS

TABLE A10.1 Reduced Collision Integrals
for Calculating Transport Properties
from the Enskog Theory

T^+	$\Omega^{+(1,1)}$	$\Omega^{+(2,2)}$
0.60	1.877	2.065
0.80	1.612	1.780
1.00	1.439	1.587
1.20	1.320	1.452
1.40	1.233	1.353
1.60	1.167	1.279
1.80	1.116	1.221
2.00	1.075	1.175
2.20	1.041	1.138
2.40	1.012	1.107
2.60	0.9878	1.081
2.80	0.9672	1.058
3.00	0.9490	1.039
3.20	0.9328	1.022
3.60	0.9058	0.9932
4.00	0.8836	0.9700
5.00	0.8422	0.9269
6.00	0.8124	0.8963
8.00	0.7712	0.8535
10.00	0.7424	0.8242
20.00	0.6640	0.7432
40.00	0.5960	0.6718
50.00	0.5756	0.6504

APPENDIX 11

CORRESPONDING STATES

A11.1 CORRESPONDING STATES TABLES

The tables in this section can be used with two-, three-, or four-parameter corresponding states. For each property, there are four sets of tables:

1. Simple reference fluid J_0 values for use with two-parameter corresponding states.
2. Size/shape deviation $J^{(1)}$ values. Three-parameter corresponding states or the LK method can be used with these values employing $J = J_0 + \omega J^{(1)}$.
3. Polar deviation $J^{(2)}$ values. Four-parameter corresponding states or the ELK method can be used with these values employing $J = J_0 + \alpha J^{(1)} + \beta J^{(2)}$. β_H, rather than β, should be used when calculating enthalpy and entropy.
4. Auxiliary tables are included for all three types of tables. These tables show values near the vapor–liquid line for J_0, $J^{(1)}$, and $J^{(2)}$ in the opposite phase given in the primary tables. These tables can be useful for interpolation near saturation and when the phase boundary of the test fluid does not exactly match that of the reference fluids.

TABLE A11.1 Enthalpy Departure Function—Simple Reference Fluid, $\left(\dfrac{H^* - H}{RT_c}\right)_0$

h_0							P_r							
T_r	0.01	0.05	0.10	0.20	0.40	0.60	0.80	1.00	1.20	1.50	2.00	4.00	7.00	10.00
0.45	5.615	5.612	5.609	5.603	5.590	5.577	5.564	5.551	5.538	5.519	5.486	5.354	5.154	4.950
0.50	5.465	5.462	5.459	5.453	5.440	5.427	5.414	5.401	5.388	5.369	5.336	5.203	4.999	4.791
0.55	0.032	5.312	5.308	5.303	5.290	5.278	5.265	5.252	5.239	5.220	5.187	5.054	4.849	4.638
0.60	0.027	5.162	5.159	5.153	5.141	5.129	5.116	5.104	5.091	5.073	5.041	4.910	4.704	4.492
0.65	0.022	0.118	5.008	5.002	4.991	4.980	4.968	4.956	4.945	4.927	4.896	4.769	4.565	4.353
0.70	0.020	0.101	0.214	4.848	4.839	4.829	4.818	4.808	4.797	4.781	4.752	4.631	4.432	4.221
0.75	0.017	0.088	0.184	4.687	4.679	4.672	4.664	4.655	4.646	4.632	4.607	4.495	4.303	4.095
0.80	0.015	0.078	0.160	0.345	4.507	4.504	4.499	4.494	4.488	4.478	4.459	4.361	4.178	3.974
0.85	0.014	0.069	0.141	0.300	4.309	4.313	4.316	4.316	4.316	4.312	4.302	4.225	4.056	3.857
0.90	0.012	0.062	0.126	0.264	0.596	4.074	4.094	4.108	4.118	4.127	4.132	4.086	3.835	3.744
0.93	0.011	0.058	0.118	0.246	0.545	0.960	3.920	3.953	3.976	4.000	4.020	4.001	3.863	3.678
0.95	0.011	0.056	0.113	0.235	0.516	0.885	3.763	3.825	3.865	3.904	3.940	3.943	3.815	3.634
0.97	0.011	0.054	0.109	0.226	0.490	0.824	1.356	3.658	3.732	3.796	3.853	3.884	3.767	3.591
0.98	0.010	0.053	0.107	0.221	0.478	0.797	1.273	3.544	3.652	3.736	3.806	3.853	3.743	3.569
0.99	0.010	0.052	0.105	0.216	0.466	0.773	1.206	3.376	3.558	3.670	3.758	3.823	3.720	3.548
1.00	0.010	0.051	0.103	0.212	0.455	0.750	1.151	2.592	3.441	3.598	3.706	3.792	3.696	3.526
1.01	0.010	0.050	0.101	0.208	0.445	0.728	1.102	1.796	3.283	3.516	3.652	3.760	3.671	3.505
1.02	0.010	0.049	0.099	0.204	0.435	0.708	1.060	1.627	3.039	3.422	3.595	3.729	3.647	3.484
1.05	0.009	0.046	0.094	0.192	0.407	0.654	0.955	1.359	2.034	3.030	3.398	3.631	3.575	3.420
1.10	0.008	0.042	0.086	0.175	0.367	0.581	0.827	1.120	1.487	2.203	2.965	3.456	3.453	3.315
1.20	0.007	0.036	0.073	0.148	0.305	0.474	0.657	0.857	1.076	1.443	2.079	3.066	3.202	3.107
1.30	0.006	0.031	0.063	0.127	0.260	0.349	0.545	0.698	0.860	1.116	1.560	2.645	2.942	2.899
1.50	0.005	0.024	0.048	0.097	0.196	0.297	0.400	0.505	0.612	0.774	1.046	1.927	2.421	2.486
2.00	0.003	0.014	0.028	0.056	0.111	0.167	0.222	0.276	0.330	0.411	0.541	0.993	1.411	1.577
2.50	0.002	0.009	0.018	0.035	0.070	0.104	0.137	0.170	0.203	0.250	0.326	0.585	0.838	0.954
3.00	0.001	0.006	0.012	0.023	0.045	0.067	0.088	0.109	0.129	0.159	0.205	0.357	0.495	0.545
4.00	0.001	0.002	0.005	0.009	0.018	0.026	0.033	0.041	0.048	0.058	0.072	0.109	0.110	0.061

TABLE A11.2 Enthalpy Departure Function—Size/Shape Deviation, $\left(\dfrac{H^* - H}{RT_c}\right)^{(1)}$

$h^{(1)}$

T_r \ P_r	0.01	0.05	0.10	0.20	0.40	0.60	0.80	1.00	1.20	1.50	2.00	4.00	7.00	10.00
0.45	9.513	9.514	9.519	9.515	9.518	9.520	9.522	9.525	9.527	9.531	9.537	9.564	9.611	9.663
0.50	8.867	8.868	8.869	8.871	8.875	8.879	8.883	8.887	8.891	8.897	8.908	8.954	9.030	9.111
0.55	0.079	8.213	8.214	8.216	8.222	8.227	8.232	8.239	8.243	8.252	8.266	8.327	8.426	8.532
0.60	0.059	7.569	7.570	7.573	7.579	7.585	7.592	7.569	7.605	7.615	7.632	7.705	7.825	7.950
0.65	0.045	0.240	6.949	6.952	6.959	6.966	6.973	6.980	6.987	6.999	7.018	7.102	7.239	7.383
0.70	0.034	0.184	0.393	6.360	6.366	6.373	6.381	6.388	6.396	6.408	6.430	6.523	6.677	6.837
0.75	0.027	0.142	0.305	5.797	5.803	5.809	5.816	5.824	5.832	5.845	5.868	5.971	6.141	6.319
0.80	0.021	0.110	0.234	0.533	5.266	5.271	5.277	5.285	5.293	5.306	5.330	5.444	5.632	5.824
0.85	0.017	0.087	0.182	0.401	4.754	4.754	4.758	4.764	4.771	4.784	4.810	4.939	5.149	5.358
0.90	0.014	0.070	0.144	0.308	0.751	4.254	4.248	4.249	4.255	4.268	4.298	4.450	4.688	4.916
0.93	0.012	0.061	0.126	0.265	0.613	1.219	3.941	3.934	3.937	3.951	3.987	4.163	4.422	4.662
0.95	0.011	0.056	0.113	0.241	0.542	0.994	3.763	3.712	3.713	3.730	3.773	3.972	4.248	4.498
0.97	0.010	0.052	0.105	0.219	0.483	0.837	1.607	3.471	3.467	3.492	3.551	3.782	4.077	4.336
0.98	0.010	0.050	0.101	0.209	0.457	0.776	1.324	3.332	3.327	3.363	3.434	3.686	3.992	4.257
0.99	0.009	0.048	0.097	0.120	0.433	0.722	1.154	3.164	3.164	3.223	3.313	3.591	3.909	4.178
1.00	0.009	0.046	0.093	0.191	0.410	0.675	1.034	2.341	2.952	3.065	3.186	3.495	3.825	4.100
1.01	0.009	0.044	0.089	0.183	0.389	0.632	0.940	1.375	2.595	2.880	3.051	3.399	3.743	4.023
1.02	0.009	0.042	0.085	0.175	0.370	0.594	0.863	1.180	1.723	2.650	2.906	3.303	3.660	3.947
1.05	0.007	0.037	0.075	0.153	0.318	0.498	0.691	0.877	0.878	1.496	2.381	3.010	3.418	3.723
1.10	0.006	0.030	0.061	0.123	0.251	0.381	0.508	0.617	0.673	0.617	1.261	2.507	3.023	3.362
1.20	0.004	0.020	0.040	0.080	0.158	0.232	0.297	0.349	0.381	0.381	0.361	1.489	2.273	2.692
1.30	0.003	0.013	0.026	0.052	0.100	0.142	0.177	0.203	0.218	0.218	0.178	0.693	1.592	2.086
1.50	0.001	0.005	0.009	0.018	0.032	0.042	0.048	0.049	0.046	0.032	-0.008	-0.023	0.556	1.080
2.00	-0.001	-0.004	-0.007	-0.015	-0.030	-0.047	-0.066	-0.085	-0.105	-0.136	-0.190	-0.379	-0.424	-0.255
2.50	-0.001	-0.006	-0.012	-0.025	-0.050	-0.075	-0.100	-0.125	-0.150	-0.188	-0.250	-0.465	-0.661	-0.704
3.00	-0.001	-0.007	-0.014	-0.029	-0.058	-0.086	-0.114	-0.143	-0.170	-0.211	-0.278	-0.514	-0.763	-0.899
4.00	-0.002	-0.008	-0.016	-0.032	-0.064	-0.096	-0.127	-0.158	-0.188	-0.233	-0.306	-0.567	-0.874	-1.097

TABLE A11.3 Enthalpy Departure Function—Polar Deviation, $\left(\dfrac{H^* - H}{RT_c}\right)^{(2)}$

$h^{(2)}$								P_r						
T_r	0.01	0.05	0.10	0.20	0.40	0.60	0.80	1.00	1.20	1.50	2.00	4.00	7.00	10.00
0.45	2.378	2.381	2.380	2.377	2.376	2.376	2.372	2.371	2.374	2.369	2.370	2.366	2.379	2.401
0.50	2.293	2.296	2.295	2.295	2.294	2.295	2.294	2.295	2.296	2.296	2.296	2.306	2.324	2.352
0.55	0.086	2.209	2.210	2.211	2.212	2.213	2.215	2.215	2.217	2.218	2.222	2.235	2.266	2.301
0.60	0.051	2.125	2.125	2.126	2.128	2.129	2.131	2.132	2.134	2.137	2.140	2.161	2.198	2.242
0.65	0.032	0.209	2.037	2.037	2.039	2.041	2.044	2.045	2.047	2.050	2.055	2.081	2.126	2.176
0.70	0.021	0.130	0.334	1.944	1.947	1.948	1.951	1.953	1.956	1.959	1.967	1.995	2.046	2.103
0.75	0.014	0.084	0.207	1.847	1.849	1.851	1.854	1.856	1.859	1.863	1.870	1.903	1.961	2.025
0.80	0.010	0.056	0.130	0.365	1.747	1.749	1.751	1.753	1.756	1.760	1.768	1.806	1.871	1.941
0.85	0.007	0.039	0.085	0.218	1.639	1.640	1.641	1.643	1.641	1.650	1.659	1.701	1.774	1.852
0.90	0.005	0.027	0.059	0.139	0.418	1.523	1.522	1.523	1.525	1.529	1.539	1.588	1.671	1.757
0.93	0.004	0.022	0.048	0.109	0.296	0.727	1.446	1.445	1.455	1.450	1.460	1.516	1.607	1.698
0.95	0.004	0.020	0.041	0.093	0.241	0.514	1.396	1.389	1.388	1.392	1.404	1.465	1.562	1.657
0.97	0.003	0.017	0.036	0.080	0.199	0.390	0.879	1.330	1.326	1.334	1.344	1.413	1.516	1.616
0.98	0.003	0.016	0.033	0.074	0.181	0.345	0.664	1.300	1.292	1.297	1.313	1.386	1.493	1.595
0.99	0.003	0.015	0.031	0.068	0.165	0.307	0.545	1.268	1.255	1.261	1.280	1.359	1.470	1.574
1.00	0.003	0.014	0.029	0.063	0.151	0.275	0.463	1.171	1.210	1.222	1.245	1.331	1.446	1.552
1.01	0.003	0.013	0.027	0.059	0.139	0.247	0.401	0.631	1.148	1.178	1.209	1.303	1.422	1.531
1.02	0.002	0.012	0.025	0.054	0.127	0.223	0.351	0.515	0.986	1.127	1.170	1.274	1.397	1.509
1.05	0.002	0.010	0.020	0.043	0.098	0.166	0.246	0.330	0.360	0.831	1.030	1.183	1.323	1.443
1.10	0.001	0.007	0.014	0.029	0.064	0.104	0.146	0.184	0.205	0.221	0.650	1.019	1.194	1.329
1.20	0.001	0.003	0.005	0.011	0.024	0.037	0.049	0.058	0.061	0.054	0.070	0.643	0.925	1.095
1.30	0.000	0.000	0.000	0.001	0.002	0.004	0.004	0.003	-0.001	-0.012	-0.032	0.275	0.656	0.863
1.50	-0.000	-0.002	-0.005	-0.009	-0.017	-0.026	-0.034	-0.043	-0.052	-0.067	-0.091	-0.073	0.212	0.450
2.00	-0.001	-0.003	-0.007	-0.013	-0.026	-0.039	-0.052	-0.064	-0.076	-0.094	-0.120	-0.182	-0.156	-0.054
2.50	-0.001	-0.003	-0.006	-0.012	-0.024	-0.035	-0.047	-0.058	-0.069	-0.085	-0.109	-0.175	-0.191	-0.145
3.00	-0.000	-0.002	-0.005	-0.010	-0.020	-0.029	-0.039	-0.045	-0.058	-0.071	-0.092	-0.150	-0.173	-0.146
4.00	-0.000	-0.002	-0.003	-0.007	-0.013	-0.020	-0.026	-0.033	-0.039	-0.048	-0.061	-0.100	-0.112	-0.084

TABLE A11.4 Enthalpy Departure Function—Auxiliary
(Opposite Phase) Tables

h_0 – aux	P_r						
T_r	0.01	0.05	0.10	0.20	0.40	0.60	0.80
0.45	0.048	0.266					
0.50	0.039	0.207					
0.55	5.315	0.168	0.361				
0.60	5.163	0.140	0.297				
0.65	5.001	5.011	0.250	0.555			
0.70	4.798	4.852	4.853	0.471	1.160		
0.75	4.487	4.668	4.686	0.403	0.973		
0.80	3.943	4.415	4.483	4.508	0.832	1.531	
0.85		3.991	4.179	4.277	0.708	1.306	
0.90			3.628	3.891	4.037	1.100	1.908
0.93				3.472	3.762	3.869	1.726
0.95				3.027	3.455	3.654	1.573
0.97					2.895	3.251	3.505
0.98					2.373	2.853	3.249
0.99					1.441	1.999	2.654

$h^{(1)}$ – aux	P_r						
T_r	0.01	0.05	0.10	0.20	0.40	0.60	0.80
0.45	0.150	1.004					
0.50	0.109	0.667					
0.55	8.212	0.450	1.105				
0.60	7.572	0.321	0.734				
0.65	6.976	6.948	0.522	1.315			
0.70	6.480	6.364	6.356	0.915	2.878		
0.75	6.202	5.848	5.803	0.683	1.856		
0.80	6.141	5.439	5.322	5.266	1.323	2.728	
0.85		5.192	4.953	4.810	1.013	1.910	
0.90			4.672	4.457	4.294	1.441	2.476
0.93				4.271	4.077	3.974	2.090
0.95				4.096	3.965	3.825	1.884
0.97					3.832	3.723	3.571
0.98					3.733	3.703	3.536
0.99					3.235	3.674	3.616

$h^{(2)}$ – aux	P_r						
T_r	0.01	0.05	0.10	0.20	0.40	0.60	0.80
0.45	0.330	6.489					
0.50	0.159	1.741					
0.55	2.210	0.709	2.887				
0.60	2.127	0.361	1.144				
0.65	2.022	2.036	0.577	2.302			
0.70	2.003	1.946	1.943	1.094	6.382		
0.75	1.927	1.859	1.850	0.608	2.744		
0.80	2.572	1.884	1.787	1.747	1.377	3.705	
0.85		1.722	1.675	1.650	0.769	2.013	
0.90			1.659	1.582	1.534	1.093	2.272
0.93				1.636	1.509	1.455	1.683
0.95				1.537	1.458	1.418	1.300
0.97					1.390	1.373	1.359
0.98					1.349	1.394	1.355
0.99					0.937	1.263	1.385

TABLE A11.5 Entropy Departure Function—Simple Reference Fluid, $\left(\dfrac{S^* - S}{R}\right)_0$

T_r \ P_r	0.01	0.05	0.10	0.20	0.40	0.60	0.80	1.00	1.20	1.50	2.00	4.00	7.00	10.00
0.45	10.453	8.847	8.158	7.472	6.795	6.405	6.132	5.924	5.757	5.557	5.306	4.757	4.401	4.234
0.50	10.137	8.531	7.842	7.156	6.479	6.084	5.816	5.608	5.441	5.240	4.989	4.438	4.074	3.899
0.55	0.038	8.245	7.555	6.870	6.193	5.804	5.531	5.324	5.157	4.956	4.706	4.154	3.788	3.607
0.60	0.029	7.983	7.294	6.610	5.933	5.544	5.273	5.066	4.900	4.700	4.451	3.903	3.537	3.354
0.65	0.025	0.122	7.052	6.328	5.694	5.306	5.036	4.830	4.665	4.467	4.220	3.677	3.315	3.131
0.70	0.018	0.096	0.206	6.140	5.468	5.082	4.814	4.610	4.446	4.250	4.007	3.473	3.117	2.935
0.75	0.015	0.078	0.164	5.917	5.248	4.866	4.600	4.399	4.238	4.046	3.807	3.286	2.939	2.761
0.80	0.013	0.064	0.134	0.294	5.026	4.649	4.388	4.191	4.034	3.846	3.615	3.112	2.777	2.605
0.85	0.011	0.054	0.111	0.239	4.785	4.418	4.166	3.976	3.825	3.646	3.425	2.947	2.629	2.463
0.90	0.009	0.046	0.094	0.199	0.463	4.145	3.912	3.738	3.599	3.434	3.231	2.789	2.491	2.334
0.93	0.008	0.042	0.085	0.179	0.408	0.750	3.723	3.569	3.444	3.295	3.108	2.646	2.412	2.612
0.95	0.008	0.039	0.080	0.168	0.377	0.671	3.556	3.433	3.326	3.193	3.023	2.634	2.362	2.215
0.97	0.007	0.037	0.075	0.158	0.350	0.607	1.056	3.259	3.188	3.081	2.932	2.572	2.312	2.170
0.98	0.007	0.036	0.073	0.153	0.337	0.580	0.971	3.142	3.106	3.019	2.885	2.541	2.287	2.148
0.99	0.007	0.035	0.071	0.148	0.326	0.555	0.903	2.972	3.010	2.953	2.835	2.510	2.263	2.126
1.00	0.007	0.034	0.069	0.144	0.315	0.532	0.847	2.186	2.893	2.879	2.784	2.479	2.239	2.105
1.01	0.007	0.033	0.067	0.139	0.304	0.510	0.799	1.391	2.736	2.798	2.730	2.448	2.215	2.083
1.02	0.006	0.032	0.065	0.135	0.294	0.491	0.757	1.225	2.495	2.706	2.673	2.416	2.191	2.062
1.05	0.006	0.030	0.060	0.124	0.267	0.439	0.656	0.965	1.523	2.328	2.483	2.322	2.121	2.001
1.10	0.005	0.026	0.053	0.109	0.230	0.371	0.537	0.743	1.012	1.557	2.081	2.160	2.007	1.903
1.20	0.004	0.021	0.042	0.085	0.177	0.277	0.389	0.512	0.651	0.890	1.308	1.820	1.789	1.722
1.30	0.003	0.017	0.034	0.068	0.140	0.217	0.298	0.385	0.478	0.628	0.891	1.484	1.582	1.556
1.50	0.002	0.011	0.023	0.046	0.094	0.143	0.194	0.246	0.299	0.381	0.520	0.967	1.208	1.260
2.00	0.001	0.006	0.011	0.022	0.045	0.067	0.089	0.111	0.134	0.167	0.221	0.417	0.620	0.733
2.50	0.001	0.003	0.007	0.013	0.026	0.038	0.051	0.064	0.076	0.094	0.124	0.233	0.362	0.453
3.00	0.000	0.002	0.004	0.008	0.017	0.025	0.033	0.041	0.049	0.061	0.080	0.150	0.236	0.303
4.00	0.000	0.001	0.002	0.004	0.009	0.013	0.017	0.021	0.025	0.031	0.041	0.077	0.123	0.162

TABLE A11.6 Entropy Departure Function—Size/Shape Deviation, $\left(\dfrac{S^* - S}{R}\right)^{(1)}$

$S^{(1)}$							P_r							
T_r	0.01	0.05	0.10	0.20	0.40	0.60	0.80	1.00	1.20	1.50	2.00	4.00	7.00	10.00
0.45	12.562	12.559	12.556	12.549	12.535	12.521	12.508	12.494	12.481	12.462	12.429	12.308	12.144	11.998
0.50	11.201	11.198	11.196	11.191	11.181	11.171	11.161	11.151	11.142	11.128	11.105	11.023	10.920	10.836
0.55	0.113	9.949	9.947	9.943	9.936	9.928	9.921	9.914	9.907	9.897	9.881	9.828	9.770	9.732
0.60	0.078	8.828	8.827	8.823	8.817	8.811	8.806	8.800	8.795	8.788	8.777	8.746	8.723	8.720
0.65	0.055	0.297	7.832	7.829	7.824	7.819	7.815	7.810	7.807	7.801	7.794	7.779	7.785	7.811
0.70	0.040	0.215	0.460	6.951	6.946	6.941	6.937	6.933	6.930	6.926	6.922	6.921	6.952	7.002
0.75	0.030	0.156	0.339	6.173	6.167	6.162	6.158	6.155	6.152	6.149	6.147	6.159	6.213	6.285
0.80	0.022	0.116	0.246	0.568	5.474	5.467	5.462	5.458	5.455	5.452	5.452	5.478	5.556	5.648
0.85	0.017	0.088	0.184	0.408	4.853	4.841	4.832	4.826	4.822	4.820	4.822	4.866	4.969	5.083
0.90	0.013	0.068	0.140	0.301	0.744	4.269	4.250	4.238	4.232	4.230	4.236	4.307	4.442	4.578
0.93	0.012	0.059	0.120	0.254	0.593	1.200	3.914	3.893	3.885	3.884	3.896	3.993	4.151	4.300
0.95	0.011	0.053	0.109	0.228	0.517	0.961	3.697	3.658	3.647	3.648	3.667	3.790	3.966	4.125
0.97	0.010	0.048	0.099	0.206	0.456	0.797	1.561	3.406	3.391	3.401	3.437	3.592	3.788	3.957
0.98	0.009	0.046	0.094	0.196	0.429	0.735	1.270	3.264	3.247	3.268	3.318	3.494	3.702	3.875
0.99	0.009	0.044	0.090	0.186	0.405	0.680	1.098	3.093	3.082	3.126	3.195	3.397	3.616	3.795
1.00	0.008	0.042	0.086	0.177	0.382	0.632	0.977	2.269	2.868	2.967	3.067	3.301	3.532	3.717
1.01	0.008	0.040	0.082	0.169	0.361	0.590	0.883	1.306	2.513	2.784	2.933	3.206	3.450	3.641
1.02	0.008	0.039	0.078	0.161	0.342	0.552	0.807	1.113	1.655	2.557	2.790	3.110	3.369	3.565
1.05	0.007	0.034	0.069	0.140	0.292	0.460	0.642	0.820	0.831	1.443	2.283	2.827	3.135	3.348
1.10	0.006	0.028	0.056	0.112	0.230	0.350	0.470	0.578	0.640	0.618	1.241	2.360	2.767	3.013
1.20	0.004	0.019	0.038	0.075	0.149	0.220	0.286	0.343	0.385	0.412	0.447	1.473	2.115	2.430
1.30	0.003	0.013	0.026	0.052	0.102	0.148	0.190	0.226	0.254	0.282	0.300	0.835	1.569	1.944
1.50	0.001	0.007	0.014	0.028	0.053	0.076	0.097	0.115	0.130	0.147	0.166	0.315	0.823	1.222
2.00	0.000	0.002	0.004	0.008	0.016	0.023	0.029	0.035	0.040	0.048	0.058	0.101	0.238	0.434
2.50	0.000	0.001	0.002	0.004	0.007	0.011	0.014	0.017	0.020	0.024	0.031	0.060	0.130	0.230
3.00	0.000	0.001	0.001	0.002	0.004	0.006	0.008	0.010	0.012	0.015	0.020	0.044	0.093	0.158
4.00	0.000	0.000	0.001	0.001	0.002	0.003	0.005	0.006	0.007	0.009	0.012	0.028	0.060	0.100

TABLE A11.7 Entropy Departure Function—Polar Deviation, $\left(\dfrac{S^* - S}{R}\right)^{(2)}$

$S^{(2)}$

T_r	P_r													
	0.01	0.05	0.10	0.20	0.40	0.60	0.80	1.00	1.20	1.50	2.00	4.00	7.00	10.00
0.45	2.856	2.860	2.852	2.845	2.832	2.819	2.800	2.787	2.781	2.757	2.732	2.608	2.465	2.334
0.50	2.678	2.681	2.675	2.671	2.659	2.649	2.636	2.627	2.618	2.601	2.575	2.482	2.349	2.232
0.55	0.133	2.517	2.515	2.511	2.502	2.493	2.485	2.474	2.468	2.453	2.433	2.347	2.237	2.135
0.60	0.072	2.369	2.368	2.363	2.355	2.347	2.339	2.331	2.134	2.311	2.290	2.218	2.120	2.032
0.65	0.042	0.280	2.226	2.221	2.213	2.206	2.199	2.191	2.183	2.172	2.159	2.090	2.003	1.926
0.70	0.026	0.163	0.420	2.083	2.076	2.068	2.062	2.054	2.048	2.038	2.021	1.962	1.885	1.819
0.75	0.017	0.098	0.245	1.950	1.942	1.935	1.928	1.921	1.915	1.905	1.890	1.836	1.768	1.710
0.80	0.011	0.062	0.146	0.412	1.810	1.802	1.795	1.788	1.782	1.773	1.758	1.710	1.651	1.602
0.85	0.008	0.041	0.092	0.234	1.679	1.670	1.662	1.655	1.648	1.639	1.625	1.583	1.534	1.494
0.90	0.005	0.028	0.061	0.144	0.432	1.537	1.526	1.517	1.510	1.501	1.488	1.454	1.417	1.386
0.93	0.004	0.023	0.048	0.110	0.299	0.741	1.443	1.432	1.432	1.414	1.402	1.375	1.346	1.321
0.95	0.004	0.020	0.042	0.093	0.240	0.514	1.390	1.372	1.363	1.353	1.343	1.321	1.299	1.278
0.97	0.003	0.017	0.036	0.079	0.196	0.385	0.874	1.311	1.298	1.288	1.281	1.267	1.251	1.235
0.98	0.003	0.016	0.033	0.073	0.178	0.339	0.654	1.279	1.263	1.254	1.248	1.239	1.227	1.214
0.99	0.003	0.015	0.031	0.068	0.162	0.300	0.533	1.248	1.225	1.218	1.215	1.211	1.204	1.192
1.00	0.003	0.014	0.029	0.063	0.148	0.268	0.450	1.151	1.180	1.179	1.180	1.183	1.180	1.171
1.01	0.003	0.013	0.027	0.058	0.136	0.241	0.388	0.612	1.118	1.135	1.144	1.155	1.156	1.149
1.02	0.002	0.012	0.025	0.054	0.124	0.217	0.339	0.498	0.959	1.084	1.105	1.127	1.132	1.128
1.05	0.002	0.010	0.020	0.043	0.096	0.161	0.238	0.319	0.350	0.799	0.971	1.039	1.060	1.064
1.10	0.001	0.007	0.014	0.030	0.064	0.103	0.144	0.182	0.206	0.229	0.618	0.887	0.940	0.958
1.20	0.001	0.003	0.007	0.014	0.029	0.045	0.059	0.072	0.079	0.081	0.107	0.559	0.706	0.755
1.30	0.000	0.001	0.003	0.006	0.012	0.018	0.023	0.027	0.029	0.029	0.025	0.265	0.490	0.568
1.50	0.000	-0.000	-0.001	-0.001	-0.002	-0.003	-0.004	-0.006	-0.008	-0.011	-0.018	0.012	0.172	0.273
2.00	0.000	-0.001	-0.002	-0.004	-0.008	-0.012	-0.015	-0.019	-0.022	-0.028	-0.036	-0.056	-0.051	-0.027
2.50	0.000	-0.001	-0.002	-0.003	-0.007	-0.010	-0.013	-0.016	-0.019	-0.024	-0.031	-0.052	-0.067	-0.071
3.00	0.000	-0.001	-0.001	-0.003	-0.005	-0.008	-0.010	-0.013	-0.015	-0.019	-0.025	-0.044	-0.061	-0.070
4.00	0.000	-0.000	-0.001	-0.002	-0.003	-0.005	-0.007	-0.008	-0.010	-0.012	-0.016	-0.029	-0.043	-0.053

TABLE A11.8 Entropy Departure Function—Auxiliary (Opposite Phase) Tables

$S_0 - \text{aux}$	P_r						
T_r	0.01	0.05	0.10	0.20	0.40	0.60	0.80
0.45	0.072	0.800					
0.50	0.051	0.278					
0.55	9.851	0.204	0.442				
0.60	9.586	0.156	0.334				
0.65	9.329	7.741	0.260	0.584			
0.70	9.032	7.506	6.823	0.462	1.157		
0.75	8.622	7.253	6.593	0.370	0.917		
0.80	7.986	6.934	6.332	5.687	0.742	1.390	
0.85		6.441	5.971	5.408	0.592	1.135	
0.90			5.360	4.972	4.475	0.904	1.634
0.93				4.518	4.176	3.922	1.442
0.95				4.029	3.848	3.692	1.282
0.97					3.246	3.271	3.288
0.98					2.659	2.852	3.025
0.99					1.507	1.920	2.413

$S^{(1)} - \text{aux}$	P_r						
T_r	0.01	0.05	0.10	0.20	0.40	0.60	0.80
0.45	0.256	1.721					
0.50	0.170	1.048					
0.55	9.951	0.647	1.592				
0.60	8.838	0.426	0.977				
0.65	7.880	7.834	0.647	1.631			
0.70	7.135	6.968	6.954	1.069	3.317		
0.75	6.708	6.252	6.190	0.758	2.050		
0.80	6.503	5.712	5.565	5.489	1.404	2.864	
0.85		5.374	5.105	4.933	1.041	1.951	
0.90			4.764	4.521	4.327	1.439	2.458
0.93				4.321	4.089	3.962	2.056
0.95				4.181	3.965	3.804	1.845
0.97					3.876	3.703	3.523
0.98					3.862	3.704	3.488
0.99					3.628	3.778	3.584

$S^{(2)} - \text{aux}$	P_r						
T_r	0.01	0.05	0.10	0.20	0.40	0.60	0.80
0.45	0.632	12.555					
0.50	0.273	3.030					
0.55	2.520	1.118	4.578				
0.60	2.375	0.521	1.663				
0.65	2.208	2.227	0.775	3.111			
0.70	2.176	2.094	2.087	1.382	8.002		
0.75	2.062	1.972	1.958	0.724	3.255		
0.80	2.842	1.998	1.876	1.819	1.556	4.116	
0.85		1.791	1.736	1.702	0.833	2.162	
0.90			1.712	1.622	1.559	1.138	2.328
0.93				1.680	1.530	1.462	1.708
0.95				1.585	1.477	1.424	1.309
0.97					1.415	1.378	1.351
0.98					1.397	1.405	1.347
0.99					1.028	1.295	1.389

TABLE A11.9 Viscosity—Simple Reference Fluid, $(10^3\ \eta\xi)_0$

$10^3 \times \eta\xi_0$	P_r													
T_r	0.01	0.05	0.10	0.20	0.40	0.60	0.80	1.00	1.20	1.50	2.00	4.00	7.00	10.00
0.55	351	11455	11467	11496	11557	11626	11704	11788	11880	12031	12316	13815	16948	20813
0.60	383	9224	9238	9267	9329	9397	9469	9547	9629	9761	10004	11169	13337	15681
0.65	415	409	7462	7495	7565	7639	7715	7794	7875	8002	8224	9204	10763	12163
0.70	446	437	446	6130	6710	6293	6376	6461	6547	6677	6897	7784	8986	9845
0.75	476	468	468	5060	5153	5247	5341	5435	5528	5667	5856	6750	7750	8308
0.80	505	499	496	513	4283	4392	4499	4605	4708	4861	5105	5965	6860	7255
0.85	534	529	526	532	3507	3638	3765	3887	4005	4176	4444	5336	6182	6497
0.90	562	559	557	559	595	2904	3065	3216	3357	3555	3857	4800	5632	5919
0.93	579	577	575	576	601	680	2625	2808	2973	3196	3526	4509	5342	5627
0.95	590	588	587	588	608	666	2293	2519	2709	2957	3310	4324	5161	5449
0.97	601	600	599	600	617	662	778	2195	2431	2715	3098	4146	4987	5281
0.98	607	606	605	606	622	662	757	2005	2282	2591	2992	4059	4902	5200
0.99	612	611	611	612	627	663	744	1770	2122	2464	2887	3974	4819	5122
1.00	618	617	617	618	632	666	735	1166	1945	2334	2782	3890	4738	5045
1.01	623	623	622	624	638	668	730	896	1742	2200	2678	3807	4658	4969
1.02	629	628	628	630	643	672	727	853	1496	2059	2572	3762	4579	4896
1.05	645	645	645	648	660	685	728	806	993	1610	2258	3492	4351	4682
1.10	672	672	673	677	689	711	744	795	879	1136	1767	3130	3994	4349
1.20	724	726	728	733	746	765	792	827	875	980	1275	2530	3368	3757
1.30	776	778	780	786	800	818	841	870	906	978	1152	2103	2865	3259
1.50	876	878	881	887	900	915	933	953	977	1019	1109	1629	2204	2562
1.60	925	927	930	935	947	961	976	993	1013	1047	1115	1508	2008	2348
1.70	974	976	978	983	994	1006	1019	1034	1050	1077	1131	1435	1875	2207
1.80	1021	1023	1025	1030	1040	1051	1062	1075	1089	1111	1154	1398	1793	2127
2.00	1114	1116	1118	1122	1131	1140	1150	1160	1170	1186	1218	1394	1740	2103

$\xi = (RT_c N_0^2 / P_c^4 M^3)^{1/6}$

TABLE A11.10 Viscosity—Size/Shape Deviation, $(10^3\,\eta\xi)^{(1)}$

$10^3 \times \eta\xi^{(1)}$ T_r	P_r													
	0.01	0.05	0.10	0.20	0.40	0.60	0.80	1.00	1.20	1.50	2.00	4.00	7.00	10.00
0.55	-60	33672	33712	33785	33921	34045	34150	34243	34325	34420	34512	34205	31965	28093
0.60	-76	23840	23856	23886	23940	23984	24019	24046	24065	24081	24074	23720	22590	21364
0.65	-86	-59	17901	17904	17908	17906	17901	17892	17880	17855	17803	17521	17245	17684
0.70	-94	-67	-61	13687	13656	13624	13590	13556	13522	13471	13388	13153	13388	14710
0.75	-100	-74	-56	10424	10365	10308	10252	10198	10146	10073	9963	9734	10235	11970
0.80	-105	-82	-60	-41	7748	7667	7590	7517	7448	7353	7215	6959	7571	9445
0.85	-111	-90	-67	-34	5699	5589	5488	5394	5306	5188	5021	4719	5344	7198
0.90	-117	-98	-77	-40	15	4015	3876	3754	3645	3501	3305	2952	3538	4278
0.93	-120	-103	-83	-46	15	95	3121	2970	2844	2654	2473	2089	2648	4291
0.95	-123	-106	-87	-51	12	81	2704	2518	2377	2207	1989	1606	2130	3701
0.97	-125	-110	-91	-56	7	72	239	2108	1948	1772	1554	1171	1670	3165
0.98	-127	-112	-93	-59	4	68	181	1910	1740	1567	1352	974	1461	2917
0.99	-128	-113	-96	-62	1	63	154	1694	1525	1365	1160	789	1264	2682
1.00	-129	-115	-98	-65	-3	59	138	826	1282	1163	975	617	1081	2459
1.01	-131	-117	-100	-68	-7	54	125	764	941	954	798	456	910	2248
1.02	-132	-119	-102	-71	-10	49	115	210	343	729	627	307	750	2049
1.05	-137	-124	-109	-80	-23	33	89	147	194	25	143	-80	339	1521
1.10	-144	-134	-121	-95	-45	4	51	92	112	-6	-336	-539	-150	844
1.20	-161	-159	-144	-125	-88	-53	-20	8	25	10	-191	-892	-588	90
1.30	-180	-175	-168	-155	-128	-102	-78	-57	-43	-41	-117	-756	-600	-154
1.50	-224	-221	-218	-211	-196	-180	-163	-147	-132	-114	-105	-293	-244	-60
1.60	-248	-246	-249	-239	-226	-212	-196	-179	-163	-140	-111	-144	-82	30
1.70	-273	-272	-270	-266	-255	-241	-225	-208	-190	-162	-120	-48	31	86
1.80	-299	-298	-297	-293	-283	-269	-253	-235	-215	-184	-132	6	99	96
2.00	-354	-353	-352	-347	-336	-322	-304	-289	-263	-227	-166	35	120	-14

$\xi = (RT_c N_0^2 / P_c^4 M^3)^{1/6}$

TABLE A11.11 Viscosity—Polar Deviation, $(10^3\ \eta\xi)^{(2)}$

$10^3 \times \eta\xi^{(2)}$

							P_r							
T_r	0.01	0.05	0.10	0.20	0.40	0.60	0.80	1.00	1.20	1.50	2.00	4.00	7.00	10.00
0.55	12	12840	12852	12870	12900	12916	12916	12904	12882	12825	12672	11451	8083	3392
0.60	16	7977	7979	7981	7978	7966	7945	7917	7880	7812	7665	6744	4716	2481
0.65	23	25	5565	5591	5520	5484	5442	5397	5348	5266	5115	4382	3236	2513
0.70	32	41	21	4108	4052	3994	3933	3871	3807	3709	3544	2897	2256	2356
0.75	44	54	52	3128	3049	2969	2890	2811	2733	2617	2430	1804	1431	1948
0.80	57	67	72	50	2335	2235	2136	2040	1946	1811	1599	952	707	1409
0.85	71	80	87	86	1856	1730	1609	1493	1382	1224	984	297	97	853
0.90	85	93	100	107	87	1433	1277	1135	1002	819	548	−186	−383	348
0.93	94	101	108	117	113	82	1168	999	848	647	357	−402	−607	86
0.95	100	106	113	122	125	106	1140	938	771	595	253	−519	−731	−68
0.97	106	112	118	128	135	125	138	898	708	477	165	−616	−835	−207
0.98	109	115	121	130	139	133	127	883	678	441	125	−658	−880	−270
0.99	112	118	123	133	142	140	130	865	643	405	87	−696	−920	−329
1.00	115	120	126	135	146	145	137	455	593	367	51	−730	−956	−384
1.01	119	123	129	135	149	150	143	132	488	322	17	−760	−988	−436
1.02	122	126	131	140	151	155	149	131	202	265	−18	−787	−1016	−483
1.05	131	135	139	147	159	165	164	150	66	−17	−128	−848	−1077	−603
1.10	146	149	153	159	170	176	178	170	139	−23	−280	−895	−1113	−734
1.20	176	178	180	184	191	195	195	189	173	117	−106	−829	−1009	−796
1.30	205	206	207	209	213	215	214	209	198	165	48	−608	−779	−689
1.50	260	260	260	261	262	264	264	263	260	251	216	−91	−266	−330
1.60	285	285	285	285	287	289	291	293	294	292	279	102	−61	−179
1.70	309	309	309	309	311	314	318	322	325	330	331	245	96	−73
1.80	331	331	331	332	335	338	343	349	355	363	374	347	205	−16
2.00	373	373	373	374	377	382	389	396	404	416	437	462	304	−40

$\xi = (RT_c N_0^2 / P_c^4 M^3)^{1/6}$

TABLE A11.12 Viscosity—Auxiliary (Opposite Phase) Tables

$10^3 \times \eta\xi_0$ aux T_r	P_r						
	0.01	0.05	0.10	0.20	0.40	0.60	0.80
0.55	11444	386	744				
0.60	9203	387	489				
0.65	7373	7445	442	854			
0.70	5777	6050	6090	575	5145		
0.75	4209	4874	4994	515	1233		
0.80	2899	3705	3996	4165	734	2191	
0.85		2460	2918	3281	616	1994	
0.90			1828	1828	2700	735	1184
0.93				1385	2107	2412	951
0.95				1316	1665	2006	854
0.97					1246	1510	1860
0.98					1020	1243	1557
0.99					729	910	1171

$10^3 \times \eta\xi^{(1)}$ aux T_r	P_r						
	0.01	0.05	0.10	0.20	0.40	0.60	0.80
0.55	33643	−44	−382				
0.60	23853	−52	−150				
0.65	18054	17899	−83	−590			
0.70	14327	13762	13702	−194	−6419		
0.75	12014	10752	10504	−79	−856		
0.80	9223	8681	8162	7854	−487	−1365	
0.85		7074	6578	6028	−20	−161	
0.90			4866	4866	4247	66	308
0.93				3086	3627	3319	303
0.95				2652	3114	2970	290
0.97					2182	2501	2393
0.98					1549	2019	2220
0.99					795	1267	1747

$10^3 \times \eta\xi^{(2)}$ aux T_r	P_r						
	0.01	0.05	0.10	0.20	0.40	0.60	0.80
0.55	12832	−48	−584				
0.60	7995	0	−169				
0.65	5562	5571	−37	−683			
0.70	4684	4188	4135	−186	−7106		
0.75	4228	3381	3205	−22	−1048		
0.80	4975	3311	2757	2454	−239	−1977	
0.85		2980	2569	2136	−2	−371	
0.90			2326	2326	1656	−3	−14
0.93				1648	1699	1372	84
0.95				1328	1580	1397	124
0.97					1080	1292	1180
0.98					759	1069	1183
0.99					427	617	922

A11.2 CRITICAL PROPERTIES OF FLUIDS

The table on the following pages lists the critical constants for 199 selected compounds. The values were reproduced from the data base contained in the appendix of R.C. Reid, J.M. Prausnitz, and T.K. Sherwood, *The Properties of Gases and Liquids,* 3 ed., McGraw-Hill, New York, 1977. Units for the entries in the table are: M = molecular weight (g/mol); T_c = critical temperature (K); P_c critical pressure (atm); z_c = critical compressibility factor (unitless); and ω = acentric factor (unitless).

TABLE A11.13   Critical Constants for Selected Compounds

No.	Formula	Name	M	T_c	P_c	z_c	ω
1	Ar	Argon	39.948	150.8	48.1	0.291	−0.004
2	Br_2	Bromine	159.808	584	102	0.270	0.132
3	Cl_2	Chlorine	70.906	417	76	0.275	0.073
4	Cl_4Si	Silicon tetrachloride	169.898	507	37	0.29	0.264
5	F_2	Fluorine	37.997	144.3	51.5	0.288	0.048
6	F_6S	Sulfur hexafluoride	146.050	318.7	37.1	0.281	0.286
7	HBr	Hydrogen bromide	80.912	363.2	84.4	0.283	0.063
8	HCl	Hydrogen chloride	36.461	324.6	82.0	0.249	0.12
9	HF	Hydrogen fluoride	20.006	461	64	0.12	0.372
10	HI	Hydrogen iodide	127.912	424.0	82.0	0.309	0.05
11	H_2	Hydrogen	2.016	33.2	12.8	0.305	−0.022
12	H_2O	Water	18.015	647.3	217.6	0.229	0.344
13	H_2S	Hydrogen sulfide	34.080	373.2	88.2	0.284	0.100
14	H_3N	Ammonia	17.031	405.6	111.3	0.242	0.250
15	He(4)	Helium-4	4.003	5.19	2.24	0.301	−0.387
16	I_2	Iodine	253.808	819	115	0.265	0.229
17	Kr	Krypton	83.800	209.4	54.3	0.288	−0.002
18	NO	Nitric oxide	30.006	180	64	0.25	0.607
19	NO_2	Nitrogen dioxide	46.006	431.4	100	0.480	0.86
20	N_2	Nitrogen	28.013	126.2	33.5	0.290	0.040
21	N_2O	Nitrous oxide	44.013	309.6	71.5	0.274	0.160
22	Ne	Neon	20.183	44.4	27.2	0.311	0.00
23	O_2	Oxygen	31.999	154.6	49.8	0.288	0.021
24	O_3	Ozone	47.998	261.0	55.0	0.288	0.215
25	Xe	Xenon	131.300	289.7	57.6	0.286	0.002
26	$CClF_3$	Chlorotrifluoromethane	104.459	302.0	38.7	0.282	0.180
27	CCl_2F_2	Dichlorodifluoromethane	120.914	385.0	40.7	0.280	0.176
28	CCl_4	Carbon tetrachloride	153.823	556.4	45.0	0.272	0.194
29	CO	Carbon monoxide	28.010	132.9	34.5	0.295	0.049
30	COS	Carbonyl sulfide	60.070	375	58	0.26	0.099
31	CO_2	Carbon dioxide	44.010	304.2	72.8	0.274	0.225
32	CS_2	Carbon disulfide	76.131	552	78.0	0.293	0.115
33	$CHClF_2$	Chlorodifluoromethane	86.469	369.2	49.1	0.267	0.215
34	$CHCl_2F$	Dichloromonofluoromethane	102.923	451.6	51.0	0.272	0.202
35	$CHCl_3$	Chloroform	119.378	536.4	54.0	0.293	0.216
36	CHN	Hydrogen cyanide	27.026	456.8	53.2	0.197	0.407
37	CH_2Cl_2	Dichloromethane	84.933	510	60.0	0.277	0.193
38	CH_2O	Formaldehyde	30.026	408	65		0.253
39	CH_2O_2	Formic acid	46.025	580			
40	CH_3Br	Methyl bromide	94.939	464	85		0.273
41	CH_3Cl	Methyl chloride	50.488	416.3	65.9	0.268	0.156
42	CH_3F	Methyl fluoride	34.033	317.8	58.0	0.275	0.190
43	CH_3I	Methyl iodine	141.939	528	65	0.285	0.172

TABLE A11.13 Continued

No.	Formula	Name	M	T_c	P_c	z_c	ω
44	CH_3NO_2	Nitromethane	61.041	588	62.3	0.224	0.346
45	CH_4	Methane	16.043	190.6	45.4	0.288	0.008
46	CH_4O	Methanol	32.042	512.6	79.9	0.224	0.559
57	CH_4S	Methyl mercaptan	48.107	470.0	71.4	0.268	0.155
58	CH_5N	Methylamine	31.058	430	73.6	0.292	0.275
59	C_2Cl_4	Tetrachloroethylene	165.834	620	44	0.25	
60	C_2F_6	Perfluoroethane	138.012	292.8			
61	C_2HCl_3	Trichloroethylene	131.389	571	48.5	0.265	0.213
62	C_2H_2	Acetylene	26.038	308.3	60.6	0.271	0.184
63	C_2H_3Cl	Vinyl chloride	62.499	429.7	55.3	0.265	0.122
64	C_2H_3ClO	Acetyl chloride	78.498	508	58	0.28	0.344
65	$C_2H_3Cl_3$	1,1,2-Trichloroethane	133.405	602	41	0.24	0.22
66	C_2H_3N	Acetonitrile	41.053	548	47.7	0.184	0.321
67	C_2H_3NO	Methyl isocyanate	57.052	491	55		0.278
68	C_2H_4	Ethylene	28.054	282.4	49.7	0.276	0.085
69	$C_2H_4Cl_2$	1,1-Dichloroethane	98.960	523	50	0.28	0.248
70	$C_2H_4Cl_2$	1,2-Dichloroethane	98.960	561	53	0.25	0.286
71	C_2H_4O	Acetaldehyde	44.054	461	55	0.22	0.303
72	C_2H_4O	Ethylene oxide	44.054	469	71.0	0.258	0.200
73	$C_2H_4O_2$	Acetic acid	60.052	594.4	57.1	0.200	0.454
74	$C_2H_4O_2$	Methyl formate	60.052	487.2	59.2	0.255	0.252
75	C_2H_5Br	Ethyl bromide	108.966	503.8	61.5	0.320	0.254
76	C_2H_5Cl	Ethyl chloride	64.515	460.4	52.0	0.274	0.190
77	C_2H_6	Ethane	30.070	305.4	48.2	0.285	0.098
78	C_2H_6O	Dimethyl ether	46.069	400.0	53.0	0.287	0.192
79	C_2H_6O	Ethanol	46.069	516.2	63.0	0.248	0.635
80	$C_2H_6O_2$	Ethylene glycol	62.069	645	76	0.27	
81	C_2H_7N	Ethylamine	45.085	456	55.5	0.264	0.284
82	C_2H_7N	Dimethylamine	45.085	437.6	52.4	0.272	0.288
83	C_2H_7NO	Monoethanolamine	61.084	614	44	0.17	
84	$C_2H_8N_2$	Ethylenediamine	60.099	593	62	0.26	0.51
85	C_3H_5Cl	Allyl chloride	76.526	514	47	0.26	0.13
86	C_3H_6	Cyclopropane	42.081	397.8	54.2	0.282	0.264
87	C_3H_6	Propylene	42.081	365.0	45.6	0.275	0.148
88	$C_3H_6Cl_2$	1,2-Dicloropropane	112.987	577	44	0.21	0.24
89	C_3H_6O	Acetone	58.080	508.1	46.4	0.232	0.309
90	C_3H_6O	Propionaldehyde	58.080	496	47	0.26	0.313
91	C_3H_6O	Propylene oxide	58.080	482.2	48.6	0.228	0.269
92	$C_3H_6O_2$	Propionic acid	74.080	612	53.0	0.242	0.536
93	$C_3H_6O_2$	Ethyl formate	74.080	508.4	46.8	0.257	0.283
94	$C_3H_6O_2$	Methyl acetate	74.080	506.8	46.3	0.254	0.324
95	C_3H_7Cl	Propyl chloride	78.542	503	45.2	0.278	0.230
96	C_3H_7Cl	Isopropyl chloride	78.542	485	46.6	0.269	0.232

TABLE A11.13   Continued

No.	Formula	Name	M	T_c	P_c	z_c	ω
97	C_3H_8	Propane	44.097	369.8	41.9	0.281	0.152
98	C_3H_8O	1-Propanol	60.069	536.7	51.0	0.253	0.624
99	C_3H_8O	Isopropyl alcohol	60.069	508.3	47.0	0.248	0.6637
100	C_3H_8O	Methyl ethyl ether	60.069	437.8	43.4	0.267	0.236
101	$C_3H_8O_2$	1,2-Propanediol	76.096	625	60	0.28	
102	$C_3H_8O_2$	1,3-Propanediol	76.096	658	59	0.26	
103	$C_3H_8O_3$	Glycerol	92.095	726	66	0.28	
104	C_3H_9N	n-Propylamine	59.112	497.0	46.8	0.267	0.229
105	C_3H_9N	Isopropylamine	59.112	476	50	0.29	0.297
106	C_3H_9N	Trimethylamine	59.112	433.2	40.2	0.287	0.195
107	C_4H_4O	Furan	68.075	490.2	54.3	0.294	0.204
108	C_4H_6	1-Butyne	54.092	463.7	46.5	0.27	0.050
109	C_4H_6	2-Butyne	54.092	488.6	50.2	0.277	0.124
110	C_4H_6	1,2-Butadiene	54.092	443.7	44.4	0.267	0.255
111	C_4H_6	1,3-Butadiene	54.092	425	42.7	0.270	0.195
112	$C_4H_6O_2$	Vinyl acetate	86.091	525	43	0.26	0.34
113	$C_4H_6O_3$	Acetic anhydride	102.089	569	46.2	0.287	
114	C_4H_8	1-Butene	56.108	419.6	39.7	0.277	0.187
115	C_4H_8	Cis-2-butene	56.108	435.6	41.5	0.272	0.202
116	C_4H_8	Trans-2-butene	56.108	428.6	40.5	0.274	0.214
117	C_4H_8	Cyclobutane	56.108	459.9	49.2	0.274	0.209
118	C_4H_8O	n-Butyraldehyde	72.107	524	40	0.26	0.352
119	C_4H_8O	Isobutyraldehyde	72.107	513	41	0.27	0.35
120	C_4H_8O	Methyl ethyl ketone	72.107	535.6	41.0	0.249	0.329
121	C_4H_8O	Tetrahydrofuran	72.107	540.2	51.2	0.259	
122	$C_4H_8O_2$	n-Butyric acid	88.107	628	52.0	0.295	0.67
123	$C_4H_8O_2$	Ethyl acetate	88.107	523.2	37.8	0.252	0.363
124	$C_4H_8O_2$	Isobutyric acid	88.107	609	40	0.23	0.61
125	C_4H_9Cl	1-Chlorobutane	92.569	542	36.4	0.255	0.218
126	C_4H_9Cl	2-Chlorobutane	92.569	520.6	39	0.28	0.30
127	C_4H_9Cl	$Tert$-butyl chloride	92.596	507	39	0.28	0.19
128	C_4H_{10}	n-Butane	58.124	425.2	37.5	0.274	0.193
129	C_4H_{10}	Isobutane	58.124	408.1	36.0	0.283	0.176
130	$C_4H_{10}O$	n-Butanol	74.123	562.9	43.6	0.259	0.590
131	$C_4H_{10}O$	2-Butanol	74.123	536.0	41.4	0.252	0.576
132	$C_4H_{10}O$	Isobutanol	74.123	547.7	42.4	0.257	0.588
133	$C_4H_{10}O$	$Tert$-butanol	74.123	506.2	39.2	0.259	0.618
134	$C_4H_{10}O$	Ethyl ether	74.123	466.7	35.9	0.262	0.281
135	$C_4H_{10}O_3$	Diethylene glycol	106.122	681	46	0.26	
136	$C_4H_{11}N$	n-Butylamine	73.139	524	41	0.27	0.396
137	$C_4H_{11}N$	Isobutylamine	73.139	516	42	0.28	
138	$C_4H_{11}N$	Diethylamine	73.139	496.6	36.6	0.270	0.299
139	C_5H_5N	Pyridine	79.102	620.0	55.6	0.277	0.24

TABLE A11.13 Continued

No.	Formula	Name	M	T_c	P_c	z_c	ω
140	C_5H_8O	Cyclopentanone	84.118	626	53	0.28	0.35
141	C_5H_{10}	Cyclopentane	70.135	511.6	44.5	0.276	0.192
142	$C_5H_{10}O$	Methyl isopropyl ketone	86.134	553.4	38.0	0.259	0.349
143	$C_5H_{10}O$	Diethyl ketone	86.134	561.0	36.9	0.269	0.347
144	C_5H_{12}	n-Pentane	72.151	469.6	33.3	0.262	0.251
145	C_5H_{12}	2-Methyl butane	72.151	460.4	33.4	0.271	0.227
146	$C_5H_{12}O$	1-Pentanol	88.150	586	38	0.26	0.58
147	$C_5H_{12}O$	2-Methyl-1-butanol	88.150	571	38	0.26	0.70
148	$C_5H_{12}O$	3-Methyl-1-butanol	88.150	579.5	38	0.26	0.58
149	$C_5H_{12}O$	2-Methyl-2-butanol	88.150	545	39	0.28	0.50
150	$C_5H_{12}O$	2,2-Dimethyl-1-propane	88.150	549	39	0.28	
151	$C_5H_{12}O$	Ethyl propyl ether	88.150	500.6	32.1		0.331
152	C_6F_6	Perfluorobenzene	186.056	516.7	32.6		0.40
153	C_6F_{12}	Perfluorocyclohexane	300.047	457.2	24		
154	C_6F_{14}	Perfluoro-n-hexane	338.044	451.7	18.8	0.224	0.73
155	$C_6H_4Cl_2$	o-Dichlorobenzene	147.004	697.3	40.5	0.255	0.272
156	$C_6H_4Cl_2$	m-Dichlorobenzene	147.004	684	38	0.24	0.26
157	$C_6H_4Cl_2$	p-Dichlorobenzene	147.004	685	39	0.26	0.27
158	C_6H_5Br	Bromobenzene	157.010	670	44.6	0.263	0.249
159	C_6H_5Cl	Chlorobenzene	112.559	632.4	44.6	0.265	0.249
160	C_6H_5F	Fluorobenzene	96.104	560.1	44.9	0.265	0.245
161	C_6H_5I	Iodobenzene	204.011	721	44.6	0.265	0.246
162	C_6H_6	Benzene	78.114	562.1	48.3	0.271	0.212
163	C_6H_6O	Phenol	94.113	694.2	60.5	0.24	0.440
164	C_6H_7N	Aniline	93.129	699	52.4	0.247	0.382
165	$C_6H_{10}O$	Cyclohexanone	98.145	629	38	0.23	0.443
166	C_6H_{12}	Cyclohexane	84.162	553.4	40.2	0.273	0.213
167	C_6H_{12}	Methylcyclopentane	84.162	532.7	37.4	0.273	0.239
168	$C_6H_{12}O$	Cyclohexanol	100.161	625	37	0.24	0.55
169	$C_6H_{12}O$	Methyl isobutyl ketone	100.161	571	32.3	0.26	0.400
170	$C_6H_{12}O_2$	n-Butyl acetate	116.160	579	31	0.26	0.417
171	$C_6H_{12}O_2$	Isobutyl acetate	116.160	561	30	0.27	0.479
172	C_6H_{14}	n-Hexane	86.178	507.4	29.3	0.260	0.296
173	C_6H_{14}	2-Methylpentane	86.178	497.5	29.7	0.267	0.279
174	C_6H_{14}	3-Methylpentane	86.178	504.4	30.8	0.273	0.275
175	C_6H_{14}	2,2-Dimethylbutane	86.178	488.7	30.4	0.272	0.231
176	C_6H_{14}	2,3-Dimethylbutane	86.178	499.9	30.9	0.270	0.247
177	$C_6H_{14}O$	1-Hexanol	102.177	610	40	0.30	0.56
178	$C_6H_{14}O$	Ethyl butyl ether	102.177	531	30	0.27	0.40
179	$C_6H_{14}O$	Diisopropyl ether	102.177	500.0	28.4	0.267	0.34
180	$C_6H_{15}N$	Dipropylamine	101.193	550	31	0.28	0.455
181	$C_6H_{15}N$	Triethylamine	101.193	535	30	0.27	0.329
182	C_7F_{14}	Perfluoromethylcyclohexane	350.055	486.8	23		0.482

TABLE A11.13   Continued

No.	Formula	Name	M	T_c	P_c	z_c	ω
183	C_7F_{16}	Perfluoro-n-heptane	388.051	474.8	16.0	0.273	0.56
184	C_7H_6O	Benzaldehyde	106.124	695	46		0.32
185	$C_7H_6O_2$	Benzoic acid	122.124	752	45	0.25	0.62
186	C_7H_8	Toluene	92.141	591.7	40.6	0.264	0.257
187	C_7H_8O	o-Cresol	108.140	697.6	49.4	0.24	0.443
188	C_7H_8O	m-Cresol	108.140	705.8	45.0	0.241	0.464
189	C_7H_8O	p-Cresol	108.140	704.6	50.8		0.515
190	C_7H_{14}	Cycloheptane	98.189	589	36.7	0.30	0.336
191	C_7H_{14}	Methylcyclohexane	98.189	572.1	34.3	0.269	0.233
192	C_7H_{16}	n-Heptane	100.205	540.2	27.0	0.263	0.351
193	C_7H_{16}	2-Methylhexane	100.205	530.3	27.0	0.261	0.330
194	C_7H_{16}	3-Methylhexane	100.205	535.2	27.8	0.256	0.324
195	C_7H_{16}	2,2-Dimethylpentane	100.205	520.4	27.4	0.267	0.289
196	C_7H_{16}	2,3-Dimethylpentane	100.205	537.3	28.7	0.256	0.299
197	C_7H_{16}	2,4-Dimethylpentane	100.205	519.7	27.0	0.265	0.306
198	C_7H_{16}	3,3-Dimethylpentane	100.205	536.3	29.1	0.274	0.270
199	$C_7H_{16}O$	1-Heptanol	116.204	633	30	0.25	0.56

INDEX